EXTRATROPICAL CYCLONES

THE ERIK PALMÉN
MEMORIAL VOLUME

Erik Herbert Palmén, 1898-1985

EXTRATROPICAL CYCLONES

THE ERIK PALMÉN MEMORIAL VOLUME

Co-Edited by

Chester W. Newton
National Center for Atmospheric Research

Eero O. Holopainen
University of Helsinki

American Meteorological Society
Boston
1990

ISBN 1-878220-03-9

Library of Congress catalog card number 90-81189

Published by the American Meteorological Society, 45 Beacon St., Boston, MA 02108

Richard E. Hallgren, Executive Director
Kenneth C. Spengler, Executive Director Emeritus
Evelyn Mazur, Assistant Executive Director
Arlyn S. Powell, Jr., Publications Manager
Jonathan Feld, Publications Production Manager

Editorial services for this book were contributed by Kim Dolphin, Linda Esche, Brenda Gray, and Leslie Keros.

Printed in the United States of America by Salina Press, Manlius, New York

Contents

Preface

This monograph comprises the twelve invited/lead papers presented at the Palmén Memorial Symposium on Extratropical Cyclones. The Symposium was held at the University of Helsinki, Finland, from 29 August to 2 September 1988. It was organized by the Geophysical Society of Finland and the American Meteorological Society in cooperation with the Danish, Norwegian and Swedish Geophysical Societies.

The initiative for the symposium came from Dr. Joseph Smagorinsky, President of the AMS in 1986. A motivation for holding the symposium during the last week of August in Finland was the fact that 31 August 1988 was the 90th anniversary of the birth of Professor Erik Palmén. The objective of the symposium was to give, on the basis of recent observational and modeling studies, a state-of-the-art picture of research on the structure and dynamics of extratropical cyclones, a topic which Palmén pioneered during the era of advances in aerological analysis.

While Palmén was primarily an ingenious "observationalist," he also closely followed developments of the theory of large-scale atmospheric circulation systems. Interested in weather forecasting since childhood, he was happy to acknowledge the rapid advances made in this area in recent decades with the aid of numerical modeling. It was therefore fully in accordance with his scientific attitude that the Palmén Memorial Symposium would include not only observational but also theoretical and numerical modeling studies of extratropical cyclones. As the content of the present monograph illustrates, the distinction between observational and modeling studies is becoming diffuse: Observationalists nowadays may use models and modelers may be conducting observational studies.

Ultimately, 62 full papers and 40 posters were presented at the symposium. A meeting review has been published in the *Bulletin of the American Meteorological Society,* Vol. 70, pp. 632–641 and, with some photos taken during the Symposium, in *Geophysica,* Vol. 24, pp. 67–87. A preprint volume of extended abstracts was published by the AMS and is available from AMS headquarters. Sixteen of the contributed papers appear in the January 1990 special issue of *Tellus A,* and some others have been published elsewhere.

The readiness of the authors of the lead papers to contribute to the present monograph was in itself a tribute to the memory of Erik Palmén. Each of the twelve contributions, put in final form after the Symposium, was reviewed by two experts in the respective areas and by the editors.

The monograph should be of interest to researchers in dynamic and synoptic meteorology, climatology and mesometeorology, as well as in numerical modeling and weather forecasting. It is also appropriate for teaching meteorology at graduate and upper undergraduate levels.

Erik Palmén was a genuine world's citizen. Finland was his home country, Swedish was his native tongue, and a lot of his research he made while working abroad. We cannot imagine any better way of commemorating the 90th anniversary of his birth than bringing together observationalists and modelers to present their most recent findings on extratropical cyclones, concerning which amazingly many new problems are still emerging. We also feel that this kind of monograph resulting from such a symposium would have been the only type of birthday present "Maestro" Palmén would have approved if still alive.

We want to acknowledge all authors and reviewers for their excellent contribution to the birth of the monograph. We appreciate the encouragement and advice of Kenneth Spengler and Evelyn Mazur, of the AMS, from the conception of the book through its later progress. The resources of the National Center for Atmospheric Research, and the supportive attitude of Warren Washington and others of the NCAR management, have been essential in carrying it to completion.

A very special acknowledgement of gratitude is due to Mrs. Dorene Howard of NCAR, for her expert and punctilious preparation of the whole text, and for her assistance with the editing. She has been a most valuable collaborator throughout, taking initiative and responding promptly and efficiently in a way that sustained the spirits of the technical editor (CWN). It is to her meticulous execution at all stages of the task, that we must attribute the high quality of the final product. Last but not least, we should acknowledge that the inspiration for a symposium to honor Erik Palmén came from a suggestion by Harriet Rodebush Newton.

CHESTER W. NEWTON
Boulder, Colorado

EERO O. HOLOPAINEN
Helsinki, Finland

Introduction

A core issue of meteorology of the atmosphere in the middle and high latitudes concerns the understanding of, and ability to predict, the behavior of extratropical cyclones. The past few decades have shown rapid development in our means of observing the atmosphere. Conventional data from synoptic and upper-air networks have been supplemented with data obtained by means of satellites, radars, remote-sensing profilers, etc. Equally fast has been the development of theoretical and numerical models of the atmospheric behavior. A comprehensive survey of the joint findings of observationalists and modelers on extratropical cyclones therefore appears timely. The present monograph, dedicated to the memory of the late Professor Erik Palmén who was a pioneer in cyclone studies, is devoted to this end.

The first two chapters have the character of a retrospection. C. W. Newton summarizes Palmén's contributions to concepts of cyclone structures and energy processes. H. Riehl describes the general circulation studies in the "Chicago school," giving a view of the emerging ideas of C.-G. Rossby, Palmén and others. Chapter 3, by R. J. Reed, is a review of the status of the cyclone problem prior to 1960 as well as during the past quarter century. It makes an excellent introduction to various aspects of the cyclone problem, such as the structures of fronts and cyclones and processes of frontogenesis and cyclogenesis. These are dealt with more extensively in later chapters which, besides reviewing recent developments in specific areas of the cyclone problem, also provide results not published earlier.

Chapters 4–10 concentrate mainly on our present understanding of various aspects of cyclones, and Chapters 11–12 on our ability to predict their behavior by numerical methods. In both groups, the presentations proceed roughly from larger to smaller scales.

Chapter 4 reviews recent observational studies of the role of cyclone-scale eddies in the general circulation of the atmosphere. The effects of cyclone-scale eddies on the zonally-averaged time-mean flow and on the stationary eddies during Northern Hemisphere winter are illustrated in terms of cyclone-induced mean-flow tendencies. The forcing effect of cyclones in cases of quasi-stationary flow, such as "blocking," is also discussed.

The theory of the structure and development of extratropical cyclones is discussed in Chapter 5 from several points of view. First, a "parcel theory" for slantwise displacements, and the quasi-geostrophic potential vorticity theory of cyclone development, are reviewed. Then, the isentropic potential vorticity perspective of cyclone development is highlighted with several illustrative examples from models and from real nature.

Chapter 6 discusses, with use of synoptic examples and sensitivity experiments, processes contributing to the rapid development of extratropical cyclones. The discussion is to a large extent based on the isentropic potential vorticity perspective. The chapter gives a vivid view of how on the one hand upper-level and low-level processes, and on the other hand physical and dynamical processes, interact with each other during explosive cyclone developments.

According to Chapter 7 lee cyclogenesis can, to a large extent, be interpreted as orographic modifications induced on baroclinic transient waves. The different characteristics of the process in various parts of the world are due to different flow conditions and mountain geometries. The chapter deals mainly with recent theoretical, numerical and observational results concerning the effect of the Alps. This emphasis is motivated by the recent international Alpine Experiment (ALPEX).

Chapter 8 discusses the synoptic/subsynoptic scale cloud and precipitation structures of extratropical cyclones as revealed by satellite and radar observations, interpreted in terms of isentropic airflows relative to the moving systems. Conceptual models, such as warm and cold "conveyor belts," play an important role in this description and in condensing the information content of huge amounts of data.

The theory of transverse circulations in frontal zones is discussed in Chapter 9. Emphasis is on the development of quasi-geostrophic, two-dimensional theory. Recent studies of frontogenesis seen as a three-dimensional process, however, are reviewed as well. Chapter 10 provides a review, and a lot of new information on the observed structures, of fronts in the upper as well as in the lower troposphere. The diagnosis presented of some synoptic cases probably provides the most accurate analyses one can make on the basis of the various kinds of data currently available.

Chapters 11 and 12 demonstrate an impressive increase in the skill of numerical forecasts during the past 10–15 years. Besides prediction, models are nowadays an indispensable tool also in diagnosing the atmospheric behavior. For example, Chapter 11 presents probably the most accurate picture so far of global energetics as well as the nature of systematic modeling errors. Both chapters demonstrate that with the aid of models one can also assess the cause-effect relationships arising from physical processes, which earlier were almost impossible to establish. As an instructive example, Palmén's famous study of the transformation of hurricane Hazel into an extratropical cyclone is analyzed in Chapter 12 using a modern limited-area model. The fact that all Palmén's major conclusions are confirmed makes a worthy tribute to the Maestro's pioneering studies.

While the individual contributions emphasize particular aspects, the monograph as a whole summarizes the major features of various kinds of extratropical cyclones that have been learned through observational analyses, theory and numerical experimentation. Comprehensive references are provided, along with a Subject Index and cross-references linking topics common to the different chapters.

A question not explicitly considered at length in this monograph concerns the feedback of subsynoptic-scale features on the larger-scale flow. For example, how sensitive is the prediction of the intensity of an extratropical cyclone to the detailed simulation of, say, the mesoscale rainbands? Such a simulation will require a much higher resolution than what we today have in global models. What we know, e.g., on the basis of results presented in this monograph, is that increased model resolution, as well as improved physics and model formulation, has so far resulted in improvement in predictions of the synoptic-scale flow. It is probably a safe forecast that scale interaction questions of this type will come up at many meetings in the future.

Chapter 1

Erik Palmén's Contributions To The Development Of Cyclone Concepts

Chester W. Newton

National Center for Atmospheric Research,* Boulder, Colorado 80307-3000

1.1 Palmén's Setting in the Evolution of Meteorology

Erik Palmén's scientific career encompassed the era during which theory and observations were brought together in a coherent conception of the global atmosphere. Earlier general circulation schemes mostly hypothesized meridional cells symmetrical about the earth, although some investigators, notably Dove and FitzRoy, emphasized air-mass exchanges by synoptic disturbances (Lorenz 1967, pp. 59–78). Contemporary studies of cyclones during the 19th and early 20th centuries, based on then-emerging thermodynamical-physical principles and fragmentary observations, established many of their significant features (Kutzbach 1979). Elements of the earlier investigations, together with new insights from observations and theory, were assimilated into the grand concept of the polar front theory of cyclones and the general circulation.

Palmén enthusiastically embraced this concept (introduced just before his entry into meteorology) and extended it through aerological studies outlined in Section 1.2. During this early part of his career, when he was affiliated with and became director of the Finnish Institute of Marine Research, he also engaged in oceanographic

*The National Center for Atmospheric Research is sponsored by the National Science Foundation.

investigations. Notable among these are the determination of interactions between wind stress and the sea-level slope, currents, and salinity and temperature distributions in the Baltic Sea; and theories of the equatorial counter-current and of the momentum balance of the antarctic circumpolar current.

Palmén's appointment in 1948 as a lifetime member of the Academy of Finland, working in the Department of Meteorology at the University of Helsinki, together with invitations from J. Bjerknes at UCLA and C.-G. Rossby at the University of Chicago, provided impetus for a "second stage" of his research in the milieu of a fresh attack on the general circulation of the atmosphere. For the first time, upper-air maps could be analyzed daily, and calculations of the statistical transfer properties over the Northern Hemisphere were initiated at UCLA and MIT. In Chicago a different approach was being taken, centering on synoptic and theoretical studies of upper waves and associated disturbances, jet streams, and lateral mixing processes, as recounted by Riehl in Chapter 2.

Thus Palmén's research took place in the settings of two major events that advanced our understanding of the atmosphere: the development of synoptic aerology in the context of polar front concepts, and the foundation of the present view of the general circulation in terms of the cooperative actions of mean meridional circulations and eddy disturbances. His contributions to these topics are epitomized by Eero Holopainen (1985):

> Almost all Erik Palmén's scientific papers are observational studies. However, the core of his papers was always the physical interpretation of the observational data and the

diagnostic results derived from them. He had an intuitive ability to distinguish important aspects of a problem from minor ones. This is one of the reasons why also pure theoreticians such as Jule Charney highly valued discussions with him. In many of his pioneer studies Palmén had the magical skill of deriving from a small amount of data results which later research, based on a much larger body of data, has shown to be essentially correct.

Here, I shall selectively review only Palmén's contributions related to the subjects of this volume. Some of his other works, including investigations of tropical systems and jet streams, are outlined in Newton (1986; N86 below). A complete listing is given in the posthumously-published article "In my opinion . . . ," in which Palmén (1985) presents a retrospective appraisal of his own work. Here I cannot include his citations of contemporary or precedent investigations and thus fail to do justice to his own recognition of his fellow scientists. The sequence of topics more or less follows the evolution of Palmén's interests, from the structures of individual disturbances to the overall hemispheric circulation and the energy conversion processes.

1.2 Early Aerological Studies

Palmén's synoptic investigations in 1923–28, on the movements of cyclones, confirmed the Bergen school view that they move generally along the direction of the wind in the warm sector. He established further that their speeds are correlated with the anemometer-level wind and the temperature contrast between cold and warm air, and

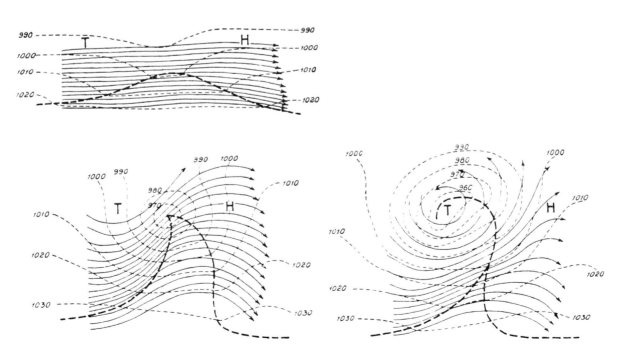

Fig. 1.1. Streamlines at cirrus level, at successive stages of cyclone development. Dashed lines are sea-level isobars (mb) and surface fronts (Palmén 1931).

diminish during their evolution to the occluded stage. These studies led to enquiries into the nature of pressure changes involved in the movement and development of disturbances.

The German–Austrian school had emphasized the concepts that disturbances are steered by the flow aloft, and that cyclones are "secondary" developments in response to the superposition of a "primary" pressure wave at substratospheric levels. Within this general framework, Palmén analyzed surface pressure tendencies as the effect of pressure change at the upper level, combined with temperature change in the intervening layer. This was attributed to "thermal" (horizontal advection) and "dynamical" (vertical motion) components, and he considered their combined effects in modifying the vertical structures of air masses as well as the horizontal temperature distribution in the troposphere.

Palmén's (1931) conception of the evolution of the cirrus-level flow, in relation to the life cycle of a polar-front cyclone, is portrayed in Fig. 1.1. As can be inferred from the crossings of sea-level isobars and upper streamlines, warm and cold advection are prominent in the developing stages. At the fully occluded stage when cold air has advanced to the south of the cyclone center and warm-sector air has been displaced upward, the low aloft has overtaken the surface center. This evolution is in accord with the original polar-front concept, in which a cyclone becomes surrounded by cold air and the potential energy of air-mass distribution is diminished (in present parlance, an "equivalent-barotropic" vortex).

Palmén remarks that "In the beginning of the development the streamlines at cirrus level show an increasing curvature [change downstream] above the cyclone center," a feature he elaborated later in terms of the increase of upper divergence during cyclone development (Section 1.4.1). In relation to later descriptions, the evolution in

Fig. 1.1 is similar to Sutcliffe's "self development" process; and, at the mature stage, it is consistent with Petterssen's finding that development ceases when an upper trough overtakes a cyclone and there is no longer positive vorticity advection above its center.

Palmén had earlier carried out statistical studies of soundings, demonstrating (as did W. H. Dines and others) that the tropopause is systematically lower and warmer, the lower the surface pressure. Unlike Dines, he emphasized the thermally asymmetric structure of cyclones, as in Fig. 1.2, with a high cold tropopause over the warm front and a low warm tropopause over the forward part of the cold air mass. In this example, Palmén concluded that the extremely warm (−30°C) and low (5 km) tropopause could not be explained by advection, and hence must be attributed to sinking in the stratosphere. In a 1928 paper, he had invoked this process in support of his view that cyclogenesis is not entirely a result of superposition of a preexisting "primary" upper-level disturbance. Rather, during the development, the warm substratospheric low also intensifies in response to a vertical circulation linked to divergence in the upper troposphere (further shown by Nyberg and Palmén 1942).

Bjerknes and Palmén (1937) presented the first comprehensive aerological analyses over an entire extratropical cyclone, enabled by an international effort in "swarm ascents" of recording meteorographs. Based on geostrophic winds at various isobaric surfaces, and fronts identified from soundings, the 3-D airflow at the upper surface of the polar-front layer is illustrated in Fig. 1.3. These streamlines show the trend to cyclonic curvature in air descending the cold front, and to anticyclonic curvature in the upper troposphere above the warm front. This turning was attributed to moist-adiabatic ascent through a layer in which, above the warm front, the wind veers with height. Analysis of winds *relative to the moving system*

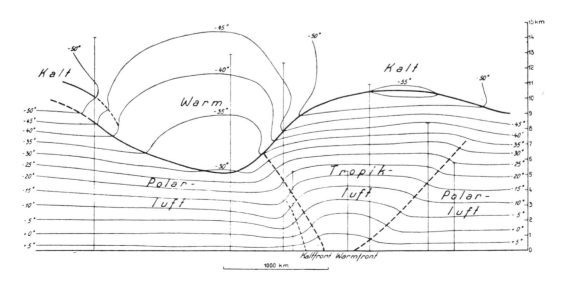

Fɪɢ. 1.2.   W-E cross section through a cyclone over western Europe (Palmén 1931).

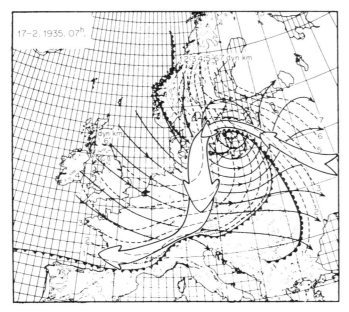

FIG. 1.3. At 07ʰ 17 February 1935, "Approximate flow of the tropical air in the warm sector above the frictional layer and at the slopes of the polar front surface," contoured in kilometers. Broad arrow, based on another figure, indicates central axis of geostrophic flow, at gradient-wind level in cold air, relative to the moving cyclone (Bjerknes and Palmén 1937).

revealed that the relative streamlines became parallel to the frontal contours in the upper troposphere; the corresponding cessation of upslope motion "restricts the space inside which the altostratus can exist" (on the anticyclonic flank of the jet stream, in later analyses; see Fig. 3.12).

The relative airflow in the cold air mass at gradient-wind level is indicated by a broad arrow. Taken together, the streamlines above and beneath the front in Fig. 1.3 indicate upper-level divergence and lower-level convergence east of the cyclone, and vice versa to its west. This interpretation was formulated in the simultaneous paper by Bjerknes (1937), in terms of gradient-wind divergence patterns associated with changes of curvature and coriolis parameter (in later but equivalent terms, absolute vorticity variations) along the current. The Bjerknes–Palmén monograph is thus historically important both as an exposition of the principles of aerological analysis (its direct emphasis), and as a basis for theoretical interpretation that served as a starting point for Rossby's planetary wave theory and Charney's baroclinic instability theory.

Aerological analyses were further advanced in collaboration with various investigators. Notably, Nyberg and Palmén (1942) introduced a new interpretation (illustrated by more recent analyses in Section 10.2.1) embodying a frontal zone that extends from the troposphere into the stratosphere, with reversing slope at tropopause level. The front then distinguishes the thermal contrast between warm and cold air in the troposphere, the opposite thermal contrast in the lower stratosphere, and tropopauses at different potential temperatures in the air masses; these

features remain coherent during distortions of the frontal zone during disturbance development.

Both Bjerknes and Palmén, and Nyberg and Palmén, take note of geostrophic winds of 60–70 m s⁻¹ in the upper troposphere, which their isobaric analyses clearly show to be concentrated in a narrow current later to be called the jet stream. These investigations set the stage for exploitation of the much more abundant aerological observations established in the late 1940s.

1.3 Large-Amplitude Upper-Level Disturbances

At the University of Chicago, Palmén's first investigations concerned the structural properties of jet streams and fronts (N86; see Fig. 3.4). He then turned his attention to the evolution of meanders of the jet stream-frontal zone that, at their extreme development, form large-scale cold and warm vortices in the upper troposphere. These are obvious manifestations of the bulk meridional exchange of air masses.

The evolution of a cutoff upper-level cyclone (Palmén 1949a) is shown in Fig. 1.4. In the earlier stages (a,b), a thermally asymmetrical trough, in which the NW winds on the west side are much stronger than the SW winds to the east, grows to a very large amplitude. At an intermediate stage (not shown), a closed low forms over the SW U.S. and expands to form the large, nearly circular, vortex seen in (c). In the process, subsidence takes place in the connecting cold tongue. "At an upper chart the phenomenon thus appears as a *'cutting-off'* of the cold air from its polar source region."

At this stage, the thermal structure is nearly symmetrical in a W-E section (d), although it is asymmetrical in the N-S direction where there is a greater overall temperature contrast with tropical air to the south. Explaining the maintenance of a deep polar air mass while it moves to a low latitude, Palmén observes:

> The fact that the [vertical shrinking of the polar air mass] often is much slower in the southern than in the central parts of a trough must depend upon the very strong combined effect of the Coriolis and centrifugal accelerations at the southern boundary of the cold air tongue. This effect tends to produce a cross-stream vertical circulation opposite to the direct solenoidal circulation .... The center over New Mexico shows a very low temperature (−29°C) for this latitude, but the temperature has risen about 6°C in the centre, indicating a subsidence in the southern parts of the cold air at the level around 500 mb. Farther to the north, however, the temperature rise was extremely strong, at the latitude 45°N from −36°C on November 2, to about −16°C two days later [due to encroachment of warm air above the subsided neck of polar air].

With this kind of cutoff cyclone, which formed above a massive polar anticyclone at the surface,

> the weak surface wind reduces the dissipation of kinetic energy to a minimum, and because of the symmetry of the

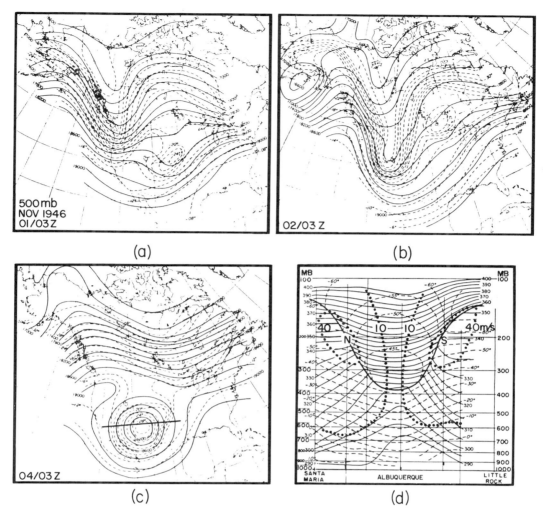

Fig. 1.4. (a–c) 500-mb contours (400 ft ≈ 120 m interval) and isotherms (dashed, °C) at 03 UTC 1, 2 and 4 November 1946; (d) W-E section through cutoff low center in (c). Thin solid and dashed lines are isentropes (°K) and isotherms; heavy line, tropopause (simplified as a continuous surface); dotted lines, isotachs (Palmén 1949a).

formation there can be no strong tendency for the vortex to move.... The symmetric .... distribution [in Fig. 1.4d] ... does not carry with it a similar symmetry in the weather phenomena. On the contrary, the high-level cyclone was accompanied by heavy precipitation on its east side and clear skies on its west side, indicating the existence of a strong upper divergence field compensated by convergence in the lower levels on the east side, and vice versa on the west side. The combined effect of the horizontal divergence and the vertical motion must have been such that the local pressure changes [aloft] practically vanished.

When the N-S asymmetry increases, "... the disturbance begins to move rather rapidly in the ENE direction, and the whole synoptic situation changes quickly."

Cutoff cyclones of this kind, forming above a cold air mass distant from the polar front at the surface, result from development in the middle and upper troposphere that is not immediately accompanied by a corresponding development at the surface. Hsieh (1949), in a study of a similar

situation, shows that the upper-level cyclone induced a weak perturbation beneath its east side, in the easterly current south of the surface anticyclone. This gradually developed into a cyclone within the polar air mass, which then ingested the lower-level front from the south. Thus, while the end product resembled a frontal cyclone, the process of its formation was entirely different from the ordinary development of a cyclone on the front itself.

Palmén remarks on the role of cutoff lows and their counterpart, warm upper-level highs:

The cut-off cold low can be regarded as a cell in a large-scale meridional exchange of air masses. A corresponding transport of tropical air masses to the north can often be observed .... Because of the difference in absolute vorticity ... between air masses in their original source regions it is obvious that the northward moving tropical air in higher latitudes must be characterized by low absolute vorticity. The tongues or cut-off islands of tropical air thus always show a pronounced anticyclonic relative vorticity and appear therefore as high-level anticyclones formed to the north of the original maximum westerlies.

An extreme example of the latter, paired with a cutoff cyclone (Palmén and Nagler 1949), is shown in Fig. 1.5, with an interpretation of its formation in terms of distortion from a "sinusoidal" wave pattern as a result of convergence above a sinking cold air mass beneath the trough at earlier stages. As discussed extensively by Hoskins et al. (1985), such cutting-off processes manifest systematic intrusions of high isentropic potential vorticity into lower latitudes, and of low PV characteristic of tropical air masses into higher latitudes. Near jet-stream level, the association of high PV with cutoff lows is evident from the isentropes and isotachs in Fig. 1.4d.

1.4 Cyclone Development and Air-Mass Exchange

1.4.1 Evolution of 3-D Frontal Structure and Airflow

Alluding to theoretical studies of the instability of perturbations on a westerly current, Palmén (1951a) questions

whether it is, in principle, permissible to start from infinitely small perturbations in discussing the cyclone problem. If such an infinitely small perturbation could cause the development of strong cyclones, it would indicate that the atmosphere is extremely unstable ... in an atmosphere where

rather strong perturbations of all kinds are always present ... it seems more likely that extratropical cyclones are induced by rather large migrating disturbances ... the question then arises whether a migrating disturbance would induce an irreversible process of the type observed in the development of cyclonic disturbances.

While emphasizing the great value of synoptic studies that had established the vertical motions relative to cyclones, Palmén comments that this distribution alone

does not describe very well the real movement in a disturbance which necessarily must contain a component of an *irreversible process* ... , [for which] it would be necessary to follow the three-dimensional air trajectories ... combined with a careful three-dimensional frontal analysis and applied to synoptic situations of well-defined types.

These precepts comprised the basis for Palmén's analyses of cyclone processes outlined below.

Figure 1.6 illustrates the evolution of frontal contours and the 500-mb flow pattern, during the development of a major cyclone. Palmén observes that

the occluded frontal cyclone can be the result of processes other than the occlusion of wave-shaped frontal perturbations .... At the beginning ... there are two surface fronts, one western front [from the Pacific] connected with the developing disturbance and one eastern front corresponding to the northern boundary of the moist warm Gulf air .... The three-dimensional fields of temperature, pressure, and

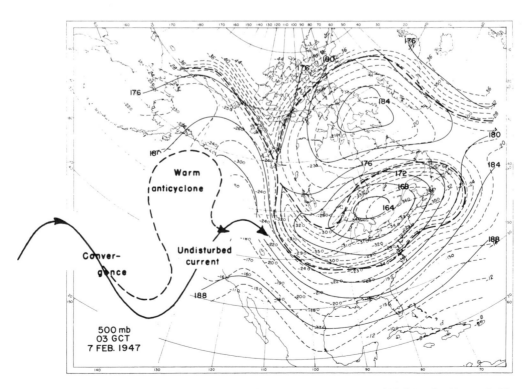

FIG. 1.5.   500-mb chart at 03 UTC 7 February 1947, with isotherms at 2°C intervals and contours at 200-ft (≈ 60-m) intervals. Heavy line is warm-air boundary of frontal layer. For inset, see text (Palmén and Nagler 1949).

wind [on 19 November] ... are, however, characteristic of every "occluded" cyclone whether it has passed through a regular process of occlusion or not. Essential for the whole development of a mature cyclone is the formation of the upper disturbance associated with the deformation of the upper front ... with the formation of an upper cyclone or a very deep trough. Obviously a well-marked surface front is not so essential for the development as was generally assumed formerly.

With this view, surface cyclogenesis ensues from "the rapid development of a deep upper cyclone from a relatively weak trough ... over the western part of the United States" (12 h prior to Fig. 1.6a). Cross sections during growth of the cold trough showed that the frontal layer was very pronounced on its west side where the jet stream was also stronger, and weak on the east side where the surface front was located. Thus, as noted by Palmén, both the thermal contrast and vorticity in the upper troposphere were more concentrated in the northwesterly current on the west side. Later interpretations of related upper-level features, in connection with ensuing cyclone development, are discussed in Section 6.3.2.

In connection with the evolution in upper levels, it is essential that

the three-dimensional structure of the cyclone is such that the upper current can remove the air accumulating in the region of lower convergence. This removal is not possible if the extratropical cyclones are symmetrical and, at the same time, the cyclonic circulation is increasing in depth.

Palmén discusses this requirement in terms of the tendency equation and the vorticity equation, concluding that, in the upper flow over a deepening cyclone,

If we neglect [lateral] shear, the cyclonic curvature must decrease in the direction of a streamline .... If we could follow the development over an individual cyclone, the decrease of vorticity along upper streamlines should intensify when the upper divergence field intensifies .... In the final stage of occlusion the low at the upper levels nearly coincides with the surface low, [giving] a phase displacement with height which gradually diminishes during the occlusion process.

The quoted passages describe features that appear in Palmén's 1931 conception of the evolution of upper-level flow in Fig. 1.1, interpreted in terms of the vorticity-divergence distribution in cyclones according to Bjerknes' (1937) model. Palmén's analysis now linked this evolution to the growth, starting with a preexisting minor trough, of a large-amplitude perturbation of a polar front extending through most of the troposphere, and the associated jet stream. Development of the cold tongue resulted in its separation, in the middle troposphere, from the main body of polar air with formation of a cutoff low aloft.

The process of seclusion of the polar air at the 500-mb level thus corresponds to the occlusion process in lower layers. In the upper atmosphere the warm air gains area, in the lower atmosphere the cold air gains area. This process corresponds to the scheme for release of energy of storms proposed by Margules in his classical studies.

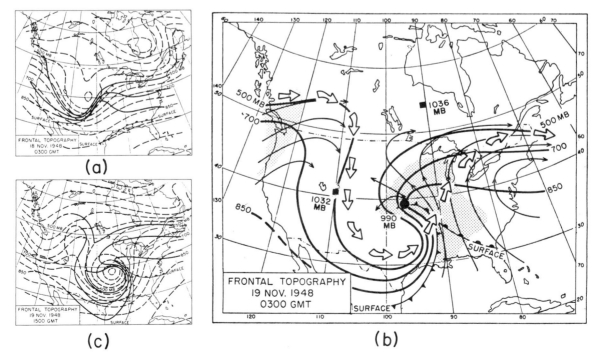

(a)

(c)

(b)

FIG. 1.6.　Frontal contours (labeled in decibars) and 500-mb geopotential contours (200-ft intervals) at (a) 03 UTC 18 November 1948 and (c) 36 h later. In (b), at an intermediate time, frontal contours, warm-air streamlines at upper surface of frontal layer and (broad arrows) jet stream axis are shown. Frontal contours are partly idealized, where the frontal layer was indistinct (Palmén 1951a, redrawn combining original figures).

Along with the growth of the cold tongue, the upper ridge downstream increased in amplitude. This represents an increase in vorticity variation along the current. Palmén pointed out that this feature is partly a result of the production of anticyclonic vorticity by upper-level divergence, owing to the enhancement of ascending motions in the troposphere associated with latent heat release in the precipitation region east of the upper trough. (See Section 6.4.)

Palmén emphasized that the vertical motion field of cyclones must be connected with systematic characteristics of the airflow when viewed in three dimensions: Both the descending trajectories in the cold air, and ascending trajectories in the warm air, take on anticyclonic curvatures related to lower- and upper-level divergence in the respective air masses. ("Conveyor belt" flow with these characteristics is extensively illustrated by Browning in Chapter 8.) Thus the 3-D trajectories, whose characters differ basically from the wave-shaped horizontal flow aloft because of the vertical motion field, represent a systematic exchange of warm and cold air, both in the vertical and across the meandering polar-front zone. This demonstrates the "irreversible process" in which warm air ascends predominantly in regions of precipitation and latent heat release, remaining in upper levels, and cold air subsides to low levels as it streams into lower latitudes.

1.4.2 Meridional and Vertical Mass Fluxes in Polar Outbreaks

Palmén and Newton (1951) assessed the general magnitude of the air-mass exchange, and the nature of the 3-D airflow, in a major polar-air outbreak. Frontal contours in Figs. 1.7a and c (60 h apart) show an expansion of the volume of polar air S of 45°N, to the west of a developing cyclone. Above about 700 mb the area of cold air at first expanded then contracted, whereas a continuous vast expansion took place in lower levels. This behavior indicates a general collapse of the polar-air extrusion. The southward flow into the cold tongue was greatest in upper levels where expansion was least, and vice versa in lower levels. From mass continuity, the inflow across 45°N minus expansion of the cold tongue within a given layer must equal the vertical divergence of mass flux.

For a 24-hour period, the overall southward mass flux across 45°N below 300 mb was evaluated as 96 Mt s^{-1}. Considering that this outbreak was extreme, Palmén concluded that about five more-ordinary disturbances around the hemisphere would exchange, across middle latitudes, around 3–5 percent of the polar air mass in a day. With a compensating poleward flux of warm air, and with typical differences of temperature and of zonal wind in the warm and cold air masses, these disturbances could

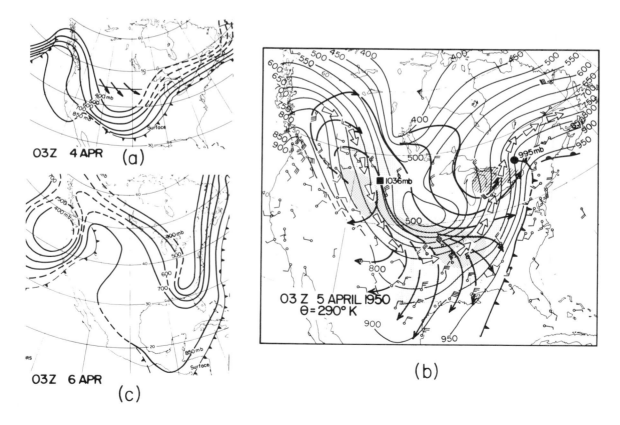

FIG. 1.7. (a, c) Frontal contours at 03 UTC 4 April 1950 and 60 h later; (b) at an intermediate time, pressure contours and streamlines on isentropic surface $\theta = 290$ K, in upper part of cold air. Winds (full barb 10 knots) are at θ surface, contoured in mb. Broad arrows (added), jet axis. Stippling shows region of descent exceeding 200 mb per day; hachures, ascent (Palmén and Newton 1951).

essentially account for the required hemispheric poleward fluxes of sensible heat and angular momentum.

The downward mass flux in the cold tongue, south of 45°N, was evaluated as a maximum of 56 Mt s^{-1} at 750 mb, comparable to but smaller than the equatorward flux. Streamlines and vertical motions on the $\theta = 290$ K isentropic surface (Fig. 1.7b) show further that descent is most prominent in the lower-latitude portion of the cold outbreak, where changes toward anticyclonic curvature along the flow are consistent with vertical shrinking in the lower troposphere. Along with the characteristic ascending streamlines in the warm air (Fig. 1.6b), they illustrate the "irreversible" character of the airflow in disturbances noted above.

1.5 Cooperative Roles of Extratropical Disturbances and Meridional Cells in the General Circulation

Palmén's investigations of the 3-D airflow in disturbances, together with his earlier evaluation (at UCLA) of the Hadley-cell circulation and his studies of jet streams, led to a synthesis of these features in his Symons Memorial Lecture (1951b). At the time, statistical calculations had demonstrated the dominance of eddy fluxes in tropical and extratropical latitudes, but the role of mean meridional circulations had received little attention. Palmén considered a more comprehensive description of the overall processes, in terms of the characteristics of synoptic circulation systems, as necessary to mitigate "a tendency to regard what is commonly called the general circulation as nothing but the statistical manifestation of currents as they appear in the actual atmosphere."

1.5.1 Palmén's Scheme of the General Circulation

Palmén (1951b) summarizes the 3-D airflows in dis-

turbances relative to the polar-front zone, based on the synoptic studies outlined above. These features are incorporated in his conception of the general circulation, shown at the right of Fig. 1.8 in relation to the surface airflow as portrayed by Defant and Defant (1958).

> In this schematic figure which refers to the northern winter the circulation has been divided into three cells: the tropical cell, the extratropical or polar-front cell and the polar or subpolar region. The tropical cell is the principal source region of angular momentum and appears in our scheme essentially in the classical shape. At the northern end of this cell the quasi-permanent subtropical jet can be observed . . . . The whole region between the North Pole and latitude 60°N. is marked as a region where large-scale horizontal mixing processes are dominant; that is the region of quasi-constant absolute vorticity (Rossby 1947). (See Section 2.3.)

Concerning the middle-latitude linkage between the subpolar and tropical regions, Palmén adduces the results in Section 1.4 and observes that:

> Analyses of the three-dimensional movements of the polar air thus give a picture of the flow pattern which is rather different from the common idea of a large-scale quasi-horizontal swaying around a mean latitude. The meridional amplitude of real trajectories seems to be much larger than the amplitude of upper stream lines, and the vertical component of the movement appears as an essential link in the whole development . . . there is no doubt about the fact that there must be a discontinuous inflow of tropical air masses into the polar region and that these, on the average, must ascend. Well-known phenomena such as the occlusion process, the distribution of precipitation areas, and the invasion of tropical air masses in the upper troposphere and lower stratosphere in very high latitudes in connection with the formation of strong disturbances show a discontinuous injection of upper tropical air in the polar region as a counterpart to the outflow of polar air [into the tropics] in the lower part of the troposphere.

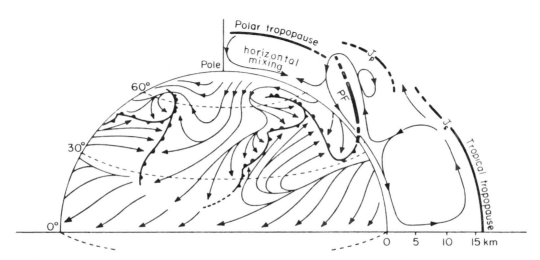

FIG. 1.8. Palmén's (1951a) model of the general circulation in winter in relation to surface streamlines (Defant and Defant 1958). In middle latitudes the "mean circulation" is relative to the meandering polar-front zone regardless of its orientation, rather than with respect to latitude.

The principal circulation in the middle-latitude belt is shown as solenoidally direct relative to the polar-front zone. This zone meanders northward and southward, and hence

> the polar-front circulation in the form presented ... could never be found from mean data computed in the common fashion [zonal averaging]; if however one referred the motions to the polar front at its mean latitude the characteristic circulation would more readily appear.

Compatibility of the circulation in Fig. 1.8 with the opposite (meridionally indirect) Ferrel cell depends on the framework in which the motions are averaged (see Section 2.6). This interpretation is further supported in principle by calculations of the mean circulation relative to an *isentropic* coordinate system, derived from the distribution of heat sources and sinks (Gallimore and Johnson 1981; see their Fig. 2). In this system, the Ferrel cell vanishes and the mean hemispheric circulation appears as a single Hadley-type cell that extends from the tropics to higher latitudes. The distinction in Fig. 1.8, between meridional overturning and overturning relative to the polar-front zone, explained the compatibility of dissipation of westerly momentum by the Ferrel cell and maintenance of the meandering polar jet by direct circulations in these latitudes (discussed further in Section 1.7).

1.5.2 Angular Momentum Processes

As a fundamental aspect of the general circulation scheme in Fig. 1.8, Palmén (1951b) described the connection between extratropical disturbances and the tropics, "the principal source region of angular momentum," and introduced the concept of the subtropical jet stream. Calculations at MIT and UCLA had shown that eddies effectively account for the meridional *transfer* of relative angular momentum (AM). Palmén perceived, however, that they could not account for the *origin* of the relative AM that is transferred; and hence the joint action of mean meridional circulations and eddy disturbances is required. His argument was first presented in a comment (1949b) on a note by Rossby and Starr (1949) in which they disclaimed the importance of mean meridional circulations. Considering a long-term mean state,

> the conditions for the constancy of total angular momentum contained in an annular zonal strip reduce to

$$\int r\rho u c_n dS + \int r^2 \Omega \rho c_n dS = \int T dV \qquad (1.1)$$

[wherein $r = a \cos \phi$, c_n is the component of meridional flow across a unit surface dS of a vertical wall at a latitude boundary, T is torque per unit mass within the volume V of the annulus]. Furthermore, if the contribution of the second integral is not zero, there are *mean meridional circulations*. The authors then agree that it is the importance of this term which they call into question.

Considering the flux of AM *into a layer of limited depth*, across the southern boundary of a volume extending to the pole, c_n becomes $v = v_g + v_a$ and the transport on the l.h.s. of (1.1)

is then

$$\int r\rho u v_g dx + \int r\rho u v_a dx + \int r^2 \Omega \rho v_a dx , \qquad (1.2)$$

the geostrophic contribution to the Ω-integral vanishing [for a complete annulus]. [For the entire depth of the atmosphere, the last integral] must practically vanish if there is to be no net transfer of mass across the latitude. However [considering the middle integral], mean meridional circulations can still give a net transport of AM across the latitude if the mean v_a is positively correlated "in the vertical" with the mean west wind.

A hypothetical example demonstrated that even a modest meridional circulation could account for a significantly large transport (Palmén later showed that this form of AM transfer is dominant in central latitudes of the Hadley cell). Since the eddy AM transfer takes place mostly in the upper troposphere, he concluded that ". . . *to maintain the wind distribution necessary for the first integral [of (1.1)] to operate, it is essential that the second integral be different from zero if computed for layers of limited thickness*." Correspondingly, maintenance of the zonal winds ultimately depends upon mean meridional circulations. In a reply, Starr made it plain that he was not persuaded. Starr (1948), in an elegant and otherwise comprehensive essay on the general circulation, had invoked ascent and descent at different latitudes in disturbances as a mechanism for vertical transfer of absolute AM but made no mention of mean meridional circulations.

This controversy may seem curious to meteorologists accustomed to the present, firmly established observational description, but it must be realized that in 1949 diverse views of the mechanisms of the general circulation were still being explored. In later papers (see N86) Palmén elaborated the theoretical and observational basis, demonstrating that the westerlies are generated by the Hadley cell through an Ω-AM to $\bar{u}$-AM conversion which accounts for the strongest mean winds in the subtropical jet stream; and that this generation in tropical latitudes is necessary as a *source* for the AM transferred by eddy fluxes to maintain the westerlies in extratropical latitudes. This concept of the cooperative actions of mean meridional circulations and disturbances harmonized the diverse views of the general circulation.

1.6 Energy Conversions in Extratropical Disturbances

A series of publications during 1958–1966 was devoted to a systematic effort to assess conversions between potential energy (PE) and kinetic energy (KE), both in individual disturbances and in their combined role with the mean meridional circulations. Evaluations of conversions in the Northern Hemisphere winter Hadley cell (see N86), and in hurricanes, had been carried out earlier. As predominantly symmetrical systems, the most essential part of their momentum and energy processes could be calculated from azimuthally-averaged circulations and pressure fields by use of expression (1) in Fig. 1.9. In extratropical disturbances, estimation of ageostrophic winds is not so readily accomplished; in addition, very large energy fluxes take place across the boundaries of any region chosen to include an extratropical system. Other approaches, using expressions (2) and (3), involve calculation of the divergence and vertical motion distribution within the region so that, by either method, estimation of energy conversions is more complex.

Palmén had earlier commented on the collective roles of extratropical disturbances, e.g. (Palmén and Newton 1951), that a conceptual model incorporating the features of Fig. 1.7

represents a mechanism for direct solenoidal circulations between the sinking cold and ascending warm air-masses. This process of direct circulation appeared . . . as an empirical fact [in the calculation of sinking in the cold air mass] . . . cold tongues undergo continuous changes associated with change in amplitude and [their] ultimate elimination . . . as a result of the vertical shrinking and horizontal spreading of the cold air in lower latitudes. This process of discontinuous formation of cold tongues of sinking air represents statistically a type of meridional circulation in which the descending cold air flows southwards, and the ascending warm air northwards, in the vicinity of the polar front.

Palmén (1951a) further observes that

the vertical circulation necessary to maintain the kinetic energy of the atmosphere . . . is mainly associated with cyclones and anticyclones. The principal regions of descending polar air are the cold anticyclones separating cyclone families (or individual cyclones) and their counterparts in the free atmosphere, the cold troughs. The tropical air ascends in the regions where condensation and precipitation are observed. . . . The ascending warm air must form a diverging current in the upper troposphere. The convergence at lower levels and the divergence at upper levels . . . represent one branch of the solenoidal circulation, the other branch being the combined lower divergence and upper convergence associated with descending movement in the surrounding cold anticyclonic areas.

1.6.1   Energy Conversions in Cyclone Hazel

Palmén's (1958) first calculations were for a hybrid storm that resulted from the transformation of the 1954 Hurricane Hazel into an extratropical cyclone. This event occurred as Hazel, moving onshore from SSE, was overtaken by a well-marked polar front ahead of a deep, slow-moving upper trough. At the time of Fig. 1.10a the cyclone had already ingested the surface front, and thus had both the characteristics of heavy convective precipitation associated with the hurricane, and a strong air-mass contrast (almost 30°C between the warmest and coldest air at 500 mb). These combined circumstances resulted in a devastating extratropical cyclone that moved northward into Canada. Sequential maps are reproduced in Chapter 12, where Anthes presents numerical simu-

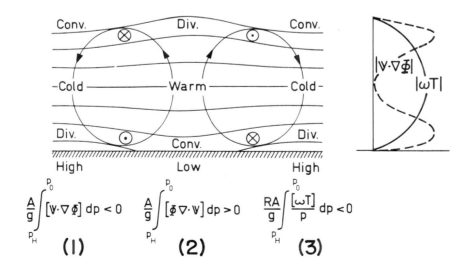

$$\frac{A}{g}\int_{P_H}^{P_0}[\mathbf{v}\cdot\nabla\Phi]\,dp<0 \qquad \frac{A}{g}\int_{P_H}^{P_0}[\Phi\nabla\cdot\mathbf{v}]\,dp>0 \qquad \frac{RA}{g}\int_{P_H}^{P_0}\frac{[\omega T]}{p}\,dp<0$$

$$(1) \qquad\qquad (2) \qquad\qquad (3)$$

FIG. 1.9.   Illustrating three equivalent expressions for conversion of available potential energy to kinetic energy (Palmén and Newton 1969, p. 535). Ordinate is height, thin lines are isobaric surfaces. Added features: In a rotating (Northern Hemisphere) system, the ageostrophic circulation generates motions normal to the section (⊗ into page, ⊙ out of page). At right, the associated profiles of [ωT], expressing vertical transfer of sensible heat, and [$\mathbf{V}\cdot\nabla\Phi$], kinetic energy generation.

lations of Hazel that support Palmén's views of the physical processes.

With sinking in the cold tongue and ascent associated with copious release of latent heat in the warm air to its east, the situation represented an unusually intense production of KE according to expression (3) in Fig. 1.9. Direct solenoidal overturning is indicated by the divergence profiles in the cold- and warm-air regions (Fig. 1.10b) and by the pronounced cross-contour flow in the upper branch at 300 mb in Fig. 1.10a. This accounts for most of the PE to KE conversion (Fig. 1.10c) in an airstream along a path suggested by the broad arrow (see cross section of the model-simulated airflow in Fig. 12.25b). This represents upper-level outflow from the convectively-ascending tropical air of the hurricane which, entering the anticyclonic flank where inertial stability is weak, and traversing a strong geopotential gradient, feeds into and increases the KE of the jet stream. As pointed out by Palmén this KE may be partly reconverted to APE by indirect circulations in the regions between KE-producing disturbances, but a net generation of KE must result since the initial ascent takes place through an irreversible process of condensation and latent heat release.

1.6.2 Kinetic Energy Budget for a Limited Region

The expressions in Fig. 1.9 give the energy conversion for a closed system, for which (e.g., for the circulation illustrated or for the entire atmosphere) there are no

energy fluxes across boundaries. For an open system, such as a cyclone-anticyclone couplet, the total energy budget comprises the generation, surface and internal dissipation, and the net flux of energy across the boundaries of the volume considered, which can be large especially in the neighborhood of the jet stream as illustrated by the Hazel case. Palmén's (1959) formulation for application to open systems is summarized briefly (see also Palmén and Newton 1969, Chap. 16).

The change of horizontal KE (denoted by k for unit mass) in a fixed volume V with area A bounded by a vertical wall with periphery L, an upper isobaric surface p_T, and p_S at the earth's surface, is expressed by

$$\frac{\partial}{\partial t} \int_V \rho k \, dV = -\frac{1}{g} \int_{p_T}^{p_S} \oint_L k v_n \, dL \, dp - \frac{1}{g} \int_A \omega_T k_T \, dA$$
$$\text{(1.3)}$$
$$-\frac{1}{g} \int_{p_T}^{p_S} \int_A \mathbf{V} \cdot \nabla \Phi \, dA \, dp + \frac{1}{g} \int_{p_T}^{p_S} \int_A \mathbf{V} \cdot \mathbf{F} \, dA \, dp.$$
$$\text{(GKE)} \qquad\qquad\qquad \text{(DKE)}$$

Here the l.h.s. and first two r.h.s. terms represent the change of total KE within the volume and (with v_n the outward component across L) the KE imports through the lateral and top boundaries. Together, these three terms balance the total change of KE resulting from generation GKE and frictional dissipation DKE. (The last term, in which $\mathbf{F}$ is "frictional" force, represents dissipation for $\mathbf{V} \cdot \mathbf{F} < 0$.)

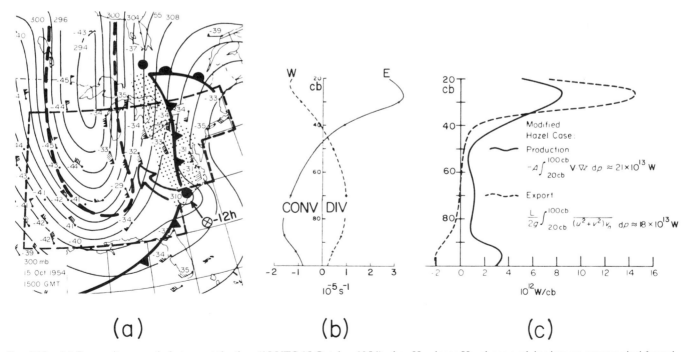

(a)   (b)   (c)

Fig. 1.10. (a) Composite synoptic features at the time (15 UTC 15 October 1954) when Hurricane Hazel was evolving into an extratropical frontal cyclone: winds and contours (200-ft interval) at 300 mb; surface fronts; heavy dots, centers of Hazel and an extratropical cyclone near James Bay; ⊗ Hazel center 12 h earlier; heavy dashed line, frontal contour at 500 mb; stippling, area of precipitation >2.5 cm during 24 h ending 15 h after time of figure. Broad arrow suggests outflow from upper levels of cyclone into anticyclonic flank of polar jet. Dashes outline computation area comprising 15, 5°× 5° lat-long blocks. (b) Mean divergence over 6 eastern (solid) and 9 western blocks. (c) KE production within (solid), and export from, the entire computation region and their vertically-integrated totals (Palmén 1958, left figure redrawn).

With the transformations

$$\mathbf{V} \cdot \nabla \Phi \equiv \mathbf{V}_a \cdot \nabla \Phi = \nabla \cdot (\Phi \mathbf{V}) - \Phi \nabla \cdot \mathbf{V},$$

$$\Phi \nabla \cdot \mathbf{V} = -\Phi \frac{\partial \omega}{\partial p} = -\frac{\partial(\omega \Phi)}{\partial p} + \omega \frac{\partial \Phi}{\partial p} = -\frac{\partial(\omega \Phi)}{\partial p} - \omega \alpha,$$

and $\alpha = RT/p$; and application of Gauss' theorem to express $(\nabla \cdot \Phi V)$ as geopotential flux across the lateral boundary, (1.3) can be written

$$\frac{\partial K}{\partial t} = -\frac{1}{g} \int_{P_T}^{P_S} \oint_L k v_n dL dp - \frac{1}{g} \int_A \omega_T k_T dA$$

$$-\left[\frac{1}{g} \int_A \omega_T \Phi_T dA + \frac{1}{g} \int_{P_T}^{P_S} \oint_L \Phi v_n dL dp \right. \qquad (1.4)$$

$$\left. + \frac{R}{g} \int_{P_T}^{P_S} \int_A \frac{\omega T}{p} dA dp \right] + \frac{1}{g} \int_{P_T}^{P_S} \int_A \mathbf{V} \cdot \mathbf{F} dA dp.$$

Here, K denotes total KE within the volume expressed by the l.h.s. of (1.3). In this transformation, the three terms within brackets comprise the total generation GKE (the first two expressing work upon the boundaries of an open system by the surrounding atmosphere).

For a closed system, e.g. the whole atmosphere, the flux [first four r.h.s.] terms disappear, and the increase of KE equals the conversion of [available] PE into KE diminished by the frictional dissipation of KE (e.g. White and Saltzman 1956). For a closed system the change of KE can be computed either from the work term [$\mathbf{V} \cdot \nabla \Phi$ in (1.3)] or from the conversion terms [(2) or (3) in Fig. 1.9]. For open systems it seems most practical to use the [latter] terms, since the flux of PE could be difficult to evaluate. It should especially be

pointed out that the local change of KE hardly can be computed, or even estimated, from the local change of potential energy between consecutive synoptic times .... In real atmospheric processes an increase of KE through conversion of PE into KE does not necessarily mean that the PE actually decreases even when radiational processes and advection of PE are disregarded. The vertical circulation associated with conversion between PE and KE very commonly is accompanied by liberation of latent heat, thus adding a heat source as a result of the conversion process, [as in tropical cyclones in which] PE, KE and internal energy increase simultaneously.

1.6.3   Energy Conversion in a Developing Cyclone

Palmén and Holopainen (1962) employed a modified version of (1.4) to evaluate the energy budget of a cyclone whose composite features are shown in Fig. 1.11. Vertical motions were calculated from the divergence field derived from kinematic analyses, by use of the continuity equation. Arrows on the map show only the general regions of maximum vertical motion at 500 mb. Descent is present within the polar-air tongue outlined by the frontal contour; and ascent, about twice as large, over a region surrounding the cyclone center and cold front. These features are illustrated in the cross section of Fig. 1.12, along latitude 40°N.

Because of the unreliability of high-level winds, computations were stopped at the 300-mb level. A summary of the energy budget for the volume beneath that level is sketched in the inset of Fig. 1.11. Fluxes across the boundaries are large for both KE and PE. (Referring to Fig. 1.12 and the second and third r.h.s. terms of (1.4), upward

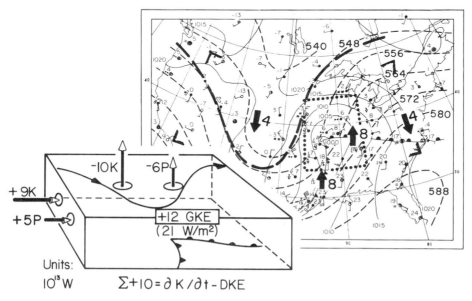

FIG. 1.11. Surface map and 500-mb contours (dam) 12 UTC 18 November 1957, a composite of analyses in Palmén and Holopainen (1962). Heavy dashed line, warm boundary of 500-mb front; thick arrows indicate locations and magnitudes (μb s^{-1}) of maximum upward and downward motions at 500 mb. The inset sketch, based on their tabulated evaluations, shows energy budget components for the volume up to 300 mb, inside area whose corners are shown as heavy triangles. Boxed value is KE generation within volume in units of 10^{13} W; GKE per unit area in parentheses. Arrows (whose locations are not related to the wave pattern) indicate overall fluxes of kinetic (K) and potential (P) energy across the four lateral walls and through the 300-mb surface. Dissipation at ground was about 2 units; internal dissipation not estimated.

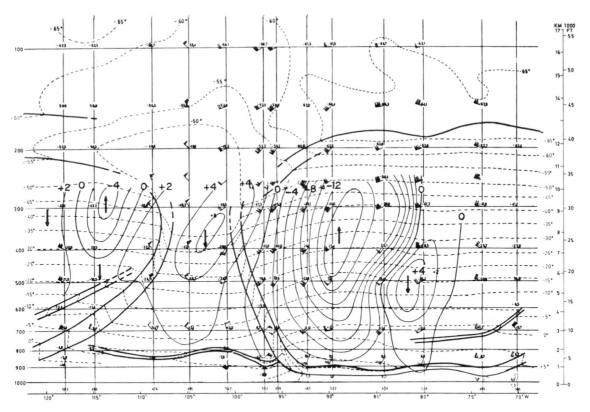

FIG. 1.12. Vertical cross section along 40°N in Fig. 1.11, with tropopauses, frontal layers and isotherms. Vertical motions (thin solid lines) were calculated by a different method and exceed those in Fig. 1.11 (Palmén and Holopainen 1962).

fluxes through the 300-mb surface are due to the association of ascent, within the warm air, with both greater geopotential and stronger winds in the jet stream.) In this instance the horizontal influxes of KE and PE almost balanced the outfluxes through 300 mb, so that their total value, −1.5 units (in units of 10^{13}W), is much smaller than the generation GKE = +11.7 units within the volume. The overall sum, +10.2 units, is thus almost equivalent to the generation of KE arising from the $\omega''T''$ correlation (wherein double primes denote local deviations from the areal mean at a given level) in the next-last term of (1.4).

This overall value represents $(\partial K/\partial t -$ DKE) in (1.4). Although neither of these components was evaluated except for surface dissipation, the surely much smaller value of DKE than GKE suggested that most of the KE generation was consumed in increasing the KE of the cyclone (which deepened 20 mb in 24 h).

The large value of the $[\omega''T'']$ term which gives the conversion between available potential and kinetic energy inside the region shows that an important role in the deepening of the cyclone was played by ascent of warm air and descent of cold air. This process of solenoidal circulation occurred essentially in a zonal plane, as can be seen from the cross section in [Fig. 1.12].

The authors emphasized the importance of latent heat release in driving the vertical circulation; over the dotted

inner area in Fig. 1.11, this averaged about 60 percent of the solar constant. The observed rate of precipitation was close to the amount calculated from the convergence of water vapor $(-\overline{\nabla \cdot q\mathbf{V}})$ integrated over pressure; 84 percent of it being accounted for by $(-\overline{q}\overline{\nabla \cdot \mathbf{V}})$. This agreement substantiated the validity of the calculations of divergence, and thus supported the estimate of KE generation, over the region of the cyclone. Acknowledging uncertainties over other regions, it is clear that the KE generation in this case (21 W m^{-2} over the entire cyclone-anticyclone couplet, omitting additional GKE above 300 mb), and in others giving comparable values, greatly exceeds the mean value of generation and dissipation over the extratropical region as a whole as discussed below. Further studies of kinetic energy budgets of cyclones are reviewed in Section 12.3.4.

1.7 Role of Extratropical Disturbances in Hemispheric Energy Processes

1.7.1 Maintenance of Extratropical Jet Stream

The dominance of disturbances in the extratropical KE budget was exemplified by Palmén (1959) in terms of Cyclone Hazel. At the time when it was being transformed from a hurricane to an extratropical cyclone, the conversion rate over the area considered (Fig. 1.10a) was about 200 TW (TW = 10^{12}W). The computation area was $1/35$

the area of the "polar cap" north of 30°N. For this total area, considering the KE influx from the tropics, partial reconversion to APE by the Ferrel cell, and an estimate (by Brunt) of 5 W m^{-2} for the average KE dissipation,

> the conversion of potential energy into kinetic energy should be of the order of magnitude [500–550 TW]. Hence, only about 3 active extratropical disturbances of the same intensity of "Hazel" would suffice in producing the KE necessary for the maintenance of the total KE of the whole cap.

More generally, considering the small area involved, "This conclusion still holds if we consider the development in 'Hazel' to be strong compared with average cyclones." Further, "one has to conclude ... that every region of strong conversion of PE into KE must be surrounded by areas of [weaker] reconversion of the exported KE into PE," exemplified by the alternating accelerations and decelerations along the polar-front jet stream.

On the whole, however, the conversion is dominated by the strong and systematically-arranged vertical motions in synoptic disturbances. Citing computations which showed a mean direct solenoidal circulation relative to the jet-stream waves in a rotating annulus experiment (see Section 2.6), Palmén observes that:

> Applied on the atmosphere an averaging with reference to the polar-front jet would probably give the same result. Since the high-tropospheric northern jet, on the average, is situated vertically above the polar-front zone around the 500-mb level the result would correspond to mean ascending movement of warm air to the right (looking in the direction of the general air motion) and mean descending motion of cold air to the left of the polar front at that level [as in Fig. 1.8]. The maintenance of the northern or polar-front jet could then also be considered as the result of a mean vertical circulation just as the subtropical jet is maintained by the Hadley circulation.

The localization of KE generation along cyclone tracks (see Section 4.2.2) where strong vertical motions and temperature contrasts are concentrated, with little conversion elsewhere, has been confirmed by more recent general circulation statistics (e.g., Lau 1979, Fig. 4).

1.7.2 Hemispheric Energy Conversions

Palmén (1960) presented preliminary estimates of energy conversions over the hemisphere, considering the dominance of a mean meridional circulation in lower latitudes and of eddies in higher latitudes owing to their different thermal Rossby numbers (as established experimentally by D. Fultz), and the generation of eddy KE according to E. Lorenz. The conversion in the Hadley cell had been calculated by Palmén, Riehl and Vuorela (1958). Based on crude estimates of surface frictional and internal dissipation, Palmén concluded that "the total frictional dissipation in the cap north of 30°N in winter probably is larger than 60×10^{13} W and smaller than 100×10^{13} W." Existing estimates of KE generation were generally much

smaller; in an examination of their basis, Palmén concluded that underestimates of vertical velocity resulted from "approximations used in the model and the necessary smoothing technique used in the computations."

Since (3) in Fig. 1.9 expresses the vertical flux of sensible heat, however, it can be used if the total heat sources and sinks over an extensive area are known, without appeal to the detailed circulations inside the region. This was the method used by Palmén (1966) in an evaluation of energy conversions over the extratropical region. If its boundary is chosen at the subtropical latitude ϕ_S where the mean meridional wind $[\bar{v}]$ vanishes, the first r.h.s. term of (1.4) comprises only the meridional eddy flux. If the whole depth of the atmosphere is considered, the second and third r.h.s. terms vanish. In the fourth term $[\bar{v}][\bar{\Phi}] = 0$ at ϕ_S, and $[\overline{v'\Phi'}]$ was neglected on the assumption that $v' \approx v'_g$. (Later calculations indicate that this term is not negligible; in effect, it reduces the poleward flux of KE across ϕ_S.) Then, for the extratropical region,

$$\frac{\partial K}{\partial t}\bigg|_{\phi_S}^{90°} \approx \frac{2\pi a \cos \phi_S}{g} \int_0^{p_S} [\overline{k'v'}]_S \, dp + H_z + DKE, \quad (1.5)$$

equivalent to Palmén's Eq. (7) which is the basis of the ensuing discussion.

The integral term expresses the import into the region, by eddy flux across ϕ_S, of KE generated by the Hadley circulation minus the portion dissipated within the tropics. H_z, symbolizing the next-last term of (1.4), represents the conversion from APE to KE associated with vertical heat flux; and DKE denotes dissipation by surface and internal friction, within the extratropical region. If $\partial K/\partial t$ is assumed small, as in the extreme seasons, an estimate of DKE is obtained as a residual of the import and generation terms.

The overall heat sources and sinks for the tropical and extratropical regions, above and below 500 mb, and sensible heat fluxes across 32°N and from the earth's surface, are summarized in Fig. 1.13a for Northern Hemisphere winter. Heat fluxes through the 500-mb surface by the mean meridional cells, based on their mass circulations determined by Palmén and Vuorela (1963), are also shown. Vertical eddy heat fluxes are estimated as a residual of these quantities. Based on evaluations for thinner layers, the total heat flux per unit area in Fig. 1.13b is obtained as an average for the extratropical area 32°–90°N. Small turbulent eddies account for the entire upward flux of sensible heat near the earth's surface, with contributions by convective clouds higher up (diminishing with height through the lower troposphere). In the upper troposphere, mechanical turbulence carries heat downward. Small eddies, if randomly distributed, transmit a portion of the vertical heat flux but do not contribute to KE generation on the synoptic scale. Thus their estimated contribution is subtracted from the total to obtain the vertical heat flux shown for large eddies and the Ferrel cell.

Evaluations of the next-last term of (1.4), for 100-mb layers, are shown in Fig. 1.13c. When integrated through

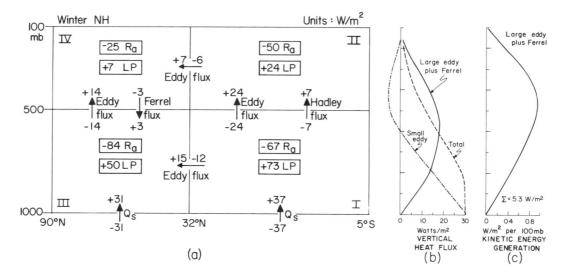

FIG. 1.13.   (a) Winter heat budget in the belts 5°S–32°N and 32° N–90°N, and the vertical fluxes of sensible heat through the 500-mb surface and from the earth surface (Q_S). All quantities are expressed in W m^{-2} averaged over the areas concerned (fluxes across 32°N are consistent, considering the different areas). Heat sources and sinks are denoted by R_a for net radiation, LP for condensation heat release. (b) Components of vertical flux of sensible heat over the extratropical region. (c) Contribution to KE generation, associated with vertical heat flux, per 100-mb layer (Palmén 1966, with revised values from Palmén and Newton 1969).

the whole depth this gives, for H_z in (1.5), an average KE generation of 5.3 W m^{-2} over the area poleward of 32°N. Taking into account the negative generation of KE by the indirect Ferrel circulation (-11×10^{13} W or -0.9 W m^{-2} average over the area), the production by eddies is 6.2 W m^{-2}. Citing energy conversion rates for individual cyclones such as in Section 1.6.3 and the fractional area of the extratropical region they occupy, Palmén concluded that "five such cyclones would suffice to produce the amount of kinetic energy computed from [Fig. 1.13c]." This is compatible with the conclusion in Section 1.4.2, that about five disturbances around the hemisphere can accomplish the required poleward transfers of heat and zonal momentum.

The above evaluations (multiplied by the area of the polar cap) are used in a revision of the idealized scheme (Fig. 1.14) presented by Palmén (1961), to portray the contributions of disturbances and mean meridional circulations in energy conversions over the hemisphere as a whole. Direct solenoidal circulations in the extratropical disturbances are mainly in a W-E plane, generating KE of the meridional flow in these eddies. In units of 10^{13} W, KE generation in the Hadley cell is 30 units, about a third being dissipated by friction within the tropics and 20 units exported to the extratropical cap. About half this amount is degenerated by the Ferrel cell, so that the much larger KE generation by disturbances (75 units) approximately equals the frictional dissipation within the extratropical region.

The total KE generation over the hemisphere (to 5°S) in Fig. 1.14 is 94 units, or an areal mean of 3.4 W m^{-2}. This may be compared with the ECMWF model conversion

from available potential to kinetic energy (for the corresponding season) in Fig. 11.23, which is 2.7 W m^{-2}. While this value is for the whole globe and the comparison is thus not direct, it lends support to Palmén's evaluation derived from the vertical heat flux. (This larger estimate is compatible with both the more vigorous eddy activity and more intense Hadley circulation in the winter hemisphere.) It must be concluded that in this and his earlier investigations, Palmén achieved his objective of establishing firmly the role of extratropical cyclones in the general circulation.

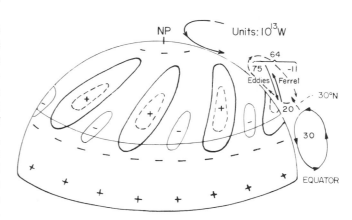

FIG. 1.14.   Schematic field of vertical velocity over the Northern Hemisphere in winter (not considering actual distribution of disturbances around hemisphere). Plus signs denote ascent, minus signs descent. Numbers at right represent estimated values of conversion between PE and KE in tropical and extratropical latitudes, and eddy flux of KE across 30°N. (Modified from Palmén 1961, with revised budget values).

1.8   An Appreciation

Erik Palmén stands as one of the preeminent contributors to our present conceptions of cyclones and the general circulation of the atmosphere. While these have emerged from the efforts of many investigators, his special contributions are unique in their scope and insight, in respect both to the aerological description of atmospheric circulation systems and to the interpretation of their physical processes. His works embrace both tropical and extratropical systems, including fronts and jet streams; the structures of cyclones in their framework; the natures of three-dimensional circulations and their role in air-mass exchanges; discrimination of the subtropical and extratropical wind systems and the processes that sustain them; and illumination of the mechanisms of angular momentum and energy conversions in the perspectives of synoptic disturbances and mean meridional circulations.

Through these multifarious investigations, Palmén played a leading role in the era when the polar-front concepts were extended through three-dimensional aerological analyses and during the emergence of a unified view of the linkages among the various components of the general circulation.

Along the way, Palmén not only trained his students in the techniques and principles of analysis but, more important, his contagious enthusiasm for the scientific enterprise conferred upon them a lasting sense of curiosity and purpose. I am deeply grateful for the special privilege of having been among his students, and of enjoying his and Synnöve Palmén's warm friendship over a period of many years.

Acknowledgments

I am grateful to Dr. Alf Nyberg for reading and giving his judgment of this chapter from the viewpoint of a scientific colleague and esteemed friend of Erik Palmén. Professor Eero Holopainen provided many perceptive comments that led to material improvements. Mrs. Dorene Howard has been most helpful and supportive at every stage, not only in the preparation of this manuscript, but also in editing and setting in final form all the others in this volume.

REFERENCES

Bjerknes, J., 1937: Theorie der aussertropischen Zyklonenbildung. *Meteor. Zeits.,* **54,** 462–466.

――――, and E. Palmén, 1937: Investigations of selected European cyclones by means of serial ascents. Case 4: February 15–17, 1935. *Geofys. Publ.,* **12,** No. 2, 1–62.

Defant, A., and F. Defant, 1958: *Physikalische Dynamik der Atmosphäre.* Akademische Verlag, 527 pp.

Gallimore, R. G., and D. R. Johnson, 1981: The forcing of the meridional circulation of the isentropic zonally averaged circumpolar vortex. *J. Atmos. Sci.,* **38,** 583–599.

Holopainen, E. O., 1985: Erik Herbert Palmén in memoriam. *Geophysica,* **21,** 1–3.

Hoskins, B. J., M. E. McIntyre and A. W. Robinson, 1985: On the use and significance of isentropic potential vorticity maps. *Quart. J. Roy. Meteor. Soc.,* **111,** 877–946.

Hsieh, Y.-P., 1949: An investigation of a selected cold vortex over North America. *J. Meteor.,* **6,** 401–410.

Kutzbach, G., 1979: *The Thermal Theory of Cyclones.* American Meteorological Society, 255 pp.

Lau, N.-C., 1979: The structure and energetics of transient disturbances in the Northern Hemisphere wintertime circulation. *J. Atmos. Sci.,* **36,** 982–995.

Lorenz, E. N., 1967: *The Nature and Theory of the General Circulation of the Atmosphere.* WMO No. 218.TP.115, World Meteorological Organization, Geneva, 161 pp.

Newton, C. W., 1986: Erik Palmén: Synthesizer of the atmospheric general circulation. *Bull. Amer. Meteor. Soc.,* **67,** 282–293.

Nyberg, A., and E. Palmén, 1942: Synoptisch-aerologische Bearbeitung der Internationalen Registrierballonaufstiege in Europa in der Zeit 17–19 October 1935. *Geografiska Annaler,* **24,** 51–93.

Palmén, E., 1931: Die Beziehung zwischen troposphärischen und stratosphärischen Temperatur- und Luftdruckschwankungen. (Über die Natur der sog. primären und sekundären Druckwellen). *Beitr. Phys. fr. Atmos.,* **17,** 102–116.

――――, 1949a: Origin and structure of high-level cyclones south of the maximum westerlies. *Tellus* **1(1),** 1–10.

――――, 1949b: Meridional circulations and the transfer of angular momentum in the atmosphere (with Reply by V. P. Starr). *J. Meteor.,* **6,** 429–430.

――――, 1951a: The aerology of extratropical disturbances. *Compendium of Meteorology,* T. F. Malone, Ed. American Meteorological Society, 599–620.

――――, 1951b: The rôle of atmospheric disturbances in the general circulation (Symons Memorial Lecture). *Quart. J. Roy. Meteor. Soc.,* **77,** 337–354.

――――, 1958: Vertical circulation and release of kinetic energy during the development of hurricane Hazel into an extratropical storm. *Tellus,* **10,** 1–23.

――――, 1959: On the maintenance of kinetic energy in the atmosphere. *The Atmosphere and the Sea in Motion* (Rossby Memorial Volume), B. Bolin, Ed. Rockefeller Institute Press, 212–224.

――――, 1960: On generation and frictional dissipation of kinetic energy in the atmosphere. *Soc. Sci. Fennica, Comm. Phys.-Math.,* **24** (11), 3–15. (Reprinted as *Univ. Helsinki, Inst. Meteor., Papers* No. 87).

――――, 1961: On conversion between potential and kinetic energy in the atmosphere. *Geofis. Pura e Applic.,* **49,** 167–177.

――――, 1966: On the mechanism of the vertical heat flux and generation of kinetic energy in the atmosphere. *Tellus,* **18,** 838–845.

――――, 1985: In my opinion . . . . *Geophysica,* **21,** 5–18.

――――, and K. M. Nagler, 1949: The formation and structure of a large-scale disturbance in the westerlies. *J. Meteor.,* **6,** 227–242.

――――, and C. W. Newton, 1951: On the three-dimensional motions in an outbreak of polar air. *J. Meteor.,* **8,** 25–39.

――――, and E. O. Holopainen, 1962: Divergence, vertical velocity and conversion between potential and kinetic energy in an extratropical disturbance. *Geophysica,* **8,** 89–113.

――――, and L. A. Vuorela, 1963: On the mean meridional circulations in the Northern Hemisphere during the winter season. *Quart. J. Roy. Meteor. Soc.,* **89,** 131–138.

——, and C. W. Newton, 1969: *Atmospheric Circulation Systems.* Academic Press, 603 pp.

——, H. Riehl and L. A. Vuorela, 1958: On the meridional ciculation and release of kinetic energy in the tropics. *J. Meteor.,* **15,** 271–277.

Rossby, C.-G., and V. P. Starr, 1949: Interpretation of the angular-momentum principle as applied to the general circulation of the atmosphere. *J. Meteor.,* **6,** 288.

Starr, V. P., 1948: An essay on the general circulation of the earth's atmosphere. *J. Meteor.,* **5,** 39–43.

White, R. M., and B. Saltzman, 1956: On conversion between potential and kinetic energy. *Tellus,* **8,** 357–363.

Chapter 2

General Circulation Studies in Chicago from the 1940s into the 1950s

Herbert Riehl

1200 Humboldt Street, Denver, Colorado 80218

2.1 Introduction

In the forty years that have passed since the time when Erik Palmén began his period of highest research productivity, the methods of general circulation research have changed drastically. Because of the technical aids that have become available through ever more sophisticated high-speed computers and satellites, nonlinear models of various forms can now be run and tested for time periods often of great length and even involving varying climate conditions over the earth.

In those early days, a concept of the actual general circulation was being pieced together gradually, at first mainly from surface observations, then from upper-air temperatures and pressures as these gradually became available, and finally using the upper winds which previously had been completely missing in cyclones with their cloud shields, just where they were needed most.

The expanding knowledge about the atmosphere and oceans was the subject of many research papers, also the objective of various expeditions into uncharted areas with a variety of aims. Theory, already a main method for attacking the cyclone problem in the Bergen school of Vilhelm Bjerknes, demanded almost visionary insight into the general circulation. The main theoretical tool was to linearize the basic equations, mostly already known from the physicists of the preceding century, and to integrate them with different objectives, of which the formulation of "conservation theorems" was perhaps the most far reaching and successful.

Probably there will be little disagreement in saying that among the researchers of those days Carl-Gustaf Rossby was one of the most outstanding personalities, certainly the best-known leader of such activity for a number of years. He had written an extensive monograph (Rossby 1941) on the general circulation just before the onset of the 1940s war. Like all authors following the original Hadley presentation, he aimed to show the then up-to-date three-cell ageostrophic flow (Fig. 2.1)—very similar to Bergeron's version (1928). In a later interpretation (Rossby 1949), however, a small fourth equatorial cell was included similar to Fletcher's (1945), to depict the widespread existence of double equatorial troughs. This interpretation was later rejected by the Indian meteorologist Asnani (1968) and replaced by him with a new model.

2.2 Rossby's General Circulation Concepts

Rossby seriously reacted to a suggestion by Albert Defant (1921) that a large-scale mixing coefficient should be

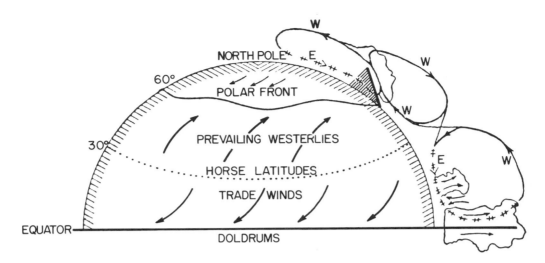

Fig. 2.1. Mean meridional circulation in the Northern Hemisphere atmosphere and mean surface currents (Rossby 1941).

introduced into the flow equations which would confer on the large cyclones and anticyclones of the lower atmosphere more importance in the general circulation scheme than was previously accorded to them. Rossby (1941, Figs. 11 and 12) shows a moving trough in the westerlies, and even a trough with marked northeast-southwest slant which he called a preferential mode for transport of low-latitude heat and moisture into the higher latitudes. But he did not take up the possible importance of the slanting axis as a means for turbulent exchange of momentum across the latitude circles (although he evoked mixing by synoptic-scale eddies to transfer westerly momentum into middle latitudes, from the direct-circulation generating cells to the south and north in Fig. 2.1). One may surmise that the then Assistant Professor V. P. Starr in Chicago derived therefrom an early impetus for his later, now widely known, calculations of cross-latitude mixing processes.

Rossby pursued what had been a central subject to him for years: the "zonal index" (the pressure difference between latitudes 35° and 55° indicating geostrophically the strength of the westerlies), its variations and persistences. He also considered ocean-continent differences and proceeded to his favorite subject of isentropic charts which, after a long interlude, are again receiving attention. He also worked energetically at long range prediction, a subject which his principal assistant, Jerome Namias, has pursued to the time of this writing.

A word should be said here about the choice of coordinate representation at the time. Due to the decrease of absolute angular momentum poleward on the almost spherical earth, the earth's axis of rotation doubtless was suited as one coordinate on a two-dimensional diagram. With height as the other coordinate, variations with longitude were thereby excluded (though they were later included as averages around a latitude circle). The original form of the presentation raised doubts about the middle latitude "reverse cell" in Fig. 2.1. As variously pointed out,

the west winds, without frictional constraint, should decrease rapidly equatorward and go over into easterlies just about where Palmén and others show the maximum subtropical jet stream of winter. This subject, namely the dependence of the sense of circulation upon the coordinate system used, will recur in Section 2.6.

About 1945, as observations kept increasing, Rossby had seen enough of the new high-tropospheric winds and their variations over the globe to voice this criticism of the school of meteorology where he had grown up (Rossby 1947):

It has become increasingly apparent that the original Norwegian model of a deepening storm center, depicted as drawing its kinetic energy from potential energy supplies in the lower troposphere and gradually extending its influence to higher levels, must be supplemented with other models which permit us to account for those cases in which intense circulations first appear at higher levels and then gradually set the lower strata in motion. The dynamic instability of the high-level west wind belt appears to provide an opportunity for the development of such a supplementary model.

This is a radical shift, worth quoting, which Palmén apparently also had to make. The "supplementary model" was provided by Charney's (1947) work on instability in the polar westerlies. Charney had interrupted a journey from California to Scandinavia for the best part of a year, fascinated by the variety of ideas and thrusts in the Chicago offices. One cannot ignore the vast impetus which Palmén and others received from the "ground breaking machine" which was Rossby.

In an initial paper, Rossby (1947) considered at length horizontal mixing in the very shallow atmosphere—a very small vertical scale compared to the horizontal planetary scale—as an agent for equalizing absolute vorticity in the polar latitudes, and various transfer rates equatorward from different latitudinal positions of the maximum wind created by the mixing in the "thin atmospheric shell" on the poleward side. Rossby used scale analysis to relate his calculations to solar rotation data, based on the ratio U/C_E between the zonal motion of the flow (U) and the equatorial velocity of the rotating body (C_E) or a reasonable alternative; this approach also opened the possibility for experimental exploitation of his ideas under various conditions of rotation rates and heat and cold sources.

For this purpose the laboratory of Professor Dave Fultz was established. At first, glass spherical half-shells were reproduced (it was technically very difficult to make them exactly) for his rotating apparatus. Later, and strangely, very useful results were extracted from rotating fluid basins with a flat bottom, which meant that the variation of the Coriolis parameter, which plays so large a role in Rossby's wave analyses, was excluded. A simple approximation to the variation of the Coriolis parameter was obtained at Woods Hole Oceanographic Institution using a curved bottom configuration for water experiments. Despite the promising early results, most of these experiments died out when electronic computers began competing seriously. But the foregoing shows the ultimate strides taken, given the limit to theoretical integrations at the time.

2.3   The Milieu at Chicago

Rossby had the gift of attracting a large number of visitors, most of them passing from Europe westward, to spend some time at the University of Chicago on their travel route; apparently that was a "must" in the late 1940s. Charney's interruption at Chicago on an eastbound route has already been mentioned. The most enduring visitor, at first accompanied by Dr. Alf Nyberg, was Palmén, who kept returning to Chicago for prolonged periods for some 20 years.

I first met Palmén in the autumn of 1946 after returning from a long Caribbean assignment. In the whole winter of 1946–47 there existed a veritable forum in the Chicago meteorology department, centered on a large table on the first floor of the building. There George Cressman offered daily discussions and forecasts with all available maps. The number of attendees was rather variable, perhaps averaging 15 including advanced students, and there was no end to the arguments about general and cyclone circulations which followed the initial discussion. Such a profitable arrangement is found very rarely. Rossby and Palmén were almost always present and they joined in leading the arguments.

2.4   Palmén's and Other Views on Jet Streams

Palmén displayed an early and continuing opposition to the single polar jet stream concept that was so simple and convenient. He thought that the great mass of air convected to the upper troposphere in the tropics could not descend entirely in the subtropics, in disagreement with Fig. 2.1. In fact, when drawing north-south cross sections to the high troposphere became possible over the North American continent, one did find that, with one jet axis centered at, say, the vicinity of the U.S.–Canadian border, a secondary increase in westerly speed was encountered along and around the Gulf Coast to Brownsville, Texas, the southernmost point with sounding data at the time. Palmén saw this secondary rise as indicative of a second wind maximum which executed the entire momentum transfer poleward from the whole tropical zone, with its limit roughly above the surface subtropical highs. As evidence kept accumulating, one began to speak of the "subtropical jet stream," found mainly above 500 mb, at a mean latitude about 27° in the Northern Hemisphere (near 45°N in many regions in summer) and not undergoing the many violent north-south oscillations of the northern, soon to be called "polar," jet stream. The wave length of the latter is in general shorter than in the subtropical jet stream, and a large fraction of the kinetic energy often is contained in the meridional component of motion. Thus, in depictions of the mean distribution of the zonal component (Willett 1944, pp. 131–135), the subtropical jet stream dominates. Due to the land mass topography, mean troughs in the polar and ridges in the subtropical, jet streams sometimes coincide, especially at the east coasts of North America and Asia. Here, then, the greatest mean zonal maxima tend to be observed (Fig. 2.2).

If the flow from the tropics is taken into account as demanded by Palmén, its motion, if frictionless, would be at constant absolute angular momentum, especially when tracked on isentropic surfaces. A fairly good approximation to such motion has been found in limited regions, especially eastern Asia. An idealized profile of zonal wind speed in the 300–200 mb range, near the United States east coast, is presented in Fig. 2.3 in nondimensional coordinates to accommodate many perspectives. The region of the core of strongest wind is a mixture of polar and subtropical jet streams; constant absolute angular momentum is a rather good approximation farther southward. But the lack of isentropic computations as well as frictional dissipation and downward currents rather modify some of the actual profiles.

There was much argument about the origin and maintenance of jet streams. In addition to Rossby and Palmén, principal scientists who were concerned were Victor P. Starr and Jerome Namias. J. Bjerknes should also be noted but he carried out his work more quietly—it had many similarities to Starr's—and he left the arguments to others on his staff. The principal initial bone of contention was the mechanism of absolute angular momentum transport poleward (see Section 1.5.2). Starr insisted that there were no ageostrophic meridional wind components [v] averaged around a latitude circle, and that all angular momentum transport was carried out through the correlation of the relative momentum (u') with its corresponding values of meridional wind (v') around latitude circles. Computations on such circles began deep in the tropics at 10° longitude intervals (i.e., 36 correlations summed for each resultant number) in the winter season, using geostrophic winds instead of actual observations which were still scarce (Starr and White 1951). Indeed, in those days, one could always place the polar jet stream on an upper-air map where there was a big hole in the high-level data; this was even more true for the subtropical current. The early tracking instruments lost the balloons, drifting rapidly eastward.

Palmén took the momentum transport problem very seriously. In the well-known text *Atmospheric Circulation Systems* by Palmén and Newton (1969), these authors take up this subject beginning already on p. 8 and with a large series of references on pp. 23–25 which obviates the need for much repetition here. One of Palmén's outstanding results was that he could show that the subtropical descent of the mass ascended in the deep tropics was at a latitude sufficiently far from the equator so that no $u'w'$ (w denoting vertical motion) meridional correlation was needed (beyond a small friction term) as a mechanism for the vertical transfer of momentum. The difference in latitude between ascent and descent was sufficient so that, of the vast absolute angular momentum transported toward the subtropics, only the quantity forming the jet stream momentum was left in the high troposphere and the balance returned to the surface in slow sinking motion, a significant ageostrophic process.

The constraint for the sinking motion was based on London's (1957) calculations for net cooling in the subtropics. For steady state, there had to be a balance between the dry-adiabatic heating due to sinking and the radiational cooling.

2.5 Lateral Mixing and Meridional Circulations

It was quite typical of the times that theoretical arguments occurred on a variety of topics without the simplest calcu-

lations; ageostrophic motion was one of these. In the present case, the ageostrophic meridional circulation at the surface between latitudes 40°N and 40°S was not determined until 1950, based on a 1938 U.S. Weather Bureau Atlas of the Climatic Charts of the Oceans (Riehl and Yeh 1950). Clearly, an ageostrophic meridional circulation of 1–2 m s^{-1} was found to exist at the surface, especially in winter in both hemispheres. Palmén and Vuorela (Fig. 1.3 of the Palmén–Newton book) later found even somewhat larger components at low levels with completely matching components from the south in the high troposphere centered at 200–300 mb, as far north as latitude 30°N, roughly the mean latitude of the subtropical jet stream axis around the globe.

Rossby's theory of establishing a jet stream maximum through horizontal mixing over a thin polar cap (Fig. 2.4) encountered difficulties. Since the circulation around the boundary is strengthened, the total vorticity over the polar cap must increase from Stokes' theorem. Hearsay has it that this matter was first brought up by a Scandinavian scientist. Possible mechanisms to overcome the problem were offered by Kuo (1951) and Yeh (1951), both located in Chicago at that time. It is necessary to import vorticity poleward by large-scale eddies to and across the jet stream axis. This may seem contradictory a priori but, according to Yeh, it can indeed be a solution. At the surface, he says, friction with the ground perpetually seeks to reduce all wind motion. Since one finds quasi-permanent anticyclones in the subtropics and quasi-permanent cyclones in the subpolar belt, friction tends to destroy anticyclonic vorticity in low latitudes and cyclonic vorticity in high latitudes. Thus cyclonic relative vorticity is transferred from the earth to the atmosphere at low latitudes and is absorbed by the surface at high latitudes. Herewith we obtain the

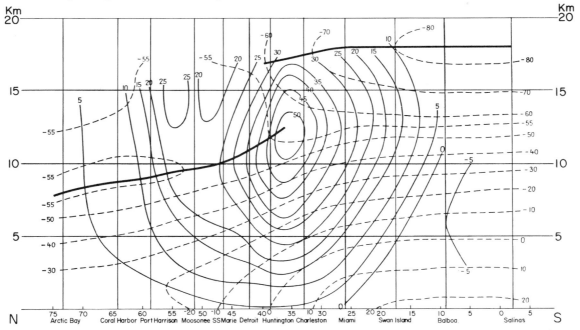

FIG. 2.2. Observed mean temperatures and geostrophic zonal wind component in a vertical cross section along meridian 80°W for January–February 1941–45 (Rossby 1949, analysis by S. L. Hess).

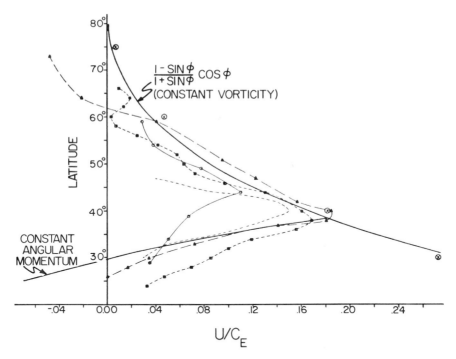

Fig. 2.3. Comparison between theoretical north-south profiles obtained from vorticity and momentum considerations (heavy solid lines) and some observed geostrophic profiles near the tropopause level. The full line represents the average for nine days with fairly straight west winds over North America. Abscissa labeled in U/C_E where C_E is equatorial velocity of the earth's surface. Large circles denote solar rotation data (Staff Members 1947).

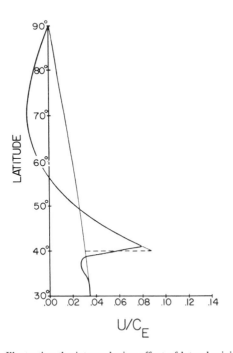

Fig. 2.4. Illustrating the jet-producing effect of lateral mixing over the polar cap. Initial wind distribution (thin) is assumed to represent constant angular velocity; the final distribution is shown by the heavy line. The total absolute angular momentum of the two profiles is the same, but in the final distribution the vertical vorticity has been redistributed by mixing and has assumed a constant value. The discontinuity at latitude 40° is presumably spread out as a result of meridional circulations. Abscissa as in Fig. 2.3 (Staff Members 1947).

needed distribution of sources and sinks to permit a mean relative vorticity flux from the subtropics to the polar belt, against the mean absolute vorticity gradient.

While Yeh's argument helps us overcome the crucial point concerning Fig. 2.4, there remains the problem of how the sharp lateral tropospheric temperature concentration is obtained which, in accord with the geostrophic thermal wind, makes it possible for the strong and narrow wind center to occur. This discussion concerns itself mainly with the polar jet stream, with its many smaller-scale high and low velocity centers moving along the axis of the current. Rossby evidently followed his Gulf Stream picture (1936) with cold temperatures raised from lower depths near the shore, and warm temperatures depressed farther out (eastward) giving rise to a strong current, above 1 m s^{-1}, in the area of concentrated isotherms and even a weak countercurrent near shore. Applying this model to the atmosphere, he arrives at Fig. 2.5 for the troposphere, with the reverse for the stratosphere implying a tropopause height increasing equatorward. With this model the current can decrease above its core. Such a structure is found widely but not exclusively, with respect to the distinct high and low speed centers along the jet stream axis. The wide area of descent in Fig. 2.5 ties in closely with Rossby's work on supergradient westerly winds, to the right of the current in the Northern Hemisphere down the isentropic slopes. The high wind center develops along the main axis in a narrow "reverse cell," similar to the Gulf Stream.

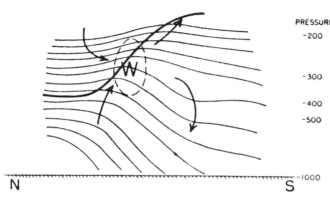

FIG. 2.5. Probable meridional displacements and adjustments with intensification of jet stream (W). Lines of constant potential temperature given by thin lines, tropopause by heavy line. It is probable that meridional arrangements of this type might give rise to frontal waves (Staff Members 1947).

Another view is taken by Namias and Clapp (1949) whose approach is kinematic. Consider, for instance, two bands of waves in the lower and middle troposphere, one in middle latitudes but the other one much farther north. For different wavelengths and speeds, situations can and do arise when a trough in the south becomes situated underneath a ridge in the north. Then the southwest winds of the lower-latitude wave and the northwest winds of the northern one will point toward each other, an arrangement which the authors call "confluence." Bringing their isotherm fields with them, the width of the isotherm concentration is narrowed, the thermal wind is increased and the winds become subgradient, so they are accelerated toward lower pressure. This effect can extend to high levels and thereby lead to the generation or intensification of a longitudinally restricted high wind core along the main jet axis. The high wind core will move forward from the confluence area, and it is here that Rossby's mechanism often applies strongly, more so than the divergence on the forward side postulated by Namias.

It is seen, with such combinations, that the two approaches are not mutually exclusive and also supply a mechanism for the movement of the whole jet stream system. Rossby's approach leads to strengthening of the jet stream nose, while Namias and Clapp (in their Fig. 4) have the perfect picture of the solenoidal circulation and wind field in the rear. Two regions of greatest cloudiness and precipitation should be found to the left forward and right rearward sectors of the high-speed core. The precipitation itself could affect the speed of the whole system. The jet stream maximum should lead to the formation of a new trough of the polar jet downstream and, by means of such "energy dispersion," should rapidly affect the whole hemisphere. Rossby (1949) also proceeds briefly into the subject of blocking action. It may merely be mentioned that, very early on, Rossby spoke of extreme current concentrations resulting in a "hydraulic jump" as the origin of blocks, but I have not been aware of further development of this hypothesis. Thus it will now be preferable to turn to

a few energy calculations and modifications of the earlier three-cell meridional structure concept.

2.6 Meridional versus Jet Stream-Relative Circulations

Both Rossby and Palmén have demonstrated that injection of energy (potential + sensible + latent) into the higher latitudes from longitudinally very limited waves along the westerly jet stream can suffice for energy balance over the "polar cap" (see Section 1.4.2). High-energy air is drawn from latitudes as low as 30° or less to as far as 60° and beyond in narrow channels, with compensating mass balance by reverse cold currents. It has been estimated that a four-wave pattern, marked and persistent, could take care of the whole energy exchange between high and low latitudes in winter. Of course, patterns do not persist in such enhanced forms, so many smaller perturbations must also contribute.

Within the tropics, in contrast, the ageostrophic meridional motion suffices for a steady poleward energy transport to about the poleward limit of the tropics (Palmén et al. 1958). Fig. 2.6a shows the vertical profile of mean thermodynamic energy and Fig. 2.6b the net meridional transport approximately to latitude 30°N in winter. At low levels equatorward winds carry low energy toward the equator; at upper levels the poleward circulation carries high energy. Once again, the difference between tropical and extratropical processes is demonstrated. The picture, however, is not consistent with the three-cell meridional general circulation structure in Fig. 2.1. Again the problem is the middle cell. While it does carry warm air and moisture poleward near the surface, it is generally quite statically stable, so that the upper return current carries more energy than the lower poleward one. This, of course, cannot be correct.

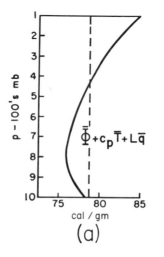
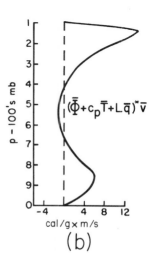

FIG. 2.6. (a) Vertical distribution of total heat content of the air (cal/g) at 15°N for January 1956. (b) Heat transport across 15°N in winter (Palmén, Riehl and Vuorela 1958).

In water basin experiments under imposed conditions of heating and basin rotation rate, structures very similar to those in the atmosphere have been found. Averaging zonally around the basin for a steady three-wave case (Riehl and Fultz 1957), one obtains the vertical motions described in Fig. 2.7a. The strongest westerly flow lies between 0.6 and 0.7 of the non-dimensional radius. If, however, distance from the jet stream axis is plotted as the abscissa, the picture of Fig. 2.7b emerges. The view near the middle of the thickness of the water layer (~500 mb in the atmosphere) is that of Fig. 2.7c. Ascent is concentrated near the ridge, descent around the trough, at a lower latitude. As cyclonic vorticity decreases from trough to ridge, descending changes to ascending motion in the flow paralleling the jet axis. The reverse change occurs during passage from ridge to trough, a very realistic portrayal of the tropospheric motions.

Thus, while a reverse circulation does occur across the jet stream axis in the northwest sector to the trough of the wave, upward motion predominates equatorward of the jet axis upon integration over the whole wave, and a thermally direct total circulation is obtained. It is readily seen that the choice of a coordinate system representing a perceived "mean" circulation and its deviations ("eddies") basically affects the interpretation of the transport mechanism,

although statistically an identical result would be obtained for total transport. Therefore it is very important to differentiate between computational results arising from the choice of a coordinate system and the interpretation of those results to describe actual physical processes in the atmosphere. The jet stream coordinate system just described cannot be used practically for computerized global analysis. But this does not invalidate the reality of Fig. 2.7b compared to Fig. 2.7a, or many other comparisons that could be made.

2.7 Conclusion

Finally, Fig. 2.8 shows Palmén's (1951) well-meaning attempt to present an acceptable compromise to the general circulation description (see discussion in Section 1.5.1). This may serve as a good close to this presentation of the turbulent events in general circulation research for a few years following the order-of-magnitude increase of meteorological observations in the 1940s. Only a few of the more outstanding features could be highlighted here. The possible role of a large contribution of the oceans to energy balance, for instance, was not considered. Matters such as the Southern Oscillation were brought up only intermittently. But that feature was not

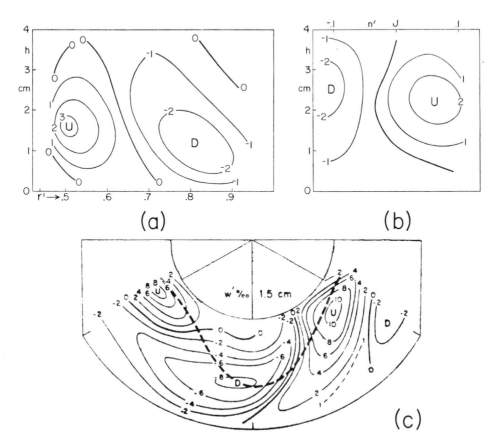

FIG. 2.7.   Rotating 3-wave steady experiment in a circular basin. Nondimensional radius is comparable to that of Figs. 2.3–2.4. (a) Vertical cross section of vertical motion ($^0/_{00}$ of Ωr at the basin rim) when longitudinal averaging follows latitude circles. (U denotes upward, D downward motion.) (b) When longitudinal averaging follows the jet stream axis. (c) Vertical motion at 1.5 cm from basin bottom. Dashed line corresponds to jet axis at top surface (4 cm) (Riehl and Fultz 1957).

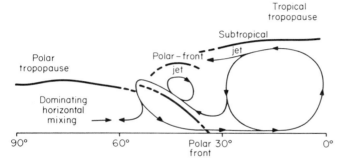

Fig. 2.8. Palmén's (1951) scheme of the general circulation in winter. The solenoidally-direct transverse circulation relative to the meandering polar-front zone is analogous to the circulation in Fig. 2.7b relative to jet-stream waves. This kinetic energy-producing mean circulation contrasts with that of the Ferrel cell, which is analogous to the zonally-averaged Fig. 2.7a.

very well-known and it did not fit into a latitudinal cross section. Palmén's research, continued for a long time after the period covered by this brief summary, has remained a mainstay in widely expanding efforts to model the general circulation with various methods. The impetus started by Rossby's initiative in the middle 1940s, which served as an important stimulus to Palmén's many accomplishments, did not die suddenly with his return from Chicago to Sweden. The big trends of thinking set in motion during that period have only slowly diminished with time and have not disappeared to this day.

REFERENCES

Asnani, G. C., 1968: The equatorial cell in the general circulation. *J. Atmos. Sci.,* **25**, 133–134.

Bergeron, T., 1928: Über die dreidimensional verknüpfende Wetteranalyse (I). *Geofys. Publ.,* **5**, No. 6, 1–111.

Charney, J. G., 1947: The dynamics of long waves in a baroclinic westerly current. *J. Meteor.,* **4**, 135–162.

Defant, A., 1921: Die Zirkulation der Atmosphäre in den gemässigten Breiten der Erde. *Geogr. Annaler,* **3**, 209–265.

Fletcher, R. D., 1945: The general circulation of the tropical and equatorial atmosphere. *J. Meteor.,* **2**, 167–174.

Kuo, H. L., 1951: Vorticity transfer as related to the development of the general circulation. *J. Meteor.,* **8**, 146–150.

London, J., 1957: A study of the atmospheric heat balance. Dept. Meteor., New York University, Final Rep., Contr. AF19(122)–165, 99 pp.

Namias, J., and P. F. Clapp, 1949: Confluence theory of the high-tropospheric jet stream. *J. Meteor.,* **6**, 330–336.

Palmén, E., 1951: The role of atmospheric disturbances in the general circulation. *Quart. J. Roy. Meteor. Soc.,* **77**, 337–354.

——, and C. W. Newton, 1969: *Atmospheric Circulation Systems.* Academic Press, 603 pp.

——, H. Riehl and L. A. Vuorela, 1958: On the meridional circulation and release of kinetic energy in the tropics. *J. Meteor.,* **15**, 271–277.

Riehl, H., and T. C. Yeh, 1950: The intensity of the net meridional circulation. *Quart. J. Roy. Meteor. Soc.,* **76**, 182–188.

——, and D. Fultz, 1957: Jet stream and long waves in a steady rotating dishpan experiment. *Quart. J. Roy. Meteor. Soc.,* **83**, 215–231.

Rossby, C.-G., 1936: Dynamics of steady ocean currents in the light of experimental fluid dynamics. *Papers in Phys. Ocean. and Meteor.,* MIT–Woods Hole Oceanogr. Inst., **5**, No. 1, 43 pp.

——, 1941: The scientific basis of modern meteorology. *Climate and Man, Yearbook of Agriculture.* U.S. Gov't Printing Office, 599–655.

——, 1947: On the distribution of angular velocity in gaseous envelopes under the influence of large-scale horizontal mixing processes. *Bull. Amer. Meteor. Soc.,* **28**, 53–68.

——, 1949: On the nature of the general circulation in the lower atmosphere. *The Atmosphere of the Earth and Planets,* G. P. Kuiper, Ed. University of Chicago Press, 16–48.

Staff Members, Dept. Meteor., Univ. Chicago, 1947: On the general circulation of the atmosphere in middle latitudes. *Bull. Amer. Meteor. Soc.,* **28**, 255–280.

Starr, V. P., and R. M. White, 1951: A hemispheric study of the angular momentum balance. *Quart. J. Roy. Meteor. Soc.,* **77**, 216–226.

Willett, H. C., 1944: *Descriptive Meteorology.* Academic Press, 310 pp.

Yeh, T.-C., 1951: On the maintenance of the zonal circulation in the atmosphere. *J. Meteor.,* **8**, 146–150.

Chapter 3

Advances in Knowledge and Understanding of Extratropical Cyclones during the Past Quarter Century: An Overview

Richard J. Reed

Department of Atmospheric Sciences, University of Washington, Seattle, Washington 98195

3.1 Introduction

The purpose of this chapter is to present an overview of the progress that has been made in knowledge and understanding of the extratropical cyclone in the roughly quarter-century that has elapsed since Palmén worked actively on the subject. It is recognized that other contributors to this volume will describe more fully Palmén's own contributions to the subject and will treat in greater detail various aspects of the subject that are only touched upon here.

With the purpose of keeping the overview to manageable size, it has been decided to focus on only certain aspects of the cyclone problem. Topics to be emphasized are the structures of fronts and cyclones and the processes of frontogenesis and cyclogenesis. Such important topics as the role of cyclones in the general circulation, orographic cyclogenesis and mesoscale precipitation features within cyclones will be left for others to discuss. With the purpose of putting the advances of the past quarter-century into perspective, the development of knowledge and understanding of the extratropical cyclone prior to 1960 will first be sketched.

3.2 Status of the Cyclone Problem Prior to 1960

As documented by Gisela Kutzbach (1979) in her treatise, *The Thermal Theory of Cyclones: A History of Meteorological Thought in the Nineteenth Century,* a considerable knowledge of cyclone structure and behavior existed prior to World War I and many relevant thermodynamic and dynamic principles were understood. Espy, Ferrel, Dove, Loomis, Buchan, Mohn, Ley, Köppen, Bigelow, Margules, von Ficker, Dines and Shaw are among the many early meteorologists whose substantial contributions are described in Kutzbach's book. The picture of cyclones gleaned from the efforts of these early investigators, however, seems fragmentary when viewed against the remarkable synthesis achieved by the Bergen school of meteorologists under V. and J. Bjerknes in the period following World War I. In the polar front theory of cyclones, which they put forth at that time (Bjerknes and Solberg 1922), the cyclone forms as a result of an instability of the polar front, a surface of discontinuity separating tropical and polar air masses. Beginning as a wave on the front, the cyclone undergoes a characteristic life cycle that terminates in the occluded stage in which the tropical air has been lifted aloft by the sinking and spreading of the polar air. The kinetic energy of the cyclone derives from the potential energy released in the rearrangement of the air masses.

These concepts are illustrated in Figs. 3.1 and 3.2, taken from the paper of Bjerknes and Solberg. The first figure depicts the structure of the developing cyclone, showing the arrangement and motion of the warm and cold air masses at the surface (middle panel) and the cloud and precipitation distribution in vertical sections taken to the north (upper panel) and south (lower panel) of the cyclone center. A broad region of cloud and precipitation is seen to form from the upgliding of the warm air along the sloping warm front. A narrower band is produced by the up-thrusting of the warm air by the advancing cold front. The figure represents a slightly revised version of the diagram appearing in J. Bjerknes' (1919) pioneering paper on the subject. Figure 3.2 illustrates the life cycle of the cyclone from its birth as a wave on the polar front to its demise as a decaying vortex within the cold air.

Although a number of features of the polar-front theory remain essentially intact, many modifications and extensions have become necessary as new knowledge has been gained. Swarm or serial ascents by balloon-borne mete-orographs, taken in the late 1920s and early 1930s, gave the first adequate picture of upper-air structure in cyclones. Some knowledge of the structure had been obtained earlier from cloud motions, from mountain observations, from occasional balloon and kite soundings and from manned ascents. The serial ascents revealed, not surprisingly, that the depiction of the polar front as a discontinuity surface separating tropical and polar air masses was an

over-idealization. A narrow layer of transition constituted a more fitting (but still idealized) description of the thermal structure. The altered manner of depicting the polar front is illustrated in Fig. 3.3, taken from a familiar paper of Bjerknes and Palmén (1937).

The serial ascents also revealed the existence of an upper-tropospheric wave located over and rearward of the surface cyclone and the presence of considerable baro-clinity in the warm air above the frontal surface. Thus Bjerknes (1937), in a theoretical paper published con-currently with the aforementioned observational study, recognized two components to cyclogenesis: the pre-viously hypothesized frontal instability and the instability of the upper-level wave in the baroclinic westerlies. The underlying concepts were later elaborated in a joint paper with Holmboe (Bjerknes and Holmboe 1944).

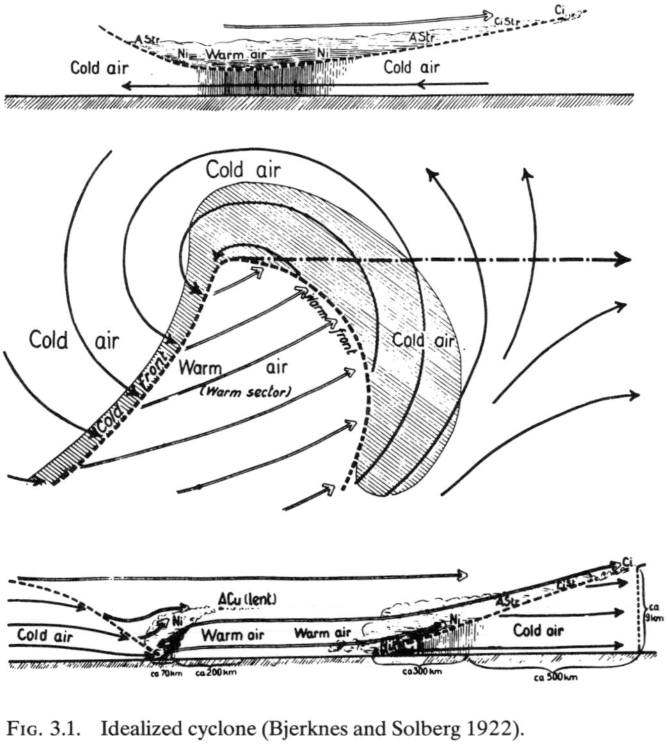

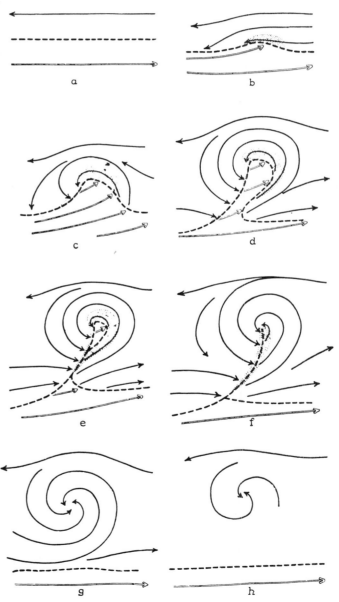

FIG. 3.2.   The life cycle of cyclones (Bjerknes and Solberg 1922). See also Fig. 10.12.

FIG. 3.1.   Idealized cyclone (Bjerknes and Solberg 1922).

With the establishment of radiosonde networks in the late 1930s and 1940s, the stage was set for even more rapid advance in defining the three-dimensional structure of the atmosphere. Particularly notable was the work of the Chicago school under the leadership of Rossby and Palmén (see Chapter 2). Many of the ideas and findings of this school were summarized in a famous paper which they coauthored with nine other distinguished meteorologists (Staff Members 1947). This paper introduced the concept of a jet stream and related the new entity to frontal and tropopause structure. In discussing the meanderings of the upper westerlies (and jet stream) the authors distinguished between slow-moving, long waves with lengths of 50 to 120 degrees of longitude and shorter frontal waves that moved through them and were steered by them. Defant (1912) had earlier speculated on the existence of long circumpolar waves based on his finding of a 5.7-day periodicity in rainfall records, and Bjerknes and Solberg related their idea of cyclone families to the hypothesized waves. The Chicago investigators also discussed the important phenomena of cutoff lows and highs (or blocks) and of downstream development caused by energy dispersion. A feature of the Chicago school, particulary evident in Palmén's work (1951), was the view of synoptic disturbances as vital elements in the exchange processes of the general circulation (Section 1.4). This view also had antecedents in the work of the Bergen school (e.g., Bjerknes and Solberg 1922).

The discovery of the jet stream tended to draw attention away from thermal discontinuities, whether in the temperature itself or in the temperature gradient, and to focus it instead on less sharply bounded zones of enhanced baroclinity. Such a zone is illustrated in Fig. 3.4 which shows a mean cross section through the jet stream on a particular day over North America (Palmén and Nagler 1948). It is evident that the heavy lines, representing the boundaries of the principal frontal layer, are not surfaces of discontinuity

and that a substantial portion of the temperature contrast between the polar and tropical regions resides outside the layer.

Simultaneously with the expanded view of atmospheric structure came a theoretical development of first magnitude: the introduction of the theory of baroclinic instability by Charney (1947) and Eady (1949). This theory shifted emphasis away from frontal discontinuities as the seat of the instability responsible for cyclogenesis to the instability of the broad baroclinic westerlies. The theory successfully predicted the structure of the incipient waves, gave realistic growth rates for their development and accounted for their characteristic wavelengths. The success of the baroclinic theory, coupled with the failure of earlier works on frontal instability (Solberg 1928; Kotschin 1932; Bjerknes and Godske 1936) to obtain a satisfactory solution to the cyclone problem, resulted in general acceptance of baroclinic instability as the fundamental cause of cyclogenesis.

A further change in perspective regarding fronts occurred in the 1950s with Phillips' (1956) first successful numerical simulation of the atmospheric general circulation. In this experiment, started from a simple initial state, baroclinic disturbances formed which later acquired front-like features. Thus the typical frontal structure was seen as a consequence of the cyclogenesis rather than as a cause. Of course, this finding did not change the observational fact that in nature preexisting fronts are a favored seat of cyclogenesis. Cyclones can create fronts that in turn aid in the formation of new cyclones (Eliassen 1966). Actually, this idea was also contained in Bjerknes and Solberg's (1922) description of the cyclone family which required a "mother" cyclone to initiate the wave developments. Later numerical studies by Edelmann (1963), Hoskins and West (1979) and Takayabu (1986), begun from simple initial states featuring continuous but concentrated thermal fields and associated overlying jet streams, have confirmed Phillips' finding. Phillips' early

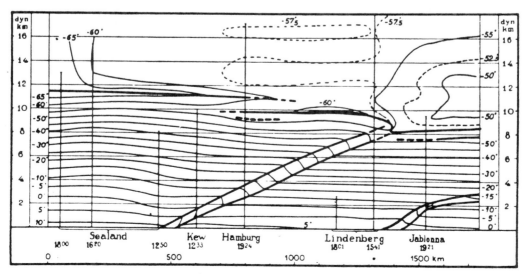

FIG. 3.3. "The 'zonal cross-section,' evening of the 15th of February, 1935" (Bjerknes and Palmén 1937).

picture, with fronts subjectively added, is reproduced in Fig. 3.5.

As the view of the polar front as a semipermanent discontinuity surface diminished and sharp fronts came increasingly to be regarded as transient features of the circulation, interest grew in the process of frontogenesis. Studies by Reed and Sanders (1953), Newton (1954), Reed (1955) and Sanders (1955) looked at the frontogenetical process in actual cases and in three dimensions. These studies made use of kinematical concepts developed by Bergeron (1928), Petterssen (1936) and Miller (1948) and also took account of vorticity considerations (Petterssen and Austin 1942). The studies of Reed and Sanders (1953) and Reed (1955) revealed that, in certain cases at least, strong upper-level frontal zones contained air with potential vorticity values typical of stratospheric air, suggesting an immediate stratospheric origin. The studies also revealed that in such cases a tilting of the isentropic surfaces by differential vertical motion, rather than the classical deformation process, was the prime mechanism in the frontogenesis. Sanders' work (1955) called attention to the extreme intensity that surface fronts can achieve, the rapidity with which the frontal intensity diminishes away from the surface, and the great strength of the frontogenetical process next to the ground, even under apparently steady-state conditions. It does no discredit to his work to state that part of its novelty stemmed from the excessive hold that the idealized picture of a more or less permanent and pervasive polar front had on the meteorological thinking of that era.

The idea that frontal zones are better regarded as regions of active frontogenesis than as semipermanent phenomena had another important consequence. It provided the impetus for Sawyer (1956) to formulate a diagnostic equation that can be used to measure the cross-front, ageostrophic circulation that forms in response to a prescribed frontogenetical forcing. As modified by Eliassen's elegant treatment (1962), this equation, which has come to be known as the Sawyer–Eliassen equation, has received wide application in later treatments of the frontal problem. The physical basis of the equation, first enunciated by Namias and Clapp (1949), is illustrated in Fig. 3.6.

This account of the pre-1960 period would not be complete without mention of the work of Sutcliffe (1947) and Petterssen (1956, pp. 320–339) on the problem of cyclone development. Their objective was to diagnose the factors conducive to cyclogenesis in the complex, finitely disturbed initial states that prevail in the real atmosphere, rather than to determine the growth of small perturbations in highly simplified flows, as done in theoretical studies. The provocative ideas of B type development (Petterssen et al. 1955) and A type development (Petterssen et al. 1962) have been an outcome of Petterssen's work. The former type refers to cyclone development at low levels associated with the approach of a preexisting upper-level trough to a low-level baroclinic zone. The latter type applies to development that takes place in a region of maximum baroclinity with the major contribution coming from the low-level thermal advection rather than from the vorticity advection aloft. Sutcliffe's expression for development, incidentally, was a forerunner of the much used quasi-geostrophic ω-equation (Fjørtoft 1955; Holton 1979, pp. 136–139; Trenberth 1978) which in Q-vector form (Hoskins et al. 1978) has received renewed interest.

3.3 Advances of the Past Quarter Century

As evident from the foregoing account, the post-1960 period began with a substantial knowledge of the major structural features of fronts and cyclones; with some

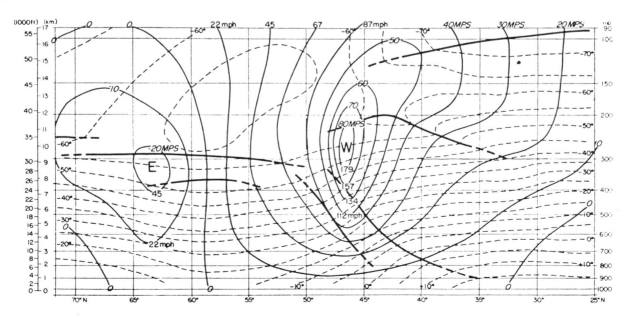

FIG. 3.4.   A mean cross-section for 03 UTC 30 November 1946, showing the geostrophic westerly wind (solid) and temperature (dashed) over North America in a case of westerly flow. Heavy solid lines indicate boundaries of principal frontal layer and tropopause surfaces (Palmén and Nagler 1948).

understanding of frontogenetical processes and their role in frontal circulations; with an accepted instability theory of cyclogenesis (baroclinic instability); and with diagnostic tools (basically the quasi-geostrophic ω-equation) for the study of cyclone development in the real atmosphere. What have been the accomplishments of the past 25 years? From the standpoint of the present overview, the two most impressive advances have been in the areas of (1) theoretical understanding of frontogenesis and (2) numerical modeling of cyclones and cyclogenesis in real situations. These and other important advances of the past quarter-century will now be reviewed.

3.3.1 Surface Fronts and Frontogenesis

As summarized in a review article by Hoskins (1982), theoretical understanding of frontogenesis advanced rapidly in the late 1960s and early 1970s, thanks largely to the work of Stone (1966), Williams (1967, 1972), Hoskins (1971) and Hoskins and Bretherton (1972). In these works, the formation and evolution of fronts were studied on the basis of either a prescribed deformation field or a deformation field produced within an amplifying baroclinic wave. Realistic frontal structures featuring extreme thermal concentrations next to the surface, reminiscent of Sanders' (1955) observational results, were obtained in

several of these studies. Stone's analytic solution, based on a prescribed deformation field and the quasi-geostrophic equations, succeeded in producing a sharp front at the surface but contained a number of unrealistic features, including the lack of a frontal slope, an unrealistic vorticity field, and a thermal gradient that grew exponentially with time so that an infinite time was required for the surface discontinuity to develop. Stone hypothesized that the lack of a frontal slope and the unrealistic vorticity distribution were consequences of the neglect of nonlinearities in the quasi-geostrophic solution, and further hypothesized that the effect of an induced cross-front, ageostrophic circulation would be to tilt the isentropes and thereby produce a realistic thermal wind field and associated vorticity distribution. This hypothesis was borne out by the later work of Williams (1967), in which the primitive equations were solved numerically, and in the work of Hoskins and Bretherton (1972), in which analytic solutions were obtained with use of the geostrophic momentum or semigeostrophic equations (see Section 9.8). A direct comparison of quasi-geostrophic and nongeostrophic frontogenesis was made by Williams (1972).

In addition, Williams' (1967) numerical results suggested that frontal discontinuities can form in finite time in the primitive equation system. Hoskins and Bretherton (1972) proved the correctness of this proposition in the case of the geostrophic momentum equations. Thus the key idea has emerged from these papers that frontogenesis may be regarded as a two-step process, in which the geostrophic deformation field of the growing baroclinic wave first concentrates the thermal gradient, and the induced secondary frontal circulation then causes a "collapse" of the thermal gradient to a true discontinuity near the ground.

Of course, when observed at sufficiently fine resolution, fronts in the real atmosphere always appear as transition zones of finite width, suggesting that some process acts to limit the intensity of the thermal gradient and thereby to bring about a steady-state condition. This process is generally considered to be turbulent diffusion (Welander 1963; Williams 1974). In a numerical experiment that included diffusion, Williams found that fronts can indeed form in a day or two and then persist in a quasi-steady state

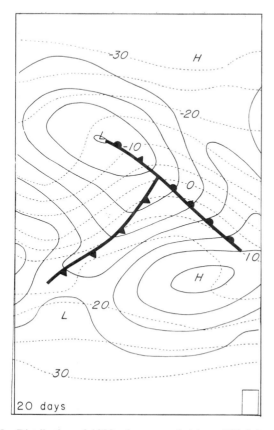

FIG. 3.5. Distribution of 1000 mb contour height at 200-ft intervals (solid lines) and 500-mb temperature at 5°C intervals (dashed lines) at 20 days (Phillips 1956). Fronts (added) have been subjectively located on the basis of the contour and isotherm configurations.

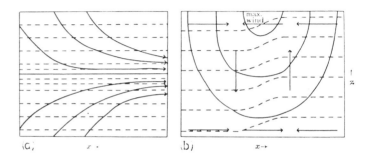

FIG. 3.6. (a) Horizontal distribution of streamlines (solid) and isotherms (dashed) in a frontogenetic confluence. (b) Vertical section showing confluent flow and the induced transverse ageostrophic circulation required to maintain thermal wind balance under the frontogenetical action (Sawyer 1956).

in which the frontogenetical processes are balanced by diffusive processes.

On the other hand, Orlanski et al. (1985) have argued that as the frontal scale becomes even moderately small, nongeostrophic accelerations (not contained in semigeostrophic theory) may lead to a reduction of the vorticity generation, thereby limiting the frontal strength. Gall et al. (1987) have recently tested this hypothesis in a nonhydrostatic, nondiffusive, primitive equation model in which the horizontal grid size was systematically reduced from 20 km to 280 m and the vertical resolution reduced from 320 m to 40 m. They found no evidence of a physical process that limits frontal collapse in the absence of diffusion, though their experiments did show some tendency for the line of maximum vorticity and line of maximum convergence to separate with time, as happened in the numerical experiments of Ross and Orlanski (1982) and Orlanski and Ross (1984).

Paradoxically, although turbulent diffusion appears to be the main mechanism limiting the frontal scale, surface friction, as demonstrated long ago by Eliassen (1959), strengthens the transverse frontal circulation near the ground and thereby contributes to surface frontogenesis. Eliassen's qualitative arguments have since been given quantitative support by aircraft measurements taken within a fully developed, quasi-steady front over the ocean (Bond and Fleagle 1985), though Eliassen (1966) later acknowledged some weaknesses in his earlier arguments (see Section 9.5). Bond and Fleagle evaluated indirectly the total forcing of the cross-front circulation by substituting observed data in the left-hand side of the Sawyer–Eliassen equation (see Section 9.2, Eqs. (9.12) and (9.13)). They then compared the inferred forcing with the forcing derived from the observed geostrophic wind and temperature fields, the forcing that ordinarily appears in the equation and estimates of the additional forcings caused by condensation heating and boundary-layer friction. The inferred forcing showed a strong maximum at 900 mb just ahead of the front (see vertical motion distribution in Fig. 8.23). A similar, but somewhat weaker, maximum appeared in the directly computed total forcing. This mainly resulted from the frictional component.

The effect of latent heat release in clouds on frontogenesis has been investigated in numerous studies (Hoskins and Bretherton 1972; Williams et al. 1981; Mak and Bannon 1984; Hsie et al. 1984; Ross and Orlanski 1978; Baldwin et al. 1984; Hsie and Anthes 1984; Bannon and Mak 1984). These studies have shown that condensation heating has a substantial enhancing effect. This result is not surprising in view of Sawyer's (1956) and Eliassen's (1959) early demonstrations that latent heat release strengthens the cross-front ageostrophic circulation.

It is evident from the Sawyer–Eliassen equation that small static stability or, more generally, small symmetric stability (Hoskins 1974) can also have a substantial enhancing effect on the secondary frontal circulation. The effect of small symmetric stability was first demonstrated

by Hoskins and Bretherton (1972) in an example that assumed the potential vorticity to be everywhere zero. Such a condition corresponds to a symmetrically neutral state. The neutral state is rarely seen in a dry atmosphere but, as these authors and others (e.g., Kleinschmidt 1941; Sawyer 1949; Bjerknes 1951; Bennetts and Hoskins 1979; Emanuel 1983; Sanders and Bosart 1985) have pointed out, it can readily be achieved along moist isentropic surfaces in cloudy air. Studies by Emanuel (1985) and Thorpe and Emanuel (1985) show the great narrowing and intensification of the frontal upglide that occurs when the moist symmetric stability is small. Their results were anticipated in a little-known work of Todsen (1964), discussed and illustrated in Section 9.7.

On the observational side, the most notable advance in knowledge of frontal structure has been the documentation from aircraft, tower and radar wind-profiler data of the remarkable intensity that fronts can achieve in the vicinity of the ground. Sudden wind shifts and sharp temperature drops with passage of cold fronts have been recognized by meteorological observers for a century or more, and examples of these can readily be found on strip charts from continuously recording instruments. Nevertheless, recent measurements of Shapiro (1984), Shapiro et al. (1985) and Bond and Fleagle (1985) have added significantly to the picture of frontal structure in the boundary layer. In particular, their results show that intense cold fronts have the appearance of the density currents seen in laboratory experiments and in their atmospheric counterpart, the squall line. A striking feature is the narrow plume of rapidly ascending air (width on the order of a kilometer or less and speed on the order of 5–10 m s^{-1}) that occurs at the nose of the front (see Figs. 8.23 and 10.9). The plume has also been measured by Doppler radar (Browning and Harrold 1970; Carbone 1982; Hobbs and Persson 1982) and is responsible for what is termed the narrow cold front band in the Houze and Hobbs (1982) classification of mesoscale rainbands. Cloud and precipitation, however, are not essential for its formation, as evidenced by its occasional occurrence in dry air (Shapiro 1984). Diagrams from Shapiro's paper are shown in Fig. 3.7. The upper panel illustrates the extreme sharpness of the front. Only ten seconds were required for the front to pass the instrumented tower from which the measurements were taken. At the observed frontal velocity of 17 m s^{-1} this time interval corresponds to a frontal width of 170 m.

The lower panel shows the vertical velocity measured at the front. Already at 300 m the velocity exceeded 5 m s^{-1} in the warm air just ahead of the narrow transition zone. It is perhaps of significance that the warm air ahead of the front and the cold air to the rear were highly unstable, possessing superadiabatic lapse rates from the heated ground to the uppermost level. Keyser and Anthes (1982) obtained a similar but much weaker plume in a numerical experiment with horizontal grid resolution of 20 km that incorporated boundary layer physics. Their diagnosis

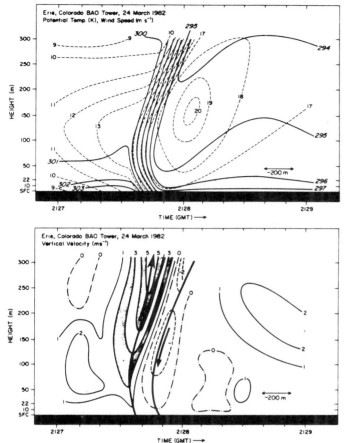

Fig. 3.7. Upper panel: Cross sectional (time series) analysis of BAO wind tower temperature and wind measurements. Lower panel: Corresponding analysis of vertical motion. Note the distance scale in lower right (Shapiro 1984).

revealed that the jet-like feature, as in the case study of Bond and Fleagle (1985) and in a later model simulation of Baldwin et al. (1984), was a consequence of surface friction.

Also worthy of mention on the observational side are the studies of the phenomenon of coastal frontogenesis by Bosart et al. (1972), Bosart (1975, 1981) and Keshishian and Bosart (1987). These highlight an additional mechanism that can produce substantial frontal circulations—the differential heating that takes place between land and sea when a cold polar anticyclone moves offshore. The process is aided by elevated terrain that traps the cold air in the vicinity of the coast and by latent heat release in cumuliform clouds that form over the warm waters. The most pronounced cases of coastal frontogenesis occur along the Carolina coast of the eastern U.S. where the coastal configuration, in combination with the proximity of the warm Gulf Stream waters and elevated terrain of the Appalachian Mountains, create an unusually favorable set of conditions. Some success in modeling the phenomenon has been achieved by Ballentine (1980), Stauffer and Warner (1987) and Uccellini et al. (1987).

3.3.2 Upper-Level Fronts and Frontogenesis

Prior to the early 1960s some doubts existed regarding the validity of the tropopause folding concept (Reed 1955), in which a tongue of stratospheric air was envisaged to descend into the upper or middle troposphere and assume the character of an upper-level frontal zone. These doubts were largely dispelled by aircraft observations made by Briggs and Roach (1963), who measured humidity and ozone mixing ratios near jet streams and found in some cases protrusions of stratospheric air with low water vapor and high ozone content within sharply-bounded frontal zones beneath the jet stream core. Briggs and Roach's results were reinforced a short time later when Danielsen (1964, 1968) succeeded in directing aircraft carrying radioactivity measuring equipment through an intense upper-tropospheric frontal zone. Having been deposited in the stratosphere in nuclear weapons tests, the radioactivity, like ozone, served as a tracer of stratospheric air.

Some of Danielsen's results are reproduced in Figs. 3.8 and 3.9. Figure 3.8 depicts traces of temperature and accumulated total β activity measured at two flight levels during back-and-forth transects through the frontal zone.

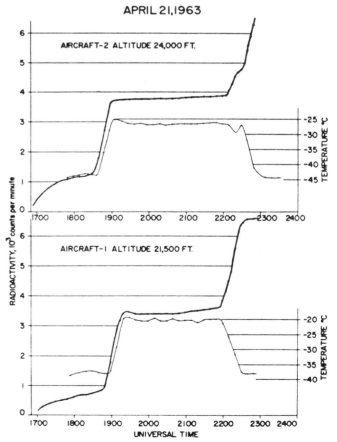

Fig. 3.8. Continuous traces of accumulated total β activity (cpm) and temperature measured along WB-50 flight paths in Fig. 3.9 (Danielsen 1968).

A nearly perfect match is seen between the two traces. On both warm and cold sides of the zone, the radioactivity is low (small slope of the curve) signifying tropospheric air. Within the zone, the extraordinary intensity of which is evidenced by the nearly 20°C temperature change across it, the radioactivity is vastly greater (steep slope). The presence of stratospheric air is proved beyond doubt.

A cross section through the tropopause fold, depicting β activity of strontium-90 and potential vorticity, appears in Fig. 3.9. Also shown are the flight paths of the WB-50 aircraft. The stratospheric extrusion is plainly evident in both the radioactivity and potential vorticity. Other equally remarkable tropopause folds have been documented in later penetrations of upper-level fronts by instrumented aircraft (Danielsen and Mohnen 1977; Shapiro 1978, 1980; Danielsen et al. 1987). Bosart (1970) has made an in-depth study of an extreme case that occurred at a time when a special series of three-hourly radiosonde ascents were taken in the eastern U.S. In the works cited, a variety of tracers have been employed including radioactivity, ozone, carbon monoxide, water vapor, condensation nuclei and potential vorticity.

Since, in general, isentropic potential vorticity is not conserved in the presence of diabatic heating and viscous and other nonconservative body forces (Staley 1960), it cannot be expected to be as conservative as some of the other tracers. In particular, Shapiro (1976, 1978) has presented examples of abnormally large stratospheric potential vorticity values, immediately on the cyclonic side of the jet core (see Fig. 10.4), that have no counterparts in the ozone distribution. He has explained these anomalous amounts in terms of the vertical divergence of turbulent heat fluxes above and below the jet core, but his interpretation has been questioned by Danielsen et al. (1987).

Because of the issue of stratospheric-tropospheric exchange, the subject of turbulent mixing in the vicinity of tropopause folds has attracted much interest, but the topic is beyond the scope of this overview.

Diagnostic studies of upper-level frontogenesis have focused on the problem of explaining the cross-stream indirect thermal circulation that observational studies (e.g., Reed and Sanders 1953) have shown is essential to the process. Two mechanisms have been proposed: (1) the mechanism introduced by Palmén and Nagler (1949), and recently revived by Newton and Trevisan (1984a), in which an indirect circulation forms in a plane normal to the jet stream as air flows from an upstream ridge to a downstream trough under the constraint of gradient wind balance; and (2) the mechanism postulated by Shapiro (1981), based on the Sawyer–Eliassen equation, in which an along-front thermal gradient within an essentially straight frontal zone produces a shift of the downward branch of the transverse circulation from the cold to the warm side of the zone. The underlying mechanism was first discussed by Eliassen (1962) with reference to lower-level warm frontal circulations. In the upper-level case the along-front thermal gradient is such that cold advection occurs (Shapiro 1983). Uccellini et al. (1985) applied the Sawyer–Eliassen equation to an actual case of tropopause folding, successfully reproducing the measured transverse circulation while isolating the effect in question.

As described by Bosart (1970) and Shapiro (1983), most cases of intense upper-level frontogenesis occur when a short-wave trough moves in a northwesterly current from an upstream long-wave ridge to an amplifying (or "digging") downstream long-wave trough. Thus the two mechanisms (if they can be regarded as dynamically independent) reinforce each other (see Section 10.2.2). Gen-

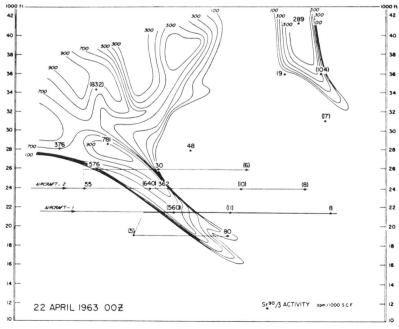

FIG. 3.9. Potential vorticity (contoured at intervals of 100×10^{-9} m s K kg^{-1}) and β activity of strontium-90 (dpm/KSCF) (Danielsen 1968).

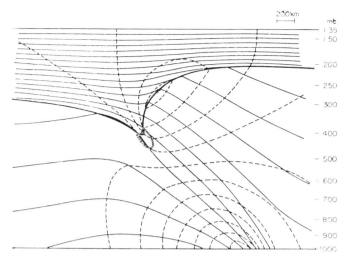

FIG. 3.10. Upper-level frontogenesis in a two-region semigeostrophic model. Solid lines, potential isotherms (interval 7.8 K); dashed lines, isotachs (interval 10.5 m s^{-1}). Richardson number contour value of 1.0 is indicated by small circles (Hoskins 1971).

erally the strongest thermal gradient is achieved in the vicinity of the trough axis, but occasionally the zone of maximum intensity advances somewhat ahead of it. Examples may be found in Reed (1955) and Bosart (1970).

Limited success has been achieved in simulating upper-level fronts and tropopause folds with two-dimensional dynamical models. The solution to the analytic model of Hoskins (1971) and Hoskins and Bretherton (1972), in which a uniform horizontal deformation field was allowed to act on an initial temperature field, is shown in Fig. 3.10. The model uses the geostrophic momentum and Boussinesq approximations and contains a tropopause separating a tropospheric region of small uniform potential vorticity below from a stratospheric region of large potential vorticity above. The solution shows a rudi-

mentary tropopause fold. Another noteworthy feature is the distinct separation of the upper- and lower-level fronts. A subsequent nonBoussinesq solution (Hoskins 1972) yielded an even more pronounced penetration of the stratospheric air into the troposphere, but neither simulation gave a fold of the magnitude seen in real cases.

Buzzi et al. (1981), using a two-dimensional semigeostrophic model in isentropic coordinates, extended Hoskins' work to include a continuous potential vorticity distribution. A jet structure was prescribed, and upper and lower boundaries were chosen to be isentropic. An internal upper-tropospheric front formed under these conditions in response to the imposed deformation field but, as the authors pointed out, the circulation transverse to the front was direct, not indirect as found in observational studies. Moore (1987) has also studied the effect of a continuously-varying potential vorticity. According to Shapiro's (1981) diagnosis, however, an indirect frontal circulation can occur in the two-dimensional case provided there exists an along-front thermal gradient with cold advection within the zone. This idea has been tested by Keyser and Pecnick (1985) in a two-dimensional primitive equation model patterned after the work of Hoskins and Bretherton (1972). Their results, shown in Fig. 3.11, confirm Shapiro's reasoning. The "cold advection" case (Fig. 3.11b) exhibits an upper-level frontal zone, after 24 hours of integration, that is stronger than that of the "pure confluence" case (Fig. 3.11a) and that has the maximum subsidence displaced toward the warm side of the zone.

A number of studies of upper-level frontogenesis have been performed using three-dimensional models (Mudrick 1974; Shapiro 1975; Buzzi et al. 1977; Hoskins and West 1979; Heckley and Hoskins 1982; Newton and Trevisan 1984b). In general these have produced realistic fronts, but none has succeeded in duplicating some of the extreme

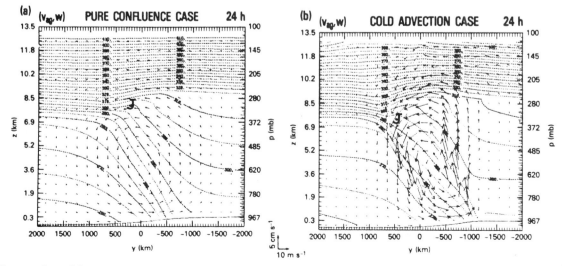

FIG. 3.11. Cross sections of the transverse ageostrophic circulation and potential temperature after the 24-h integration of a two-dimensional primitive equation model of frontogenesis due to (a) pure confluence and (b) confluence in the presence of upper-level cold advection (Keyser and Pecnick 1985). See also Fig. 10.7.

cases observed. It is possible that the oversimplified initial states used in the model simulations lack essential features of the initial states that are present in actual situations. For a more comprehensive discussion of upper-level fronts, the reader is referred to a recent review by Keyser and Shapiro (1986). A review of observational aspects of fronts, both upper and lower, can be found in Keyser (1986). Overviews of the subject are presented by Eliassen in Chapter 9 of this volume from the theoretical viewpoint, and by Shapiro and Keyser in Chapter 10 with emphasis on recent observational studies.

3.3.3 The Cyclone as Viewed from Space

Slightly more than a quarter-century has elapsed since a new observational tool of immense importance—the meteorological satellite—was introduced into meteorology. Cloud patterns seen in visible and IR images by the early polar-orbiting satellites have given a fresh perspective on cyclone structure and behavior, and the ability of satellites to view the entire globe has allowed cloud systems in cyclones over the oceans to be adequately documented for the first time. Geostationary satellites introduced later have provided time-lapse pictures that have proved particularly valuable in studying the evolution of cloud features and, with the help of water vapor imagery, moisture patterns as well (Petersen et al. 1984). Passive microwave radiometers have already shown promise in identifying integrated water vapor, cloud-water and rainwater patterns in cyclones, and doubtless will be used increasingly in both operations and research (McMurdie and Katsaros 1985).

What has been learned from this new observational tool regarding cyclone structure and evolution? One way to address this query is by posing a further question: How well has the classical picture of cloud organization put forth by members of the Bergen school (e.g., Bjerknes and Solberg 1921, 1922) stood up under the new stream of observations? Most investigators would agree that it has stood up very well, particularly over the oceans where the moisture supply is always sufficient to assure identifiable cloud masses. Numerous examples can be found in which the cloud patterns conform at each stage of development to the classical scheme. Cold, warm and occluded fronts are observed to have the expected signatures (WMO 1973).

On the other hand, numerous cases also exist in which the cloud patterns and their evolutions are complex and not easily fitted into the classical mold. In view of the expanded knowledge of cyclone structure that has been acquired since the classical picture was first propounded, the complexity is not surprising. The original cyclone model was founded on the idea of the cyclone as a wave on the polar front. Later came the idea of the upper baroclinic wave, and still later the concept of the jet stream. These new entities were viewed as being related to frontal waves and frontal zones, yet as having separate identities.

Obviously the added circulation patterns associated with the upper waves and jet stream should be expected to complicate the simple picture derived from frontal considerations alone. Also the recognition that frontogenesis and cyclogenesis often occur in tandem rather than sequentially, and that interactions between more or less independent upper- and lower-level components are involved in many instances of cyclogenesis (Petterssen Type B), opens the possibility for a still wider range of structures. Clearly, modifications and extensions of the simple classical model are warranted and indeed have flourished (perhaps excessively) in the satellite literature.

An example of a modified scheme appears in Fig. 3.12. This illustrates the separation often made by satellite meteorologists between cirrostratus decks that lie on the warm or anticyclonic-shear side of the jet axis, and frontal clouds, whose tops are located at discretely lower levels. Although it might be speculated that the presence of distinct upper and middle-to-lower cloud patterns is indicative of distinct components to the vertical motion field, it is possible that the initial moisture distribution also plays a crucial role in shaping the cloud patterns (Durran and Weber 1988). As yet no satisfactory explanation exists concerning why the cloud tops vary more or less continuously with height in some cases, as postulated in the Norwegian model, and why in other cases they are arranged in steps.

Another pattern of development, often seen in satellite pictures but not included in presatellite thinking, involves cyclogenesis in cold air masses rearward of the polar front and poleward of the jet stream axis. Occurring mainly over the oceans during the winter half-year, the disturbances in question are first seen in satellite imagery as regions of enhanced cumulus convection. Subsequently the convective elements spread and merge, and a more or less solid comma-shaped cloud mass emerges. The final shape is not unlike that of many developing frontal cyclones, but typically the cold air systems are smaller in dimension. A satellite picture of such a system is shown in Fig. 3.13.

As illustrated schematically in Fig. 3.14, the disturbances are known to form in the region of positive vorticity advection ahead of a secondary upper-level vorticity maximum (Anderson et al. 1969; WMO 1973) or, from an alternative viewpoint, in the left exit region of a jet streak. It has further been found (Reed 1979; Mullen 1979; Reed and Blier 1986a,b) that the region of formation is characterized by weak to moderate baroclinity, appreciable surface fluxes of heat and moisture, and a conditionally unstable lapse rate through a substantial depth of the atmosphere. The systems are believed to be closely related to the polar lows that have been much discussed by British and Norwegian meteorologists, and indeed they are often regarded as one category of polar low (Businger and Reed 1989).

When a cold air comma approaches sufficiently close to the polar front, it may induce a wave development on the latter (Anderson et al. 1969). In many instances the wave

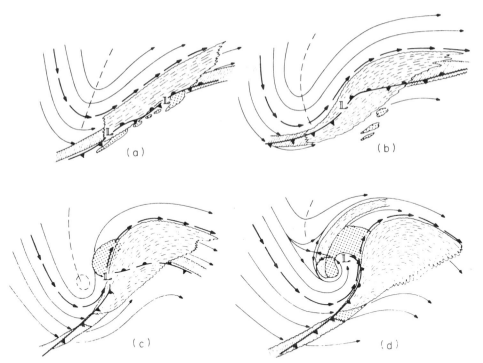

Fig. 3.12. Schematic diagram of the cloud patterns associated with an extratropical cyclone at four stages of development. Dashed lines indicate cirrostratus cloud decks, cross-hatching frontal cloud bands, and dots show low- or middle-level cloud decks. (Adapted from lecture notes of Roger B. Weldon by Wallace and Hobbs 1977, p. 262.) See also Fig. 8.11.

grows into a typical frontal cyclone, and the comma is rapidly absorbed into the frontal low. In other cases the wave and comma cloud maintain separate identities. Cases can also be found in which the polar low becomes the dominant partner (Reed 1979). In certain cases the merging of the two components have been described as "instant occlusion," the idea being that the comma supplies the low center on the poleward side of the jet axis and the frontal wave supplies the warm and cold fronts (Anderson et al. 1969). The process has been clarified in recent work by Browning and Hill (1985) and McGinnigle et al. (1988; described in Section 8.5). A case in which the merger of a comma cloud and frontal wave produced a major oceanic cyclone has been documented by Mullen (1983). The dual nature of the development is plainly evident in Figs. 3.15 and 3.16 which show satellite pictures and surface maps, respectively, of the evolving systems.

A method that has been found useful for understanding cloud patterns in cyclones is that of analyzing the flow on isentropic surfaces relative to a coordinate system moving with the storm (Kleinschmidt 1957, p. 135; Green et al. 1966; Browning and Harrold 1969; Carlson 1980). Browning presents a comprehensive discussion in Chapter 8. Provided the patterns are not undergoing rapid changes of shape, the streamlines of the relative flow represent air trajectories relative to the storm. Unfortunately, many of the most interesting situations involve rapid changes of shape, thereby complicating the interpretation. Furthermore, upper-air data needed for constructing such charts are available only at 12-hour

intervals. A possible way around these difficulties is through use of trajectories constructed from the output of numerical prediction models that provide essentially continuous fields. Of course, to yield reliable information, the models must simulate accurately the development of the weather system under study, particularly the development of the cloud fields. Fortunately, the most advanced of the current operational and research models have reached the stage where meaningful diagnosis is possible.

3.3.4 Cyclogenesis

Theoretical studies of baroclinic instability have expanded greatly in number and scope during the past quarter-century. The pioneering studies of Charney and Eady employed linearized equations, a dry atmosphere and a basic flow characterized by vertical shear only. Later studies have utilized zonal jets with meridional as well as vertical shear (Pedlosky 1964a,b; Brown 1969a,b; Song 1971; Gall 1976a,b; Simmons and Hoskins 1976), have extended the analysis into the nonlinear regime (Simons 1972; Simmons and Hoskins 1978) and have treated moist processes (Gall 1976c; Mak 1982; Emanuel et al. 1987). It has been found that the inclusion of lateral shear, and hence of barotropic energy conversion processes, has only minor effects on the properties of the unstable baroclinic modes (e.g., Simmons and Hoskins 1976). The largest impact of the studies with zonal jets, particularly those extending into the nonlinear regime, has been in the knowledge gained regarding the interactions between the disturbances and the basic flow (Brown 1969b; Song 1971; Gall 1976b) and the variation of the interactions within the life cycle of the baroclinic wave (Simons 1972; Simmons and Hoskins 1978). The extended integrations with zonal jets have, as mentioned previously, yielded realistic cyclone and frontal evolutions (Edelmann 1963; Hoskins and West 1979; Takayabu 1986).

Condensation heating has been found by Gall (1976c) to enhance the growth rates of baroclinic disturbances at all wavelengths, but not to change the wavelength of maximum growth. Mak (1982) also found that condensation heating significantly increases growth rates but, contrary to Gall, obtained a significant decrease in the size of the most unstable wave. Of particular interest in connection with the effects of moist processes is the recent paper by Emanuel et al. (1987), in which they examine baroclinic instability in conditions of small stability to slantwise moist convection. Their results show the greatly enhanced growth rates and shortened wavelengths that are obtained as the moist potential vorticity, the measure of slantwise or symmetric stability, approaches zero. As remarked by the authors, in the semigeostrophic system of equations the potential vorticity acts as an effective static stability. It is the equivalent of the static stability in the quasi-geostrophic system. In this connection, previous studies (Staley and Gall 1977; Duncan 1977) using dry quasi-geostrophic models have revealed the scale-shortening effect of reduced static stability in the lower troposphere. Hayashi and Golder (1981), in a general circulation experiment comparing dry and moist atmospheres, found that baroclinic disturbances were much more energetic in the moist atmosphere and attributed this result to the lesser static stability that prevails under moist conditions.

A preponderance of the studies cited above have dealt with perturbations of normal mode form. Farrell (1982, 1984), however, has pointed out that in order to represent the initial conditions that exist in the real atmosphere prior to cyclogenesis, for example the conditions associated with Petterssen Type B development, it is necessary to augment the discrete normal modes by a continuous spectrum of neutral modes. Transient growth depends on the continuous spectrum; only at later stages do the normal modes predominate. In later work Farrell (1985, 1989) has further explored his contention that an initial value approach, rather than a normal mode approach, is required to study cyclogenesis in the real atmosphere. Another aspect of nonmodal baroclinic wave growth has been studied by Simmons and Hoskins (1979) with the use of a nonlinear primitive-equation model. They demonstrate how a localized disturbance introduced in a baroclinically unstable flow produces downstream (and upstream) wave development through energy dispersion.

It was mentioned earlier that prior to the advent of baroclinic instability theory a number of attempts were made, but with only limited success, to solve the problem of the stability of frontal waves, that is, waves on an ideal surface of discontinuity. This problem was addressed later by Orlanski (1968) for a wide range of Rossby and Richardson numbers. Based on his analysis, Orlanski identified four distinct regions of instability that he associated with the names of Rayleigh, Helmholtz, Eady and Bjerknes. Mechoso and Sinton (1983) have shown that the Bjerknes mode results from a juxtaposition of Rayleigh and Eady modes, and Sinton and Mechoso (1984) have studied the nonlinear evolution of the frontal waves, using a two-layer, shallow-water model. They show examples of rather realistic looking frontal cyclones for the Eady and Bjerknes modes. The relevance of their results to the less than ideal frontal cyclones that occur in nature remains to be clarified. In this connection it should be mentioned that Moore and Peltier (1987), in examining the stability of realistic frontal zone/jet stream structures, found the existence of a short-wave branch of unstable normal modes that is distinct from the classical Charney-Eady modes. The fastest growing mode in the newly discovered branch has a wavelength of about 1000 km. It derives its energy from the baroclinic conversion process.

A novel approach to understanding cyclogenesis, based on the conservation of isentropic or Rossby–Ertel potential vorticity, has been put forth by Hoskins, McIntyre and Robertson (1985). Underlying their approach is the invertibility principle, earlier recognized and utilized by Kleinschmidt (1957, pp. 113–116), which states that, subject to specification of a balance condition and a suitable reference state, the potential vorticity distribution is sufficient to infer the fields of the other meteorological variables such as winds, temperatures and geopotential heights. The approach has much pedagogical appeal, in that for dry-adiabatic motion it links earlier and later atmospheric states through a single simple conservation principle. During moist-adiabatic motion the (dry) isentropic potential vorticity is not conserved, and application of the principle becomes more complicated.

The final noteworthy advance in knowledge and understanding of extratropical cyclones, and in many ways the most remarkable, is in the realm of numerical prediction of cyclone development. It is easy to lose sight of the fact that every day at forecast centers around the world our knowledge of cyclones (or, more precisely, of the laws that govern their behavior) is being tested in real situations. The general success of the forecasts in data-rich areas bears witness to the fact that the cyclogenetical process is indeed now well understood—at least by the computer! Sensitivity experiments, in which various physical processes are withheld in turn from a full-physics control forecast, offer a means for better human understanding of the processes involved (see Section 12.3.2). Such experiments are becoming increasingly common.

Because of the special importance of rapidly intensifying storms and the difficulty, at least until recently, of predicting them (Sanders 1987), explosive cyclogenesis—defined roughly as deepening in excess of 24 mb in 24 hours (Sanders and Gyakum 1980)—has attracted much attention in recent years. Sanders and Gyakum showed that

FIG. 3.13.   Example of comma-shaped cloud pattern (indicated by arrow) in a polar air mass (Reed 1979).

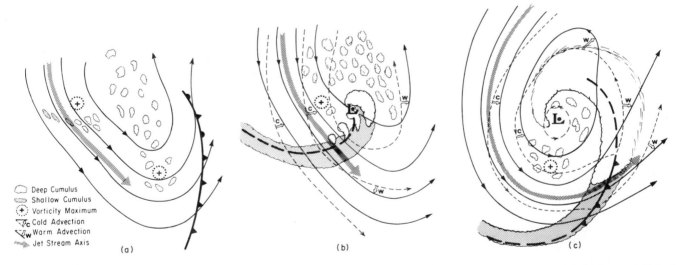

FIG. 3.14.   Schematic diagram of comma cloud development: (a) incipient stage, (b) intensifying stage, (c) mature stage. Solid lines are 500 mb contours; dashed lines are surface isobars. Heavy broken line marks the surface trough. Frontal symbol in (c) indicates that the trough may assume frontal characteristics in some cases. Further explanation at lower left (Reed and Blier 1986a).

rapidly deepening storms are primarily maritime, cold season events and that they occur usually somewhat downstream of a mobile 500 mb trough within or poleward of the maximum westerlies and within or ahead of planetary-scale troughs. They found, furthermore, that such storms occur most frequently at the western ends of the Atlantic and Pacific storm tracks, preferentially near the regions of strongest SST gradients. They concluded from their study that explosive cyclones are baroclinic events aided by diabatic heating of an unidentified character. The baroclinic nature of explosive cyclones and their association with conditions that favor deep convection has

been verified in a compositing study, based on weather ship observations, by Rogers and Bosart (1986).

Detailed case studies have been made of a number of extraordinary storm developments. Most studied has been the poorly forecasted Presidents' Day storm of 1979 which deposited a record-breaking snowfall on the middle Atlantic states. Bosart (1981) documented the crucial role of surface fluxes in moistening, heating and destabilizing the boundary layer and thereby establishing the coastal front upon which the low formed. He also documented the importance of an upper-level short-wave trough that advanced from the west and interacted with the coastal

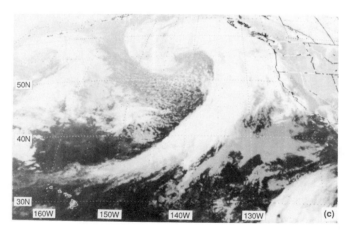

FIG. 3.15. GOES-W infrared (IR) satellite imagery at (a) 0545 UTC 7 January (b) 1745 UTC 7 January, and (c) 0546 UTC 8 January 1981 (Mullen 1983).

low, and the existence of convective activity in the vicinity of the storm center. A later diagnostic study of Bosart and Lin (1984) confirmed and extended the earlier results. Studies by Uccellini et al. (1984, 1985) called attention to the parts played in the development by an unbalanced subtropical jet streak, an induced ageostrophic low-level jet and the descent of stratospheric air in the tropopause fold beneath a polar jet streak that brought high potential

vorticity air to mid-tropospheric levels upstream of, and prior to, the rapid deepening phase (see Section 6.3.2).

A second poorly predicted storm that has received extensive study is the so-called Queen Elizabeth II storm of September 1978 which exhibited a central pressure fall of more than 50 mb in 24 hours. Gyakum's (1983a,b) analysis of the storm led him to conclude that it originated as a shallow baroclinic disturbance and that its extreme development was a consequence of the release of latent heat in organized cumulus convection. He cited evidence of hurricane-like features in the storm. Uccellini (1986) questioned Gyakum's characterization of the QE II storm as a shallow baroclinic system, presenting convincing evidence that strong upper-level baroclinic features, including a pronounced tropopause fold, existed upstream of the storm prior to its intensification.

A storm in the eastern Pacific that deepened nearly 40 mb in 12 hours has been investigated by Reed and Albright (1986). The storm was an offshoot of an earlier low pressure system in the western Pacific that weakened as it passed through a long-wave ridge and then rejuvenated suddenly upon entering the succeeding downstream long-wave trough. It too was missed by the operational forecasts. Factors found to be associated with its development were strong, deep baroclinity, small static stability and possible symmetric instability within the frontal cloud band. Preconditioning of the environment by sea-surface fluxes immediately prior to the rapid deepening was also found to be a crucial factor in the development. Although a preexisting upper-level short-wave trough or jet streak was present upstream of the incipient surface low, the intensification of the upper-level vorticity pattern appeared to occur simultaneously with the storm development rather than prior to it.

Sensitivity studies, employing fine-mesh mesoscale models, have been conducted for each of these storms. Simulations performed by Uccellini et al. (1987) and by Atlas (1987) confirm dramatically the vital role of sea-surface fluxes in producing the coastal cyclogenesis that preceded the rapidly deepening phase of the Presidents' Day storm (see Secs. 6.3.3, 12.3.2g). Kuo, Shapiro and Donall (1990), in a moderately successful simulation of the QE II storm (see Fig. 10.14), initiated at the beginning of the 24-hour period of most rapid deepening, found a much lesser, but not inconsequential, role for the surface fluxes. Latent heat release was by far the major factor in the rapid deepening. Kuo and Reed (1988), in a simulation of the eastern Pacific storm, also initialized at the beginning of the rapid deepening stage, identified latent heat release as the dominant diabatic effect. During this stage surface fluxes had little impact on the forecast despite their importance in supplying heat and moisture at an earlier stage. The simulation also showed that a symmetrically neutral or slightly unstable state existed in the region of low-level inflow ahead of the storm where rapid spin-up of vorticity occurred. A narrow sheet of rapidly rising air (with velocities exceeding 50 cm s^{-1}) was located within

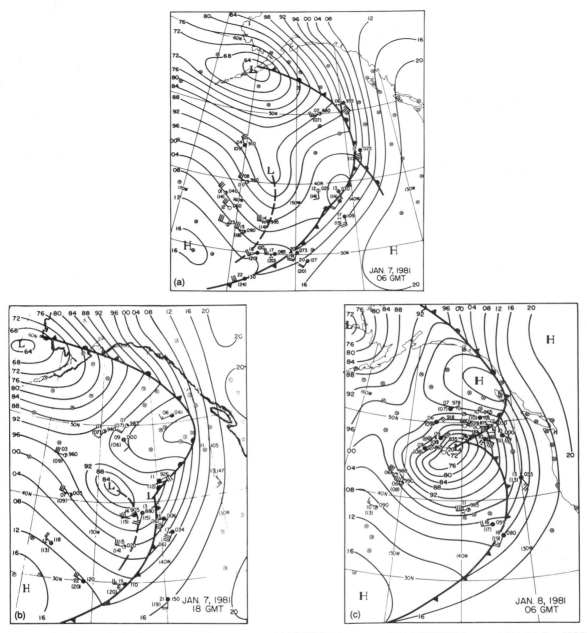

FIG. 3.16.   Surface   analysis   for   (a)   06 UTC   7 January   (b)   18 UTC 7 January, and (c) 06 UTC 8 January 1981 (Mullen 1983).

the region. Their results suggest that a key element in rapid cyclogenesis is the strength of the slantwise ascent in and above the warm frontal (or warm frontogenetical) zone.

Danard and Ellenton (1980), Chen and Dell'Osso (1987) and Reed et al. (1988) have also performed illuminating sensitivity studies of rapidly deepening cyclones. These and other studies that are in progress should lead to a rapid increase in the understanding of processes that contribute to cyclogenesis in general and explosive cyclogenesis in particular.

3.4   Concluding Remarks

From the foregoing account it is apparent that the past quarter-century has witnessed a remarkable advance in knowledge and understanding of the extratropical cyclone, an advance made possible by the solid foundations laid down by earlier workers in the field such as the man we honor at this symposium—Erik Palmén. Thanks in part to the new opportunities created by the high-speed computer and in part to the ingenuity of a large number of skilled workers, much progress has been made in understanding how fronts and cyclones form and in predicting their development. On the observational side, new instruments and new and improved observing platforms—satellites, radars, research aircraft and towers—have allowed the cyclone both to be viewed in broad perspective and to be probed in fine detail.

Looking to the future, we can be optimistic. The advanced numerical models now in existence, and many of the new instrument systems, are yet to be fully exploited. Theoreticians still have new ideas to explore. When meteorologists gather a quarter-century from now to take stock of the progress that has been made on the cyclone problem, they will no doubt have a further proud record of accomplishment to look back on.

Acknowledgments

I wish to thank Brian J. Hoskins, Chester W. Newton and Louis W. Uccellini for reading the manuscript and offering many helpful suggestions and the National Science Foundation for supporting its preparation under grant ATM8421396A04.

REFERENCES

Anderson, R. K., J. P. Ashman, F. Bittner, G. R. Farr, E. W. Ferguson, V. J. Oliver and A. H. Smith, 1969: Application of meteorological satellite data in analysis and forecasting. *ESSA Tech. Rep. NESC51*, Government Printing Office, Washington D.C. [NTIS AD-697033].

Atlas, R., 1987: The role of ocean fluxes and initial data in the numerical prediction of an intense coastal storm. *Dyn. Atmos. Oceans*, **10**, 359–388.

Baldwin, D., E.-Y. Hsie and R. A. Anthes, 1984: Diagnostic studies of a two-dimensional simulation of frontogenesis in a moist atmosphere. *J. Atmos. Sci.*, **41**, 2686–2700.

Ballentine, R. J., 1980: A numerical investigation of New England coastal frontogenesis. *Mon. Wea. Rev.*, **108**, 1479–1497.

Bannon, P. R., and M. Mak, 1984: Diabatic quasi-geostrophic surface frontogenesis. *J. Atmos. Sci.*, **41**, 2189–2201.

Bennetts, D. A., and B. J. Hoskins, 1979: Conditional symmetric instability — a possible explanation for frontal rainbands. *Quart. J. Roy. Meteor. Soc.*, **105**, 945–962.

Bergeron, T., 1928: Über die dreidimensionale verknüpfende Wetteranalyse. *Geofys. Publ.*, **5**, No. 6, 111 pp.

Bjerknes, J., 1919: On the structure of moving cyclones. *Geofys. Publ.*, **1**, No. 2, 1–8.

———, 1937: Theorie der aussertropischen Zyklonenbildung. *Meteor. Zeits.*, **54**, 186–190.

———, 1951: Extratropical cyclones. *Compendium of Meteorology*, T. F. Malone, Ed. American Meteorological Society, 577–598.

———, and H. Solberg, 1921: Meteorological conditions for the formulation of rain. *Geofys. Publ.*, **2**, No. 3, 1–60.

———, and H. Solberg, 1922: Life cycle of cyclones and the polar front theory of atmospheric circulation. *Geofys. Publ.*, **3**, No. 1, 1–18.

———, and C. Godske, 1936: On the theory of cyclone formation at extratropical fronts. *Astrophys. Norv.*, **1**, No. 6, 199–235.

———, and E. Palmén, 1937: Investigations of selected European cyclones by means of serial ascents. *Geofys. Publ.*, **12**, No. 2, 1–62.

———, and J. Holmboe, 1944: On the theory of cyclones. *J. Meteor.*, **1**, 1–22.

Bond, N. A., and R. G. Fleagle, 1985: Structure of a cold front over the ocean. *Quart. J. Roy. Meteor. Soc.*, **111**, 739–760.

Bosart, L. F., 1970: Mid-tropospheric frontogenesis. *Quart. J. Roy. Meteor. Soc.*, **96**, 442–471.

———, 1975: New England coastal frontogenesis. *Quart. J. Roy. Meteor. Soc.*, **97**, 457–482.

———, 1981: The Presidents' Day snowstorm of 18-19 February 1979: A subsynoptic scale event. *Mon. Wea. Rev.*, **109**, 1542–1566.

———, and S. C. Lin, 1984: A diagnostic analysis of the Presidents' Day storm of February 1979. *Mon. Wea. Rev.*, **112**, 2148–2177.

———, C. J. Vaudo and J. H. Helsdon, Jr., 1972: Coastal frontogenesis. *J. Appl. Meteor.*, **11**, 1236–1278.

Briggs, J., and W. T. Roach, 1963: Aircraft observations near jet streams. *Quart. J. Roy. Meteor. Soc.*, **89**, 225–247.

Brown, J. A., Jr., 1969a: A numerical investigation of hydrodynamic instability and energy conversions in the quasi-geostrophic atmosphere: Part I. *J. Atmos. Sci.*, **26**, 352–365.

———, 1969b: A numerical investigation of hydrodynamic instability and energy conversions in the quasi-geostrophic atmosphere: Part II. *J. Atmos. Sci.*, **26**, 366–375.

Browning, K. A., and T. W. Harrold, 1969: Air motion and precipitation growth in a wave depression. *Quart. J. Roy. Meteor. Soc.*, **95**, 288–309.

———, and ———, 1970: Air motion and precipitation at a cold front. *Quart. J. Roy. Meteor. Soc.*, **96**, 369–389.

———, and F. F. Hill, 1985: Mesoscale analysis of a polar trough interacting with a polar front. *Quart. J. Roy. Meteor. Soc.*, **111**, 445–462.

Businger, S., and R. J. Reed, 1989: Cyclogenesis in cold air masses. *Weather and Forecasting*, **4**, 133–156.

Buzzi, A., T. Nanni and M. Tagliazucca, 1977: Mid-tropospheric frontal zones: Numerical experiments with an isentropic coordinate primitive equation model. *Arch. Meteor. Geophys. Bioklim*, **A26**, 135–178.

———, A. Trevisan and G. Salustri, 1981: Internal frontogenesis: A two-dimensional model in isentropic semi-geostrophic coordinates. *Mon. Wea. Rev.*, **109**, 1053–1060.

Carbone, R. E., 1982: A severe winter squall line. Stormwide hydrodynamic structure. *J. Atmos. Sci.*, **39**, 258–279.

Carlson, T. N., 1980: Airflow through midlatitude cyclones and the comma cloud pattern. *Mon. Wea. Rev.*, **108**, 1498–1509.

Charney, J. G., 1947: The dynamics of long waves in a baroclinic westerly current. *J. Meteor.*, **4**, 135–162.

Chen, S.-J., and L. Dell'Osso, 1987: A numerical case study of East Asian coastal cyclogenesis. *Mon. Wea. Rev.*, **115**, 477–487.

Danard, M. B., and G. E. Ellenton, 1980: Physical influences on East Coast cyclogenesis. *Atmos.-Ocean*, **18**, 65–82.

Danielsen, E. F., 1964: Project Springfield Report. Defense Atomic Support Agency, Washington D.C. 20301, DASA 1517 (NTIS #AD-607980), 97 pp.

———, 1968: Stratospheric-tropospheric exchange based on radioactivity, ozone and potential vorticity. *J. Atmos. Sci.*, **25**, 502–518.

———, and V. A. Mohnen, 1977: Project dust storm report: ozone transport, in situ measurements and meteorological analyses of tropopause folding. *J. Geophys. Res.*, **82**, 5867–5878.

———, R. T. Hipskind, S. E. Gaines, G. W. Sachse, G. L. Gregory and G. F. Hill, 1987: Three-dimensional analysis of potential vorticity associated with tropopause folds and observed variations of ozone and carbon monoxide. *J. Geophys. Res.*, **92**, No. D2, 2103–2120.

Defant, A., 1912: Die Veränderungen in der allgemeinen Zirkulation der Atmosphäre in den gemässigten Breiten der Erde.

Wiener Akad. Wiss., Sitzungsberichte, **121**, 379-586. (Summary in *Meteor. Zeits.,* **30**, 126-138.)

Duncan, C. N., 1977: A numerical investigation of polar lows. *Quart. J. Roy. Meteor. Soc.,* **103**, 255-268.

Durran, D. R., and D. B. Weber, 1988: An investigation of the poleward edges of cirrus clouds associated with midlatitude jet streams. *Mon. Wea. Rev.,* **116**, 702-714.

Eady, E. T., 1949: Long waves and cyclone waves. *Tellus,* **1 (3)**, 33-52.

Edelmann, W., 1963: On the behavior of disturbances in a baroclinic channel. Sum. Rept. No. 2. Research in Objective Forecasting, Part F, Contract No. AF61 (052)-373, Deutscher Wetterdienst, Offenbach, 35 pp.

Eliassen, A., 1959: On the formation of fronts in the atmosphere. *The Atmosphere and the Sea in Motion,* B. Bolin, Ed. Rockefeller Institute Press, 277-287.

____, 1962: On the vertical circulation in frontal zones. *Geofys. Publ.,* **24**, 147-160.

____, 1966: Motions of intermediate scale: Fronts and cyclones. *Advances in Earth Science,* P. M. Hurley, Ed. MIT Press, 111-138.

____, and E. Kleinschmidt, 1957: Dynamic meteorology. *Handbuch der Physik,* **48**, S. Flügge, Ed. Springer-Verlag, 1-154.

Emanuel, K. A., 1983: On assessing local conditional symmetric instability from atmospheric soundings. *Mon. Wea. Rev.,* **111**, 2016-2033.

____, 1985: Frontal circulations in the presence of small moist symmetric instability. *J. Atmos. Sci.,* **42**, 1062-1071.

____, M. Fantini and A. J. Thorpe, 1987: Baroclinic instability in an environment of small stability to slantwise moist convection. Part I: Two-dimensional models. *J. Atmos. Sci.,* **44**, 1559-1573.

Farrell, B., 1982: The initial growth of disturbances in a baroclinic flow. *J. Atmos. Sci.,* **39**, 1663-1686.

____, 1984: Modal and non-modal baroclinic waves. *J. Atmos. Sci.,* **41**, 668-673.

____, 1985: Transient growth of damped baroclinic waves. *J. Atmos. Sci.,* **42**, 2718-2727.

____, 1989: Optimal excitation of baroclinic waves. *J. Atmos. Sci.,* **46**, 1193-1206.

Fjørtoft, R., 1955: On the use of space-smoothing in physical weather forecasting. *Tellus,* **7**, 462-480.

Gall, R., 1976a: A comparison of linear baroclinic instability theory with the eddy statistics of a general circulation model. *J. Atmos. Sci.,* **33**, 349-373.

____, 1976b: Structural changes of growing baroclinic waves. *J. Atmos. Sci.,* **33**, 374-390.

____, 1976c: The effects of released latent heat in growing baroclinic waves. *J. Atmos. Sci.,* **33**, 1686-1701.

____, R. T. Williams and T. L. Clark, 1987: On the minimum scale of surface fronts. *J. Atmos. Sci.,* **44**, 2562-2574.

Green, J. S. A., F. H. Ludlam and J. F. R. McIlveen, 1966: Isentropic relative-flow analysis and the parcel theory. *Quart. J. Roy. Meteor. Soc.,* **92**, 210-219.

Gyakum, J. R., 1983a: On the evolution of the QE II storm. I: Synoptic aspects. *Mon. Wea. Rev.,* **111**, 1137-1155.

____, 1983b: On the evolution of the QE II storm. II: Dynamic and thermodynamic structure. *Mon. Wea. Rev.,* **111**, 1156-1173.

Hayashi, Y., and D. E. Golder, 1981: The effects of condensational heating on midlatitude transient waves in their mature stage: Control experiments with a GFDL general circulation

model. *J. Atmos. Sci.,* **38**, 2532-2539.

Heckley, W. A., and B. J. Hoskins, 1982: Baroclinic waves and frontogenesis in a non-uniform potential vorticity semi-geostrophic model. *J. Atmos. Sci.,* **39**, 1999-2016.

Hobbs, P. V., and P. O. G. Persson, 1982: The mesoscale and microscale structure and organization of clouds and precipitation in midlatitude cyclones. V: The substructure of narrow cold-frontal rainbands. *J. Atmos. Sci.,* **39**, 280-295.

Holton, J. R., 1979: *An Introduction to Dynamic Meteorology,* 2nd ed. Academic Press, 391 pp.

Hoskins, B. J., 1971: Atmospheric frontogenesis models: Some solutions. *Quart. J. Roy. Meteor. Soc.,* **97**, 139-153.

____, 1972: Non-Boussinesq effects and further development in a model of upper tropospheric frontogenesis. *Quart. J. Roy. Meteor. Soc.,* **98**, 532-547.

____, 1974: The role of potential vorticity in symmetric stability and instability. *Quart. J. Roy. Meteor. Soc.,* **100**, 480-482.

____, 1982: The mathematical theory of frontogenesis. *Annual Review of Fluid Mechanics,* **14**, Annual Reviews Inc., 131-151.

____, and F. P. Bretherton, 1972: Atmospheric frontogenesis models: Mathematical formulation and solution. *J. Atmos. Sci.,* **29**, 11-37.

____, I. Draghici and H. C. Davies, 1978: A new look at the ω-equation. *Quart. J. Roy. Meteor. Soc.,* **104**, 31-38.

____, and N. V. West, 1979: Baroclinic waves and frontogenesis. Part II: Uniform potential vorticity jet flows—cold and warm fronts. *J. Atmos. Sci.,* **36**, 1663-1680.

____, M. E. McIntyre and A. W. Robertson, 1985: On the use and significance of isentropic potential vorticity maps. *Quart. J. Roy. Meteor. Soc.,* **111**, 877-946.

Houze, R. A., Jr., and P. V. Hobbs, 1982: Organization and structure of precipitating cloud systems. *Advances in Geophysics,* **24**, 225-315.

Hsie, E.-Y., and R. A. Anthes, 1984: Simulations of frontogenesis in a moist atmosphere using alternative parameterizations of condensation and precipitation. *J. Atmos. Sci.,* **41**, 2701-2716.

____, ____, and D. Keyser, 1984: Numerical simulation of frontogenesis in a moist atmosphere. *J. Atmos. Sci.,* **41**, 2581-2594.

Keshishian, L. G., and L. F. Bosart, 1987: A case study of extended East Coast frontogenesis. *Mon. Wea. Rev.,* **115**, 100-117.

Keyser, D., 1986: Atmospheric fronts: an observational perspective. *Mesoscale Meteorology and Forecasting,* P. S. Ray, Ed. American Meteorological Society, Ch. 10.

____, and R. A. Anthes, 1982: The influence of planetary boundary layer physics in frontal structure in the Hoskins-Bretherton horizontal shear model. *J. Atmos. Sci.,* **39**, 1783-1802.

____, and M. J. Pecnick, 1985: A two-dimensional primitive equation model of frontogenesis forced by confluence and horizontal shear. *J. Atmos. Sci.,* **42**, 1259-1282.

____, and M. A. Shapiro, 1986: A review of the structure and dynamics of upper-level frontal zones. *Mon. Wea. Rev.,* **114**, 452-499.

Kleinschmidt, E., 1941: Zur theorie der labilen Anordnung. *Meteor. Zeits.,* **58**, 157-163.

____, 1957: Cyclones and anticyclones. Chap. IV in Eliassen and Kleinschmidt, 1957 (reference listed above).

Kotschin, N., 1932: Über die Stabilität von Margulesschen Diskontinuitäts-flächen. *Beitr. Phys. Atmos.,* **18**, 129-164.

Kuo, Y.-H., and R. J. Reed, 1988: Numerical simulation of an explosively deepening cyclone in the Eastern Pacific. *Mon. Wea. Rev.,* **116,** 2081-2105.

——, M. A. Shapiro and E. Donall, 1990: Interaction of baroclinic and diabatic processes in numerical simulations of a rapidly developing marine cyclone. *Mon. Wea. Rev.,* in press.

Kutzbach, G., 1979: *The Thermal Theory of Cyclones. A History of Meteorological Thought in the Nineteenth Century.* American Meteorological Society, 255 pp.

Mak, M., 1982: On moist quasi-geostrophic baroclinic instability. *J. Atmos. Sci.,* **39,** 2028-2037.

——, and P. R. Bannon, 1984: Frontogenesis in a moist semi-geostrophic model. *J. Atmos. Sci.,* **41,** 3485-3500.

McGinnigle, J. B., M. V. Young and M. J. Baker, 1988: The development of instant occlusions in the North Atlantic. Met O 15 Internal Report No. 73, U.K. Meteorological Office, 25 pp.

McMurdie, L. A., and K. B. Katsaros, 1985: Atmospheric water distribution in a midlatitude cyclone observed by the Seasat Scanning Multichannel Microwave Radiometer. *Mon. Wea. Rev.,* **113,** 584-598.

Mechoso, C. R., and D. M. Sinton, 1983: On the energy analysis of the two-layer frontal model. *J. Atmos. Sci.,* **40,** 2069-2074.

Miller, J. E., 1948: On the concept of frontogenesis. *J. Meteor.,* **5,** 169-171.

Moore, G.W.K., 1987: Frontogenesis in a continuously varying potential vorticity fluid. *J. Atmos. Sci.,* **44,** 761-770.

——, and W. R. Peltier, 1987: Cyclogenesis in frontal zones. *J. Atmos. Sci.,* **44,** 384-409.

Mudrick, S. E., 1974: A numerical study of frontogenesis. *J. Atmos. Sci.,* **31,** 869-892.

Mullen, S. L., 1979: An investigation of small synoptic scale cyclones in polar air streams. *Mon. Wea. Rev.,* **107,** 1636-1647.

——, 1983: Explosive cyclogenesis associated with cyclones in polar air streams. *Mon. Wea. Rev.,* **111,** 1537-1553.

Namias, J., and P. F. Clapp, 1949: Confluence theory of the high tropospheric jet stream. *J. Meteor.,* **6,** 330-336.

Newton, C. W., 1954: Frontogenesis and frontolysis as a three-dimensional process. *J. Meteor.,* **11,** 449-461.

——, and A. Trevisan, 1984a: Clinogenesis and frontogenesis in jet-stream waves. Part I: Analytical relations to wave structure. *J. Atmos. Sci.,* **41,** 2717-2734.

——, and ——, 1984b: Clinogenesis and frontogenesis in jet-stream waves. Part II: Channel model numerical experiments. *J. Atmos. Sci.,* **41,** 2735-2755.

Orlanski, I., 1968: Instability of frontal waves. *J. Atmos. Sci.,* **25,** 178-200.

——, and B. B. Ross, 1984: The evolution of an observed cold front. Part II: Mesoscale dynamics. *J. Atmos. Sci.,* **41,** 1669-1703.

——, ——, L. Palinsky and R. Shaginaw, 1985: Advances in the theory of atmospheric fronts. *Advances in Geophysics,* **27,** 223-252.

Palmén, E., 1951: The role of atmospheric disturbances in the general circulation (Symons Memorial Lecture). *Quart. J. Roy. Meteor. Soc.,* **77,** 337-354.

——, and K. M. Nagler, 1948: An analysis of the wind and temperature distribution in the free atmosphere over North America in a case of approximately westerly flow. *J. Meteor.,* **5,** 58-64.

——, and ——, 1949: The formation and structure of a large-scale disturbance in the westerlies. *J. Meteor.,* **6,** 227-242.

Pedlosky, J., 1964a: The stability of currents in the atmosphere and ocean: Part I. *J. Atmos. Sci.,* **21,** 201-219.

——, 1964b: The stability of currents in the atmosphere and ocean: Part II. *J. Atmos. Sci.,* **21,** 342-353.

Petersen, R. A., L. W. Uccellini, A. Mostek and D. A. Keyser, 1984: Delineating mid- and low-level water vapor patterns in pre-convective environments using VAS moisture channels. *Mon. Wea. Rev.,* **112,** 2178-2198.

Petterssen, S., 1936: Contribution to the theory of frontogenesis. *Geofys. Publ.,* **11,** No. 6, 27 pp.

——, 1956: *Weather Analysis and Forecasting,* 2nd ed., Vol. 1. McGraw-Hill, 428 pp.

——, and J. M. Austin, 1942: Fronts and frontogenesis in relation to vorticity. *Papers in Physical Oceanography and Meteorology,* VII, No. 2. MIT and Woods Hole Oceanographic Institution, 37 pp.

——, G. E. Dunn and L. L. Means, 1955: Report of an experiment in forecasting of cyclone development. *J. Meteor.,* **12,** 58-67.

——, D. L. Bradbury and K. Pedersen, 1962: The Norwegian cyclone models in relation to heat and cold sources. *Geofys. Publ.,* **24,** 243-280.

Phillips, N. A., 1956: The general circulation of the atmosphere: A numerical experiment. *Quart. J. Roy. Meteor. Soc.,* **82,** 124-164.

Reed, R. J., 1955: A study of a characteristic type of upper-level frontogenesis. *J. Meteor.,* **12,** 542-552.

——, 1979: Cyclogenesis in polar air streams. *Mon. Wea. Rev.,* **107,** 38-52.

——, and F. Sanders, 1953: An investigation of the development of a mid-tropospheric frontal zone and its associated vorticity field. *J. Meteor.,* **10,** 338-349.

——, and M. D. Albright, 1986: A case study of explosive cyclogenesis in the Eastern Pacific. *Mon. Wea. Rev.,* **112,** 2297-2319.

——, and W. Blier, 1986a: A case study of comma cloud development in the Eastern Pacific. *Mon. Wea. Rev.,* **114,** 1681-1695.

——, and ——, 1986b: A further case study of comma cloud development in the Eastern Pacific. *Mon. Wea. Rev.,* **114,** 1696-1708.

——, A. J. Simmons, M. D. Albright and P. Undén, 1988: The role of latent heat release in explosive cyclogenesis: Three examples based on ECMWF Operational Forecasts. *Weather and Forecasting,* **3,** 217-229.

Rogers, E., and L. F. Bosart, 1986: An investigation of explosively deepening oceanic cyclones. *Mon. Wea. Rev.,* **114,** 702-718.

Ross, B. B., and I. Orlanski, 1978: The circulation associated with a cold front. Part II: Moist case. *J. Atmos. Sci.,* **35,** 445-465.

——, and ——, 1982: The evolution of an observed front. Part I: Numerical simulation. *J. Atmos. Sci.,* **39,** 296-326.

Sanders, F., 1955: An investigation of the structure and dynamics of an intense surface frontal zone. *J. Meteor.,* **12,** 542-552.

——, 1987: Skill of NMC operational dynamical models in prediction of explosive cyclogenesis. *Weather and Forecasting,* **2,** 322-336.

——, and J. R. Gyakum, 1980: Synoptic-dynamic climatology of the "bomb." *Mon. Wea. Rev.,* **108,** 1589-1606.

——, and L. F. Bosart, 1985: Mesoscale structure in the megalopolitan snowstorm of 11-12 February 1983. Part I: Frontogenetical forcing and symmetric instability. *J. Atmos. Sci.,* **42**, 1050–1061.

Sawyer, J. S., 1949: The significance of dynamic instability in atmospheric motions. *Quart. J. Roy. Meteor. Soc.,* **75**, 364–374.

——, 1956: The vertical circulation at meteorological fronts and its relation to frontogenesis. *Proc. Roy. Soc. London,* **A234**, 346–362.

Shapiro, M. A., 1975: Simulation of upper-level frontogenesis with a 20-level isentropic coordinate primitive equation model. *Mon. Wea. Rev.,* **103**, 591–604.

——, 1976: The role of turbulent heat flux in the generation of potential vorticity in the vicinity of upper-level jet stream systems. *Mon. Wea. Rev.,* **104**, 892–900.

——, 1978: Further evidence of the mesoscale and turbulent structure of upper level jet stream-frontal zone systems. *Mon. Wea. Rev.,* **106**, 1100–1111.

——, 1980: Turbulent mixing within tropopause folds as a mechanism for the exchange of chemical constituents between the stratosphere and the troposphere. *J. Atmos. Sci.,* **37**, 994–1004.

——, 1981: Frontogenesis and geostrophically forced secondary circulations in the vicinity of jet stream-frontal zone systems. *J. Atmos. Sci.,* **38**, 954–973.

——, 1983: Mesoscale weather systems of the central United States. The National STORM program: Scientific and Technological Bases and Major Objectives, R. A. Anthes, Ed. University Corporation for Atmospheric Research, Boulder, CO 80307-3000, 3.1–3.77.

——, 1984: Meteorological tower measurements of a surface cold front. *Mon. Wea. Rev.,* **112**, 1634–1639.

——, T. Hampel, D. Rotzoll and F. Mosher, 1985: The frontal hydraulic head: A micro-α scale (~1 km) triggering mechanism of mesoconvective weather systems. *Mon. Wea. Rev.,* **113**, 1166–1183.

Simmons, A. J., and B. J. Hoskins, 1976: Baroclinic instability on the sphere: Normal modes of the primitive and quasi-geostrophic equations. *J. Atmos. Sci.,* **33**, 1454–1477.

——, and ——, 1978: The life cycles of some nonlinear baroclinic waves. *J. Atmos. Sci.,* **35**, 414–432.

——, and ——, 1979: The downstream and upstream development of unstable baroclinic waves. *J. Atmos. Sci.,* **35**, 1239–1254.

Simons, T. J., 1972: The nonlinear dynamics of cyclone waves. *J. Atmos. Sci.,* **29**, 38–52.

Sinton, D. M., and C. R. Mechoso, 1984: Nonlinear evolution of frontal waves. *J. Atmos. Sci.,* **41**, 3501–3517.

Solberg, H., 1928: Integrationen der atmosphärischen Störungsgleichungen. *Geofys. Publ.,* **5**, No. 9, 1–120.

Song, R. T., 1971: A numerical study of the three-dimensional structure and energetics of unstable disturbances in zonal currents: Part I. *J. Atmos. Sci.,* **28**, 549–564.

Staff Members, University of Chicago, 1947: On the general circulation of the atmosphere in middle latitudes. *Bull. Amer. Meteor. Soc.,* **28**, 255–280.

Staley, D. O., 1960: Evaluation of potential vorticity changes near the tropopause and the related vertical motions, vertical advection of vorticity and transfer of radioactive debris from stratosphere to troposphere. *J. Meteor.,* **17**, 591–620.

——, and R. L. Gall, 1977: On the wavelength of maximum baroclinic instability. *J. Atmos. Sci.,* **34**, 1669–1688.

Stauffer, D. R., and T. T. Warner, 1987: A numerical study of cold-air damming and coastal frontogenesis. *Mon. Wea. Rev.,* **115**, 799–821.

Stone, P. H., 1966: Frontogenesis by horizontal wind deformation fields. *J. Atmos. Sci.,* **23**, 455–465.

Sutcliffe, R. C., 1947: A contribution to the problem of development. *Quart. J. Roy. Meteor. Soc.,* **73**, 370–383.

Takayabu, I., 1986: Roles of the horizontal advection on the formation of surface fronts and on the occlusion of a cyclone developing in the baroclinic easterly jet. *J. Meteor. Soc. Japan,* **64**, 329–345.

Thorpe, A. J., and K. A. Emanuel, 1985: Frontogenesis in the presence of small stability to slantwise convection. *J. Atmos. Sci.,* **42**, 1809–1824.

Todsen, M., 1964: A study of the vertical circulations in a cold front. Part IV of Final Report, Air Force Cambridge Laboratories, OAR Contr. No. AF61 (052)–525.

Trenberth, K. E., 1978: On the interpretation of the diagnostic quasi-geostrophic omega equation. *Mon. Wea. Rev.,* **106**, 131–137.

Uccellini, L. W., 1986: The possible influence of upstream upper-level baroclinic processes on the development of the QE II storm. *Mon. Wea. Rev.,* **114**, 1019–1027.

——, P. J. Kocin, R. A. Petersen, C. H. Wash and K. F. Brill, 1984: The Presidents' Day cyclone of 18-19 February 1979: Synoptic overview and analysis of the subtropical jet streak influencing the precyclogenetic period. *Mon. Wea. Rev.,* **113**, 31–55.

——, D. Keyser, K. F. Brill and C. H. Wash, 1985: Presidents' Day cyclone of 18-19 February 1979: Influence of upstream trough amplification and associated tropopause folding on rapid cyclogenesis. *Mon. Wea. Rev.,* **112**, 962–988.

——, R. A. Petersen, K. F. Brill, P. J. Kocin and J. J. Toccillo, 1987: Synergistic interactions between an upper level jet streak and diabatic processes that influence the development of a low level jet and a secondary coastal cyclone. *Mon. Wea. Rev.,* **115**, 2227–2261.

Wallace, J. M., and P. V. Hobbs, 1977: *Atmospheric Science: An Introductory Survey.* Academic Press, 417 pp.

Welander, P., 1963: Steady plane fronts in a rotating fluid. *Tellus,* **15**, 33–43.

Williams, R. T., 1967: Atmospheric frontogenesis: A numerical experiment. *J. Atmos. Sci.,* **24**, 627–641.

——, 1972: Quasi-geostrophic versus non-geostrophic frontogenesis. *J. Atmos. Sci.,* **29**, 3–10.

——, 1974: Numerical simulation of steady-state fronts. *J. Atmos. Sci.,* **31**, 1286–1296.

——, L. C. Chou and C. J. Cornelius, 1981: Effects of condensation and surface motion on the structure of steady-state fronts. *J. Atmos. Sci.,* **38**, 2365–2376.

WMO, 1973: *The Use of Satellite Pictures in Weather Analysis and Forecasting.* Tech. Note No. 124, WMO No. 333. World Meteorological Organization, Geneva, 275 pp.

Chapter 4

Role of Cyclone-Scale Eddies in the General Circulation of the Atmosphere: A Review of Recent Observational Studies

E. O. Holopainen

Department of Meteorology, University of Helsinki, SF-00100 Helsinki 10, Finland

4.1 Introduction

A main characteristic of the atmospheric circulation is its large variability in time. This "large-scale turbulence," which is vividly illustrated in any sample of consecutive weather maps, has an important effect on the time-mean circulation. Extratropical cyclones form a fundamental part in this turbulence and its effect on the mean conditions.

Erik Palmén and his collaborators used a case study approach in investigations of extratropical cyclones; the book *Atmospheric Circulation Systems* by Palmén and Newton (1969) contains many examples of illustrative case studies. This approach is a valid one even today, when various statistical methods of retrieving information are often used. While data availability and quality constrained Palmén's studies mainly to the Northern Hemisphere, recent diagnostic studies have been able to exploit global data. This has been the case particularly since the Global Weather Experiment or FGGE (First GARP Global Experiment) in 1979.

An arbitrary quantity can be formally represented as the sum of contributions from the zonally-averaged time-mean flow, stationary (i.e., time-mean) eddies (SE) and transient eddies (TE). Extratropical cyclones are part of the TEs, which contain contributions from many frequencies.

The spectrum of atmospheric eddies being essentially a continuous one, the definition of "cyclone-scale" is somewhat arbitrary. The flow field associated with such a scale is often obtained from the observed total field by applying some "band-pass" or "high-pass" temporal filter. A recent study by Wallace et al. (1988) shows that many characteristics of the cyclone-scale eddies are relatively insensitive to the exact form of the temporal filter used, provided the disturbances with periods ranging from 2 to 6 days are retained. In studies in which spatial filtering is used, this temporal filtering corresponds roughly to retaining zonal wave numbers higher than about 7–8.

The question concerning the role of cyclone-scale eddies in the general circulation is essentially the eddy-mean flow problem. It has at least two aspects: the dependence of eddy activity and eddy properties on the mean flow, and the feedback of eddies on the mean flow. This paper summarizes mainly recent observational studies on the latter.

Section 4.2 provides background information to the main theme of the paper by briefly reviewing some recent diagnostic studies on the global energetics of the atmosphere; some aspects of geographical distribution and the spatial structure of the cyclone-scale eddies are discussed as well. Techniques of illustrating the forcing effect of the TEs on the local time-mean flow are reviewed in Section 4.3. Section 4.4 illustrates the wintertime climatological forcing effect of cyclone-scale eddies on the longitudinally-averaged time-mean flow and on the SEs. In Section 4.5 studies of cyclone effects on low-frequency transients, including a blocking-type flow, are reviewed. Some comments on the parameterization of the cyclone-scale eddies are presented in Section 4.6, while Section 4.7 summarizes the discussion presented.

4.2 Background Information on Cyclone-Scale Eddies

4.2.1 Global Energetics

Since the pioneering study by Lorenz (1955) the energetics has played an important role in the diagnosis of the atmospheric circulation. Figure 4.1 shows a 5-year mean "Lorenz diagram," as worked out by Arpe et al. (1986) from truly global data.

From the viewpoint of our theme the main result in Fig. 4.1 is that the net effect of eddies on the axisymmetric component of the circulation is a damping one: eddies extract energy from the zonally-averaged flow. This damping effect is seen to arise mainly from the conversion term CA, which involves eddy heat fluxes, whereas the conversion term CK, which involves eddy momentum fluxes, has a maintaining effect. There are ambiguities in the interpretation of the energetics (e.g., Plumb 1983; Hayashi 1987). The net damping effect of eddies on the total energy of the basic zonal flow, however, is established observationally beyond any doubt.

Detailed spectral analyses of the global energetics have been carried out using the global data sets from 1979 or later years. These studies consist of classical zonal harmonic analysis (e.g., Kung and Tanaka 1984; Lambert 1988), spherical harmonic analysis (e.g., Boer and Shepherd 1983) and three-dimensional normal mode expansions (Tanaka et al. 1986; Tanaka and Kung 1988).

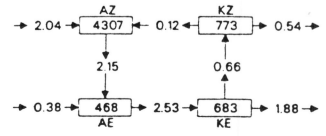

Fɪɢ. 4.1. Annual mean global "Lorenz box" energetics of the general circulation of the atmosphere. AZ and AE denote the available potential energy of the zonally-averaged flow and the eddies, respectively. KZ and KE are the corresponding kinetic energies. GZ and GE denote generation, DZ and DE denote dissipation. CA, CZ and CE represent energy conversion terms. The numbers are obtained from five years (1980-1985) of 12-hour forecasts at the ECMWF. Unit of energy, kJ m^{-2}; unit of energy change, W m^{-2}. (Adapted from Arpe et al. 1986.)

The analysis by Tanaka et al. verifies the finding, made already in the 1960s, that within the eddies energy is converted from baroclinic modes to the barotropic mode, and that the eddies also tend to barotropize the zonally-averaged flow on which they grow.

4.2.2 Geographical Distribution of the Cyclone-Scale Eddies

The geographical and seasonal distribution of some statistics of cyclone-scale disturbances, among many other general circulation characteristics, have been documented for the Northern Hemisphere, e.g., by Lau et al. (1981) and Blackmon et al. (1984a,b). The statistics exhibit in winter two distinct "storm tracks," one in the Atlantic starting from the eastern coast of North America, another in the Pacific. (For a recent discussion concerning definitions of "storm track," see Wallace et al. 1988.)

The variability associated with the cyclones of the Southern Hemisphere has been studied, e.g., by Trenberth (1982). It appears that, compared with the Northern Hemisphere, there is in the Southern Hemisphere relatively little seasonal and longitudinal variation in the cyclone activity (i.e., in all seasons the storm tracks extend virtually around the whole latitude circle). An interesting feature, revealed by the values presented in Arpe et al. (1986), is that the eddies in the Southern Hemisphere are more barotropic than those in the Northern Hemisphere in the sense that both the ratio of the eddy kinetic energy to eddy available potential energy and also the barotropic eddy-mean flow conversion term are larger in the Southern Hemisphere than in the Northern Hemisphere.

Baroclinic instability of the basic flow is known to be the main reason for the existence of cyclone-scale eddies in the atmosphere. It is therefore of interest to consider simul-

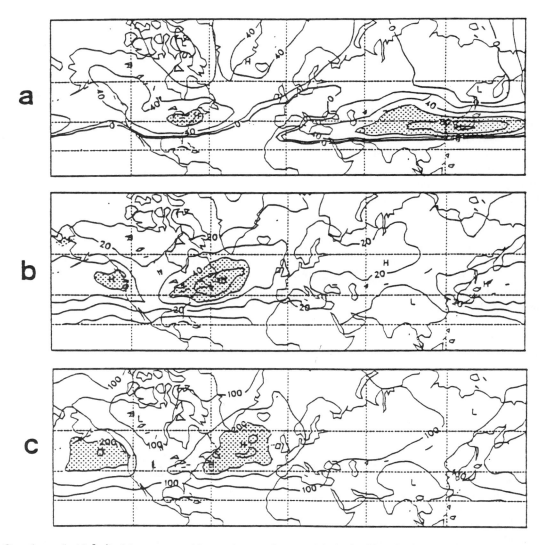

FIG. 4.2.   (a) Growth rate (in $10^{-7}s^{-1}$) of the most unstable wave in a two-layer model, obtained by using local values of the time-mean static stability and the vertical shear of the zonal wind in the Northern Hemisphere in winter. (b) Kinetic energy (J kg^{-1}) of the TEs with periods between 2.5 and 6 days at 500 mb in winter. (c) Kinetic energy (J kg^{-1}) of all TEs at 500 mb in winter. Shading indicates in (a) values larger than 60, in (b) larger than 40 and in (c) larger than 200 units. The data used are the "NMC data" as described in Lau and Holopainen (1984).

taneously the regional distribution of a measure of the instability of the time-mean flow and the distribution of the intensity of cyclone-scale eddies. These are shown for the wintertime Northern Hemisphere in Figs. 4.2a and 4.2b, respectively.

For the instability index we use the growth rate $\alpha = kc_i$ (k is the zonal wave number and c_i the imaginary component of the phase speed) of the most unstable wave in a quasi-geostrophic two-layer model (e.g., Holton 1979, pp. 216–223). In the formulation of the two-layer model the wind shear and static stability of the basic state, as well as the parameters f and β, are assumed constants. Here we consider these quantities, calculated from 300-mb and 700-mb data, as slowly varying external parameters. Thereby we get a qualitative feeling for the regions which particularly contribute to the generation of the cyclone-scale eddies. In the regions where $\alpha > 0$, instability of the observed time-mean flow to cyclone-scale eddies is suggested. Calculations of this kind have been reported earlier by Phillips (1954) for the two-dimensional (2-D) case, and by White (1982) and Dymnikov and Filin (1985) for the three-dimensional (3-D) case. (Rigorous studies of the instability of the longitudinally varying time-mean flow have been presented, e.g., by Frederiksen (1982, 1983); see also Pierrehumbert (1984)).

Figure 4.2a shows α as determined by using wintertime mean flow as the basic state. Instability ($\alpha > 0$) is indicated practically everywhere in the extratropics. Two regions stand out clearly as the main source regions of baroclinic eddies. These are the eastern coasts of the two continents around 30–40°N, long known as the principal areas of cyclogenesis. It is the longitudinal variation of the mean meridional temperature gradient that primarily determines the corresponding variation of α; the variation of the time-mean static stability has only a minor effect.

The amplitude of the developing baroclinic disturbances can be expected to be largest downstream from the main instability regions. This is verified in Fig. 4.2b, which shows the observed distribution of kinetic energy of the cyclone-scale eddies at 500 mb.

A fundamental characteristic of the atmospheric circulation is a cascade of kinetic energy from cyclone-scale to larger spatial scales (e.g., Boer and Shepherd 1983). Larger spatial scales roughly correspond to longer temporal scales. Because the energy propagation of Rossby waves is eastward (and upward), one expects the maximum of the the total TE kinetic energy to occur downstream from that of the kinetic energy of the cyclone-scale eddies. According to observations (Fig. 4.2c) this is the case, at least over the Atlantic.

Even if some crude aspects of the relationship between the mean flow and cyclone-scale eddies are known, we still lack a quantitative theory for it. Such a theory should explain, among other things, the clear difference in Fig. 4.2 between the Atlantic and Pacific regions. Why, for example, is the kinetic energy of the cyclone-scale eddies in Fig. 4.2b over the Pacific much weaker than over the Atlantic even though the contrary is true for the instability index in Fig. 4.2a? Such a theory should also elucidate to what extent the maxima of kinetic energy of all transients (Fig. 4.2c) is due to the forcing effect of cyclone-scale eddies upstream and to what extent, for example, due to tropical influences, which have been demonstrated by Simmons et al. (1983) to be a potential cause of extratropical low-frequency variability.

4.2.3   Structure of the Cyclone-Scale Eddies

Statistical characteristics of the atmospheric transient eddies have in recent years been investigated by using various techniques, among others empirical orthogonal functions expansion (e.g., Schubert 1986) and lag-correlation analysis (Blackmon et al. 1984a,b; Fraedrich and Lutz 1987; Wallace et al. 1988; Randel 1988, 1990).

Figure 4.3 illustrates the observed statistical structure of the cyclone-scale eddies in the two hemispheres during winter season. It is from the study by Randel (1988) and shows, for 51°N and 51°S, the correlation of the bandpass filtered 300-mb height with the simultaneous (lag = 0) height observations in all grid points in the longitude-latitude plane (upper panels) and longitude-height plane (lower panels).

Several characteristics of the cyclone-scale eddies are revealed by Fig. 4.3. The eddies exhibit a clear zonally-oriented wave train. They have a zonal wavelength of about 4000 km and are elongated in the meridional direction. The wave train is of limited extent in the zonal direction. Hence, these eddies are basically local phenomena which cannot be represented well by any single zonal wave number.

The patterns for the two hemispheres are seen to be quite alike. In the Southern Hemisphere, however, the eddies appear to be more wavelike and show somewhat deeper vertical penetration than in the Northern Hemisphere.

The upper panels in Fig. 4.3 indicate that cyclone-scale eddies typically have a horizontal structure such that there is a transfer of zonal momentum from the subtropics to midlatitudes. The vertical tilt of the correlation pattern in the lower panels of Fig. 4.3 indicates that these eddies transport heat poleward, particularly in the lower troposphere. It is these eddy transports of momentum and heat that create the forcing effect of eddies on the mean flow.

4.3   Methods of Illustrating the Forcing Effect of Transient Eddies on the Time-Mean Flow

The net forcing effect of eddies on the mean flow consists of the sum of direct and indirect effects. The direct eddy effect is given by the eddy flux convergence of the quantity in question. The indirect effect is created by the eddy-induced secondary circulations.

There are several diagnostic methods of illustrating the forcing effect of eddies on the mean flow. The methods fall

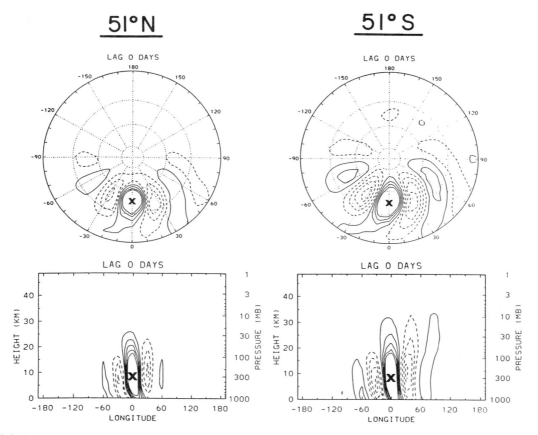

FIG. 4.3. Statistical structure of the bandpass filtered isobaric height fields at 51°N and 51°S. The upper panels show the 300-mb longitude-latitude correlation map (latitudes are drawn every 20 degrees; the outermost line is 20°). In order to facilitate comparison with the Northern Hemisphere diagram, the Southern Hemisphere grids have been reversed so that eastward is counterclockwise. The lower panels show the longitude-height correlation pattern with respect to a reference point at 300 mb. In all panels the longitude scale refers to relative distance from the zero degree reference position (not geographic longitude). The 300-mb reference point is marked with a cross. Calculations have been done for every ten degrees of longitude and the resulting 36 patterns have been averaged. (Adapted from Figs. 7 and 10 of Randel 1988.)

in two categories, denoted in the following as "conventional" and "transformed Eulerian" (or Eliassen-Palm, EP) frameworks. Although the net eddy effect is independent of the framework used, the direct and indirect eddy contributions are not.

The conventional framework has been used for the longitudinally-averaged 2-D case by Pfeffer (1981, 1987), who determined separately the direct and indirect TE effect. Another version of the conventional framework is the "tendency method" (Lau and Holopainen 1984). Here, the net forcing effect of the eddies on mean geopotential is evaluated from the interior transient eddy (TE) fluxes of potential vorticity and the TE heat fluxes at the lower and upper boundary, by inverting the associated Laplace operator. The net forcing effect of eddies on temperature and geostrophic wind can be obtained from the corresponding geopotential forcing by using the hydrostatic and geostrophic relationships. The tendency method, which has more recently been used by Mullen (1987) and Holopainen and Fortelius (1987a), bypasses the need for explicitly solving for the indirect forcing effect.

Since the study of Edmon et al. (1980) the EP method has been used extensively. The method originates from the work of Andrews and McIntyre (1976), who considered the eddy effects in the longitudinally-averaged case. The direct eddy effect is given by the EP flux divergence, a quantity normally depicted in an "EP cross section" along with EP flux vectors, which illustrate the propagation of "EP eddy activity." The indirect eddy effect is determined by the eddy-induced "residual circulation," which in the troposphere is to a large extent determined by the eddy heat fluxes at the lower boundary (see, e.g., Hoskins 1983).

Attempts to extend the EP method to the 3-D case have been reported by Hoskins et al. (1983), Plumb (1986) and Trenberth (1986). All these methods (as well as those by Holopainen et al. (1982) and Holopainen (1984) based on the eddy fluxes of potential vorticity) suffer in the troposphere from the same deficiency as in the 2-D case, in that they give quantitative information on the direct eddy effect only. This is enough if one studies only the barotropic interaction between the mean flow and eddies (e.g., Shutts 1983; Wallace and Lau 1985). In this case the indirect eddy effect is zero because there is no contribution by the eddy heat fluxes and because the vertical average of the horizontal component of the secondary circulation, induced by the variation with pressure of the eddy momentum flux convergence, disappears. This is, however, not true in the general baroclinic case.

Both the conventional method and the EP method are used in Section 4.4.1 to discuss the TE effects on the longitudinally-averaged zonal flow. When we deal with the geographical distribution of the forcing effect of the cyclone-scale TEs in the rest of the paper, however, we use only the conventional framework, more precisely the tendency method. This method seems to provide the most illuminating way of illustrating the net local forcing effect of the TEs.

4.4 Forcing Effect of Cyclone-Scale Transient Eddies on the Wintertime Climatological Circulation in the Northern Hemisphere

In this section we first consider recent studies on the forcing effect of the TEs on the longitudinally-averaged time-mean zonal flow. We then discuss the geographical distribution of the forcing effect of cyclone-scale eddies. As the third item we consider here the role of the cyclone-scale eddies in the maintenance of the climatological stationary eddies i.e., longitudinal variation of climate. Except for a few comments concerning the Southern Hemisphere, the discussion will deal with the Northern Hemisphere winter troposphere.

4.4.1   The Forcing Effect of Cyclone-Scale Eddies on the Mean Zonal Flow

The equation of zonal motion, averaged with respect to longitude $[(\ )]$ and time $(\overline{\ })$, can be symbolically written (Pfeffer 1987) as:

$$\frac{\partial [\overline{u}]}{\partial t} = \left(\frac{\partial [\overline{u}]}{\partial t}\right)_E + \left(\frac{\partial [\overline{u}]}{\partial t}\right)_H + \left(\frac{\partial [\overline{u}]}{\partial t}\right)_M + \left(\frac{\partial [\overline{u}]}{\partial t}\right)_F, \quad (4.1)$$

where the terms on the r.h.s. with subindices E, H, M and F denote, respectively, the net forcing effect due to eddies (stationary and transient), diabatic heating, mountains and friction.

Depending on whether the conventional or the transformed Eulerian framework is used, the eddy forcing $(\partial[\overline{u}]/\partial t)_E$ can be written as

$$\cos\phi\left(\frac{\partial[\overline{u}]}{\partial t}\right)_E = -\frac{1}{a}\nabla\cdot\mathbf{M} + C \quad (4.2)$$
$$\text{(conventional)}$$

or

$$\cos\phi\left(\frac{\partial[\overline{u}]}{\partial t}\right)_E = \frac{1}{a}\nabla\cdot\mathbf{F} + C^*, \quad (4.2')$$
$$\text{(transformed Eulerian)}$$

where the first and second r.h.s. terms represent the direct and indirect eddy effect, respectively; $-\nabla\cdot\mathbf{M}$ is the eddy momentum flux convergence and $\nabla\cdot\mathbf{F}$ is the EP flux divergence in the mean meridional plane (a is the radius of the Earth). C represents the effect of the eddy-induced mean meridional circulation (essentially the Coriolis force

associated with the eddy-induced mean meridional velocity), and C^* the corresponding effect of the "residual circulation" (for details, see Pfeffer 1987).

The two terms on the r.h.s. of (4.2)–(4.2') can be written as a sum of contributions from different spectral intervals. Therefore, these equations can also be used to study the contribution made by eddies of different frequencies or different zonal wave numbers. We shall first discuss the effect of all TEs and then comment on the special features of the forcing by the cyclone-scale TEs.

Figure 4.4 shows some diagnostic results derived by Pfeffer (1987) using the total observed TE fluxes estimated by Oort and Rasmusson (1971). The conventional mean meridional circulation (Fig. 4.4a) is very different from the "residual" circulation (Fig. 4.4a'). The former shows the traditional tropical Hadley cell and the extratropical Ferrel cell, whereas the latter shows a single strong Hadley cell extending through the whole hemisphere (note the difference in units!). The single Hadley-cell structure of the residual circulation is broadly similar to that of the Eulerian mass circulation in an isentropic coordinate system (e.g., Townsend and Johnson 1985). A Hadley-type direct mass circulation in midlatitudes in the isentropic framework was implied already by the early work of Palmén and Newton (1951), incorporated in Palmén's scheme of the general circulation (see Fig. 2.8).

Figures 4.4b and 4.4b' show, respectively, $-\nabla\cdot\mathbf{M}/a$ and $\nabla\cdot\mathbf{F}/a$. As is known from many studies since the late 1940s, $-\nabla\cdot\mathbf{M}/a$ exhibits a negative (positive) force on the mean zonal flow in the subtropics (midlatitudes). On the other hand, $\nabla\cdot\mathbf{F}/a$ shows a large decelerating effect in most of the middle and upper troposphere. Several other recent studies (e.g., Edmon et al. 1980; Karoly 1982; Trenberth 1987; Wu 1988) confirm that this decelerating effect is rather a robust feature of the general circulation. It is connected with the predominantly equatorward flux of potential vorticity in the atmosphere (e.g., Wiin-Nielsen and Sela 1971; Holopainen and Fortelius 1987b).

The effect of the TE-induced secondary circulation in forcing the zonal flow is shown in panels 4.4c and 4.4c'. In the conventional framework this effect counterbalances to some extent the eddy momentum flux convergence in the upper troposphere and, in a way, brings part of this direct effect downward to the lower troposphere. In the transformed Eulerian framework both $\nabla\cdot\mathbf{F}/a$ and C^* are, in the troposphere, very much influenced by the eddy heat fluxes at the lower boundary; they are individually very large. (Note that panels b' and c' have isoline spacing different from that in the other panels.) Therefore, a physical interpretation of $\nabla\cdot\mathbf{F}/a$ in the troposphere is meaningful only with simultaneous consideration of this boundary effect.

The net TE force in the conventional framework (Fig. 4.4d) is the same as in the transformed Eulerian framework (Fig. 4.4d'). (The pattern is essentially the same as that in Fig. 9c of Lau and Holopainen 1984, calculated from a different data set by using the tendency method.) It

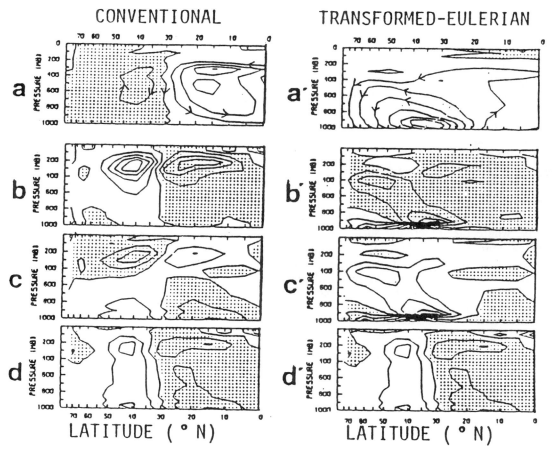

FIG. 4.4. Comparison of the "conventional" and "transformed Eulerian" frameworks of describing the TE forcing effect on the mean zonal flow in the wintertime Northern Hemisphere. Panel (a) illustrates the stream function for the "conventional" mean meridional circulation (contour interval 20 m mb s^{-1}) and panel (a') that for the "residual circulation" (contour interval 40 m mb s^{-1}). Panels (b) and (b') illustrate the first r.h.s. terms in (4.2) and (4.2'), respectively. Similarly, panels (c) and (c') illustrate the second r.h.s terms, and panels (d) and (d') the l.h.s. terms. Contour interval is 0.5 × 10^{-5} m s^{-2} in (b), (c), (d) and (d') but 2 × 10^{-5} m s^{-2} in (b') and (c'). Shading indicates negative values. (Adapted from Pfeffer 1987.)

is seen to be positive in the midlatitudes and negative in the subtropics. This results in a poleward shift of the jet stream, which in winter is located roughly at 30°N. The TE forcing is barotropic in the sense that it practically nowhere changes sign in the vertical direction.

The direct TE effect is easy to determine if circulation data are available. It is therefore of interest to compare the net TE effect with the direct TE effect in the two frameworks. It is seen that the net TE-induced force is qualitatively very much the same as $-\nabla \cdot \mathbf{M}/a$ (Fig. 4.4b), and has practically nothing in common with the pattern of $\nabla \cdot \mathbf{F}/a$ (Fig. 4.4b'). These considerations seem to suggest that, for the time-averaged conditions in the troposphere, the conventional scheme is a better indicator of the eddy-induced mean-flow effects than the transformed Eulerian scheme.

Randel (1990) has made, on the basis of daily global circulation data from a period of seven years and using the transformed Eulerian framework, a lag correlation analysis of zonal flow tendencies and eddy characteristics in the mean meridional plane. His results appear to be in good qualitative agreement with model results, reported by Edmon et al. (1980) and Hoskins (1983). These results

seem to speak for the usefulness of the transformed Eulerian approach in an analysis of this kind even in the troposphere, where it has been made questionable by studies (based on data for short periods) by Pfeffer (1985) and Baldwin et al. (1985). (In the stratosphere, the usefulness of this framework has been demonstrated earlier, e.g., by Palmer 1981).

Figure 4.4 refers to the effect of all transient eddies. Calculations leading to Lau and Holopainen (1984) showed that the zonally-averaged forcing effect of the low-frequency TEs is similar to that of the cyclone-scale TEs. The only major difference found was that in midlatitudes the net force due to the low-frequency eddies was almost uniform in the vertical; whereas the corresponding force due to cyclone-scale eddies, while eastward at all levels, has a maximum in the low troposphere (see Fig. 4c in Lau and Holopainen 1984). This means that the cyclone-scale eddies tend to reduce the baroclinicity of the basic westerly flow (i.e., the mean westerly wind shear and the associated mean meridional temperature gradient).

To summarize, according to observations, the cyclone-scale eddies have the following zonally-averaged effects:

They tend to (i) shift the time-mean jet stream poleward; (ii) enhance the barotropic component of the basic flow in middle latitudes; and (iii) reduce, in the middle latitudes, the baroclinic component of the basic flow.

A model study of the impact of baroclinic wave development on the longitudinally-averaged flow has been reported by Hoskins (1983). His model results exhibit the empirical results (i)–(iii) mentioned above. To some extent, these were demonstrated already in the pioneer modeling study by Phillips (1956).

As will become apparent in Section 4.4.3, the cyclone-scale waves in the northern troposphere interact energetically more with the stationary waves than with the zonally-averaged time-mean flow. In the Southern Hemisphere, however, where the underlying surface is more uniform and the amplitude of the stationary eddies accordingly weaker than in the Northern Hemisphere, the cyclone-scale waves sometimes clearly interact with the zonally-averaged flow (e.g., Randel and Stanford 1985).

4.4.2 Geographical Distribution of the Forcing Effect of Cyclone-Scale Eddies

Because the EP diagnostics have some shortcomings in a quantitative illustration of the eddy-mean flow interaction in the troposphere, we use in the following the TE-induced geopotential tendencies to illustrate the geographical distribution of the net cyclone effects. Traditionally one discusses separately the eddy effects on mean temperature and vorticity. The advantage of the geopotential tendencies is that the energy and vorticity aspects of the forcing are combined in, and if needed are easily derivable from, them.

Symbolically, we can write the time-averaged geopotential tendency equation in the form (see Holopainen et al. 1988)

$$\frac{\partial \overline{\Phi}}{\partial t} = 0 = \left(\frac{\partial \overline{\Phi}}{\partial t}\right)_{TE} + \left(\frac{\partial \overline{\Phi}}{\partial t}\right)_{H} + \left(\frac{\partial \overline{\Phi}}{\partial t}\right)_{M} + \left(\frac{\partial \overline{\Phi}}{\partial t}\right)_{F} + \left(\frac{\partial \overline{\Phi}}{\partial t}\right)_{ADV}$$

(4.3)

where Φ is geopotential. The l.h.s. term is the actual geopotential tendency, which is zero in steady-state conditions. The r.h.s. terms with subindices TE, H, M and F represent, respectively, the net forcing effect on mean geopotential by transient eddies, diabatic heating, mountains and friction; $(\partial \overline{\Phi}/\partial t)_{ADV}$ is the geopotential tendency arising from the mean-flow advection terms in the vorticity equation and the thermodynamic energy equation.

The net TE forcing on the time-mean geopotential, $(\partial \overline{\Phi}/\partial t)_{TE}$, can be written as the sum of contributions coming from different frequencies. Figure 4.5 shows, for the 300-mb and 1000-mb surfaces, the geopotential tendencies due to bandpass eddy momentum and heat fluxes in the Northern Hemisphere in winter. This tendency field has the largest amplitude at 1000 mb, where Fig. 4.5 shows a north-south dipole of negative and positive values at the eastern coast of North America and east of Japan. Lau and

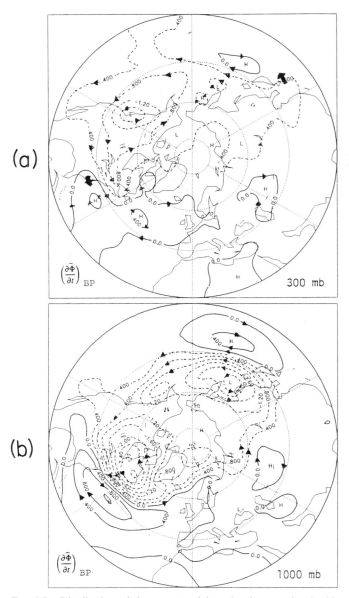

FIG. 4.5. Distribution of the geopotential tendencies associated with cyclone-scale eddies in the northern extratropics in winter at (a) 300 mb and (b) 1000 mb. The patterns are computed using the same bandpass (BP) filtered data as in Lau and Holopainen (1984); the filter originates from Blackmon (1976). Unit: 10^{-3} m^2 s^{-3}. Dashed lines indicate negative values. Arrowheads indicate the direction of the associated geostrophic wind tendencies. Thick arrows on the 300-mb map indicate the position of the two maxima of the time-mean wind on the eastern coasts of the continents.

Holopainen (1984) discussed the separate contributions to $(\partial \overline{\Phi}/\partial t)_{BP}$ by the BP eddy heat and vorticity fluxes. In the upper troposphere the two contributions counterbalance each other to some extent, but the sum effect is to a large extent dictated by the vorticity fluxes. In the lower troposphere the tendencies associated with the heat fluxes have larger magnitudes than those associated with the vorticity fluxes, and the two contributions have the same sign.

In the same way as $\overline{\Phi}$ is related to the horizontal wind $\overline{V}$, the distribution of $(\partial\overline{\Phi}/\partial t)_{TE}$ illustrates the net TE-induced force $(\partial\overline{\mathbf{V}}/\partial t)_{TE}$. Figure 4.5 implies that in the middle latitudes the cyclone-scale eddies create a time-mean eastward force. This force is particularly strong in the lower troposphere (Fig. 4.5b) on the eastern coast of North America and east of Japan, i.e., on the two main storm tracks. The maximum eastward force here is 2–3 m s^{-1} per day.

At 300 mb the mean westerly force due to the cyclone-scale eddies is much weaker than at 1000 mb. Figure 4.5 thus implies, besides an enhancement of the barotropic component of the time-mean westerly flow, a reduction of its baroclinic component on the midlatitude storm tracks. On the Pacific storm track, at about 40°N, the eastward force at 300 mb is seen to extend eastward across the whole Pacific and North America, while over the Atlantic it is almost zero east of about 50°W. Differences between the Pacific and Atlantic storm tracks were noted earlier in connection with Fig. 4.2.

In the longitudes of the main dipoles in Fig. 4.5, a westward net force due to cyclone-scale eddies is seen in the subtropics and to some extent also at high latitudes. In essence, the forcing due to cyclone-scale eddies tends to shift the time-mean wind maxima northward over the eastern coast of North America and northeastward over the eastern Pacific (see Fig. 4.5a). In the zonally-averaged case, discussed in Section 4.4.1, only the poleward shift tendency remains.

It appears that in the lower troposphere the patterns of $(\partial\overline{\Phi}/\partial t)_{BP}$ and $(\partial\overline{\Phi}/\partial t)_{TE}$ (not shown) are rather similar, the magnitude of $(\partial\overline{\Phi}/\partial t)_{BP}$ being about ¾ of $(\partial\overline{\Phi}/\partial t)_{TE}$ in the main storm track regions. The effect of the cyclone-scale eddies is thus of great importance for the maintenance of the surface westerlies and the associated mean meridional pressure gradient in the midlatitudes. Qualitatively, this fact has been clear since the early numerical general circulation experiments conducted by Phillips (1956) and Charney (1959).

A time-mean eddy-induced force as large as 2–3 m s^{-1} per day due to cyclone-scale eddies should be traceable to basic features of cyclone development. Figure 4.6 (adapt-

ed from Godske et al. 1957) shows schematically an eastward-propagating extratropical cyclone at two stages of development (the coordinate system moves eastward with the phase speed of the cyclone). The westerly geostrophic wind clearly increases in the map area from panel a to panel b. This increase is due to structural changes of the cyclone in connection with the occlusion process. The statistical effect of such increases gives the climatological effect seen in Fig. 4.5.

In real synoptic situations many processes are simultaneously operating, and the eddy-induced enhancement of westerlies cannot be clearly seen in all cases of cyclone development. A nice model demonstration of the generation of surface westerlies on the storm track as a result of eddy development in a baroclinically unstable atmosphere is given in Fig. 4.7, taken from Simmons and Hoskins (1979).

A nonzero value of any r.h.s. term in (4.3) has to be compensated for by a contribution of opposite sign arising from the other r.h.s. terms. One of the processes, which over the storm tracks compensates for the eddy-induced eastward force, is the westward force due to friction (arising from the fourth r.h.s. term in (4.3)). The advection term in (4.3) is likely to contribute to the fact that the maximum mean surface westerlies do not occur in the longitude where the eddy-induced eastward force is largest, but considerably east of it.

4.4.3 The Effect of Cyclone-Scale Eddies on the Maintenance of the Wintertime Stationary Eddies

The stationary eddies (SE) represent longitudinal variations of climate. These eddies are ultimately caused by the asymmetric forcing due to mountains, heating and transient eddies.

Diagnostic studies show that the net effect of all TEs is to damp the SE total energy, SE potential enstrophy and the SE temperature variance in the wintertime Northern Hemisphere (for a review, see Holopainen et al. 1988). There appears to be a large difference between the forcing effects on the SEs arising on one hand from the cyclone-scale transients and, on the other hand, from the low-frequency transients. We consider this difference by studying the role of two kinds of TEs in the budget of SE isobaric height variance.

Multiplying (4.3) by $g^{-2}\overline{\Phi}^*$ (here ( )* denotes deviation from zonal average and taking an area average, denoted by { }, gives (Holopainen et al. 1988)

$$\left\{\frac{\partial(\overline{Z}^{*2}/2)}{\partial t}\right\} = \left\{\overline{Z}^*\left(\frac{\partial\overline{Z}^*}{\partial t}\right)_{TE}\right\} + \{\cdots\}, \qquad (4.4)$$

in which Z is isobaric height. Let us define

$$\nu = -\left\{\overline{Z}^*\left(\frac{\partial\overline{Z}^*}{\partial t}\right)_{TE}\right\} / \left\{\frac{1}{2}\overline{Z}^{*2}\right\}, \qquad (4.5)$$

in which ν can be interpreted as a normalized measure of the net TE effect on the SE isobaric height variance. It is a

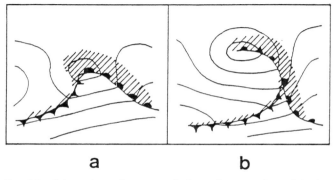

a   **b**

Fig. 4.6. Schematic surface map (isobars, fronts and precipitation areas) for two stages of an eastward-moving developing extratropical cyclone. (Fig. 15.00.1 in Godske et al. 1957.)

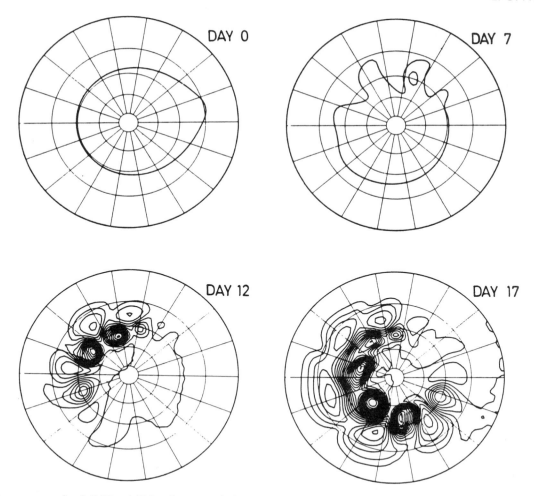

FIG. 4.7.   Surface pressure after 0, 7, 12 and 17 days in a numerical experiment in which a local disturbance of small amplitude is superimposed on a baroclinically unstable zonal flow at day 0. The contour interval is 4 mb. The North polar stereographic projection shows background lines of latitude and longitude at intervals of 20°. Note westerlies at about 40°N and easterlies at about 20°N and 60°N at day 17 (Simmons and Hoskins 1979).

kind of damping coefficient: when $\nu > 0$, the TEs tend to damp the SE isobaric height variance; when $\nu < 0$, negative damping (i.e., positive forcing) is implied. $(\partial \overline{Z}^*/\partial t)_{TE}$, and thus ν, may be written as a sum of contributions arising from transient eddies of different frequencies.

Figure 4.8 shows the coefficients ν as obtained by calculating $(\partial \overline{Z}^*/\partial t)_{TE}$ in (4.5) from bandpass (BP) and lowpass (LP) data sets, respectively. (The BP data are the same as in the case of Fig. 4.5; the LP data describe transient fluctuations with periods between 10 and 90 days.)

The two curves in Fig. 4.8 are seen to differ radically from each other. The BP eddies tend to maintain the SE isobaric height variance (negative damping coefficient!) while the corresponding effect of the low-frequency LP eddies is a damping one at all levels.

Because the area averages of isobaric height variance and kinetic energy are closely related, the difference between the two curves in Fig. 4.8 have their counterparts in the kinetic energy conversions between the TEs and the SEs. These conversions were calculated by using the same

data on which Fig. 4.8 is based. On the average between 100 and 1000 mb north of 20°N the wintertime SEs appear to gain kinetic energy from the cyclone-scale eddies at the rate of 0.1 W m^{-2}, while they lose kinetic energy to the low-frequency transients at the rate of 0.2 W m^{-2}.

Interestingly, the energy gain by the SEs from the BP transients turns out to be, relatively speaking, much larger than the corresponding gain by the axisymmetric time-mean flow: the latter conversion, so much discussed in the meteorological literature in the past (e.g., Starr 1968), was found to be only 0.02 W m^{-2}. Thus, the cyclone-scale eddies in the Northern Hemisphere interact more strongly with the stationary eddies than with the zonally-averaged time-mean flow, a fact mentioned in Section 4.4.1. It is worth pointing out, however, that energetics analysis does not reveal anything about the zonal and meridional phase shift effects the cyclone-scale eddies may have on the pattern of the time-mean flow.

The coefficient ν for the cyclone-scale eddies in Fig. 4.8

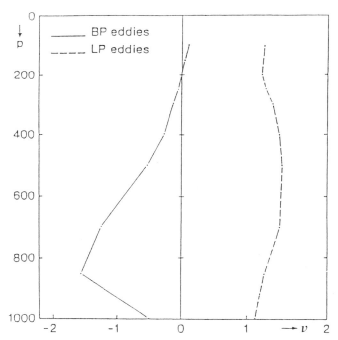

FIG. 4.8.   The stationary-eddy isobaric height "damping coefficient"

$$\nu = -\{\overline{Z}^*\left(\frac{\partial \overline{Z}^*}{\partial t}\right)_{TE}\} / \{\frac{1}{2}\overline{Z}^{*2}\}$$

(in 10^{-6} s^{-1}), due to cyclone-scale transient eddies (solid line) and due to low-frequency transient eddies (dashed line) in the winter climate case in the northern extratropics (Holopainen et al. 1988).

4.5   Effect of Cyclone-Scale Eddies on the Low-Frequency Variability of the Atmospheric Circulation

4.5.1   A General Review

Most of the variance of the atmospheric circulation occurs on time scales much longer than the lifetime of cyclone-scale eddies. The reasons for this low-frequency variability have been intensively studied in recent years (e.g., Wallace and Blackmon 1983; Frederiksen and Webster 1988). In the tropics the ocean-atmosphere interaction is a likely causal mechanism. In the extratropics potential causes are, for example, the interaction with the tropics, barotropic instability of the climatological mean flow and forcing by the cyclone-scale eddies. We consider here only the last mechanism.

Bruns (1985) showed that a large fraction of the observed tendencies associated with atmospheric large-scale variability is due to forcing by smaller synoptic scales. Egger et al. (1986) and Metz (1986, 1987) have forced a barotropic low-order model of the atmosphere with observed vorticity fluxes from the cyclone-scale eddies. The geographical distribution of the low-frequency variability in their model compared well with observations, particularly over the Atlantic. Nakamura et al. (1987) studied the interannual variability of wintertime teleconnection patterns in the Northern Hemisphere. The variability over the western Atlantic and western Pacific appeared to be connected with the fluctuations of the principal storm tracks.

has largest magnitude in the lower troposphere. This result may at first look strange when knowing that the momentum flux convergence by cyclone-scale eddies is largest in the upper troposphere (see panel 4.4b). A reason for the lower troposphere being emphasized in Fig. 4.8 is that the eddy-induced secondary circulations tend to bring part of the direct eddy force from the upper troposphere to the lower troposphere (cf. Figs. 4.4c and 4.4b). In part, however, it is due to the method of analysis used here: the denominator in (4.5) is smaller in the lower troposphere than in the upper troposphere.

Figure 4.9 shows $\overline{Z}^*$ and $(\partial \overline{Z}^*/\partial t)_{BP}$ at 850 mb, where according to Fig. 4.8 the forcing effect of the cyclone-scale eddies is largest. The maxima/minima of the eddy forcing field are seen to be located slightly west from the maxima/minima of the height field. This implies that the cyclone-scale eddies tend to shift the SEs westward. On the average, such a tendency has to be counterbalanced by an opposing tendency arising from eddies of other frequencies or from the other terms in (4.3).

The main point is that cyclone-scale transient eddies are, according to observations, important for the dynamics of the wintertime stationary eddies in the extratropics, particularly in the lower troposphere. The importance of transient eddies for the SEs in the lower troposphere has been recently noted also in a modeling study by Nigam et al. (1986, 1988).

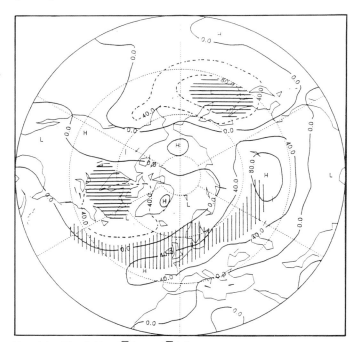

FIG. 4.9.   The fields of $\overline{Z}^*$ and $(\partial \overline{Z}^*/\partial t)_{BP}$ at 850 mb for an ensemble of several winters (the same data from which the solid curve in Fig. 4.8 has been calculated). Isolines are for $\overline{Z}^*$ with isoline spacing of 40 m, dashed lines indicate negative values. Vertical (horizontal) hatching indicates areas where $(\partial \overline{Z}^*/\partial t)_{BP}$ is larger than 0.8×10^{-4} m s^{-1} (smaller than -0.8×10^{-4} m s^{-1}) (Holopainen et al. 1988).

From these studies it would appear that a considerable part of the low-frequency variability in the wintertime northern extratropics is probably forced by the cyclone-scale eddies. At present, however, we do not have quantitative information on the relative importance of the various forcing mechanisms responsible for this variability.

4.5.2 An Example of the Forcing Effect of Cyclone-Scale Eddies During a Single Month (February 1979)

The dashed line in Fig. 4.10 shows the coefficient ν (as defined in (4.5)), obtained by calculating $(\partial \bar{Z}^*/\partial t)_{TE}$ from the highpass data in February 1979 (Holopainen and Fortelius 1987a). The coefficient exhibits a negative damping coefficient (positive forcing) at all levels, with a maximum at 850 mb. The normalized effect of the cyclone-scale eddies in February 1979 is seen to be virtually the same as that of the BP eddies in the climatological case. The effect of the cyclone-scale transients on the SEs appears thus to be a rather robust feature of the general circulation.

4.5.3 The Effect of Cyclone-Scale Eddies in "Blocking"

The "blocking" phenomenon is an important part of the atmospheric low-frequency variability in middle latitudes. It therefore appears appropriate to consider here the role played by the high-frequency cyclone-scale transients in blocking-type flows. This subject has in recent years received considerable attention.

The basic issues with regard to the role of high-frequency eddies in blocking concern their role in the onset, maintenance and breakdown phases of blocking. The effect of cyclone-scale eddies on the maintenance of blocking flows has been studied, e.g., by Dole (1983), Shutts (1983, 1986), Mullen (1987) and Holopainen and Fortelius (1987a), where further references can be found.

Figure 4.11 shows ν due to cyclone-scale eddies for two periods of February 1979. One is the blocking episode (16–25 February 1979) studied by Holopainen and Fortelius (1987a), the other is the rest of the month. During the blocking period the forcing of the SEs by cyclone-scale eddies is seen to be much larger than during the rest of the month. The maximum of the anticyclonic forcing occurred in most latitudes slightly west from the main anticyclone (see Figs. 2 and 4 in Holopainen and Fortelius 1987a). This indicates a cyclone-induced tendency to shift the blocking high westward. Such a tendency was earlier noticed by Illari (1984).

Figure 4.12 shows the geopotential forcing due to the cyclone-scale eddies at 300 mb and 1000 mb for a composite of 17 Atlantic blocking cases studied by Mullen (1987). On the blocking high itself the forcing is seen to be positive, i.e, the cyclone-scale eddies tend to strengthen the high, as expected on the basis of Fig. 4.11.

The maximum height tendency is in Fig. 4.12 seen upstream from the blocking high. Accordingly the high-frequency eddies tend, also in this composite case, to move the blocking high westward.

The role of the high-frequency eddies in the onset (and breakdown) of blocking cannot be studied in a straightforward manner with the diagnostic techniques presently available (see the discussion in Section 6 of Holopainen and Fortelius 1987a and in Section 4.7 below). Synoptically, however, it is apparent that the high-frequency eddies sometimes are important in the drastic large-scale circulation changes, that take place in connection with the establishment and disappearance of blocking (e.g., Colucci 1985).

Blocking theories not involving eddies at all (e.g., Reinhold and Pierrehumbert 1982; Frederiksen 1982, 1983; Pierrehumbert and Malguzzi 1984; Haines and Marshall

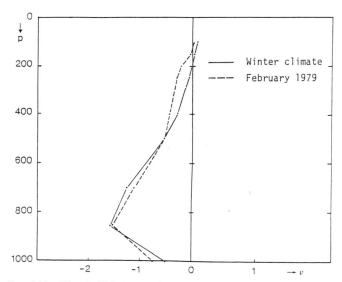

FIG. 4.10. The coefficient ν for the effect of the cyclone-scale eddies on the stationary eddies in February 1979 (dashed curve) and in an ensemble of several winters (solid curve, the same as in Fig. 4.8).

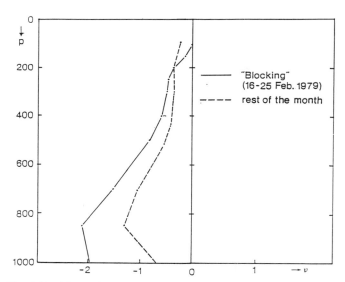

FIG. 4.11. The coefficient ν for the effect of the cyclone-scale eddies on the stationary eddies in February 1979. The solid line refers to the period 16–25 February characterized by a blocking-type flow, the dotted line to the rest of the month (Holopainen et al. 1988).

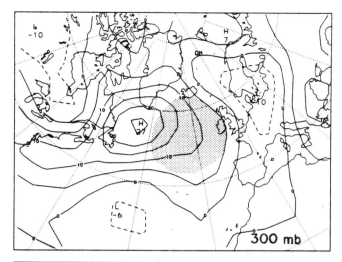

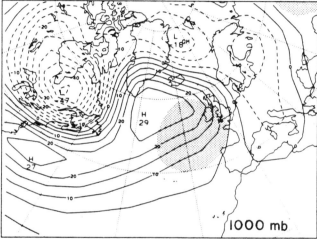

FIG. 4.12. Distribution of the geopotential tendencies associated with high-frequency TE forcing at 300 mb (upper panel) and 1000 mb (lower panel) for a composite of 17 Atlantic blocking cases. Contour interval is 5×10^{-4} m^2 s^{-3}, negative contours are dashed. Shading in the upper panel denotes regions where $\bar{Z}^*$ exceeds 300 m, in the lower panel regions where it exceeds 50 m. (Adapted from Mullen 1987.)

1987), and the empirical results showing the importance of eddies in the blocking maintenance, need not be incompatible. These theories are fundamental in showing how a blocking-type flow configuration can be an eigensolution of the equations which govern the atmospheric large-scale dynamics. The high-frequency eddies, on the other hand, seem to play a complementary role: they provide a mechanism by which these modes are maintained against surface friction, once excited, and sometimes possibly also function as the actual exciting mechanism.

4.6 Remarks on Parameterization of the Cyclone-Scale Eddies

In models which treat explicitly only the low-frequency atmospheric flow, the cyclone-scale eddies need to be parameterized. In light of the diagnostic results presented above one could expect that low-order models, which do not have a proper parameterization of cyclone effects,

would generally be deficient in simulating the time-mean flow in the lower troposphere.

With regard to the 2-D parameterization problem (i.e., parameterization of the eddy fluxes in the mean meridional plane), Green (1970) parameterized the meridional eddy fluxes of heat and potential vorticity with the aid of diffusion coefficients; the momentum fluxes were obtained as a by-product. This approach has been recently used by Wu and White (1986). According to the observational study by Lorenz (1979), however, the mean meridional heat flux correlates with the mean meridional temperature gradient in the sense of classical diffusion only on seasonal or longer time scales. Even in the 2-D case the parameterization of the effect of the cyclone-scale eddies is still an unsolved problem.

Concerning the 3-D case, data studies led Egger et al. (1986) and Metz (1986, 1987) to describe the amplitude of the forcing coming from cyclone scales as a first-order Markov process. Because their model appears to explain a lot of the observed geographical distribution of the low-frequency variance, a large fraction of the forcing caused by the cyclone-scale eddies can probably never be parameterized.

In the 3-D climate models which treat explicitly only the seasonal or longer time scales, both the cyclone-scale eddies and the low-frequency TEs should be parameterized. The low-frequency eddies have an effect on the stationary eddies that is very different from that of the high-frequency eddies (see Fig. 4.8). Furthermore, they have the largest effect on the time-mean flow outside the storm track regions (see, e.g., Lau and Holopainen 1984; Holopainen 1984). Therefore, their parameterization is a problem totally different from that of parameterizing the high-frequency, synoptic-scale eddies.

4.7 Summary and Final Remarks

The cyclone-scale eddies in the atmosphere are produced by the baroclinic instability of the planetary-scale flow. The eddy activity is organized in "storm tracks," which in the Northern Hemisphere are located downstream and polewards from the area where the instability of the time-mean flow is largest.

The cyclone-scale eddies transport heat and momentum across the storm tracks and by doing so exert a forcing effect on the background flow. In particular, in the Northern Hemisphere in winter they:

(i) tend to shift, in the mean meridional plane, the jet stream poleward. In middle latitudes they also tend to enhance the barotropic part of the time-mean westerlies and to reduce its baroclinic part (i.e., the mean meridional temperature gradient and the associated mean westerly wind shear).

(ii) tend to maintain the stationary eddy (SE) isobaric height variance and the SE kinetic energy, and to shift the SE pattern westward. This seems to apply both to the winter climate SEs and monthly SEs, as well as to "blocking" SEs.

(iii) appear to be particularly important for the time-mean circulation in the lower troposphere in the extratropics.

In this review we have confined ourselves primarily to recent observational studies of the forcing effect exerted by the cyclone-scale eddies on the time-mean circulation. A more complete review of the role of cyclone-scale eddies in the general circulation of the atmosphere should also address other issues, such as the hypothetical atmospheric circulation in the absence of the transient eddies (e.g., Held and Hoskins 1985; Schneider 1987), instability of the three-dimensional basic flow (e.g., Frederiksen 1982, 1983) and the ability of the general circulation models to simulate the cyclone-scale eddies (e.g., Lau and Nath 1987). Some of these issues were addressed in the Palmén Memorial Symposium by the contributed papers.

In this review, a statistical approach has been used to illustrate the effects of cyclone-scale eddies on stationary and quasi-stationary flow. As mentioned in the introduction, Erik Palmén and his collaborators used a synoptic, case study approach in their investigations. A composite analysis for various time lags (e.g., Dole 1983, 1986; Wallace et al. 1988) is an extension of this synoptic approach.

There is no easy way of bridging the statistical and synoptic approaches. A basic reason for this is that the spectrum of atmospheric fluctuations is a continuous one. Because of this, any partitioning of the total atmospheric flow in a given synoptic situation into "mean" and "eddy" components always involves some arbitrariness. Furthermore, the conventional Reynolds' expressions for the eddy fluxes and their mean-flow effects are not valid unless the "mean" flow is clearly separated by a spectral gap from the "eddy" part of the flow. A synthesis of the synoptic and statistical approach clearly requires some fundamental questions to be answered.

Acknowledgments

Erik Palmén was my mentor since the late 1950s. He supervised my M.S. thesis and arranged things so that I could go for postgraduate studies to the International Meteorological Institute in Stockholm. After my doctoral dissertation he also helped me, in 1965, to get a postdoctoral position in the United States. I very much value my contacts with "Maestro" Palmén, who was great not only as a scientist but also as a fellow human being.

Prof. J. M. Wallace, Dr. N-C. Lau and Dr. C. W. Newton are acknowledged for their constructive comments on the manuscript.

REFERENCES

Andrews, D. G., and M. E. McIntyre, 1976: Planetary waves in horizontal and vertical shear: The generalized Eliassen–Palm relation and the mean zonal acceleration. *J. Atmos. Sci.*, **33**, 2031-2048.

Arpe, K., C. Brankowic and E. Oriol, 1986: Variability in time and space of energetics from a long series of atmospheric data processed by ECMWF. *Contrib. Atmos. Phys.*, **59**, 321-355.

Baldwin, M. P., H. J. Edmon and J. R. Holton, 1985: A diagnostic study of eddy-mean flow interactions during FGGE-SOP1. *J. Atmos. Sci.*, **42**, 1838-1845.

Blackmon, M. L., 1976: A climatological spectral study of the 500 mb geopotential height of the Northern Hemisphere. *J. Atmos. Sci.*, **33**, 1607-1623.

——, Y-H. Lee and J. M. Wallace, 1984a: Horizontal structure of 500 mb height fluctuations with long, intermediate and short time scales. *J. Atmos. Sci.*, **41**, 961-979.

——, ——, —— and H-H. Hsu, 1984b: Time variation of 500 mb height fluctuations with long, intermediate and short time scales as deduced from lag-correlation statistics. *J. Atmos. Sci.*, **41**, 981-991.

Boer, G. J., and T. G. Shepherd, 1983: Large-scale two-dimensional turbulence in the atmosphere. *J. Atmos. Sci.*, **40**, 164-184.

Bruns, T., 1985: Contribution of linear and nonlinear processes to the long-term variability of large-scale atmospheric flows. *J. Atmos. Sci.*, **42**, 2506-2522.

Charney, J., 1959: On the theory of the general circulation of the atmosphere. *The Atmosphere and the Sea in Motion* (Rossby Memorial Volume), B. Bolin, Ed. Rockefeller Institute Press, 178-193.

Colucci, S. J., 1985: Explosive cyclogenesis and large-scale circulation changes: Implications for atmospheric blocking. *J. Atmos. Sci.*, **47**, 2701-2717.

Dole, R. M., 1983: Persistent anomalies of the extratropical Northern Hemisphere wintertime circulation. *Large-Scale Dynamical Processes in the Atmosphere*, B. J. Hoskins and R. P. Pearce, Eds. Academic Press, 95-109.

——, 1986: The life cycles of persistent anomalies and blocking over the North Pacific. *Advances in Geophysics*, **29**, 31-69.

Dymnikov, V. P., and C. K. Filin, 1985: Diagnostic analysis of the atmospheric circulation on the basis of FGGE data. *Report No. 83*. Department of Numerical Mathematics, USSR Academy of Sciences, Moscow, 61 pp. (In Russian.)

Edmon, H. J., B. J. Hoskins and M. E. McIntyre, 1980: Eliassen-Palm cross sections for the troposphere. *J. Atmos. Sci.*, **37**, 2600-2616.

Egger, J., W. Metz and G. Muller, 1986: Forcing of planetary-scale blocking anticyclones by synoptic-scale eddies. *Advances in Geophysics*, **29**, 183-198.

Fraedrich, K., and H. Lutz, 1987: A modified time-longitude diagram applied to 500 mb heights along 50° north and south. *Tellus*, **39A**, 25−32.

Frederiksen, J. S., 1982: A unified three-dimensional instability theory of the onset of blocking and cyclogenesis. *J. Atmos. Sci.*, **39**, 969-982.

——, 1983: Disturbances and eddy fluxes in the Northern Hemisphere flows: Instability of three-dimensional January and July flows. *J. Atmos. Sci.*, **40**, 836-855.

——, and P. J. Webster, 1988: Alternative theories of atmospheric teleconnections and low-frequency fluctuations. *Rev. Geophys.*, **26**, 459-494.

Godske, C. L., T. Bergeron, J. Bjerknes and R. C. Bundgaard, 1957: *Dynamic Meteorology and Weather Forecasting*. American Meteorological Society and Carnegie Institution of Washington, 800 pp.

Green, J. S. A., 1970: Transfer properties of the large-scale eddies and the general circulation of the atmosphere. *Quart. J. Roy. Meteor. Soc., 96,* 157–185.

Haines, K., and J. Marshall, 1987: Eddy forced coherent structures as a prototype of atmospheric blocking. *Quart. J. Roy. Meteor. Soc., 113,* 681–708.

Hayashi, Y., 1987: A modification of the atmospheric energy cycle. *J. Atmos. Sci., 44,* 2006–2017.

Held, I. M., and B. J. Hoskins, 1985: Large-scale eddies and the general circulation of the troposphere. *Advances in Geophysics, 28A,* 3–31.

Holopainen, E. O., 1984: Statistical local effect of synoptic-scale transient eddies on the time-mean flow in the Northern Hemisphere in winter. *J. Atmos. Sci., 41,* 2505–2515.

———, and C. Fortelius, 1987a: High-frequency transient eddies and blocking. *J. Atmos. Sci., 44,* 1632–1645.

———, and ———, 1987b: On the damping of potential enstrophy in the large-scale transient eddies in the wintertime troposphere. *J. Atmos. Sci., 44,* 1973–1980.

———, L. E. Rontu and N.-C. Lau, 1982: The effect of large-scale transient eddies on the time-mean flow in the atmosphere. *J. Atmos. Sci., 39,* 1972–1984.

———, C. Fortelius and K. Ruosteenoja, 1988: The effect of transient eddies on the stationary eddy isobaric height field. *J. Atmos. Sci., 45,* 1760–1769.

Holton, J. R., 1979: *An Introduction to Dynamic Meteorology,* 2nd ed. Academic Press, 391 pp.

Hoskins, B. J., 1983: Modeling of the transient eddies and their feedback on the mean flow. *Large-Scale Dynamical Processes in the Atmosphere,* B. J. Hoskins and R. P. Pearce, Eds. Academic Press, 169–197.

———, I. M. James and G. H. White, 1983: The shape, propagation and mean-flow interaction of large-scale weather systems. *J. Atmos. Sci., 40,* 1595–1612.

Illari, L., 1984: A diagnostic study of the potential vorticity in a warm blocking anticyclone. *J. Atmos. Sci., 41,* 3518–3526.

Karoly, D., 1982: Eliassen–Palm cross sections for Northern and Southern Hemispheres. *J. Atmos. Sci., 39,* 178–182.

Kung, E. C., and H. Tanaka, 1984: Spectral characteristics and meridional variations of energy transformations during the first and second special observing periods of FGGE. *J. Atmos. Sci., 41,* 1836–1849.

Lambert, S. J., 1988: A study of the growth and decay of eddy available potential energy and eddy kinetic energy based on temporal correlations. *Atmos.-Ocean, 26,* 40–58.

Lau, N.-C., and E. O. Holopainen, 1984: Transient eddy forcing of the time-mean flow as identified by geopotential tendencies. *J. Atmos. Sci., 41,* 313–328.

———, and M. J. Nath, 1987: Frequency dependence of the structure and temporal development of wintertime tropospheric fluctuations—Comparison of a GCM simulation with observations. *Mon. Wea. Rev., 115,* 251–271.

———, G. White and R. L. Jenne, 1981: Circulation statistics for the extratropical Northern Hemisphere. NCAR/TN-71+STR. National Center for Atmospheric Research, Boulder, Colorado, 138 pp.

Lorenz, E. N., 1955: Available potential energy and the maintenance of the general circulation. *Tellus, 7,* 157–167.

———, 1979: Forced and free variations of weather and climate. *J. Atmos. Sci., 36,* 1367–1376.

Metz, W., 1986: Transient cyclone-scale vorticity forcing of blocking highs. *J. Atmos. Sci., 43,* 1467–1483.

———, 1987: Transient eddy forcing of low-frequency atmospheric variability. *J. Atmos. Sci., 44,* 2407–2417.

Mullen, S. L., 1987: Transient eddy forcing of blocking flows. *J. Atmos. Sci., 44,* 3–22.

Nakamura, H., M. Tanaka and J. M. Wallace, 1987: Horizontal structure and energetics of Northern Hemisphere teleconnection patterns. *J. Atmos. Sci., 44,* 3377–3391.

Nigam, S., I. M. Held and S. W. Lyons, 1986: Linear simulation of the stationary eddies in a GCM. Part I: The "No-Mountain" Model. *J. Atmos. Sci., 43,* 2944–2961.

———, ——— and ———, 1988: Linear simulation of the stationary eddies in a GCM. Part II: The "Mountain" Model. *J. Atmos. Sci., 45,* 1433–1452.

Oort, A. H., and E. M. Rasmusson, 1971: *Atmospheric Circulation Statistics.* NOAA Prof. Paper No. 5, U.S. Dept. of Commerce, 323 pp.

Palmén, E., and C. W. Newton, 1951: On the three-dimensional motions in an outbreak of polar air. *J. Meteor., 8,* 25–39.

———, and ———, 1969: *Atmospheric Circulation Systems. Their Structure and Physical Interpretation.* Academic Press, 603 pp.

Palmer, T. N., 1981: Aspects of stratospheric sudden warmings studied from a transformed Eulerian-mean viewpoint. *J. Geophys. Res., 86,* 9679–9687.

Pfeffer, R. L., 1981: Wave-mean flow interactions in the atmosphere. *J. Atmos. Sci., 38,* 1340–1359.

———, 1985: Review of research on wave mean flow interactions using FGGE data. *Proc. First National Workshop on the Global Weather Experiment.* National Academy Press, Washington, D.C., 422–437.

———, 1987: Comparison of conventional and transformed Eulerian diagnostics in the troposphere. *Quart. J. Roy. Meteor. Soc., 113,* 237–254.

Phillips, N. A., 1954: Energy transformations and meridional circulations associated with a simple baroclinic wave in a two-level, quasi-geostrophic model. *Tellus, 6,* 273–286.

———, 1956: The general circulation of the atmosphere: A numerical experiment. *Quart. J. Roy. Meteor. Soc., 82,* 123–164.

Pierrehumbert, R. T., 1984: Local and global instability of a zonally varying flow. *J. Atmos. Sci., 41,* 2141–2162.

———, and P. Malguzzi, 1984: Forced coherent structures and local equilibria in a barotropic atmosphere. *J. Atmos. Sci., 41,* 246–257.

Plumb, A., 1983: A new look at the energy cycle. *J. Atmos. Sci., 40,* 1669–1688.

———, 1986: Three-dimensional propagation of transient quasi-geostrophic eddies and its relationship with the eddy forcing of the time-mean flow. *J. Atmos. Sci., 43,* 1657–1678.

Randel, W. J., 1988: Further modification of the lag-correlation diagrams: application to three-dimensional wave propagation. *Tellus, 40A,* 257–271.

———, 1990: Coherent wave-zonal mean flow interactions in the troposphere. *J. Atmos. Sci., 47,* 439–456.

———, and J. L. Stanford, 1985: The observed life cycle of a baroclinic instability. *J. Atmos. Sci., 42,* 1364–1373.

Reinhold, B. B., and R. T. Pierrehumbert, 1982: Dynamics of weather regimes: Quasi-stationary waves and blocking. *Mon. Wea. Rev., 110,* 1105–1145.

Schneider, E. K., 1987: A simplified model of the modified Hadley circulation. *J. Atmos. Sci., 44,* 3311–3328.

Schubert, S. D., 1986: The structure, energetics and evolution of the dominant frequency-dependent three-dimensional atmospheric modes. *J. Atmos. Sci.,* **43**, 1210-1237.

Shutts, G. J., 1983: The propagation of eddies in diffluent jet streams: eddy vorticity forcing of "blocking" flow fields. *Quart. J. Roy. Meteor. Soc.,* **109**, 737-761.

——, 1986: A case study of eddy forcing during an Atlantic blocking episode. *Advances in Geophysics,* **29**, 135-161.

Simmons, A. J., and B. J. Hoskins, 1979: The downstream and upstream development of unstable baroclinic waves. *J. Atmos. Sci.,* **36**, 1239-1254.

——, J. M. Wallace and G. W. Branstator, 1983: Barotropic wave propagation and instability, and atmospheric teleconnection patterns. *J. Atmos. Sci.,* **40**, 1363-1392.

Starr, V. P., 1968: *Physics of Negative Viscosity Phenomena.* McGraw-Hill, 256 pp.

Tanaka, H., and E. C. Kung, 1988: Normal mode energetics of the general circulation during the FGGE year. *J. Atmos. Sci.,* **45**, 3723-3736.

——, —— and W. E. Baker, 1986: Energetics analysis of the observed and simulated general circulation using three-dimensional normal mode expansions. *Tellus,* **38A**, 412-428.

Townsend, R. D., and D. R. Johnson, 1985: A diagnostic study of the isentropic zonally averaged mass circulation during the First GARP Global Experiment. *J. Atmos. Sci.,* **42**, 1565-1579.

Trenberth, K. E., 1982: Seasonality in Southern Hemisphere eddy statistics. *J. Atmos. Sci.,* **39**, 2507-2520.

——, 1986: An assessment of the impact of transient eddies on the zonal flow during a blocking episode using localized Eliassen-Palm flux diagnostics. *J. Atmos. Sci.,* **43**, 2070-2087.

——, 1987: The role of eddies in maintaining the westerlies in the Southern Hemisphere winter. *J. Atmos. Sci.,* **44**, 1498-1508.

Wallace, J. M., and M. L. Blackmon, 1983: Observations of low-frequency variability. *Large-Scale Dynamical Processes in the Atmosphere,* B. J. Hoskins and R. Pearce, Eds. Academic Press, 55-94.

——, and N.-C. Lau, 1985: On the role of barotropic energy conversions in the general circulation. *Advances in Geophysics,* **28A**, 33-74.

——, G.-H. Lim and M. L. Blackmon, 1988: On the relationship between cyclone tracks, anticyclone tracks and baroclinic wave guides. *J. Atmos. Sci.,* **45**, 439-462.

White, G. H., 1982: An observational study of the Northern Hemisphere extratropical summertime circulation. *J. Atmos. Sci.,* **39**, 24-40.

Wiin-Nielsen, A., and J. Sela, 1971: On the transport of quasi-geostrophic potential vorticity. *Mon. Wea. Rev.,* **99**, 447-459.

Wu, G.-X., 1988: The nature and dynamics of the general circulation of the atmosphere. *Proc. Summer School on Large-Scale Dynamics of the Atmosphere, 5-20 August 1988.* Lab. of Num. Modelling for Atmos. Sciences and Geophys. Fluid Dynamics, Chinese Academy of Sciences, Beijing, 155-227.

——, and A. A. White, 1986: A further study of the surface zonal flow predicted by an eddy parameterization scheme. *Quart. J. Roy. Meteor. Soc.,* **112**, 1041-1056.

Chapter 5

Theory of Extratropical Cyclones

Brian J. Hoskins

Department of Meteorology, University of Reading, Reading, Berkshire RG6 2AU, England

5.1 Introduction

There is no unique framework for understanding the growth and decay of extratropical cyclones. A number of useful approaches have been pursued in the huge body of literature on the subject during the past fifty years; these are reviewed also by Reed in Chapter 3 of this volume. Studies of the energetics or angular momentum budgets for a box surrounding a developing storm (Section 12.3.4) can, because of their integral nature, provide only a partial description of the processes occurring in the region. Another partial, but interesting, view is obtained by considering the work done by a parcel of air displaced in an otherwise undisturbed environment. Such a discussion, ignoring pressure forces and the continuous nature of the medium, cannot be complete but it is in accord with the spirit of synoptic descriptions in terms of the movement of conveyor belts of air, treated by Browning in Chapter 8.

The development theory of Sutcliffe (1947) and Petterssen (1956, Chap. 16) has been the basic tool of synopticians and forecasters for many years. The theory is based on approximations to the quasi-geostrophic omega and vorticity equations. With simple parameterizations of other physical processes such as latent heat release this pair of equations provides a complete set with which to discuss middle latitude synoptic systems.

An alternative, but mathematically equivalent, set is the quasi-geostrophic potential vorticity equation along with the temperature equation on the lower boundary. The linearization of this set about a basic flow has provided theoreticians with insight into the occurrence and structure of synoptic systems. These studies, however, have tended to be seen by synopticians as somewhat remote from the reality of the current weather map. With the advent of modern computers it has been possible to study linearizations of the less approximated primitive equations with more realistic basic flows, and to investigate the nonlinear

development of small amplitude synoptic systems. Data from such models, from more complicated models and from the real atmosphere can now be investigated within the framework of potential vorticity distributions on isentropic surfaces. This generalization of quasi-geostrophic potential vorticity theory, first introduced before the approximate form, can now be used routinely.

In this chapter, the potential vorticity perspective will be highlighted. Consistent with our opening statement, however, we first give an overview of insights that can be gained from parcel theory and from the omega equation. The literature on the theory of extratropical cyclones is vast and the emphasis throughout will be on the ideas rather than on an exhaustive list of references for each topic or a logical historical development of the ideas.

5.2 Parcel Theory for Slantwise Displacements

5.2.1 Symmetric Overturning

Making the Boussinesq approximation, consider the situation shown in Fig. 5.1 in which there is an x-independent zonal flow on an f-plane in thermal wind balance with static stability and baroclinity,

$$N^2 = \frac{g}{\theta_0}\frac{\partial \overline{\theta}}{\partial z}, \ B = f\frac{d\overline{u}}{dz} = -\frac{g}{\theta_0}\frac{\partial \overline{\theta}}{\partial y}, \text{ and } \zeta_a \text{ all constant.}$$

Then the slopes of the isentropes $\alpha_\theta = B/N^2$ and absolute momentum ($M = \overline{u} - fy$) surfaces, $\alpha_M = f\zeta_a/B$, are both constant. A parcel displacement in the meridional plane leads to a buoyancy force in the vertical back toward its θ-surface and an inertial force in the horizontal back toward its M-surface (see also Section 9.6). As shown in Thorpe et al. (1989) for a displacement Δs at an angle α, the integral of the buoyancy force times the displacement in the z direction and the inertial force times that in the y direction give, respectively,

$$\Delta K_z' = \frac{1}{2}(\Delta s)^2 B\frac{\sin \alpha}{\sin \alpha_\theta}\sin(\alpha_\theta - \alpha) \qquad (5.1)$$

and

$$\Delta K_y' = \frac{1}{2}(\Delta s)^2 B\frac{\cos \alpha}{\cos \alpha_M}\sin(\alpha - \alpha_M). \qquad (5.2)$$

For θ-surfaces more vertical than M-surfaces (see example in Fig. 12.13), the work done by both forces is positive, and they both act to increase displacements if these displacements are in the wedge between the two surfaces, i.e., $\alpha_M < \alpha < \alpha_\theta$. For small angles, the change in energy $\Delta K_y' + \Delta K_z'$ is maximized along isentropic surfaces. In this case the neglect of perturbation pressure forces is consistent and the dynamics are those of inertial instability on isentropic surfaces — the dynamic instability discussed by Helmholtz (1888). More generally this instability is known as symmetric (baroclinic) instability and the condition may be written in the equivalent forms:

$$\alpha_\theta > \alpha_M \text{ or } \zeta_{a\theta} < 0 \text{ or } P < 0, \qquad (5.3)$$

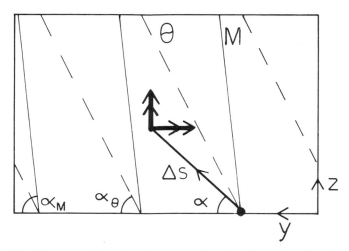

FIG. 5.1. A vertical section along a meridian for a flow with uniformly spaced isentropic surfaces (θ) and absolute momentum surfaces ($M = \overline{u} - fy$). As indicated, a parcel displacement leads to a buoyancy force in the vertical and an inertial force in the horizontal back toward the initial θ and M surfaces, respectively.

where

$$\zeta_{a\theta} = f + \left(\frac{\partial v}{\partial x}\right)_\theta - \left(\frac{\partial u}{\partial y}\right)_\theta \qquad (5.4)$$

and the potential vorticity

$$P = \frac{1}{\rho} \vec{\zeta}_a \cdot \nabla \theta. \qquad (5.5)$$

The large-scale atmosphere does not in general satisfy these criteria so that the energy available due to the thermal contrast (illustrated by $\Delta K_z'$) cannot be realized by simple overturning because of the angular momentum constraint (illustrated by $\Delta K_y'$). Symmetric instability is not necessary for cyclone growth but, as will be discussed below, locally in midlatitude weather systems it may be important.

5.2.2   Three-Dimensional Motions

On the large length-scale the angular momentum constraint can be broken by allowing variation along the basic flow (x) direction, as described by Eady (1949) and Green (1960). Suppose now that some parcels are displaced poleward as in Fig. 5.1 and at different longitudes other parcels are displaced southward along similarly sloping trajectories. In this sloping plane the motions will look like the dashed vectors shown in Fig. 5.2, with parcels curving in a clockwise sense in the Northern Hemisphere. This tendency for trajectories to curve, however, can be opposed by pressure gradients corresponding to a simple pressure pattern of the form shown. The meridional motion will then be in balance between the Coriolis and pressure gradient forces, i.e., there will be geostrophic balance.

A vertical section across the system must then look like the schematic shown in Fig. 5.3 with the warm air moving poleward and upward east of the low pressure region and the cold air moving equatorward and downward to the west. From hydrostatic balance, the lesser density of warm air corresponds to a relatively smaller change in pressure with height. This implies a tendency for the low pressure at low levels to be shifted toward the warm air region while at upper levels it is shifted away. Thus the low (and high) pressure region tilts westward with height.

From the energetics argument above we can even obtain an idea of maximum possible growth rates by assuming that such displacements are possible and that all the work done by the buoyancy force $\Delta K_z'$ can be realized by the perturbation in the kinetic energy of the N-S motion. From (5.1),

$$\frac{1}{2}(\delta\dot{y})_{max}^2 = \frac{1}{2}\delta y^2 \left(\alpha_\theta \frac{1}{4} f \frac{d\bar{u}}{dz}\right) = \frac{1}{2}\delta y^2 \left(\frac{1}{2} f \frac{d\bar{u}}{dz}\Big/N\right)^2.$$

Thus, for such a structure, the growth rate is

$$\sigma_{max} = 0.5\, f \frac{d\bar{u}}{dz}\Big/N, \qquad (5.6)$$

as derived by Eady (1949).

Taking reasonable parameter values,

$$f = 10^{-4}\text{s}^{-1},\ N = 10^{-2}\ \text{s}^{-1}\ \text{and}\ d\bar{u}/dz = 3\ \text{m s}^{-1}\text{km}^{-1}$$

(corresponding to $\partial\bar{\theta}/\partial y \approx -1\ \text{K}/100\ \text{km}$), this suggests a maximum possible growth rate of about $(0.8\ \text{day})^{-1}$. Close to a flat lower boundary, displacements must be quasi-horizontal and it is clear that σ_{max} cannot be achieved.

5.3   The Omega Equation View

5.3.1   The Equations

The usual β-plane quasi-geostrophic vorticity and thermodynamic equations may be written

$$D_g \zeta_g + \beta v_g = f_0 \frac{1}{\rho} \frac{\partial}{\partial z}(\rho w) + \mathcal{F}, \qquad (5.7)$$

$$D_g \frac{g}{\theta_0} \theta' + N^2 w = \mathcal{H}, \qquad (5.8)$$

where $D_g = \partial/\partial t + \mathbf{V}_g \cdot \nabla$ is the horizontal geostrophic advection operator, $\rho(z)$ and $N^2(z) = (g/\theta_0)d\theta_{ref}/dz$ are standard density and stratification distributions, and $\mathcal{F}$ and $\mathcal{H}$ represent frictional and diabatic heating effects, respectively. Maintenance of thermal wind balance

$$f_0\, \partial\zeta_g/\partial z = \nabla^2[(g/\theta_0)\theta'] \qquad (5.9)$$

in time implies that w must satisfy the diagnostic omega equation:

$$f_0^2 \frac{\partial}{\partial z}\left(\frac{1}{\rho}\frac{\partial}{\partial z}\rho w\right) + N^2\nabla^2 w = \mathcal{S} \qquad (5.10)$$

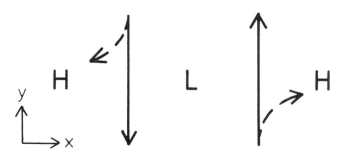

FIG. 5.2 The motions as seen in the plane of the trajectories. The dashed vectors are those that would occur in the absence of pressure variation indicated by L and H, and the continuous vectors are the actual balanced motions.

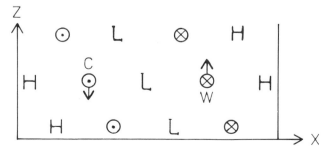

FIG. 5.3 A longitude-height section showing poleward (⊗), equatorward (⊙) and vertical motion, warm (W) and cold (C) air, and the longitudinal variation in pressure for a growing disturbance.

where

$$S = S_g + f_0\beta\, \partial v_g/\partial z - f_0\, \partial\mathcal{F}/\partial z + \nabla^2\mathcal{H}. \quad (5.11)$$

Here S_g is the source term, a function of the geostrophic variables, that would occur even in the absence of the β-effect and frictional and diabatic processes. Its form will be discussed below.

Provided that $\mathcal{F}$ and $\mathcal{H}$ can be parameterized in terms of the geostrophic variables and w, the vorticity equation (5.7) and the omega equation (5.10), along with a boundary condition $w = 0$ on $z = 0$ and suitable horizontal boundary conditions, form a complete set which is the basis of development theory. From (5.7), the growth of the cyclonic vorticity of a surface low pressure system is associated with $\partial w/\partial z$ positive and therefore ascent in the free atmosphere. The aim is then to use the omega equation to diagnose the conditions under which this occurs. Multiplying (5.10) by ρw and integrating over a domain with ρw zero at the bottom and top or tending to zero as $z \to \infty$, and zero or cyclic on horizontal boundaries, gives

$$\int S w \rho\, dV = -\int\left[\left(\frac{f_0}{\rho}\frac{\partial}{\partial z}\rho w\right)^2 + (N\nabla w)^2\right]\rho\, dV < 0. \quad (5.12)$$

Therefore S and w are negatively correlated and, provided distributions are reasonably simple, development may be expected below a region where S is negative. Simple scaling applied to (5.10) indeed suggests that

$$-\left(\frac{f_0^2}{H^2} + \frac{N^2}{L^2}\right)w \sim S. \quad (5.13)$$

However it should be noted that this estimate for w is possible only because of the simple boundary conditions and must in general be incorrect near those boundaries.

5.3.2   The Geostrophic Source Term

Sutcliffe's development theory was based on an approximation to S_g which may be written (following Hoskins et al. 1978 and Trenberth 1978)

$$S_g = 2\, B\, \partial\zeta_g/\partial s \quad (5.14)$$

where $B = |\, f\, \partial\mathbf{V}_g/\partial z| = (g/\theta_0)|\nabla\theta|$ and s is a coordinate along the thermal wind. Since significant ascent is required for development, the first deduction from (5.14) is that significant baroclinity and tropospheric vorticity gradients are a prerequisite. Also (5.14) implies that S_g is negative and w positive "ahead of" (i.e., in the direction of the thermal wind) a middle or upper tropospheric vorticity maximum, as sketched in Fig. 5.4. Since growth of a low-level vorticity maximum requires tropospheric ascent in phase with it, we may deduce also that the middle or upper tropospheric vorticity maximum must be "behind" the surface maximum, as shown in Fig. 5.4. It is also consistent with Fig. 5.3 in which the distribution of S_g will be similar to the negative of v. The elliptic equation (5.10) must then

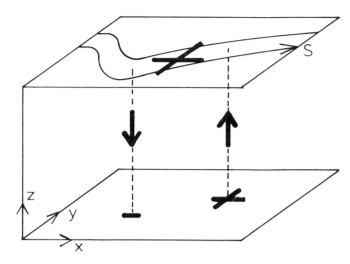

Fig. 5.4   A schematic showing a case of Northern Hemisphere surface development as described by the quasi-geostrophic vorticity equation and the Sutcliffe form of the omega equation. Shown are a free tropospheric level (z or p) and the surface. At the upper level the contours are those of θ and the coordinate s is along them. The plus sign marks a region of significant positive relative vorticity. The vertical arrows between the levels indicate the implied vertical motion and the plus and minus signs at the surface show the vorticity tendency. Note that if the vorticity develops at the surface as indicated by the tendency and if the isentropes at the surface are not too dissimilar from those on the higher surface, then there will be a forcing of descent between the two vertical arrows which will act so as to reinforce the upper positive vorticity anomaly.

yield a vertical velocity field similar in distribution to v but tilting less in the vertical. The stretching is therefore in phase with both the upper and lower tropospheric vorticity maxima.

The more usual form for S_g contains the two terms associated with thermal advection and vorticity advection. Because horizontal thermal gradients imply vertical vorticity gradients, the separation of the two terms is not a real one. Usually the simpler Sutcliffe form is superior for qualitative discussion.

The Q-vector form of S_g (Hoskins et al. 1978) is

$$S_g = 2\,\nabla \cdot \mathbf{Q}, \text{ where } \mathbf{Q} = -\,B\,\mathbf{k} \times \partial\mathbf{V}_g/\partial s. \quad (5.15)$$

This exact form again places emphasis on the baroclinity and the change in geostrophic velocity along the thermal wind, leading to the same general deductions as from the Sutcliffe form. The Q-vector form is preferable, however, in regions of significant deformation. Also $\mathbf{Q}$ pointing across a frontal region from the cold to the warm air implies a frontogenetic situation with a direct cross-frontal circulation.

5.3.3   Surface Friction

A simple view of the effect of boundary-layer turbulent momentum fluxes is obtained by considering that their convergence leads to a reduction in and turning of the wind:

$$\mathbf{V} = a\mathbf{V}_g + b\mathbf{k} \times \mathbf{V}_g \quad (5.16)$$

where $0 < a < 1$ and b has the sign of f.

Taking the divergence of (5.16), assuming the horizontal variation of a and b is negligible, and integrating over the boundary-layer depth H_{BL}, the vertical velocity at the top of the boundary layer is

$$w_{BL} = -\int_0^{H_{BL}} \nabla \cdot \mathbf{V} \, dz = \bar{b} H_{BL} \zeta_g . \quad (5.17)$$

Here $\bar{b}$ is a mean value of b and ζ_g is the geostrophic relative vorticity at the top of the boundary layer. This "Ekman pumping" condition replaces the boundary condition $w = 0$ for (5.10). In a region of positive low-level ζ_g, (5.17) implies ascent which the solution of (5.10) will generally give decreasing with height. From (5.7) this gives a tendency to decrease the vorticity.

As a quantitative example, for a sinusoidal distribution of ζ_g in the horizontal with total wavenumber K, and ρ and N^2 taken to be constant,

$$w = \bar{b} H_{BL} \, \zeta_g \exp(-z/H_R), \quad (5.18)$$

where the Rossby height scale $H_R = f/NK$. This gives a low-level vorticity rate of change $f \, \partial w/\partial z = -\bar{b} f (H_{BL}/H_R)\zeta_g$ so that the low-level vorticity spins down on a time-scale

$$T_{BL} = (\bar{b} f)^{-1} H_R/H_{BL} . \quad (5.19)$$

Taking reasonable parameter values: $\bar{b} = 0.2$, $H_{BL} = 10^3$m, $N = 10^{-2} \text{ s}^{-1}$ and $K = (5 \cdot 10^5 \text{ m})^{-1}$ gives T_{BL} to be about 3 days. This and more sophisticated analyses suggest that boundary-layer friction is significant but not in general strong enough to stabilize realistic flows (Valdes and Hoskins 1988).

5.3.4   Diabatic Heating

In general, a region of diabatic heating ($\mathcal{H} > 0$) must, from (5.10) and (5.11), lead to a vertical circulation with concentrated ascent in the region of heating and broader descent in the surrounding region. The major vorticity tendency is then positive below the heating and negative above it. Considering the simple middle-latitude weather system structure in Figs. 5.3 and 5.4, it is to be expected that the warm air moving poleward and ascending should reach its condensation level. The latent heat release will lead to extra ascent and a tendency to enhance the lower-tropospheric low pressure and the upper-tropospheric ridge.

If the latent heat release rate is proportional to w, then the diabatic heating term in (5.8) and therefore (5.10) can be absorbed into the $N^2 w$ term by using a reduced N^2_{eff} in condensation regions. Such an on-off process is difficult to handle in analytical investigations. Often, latent heat release effects are crudely modeled by considering a reduced N^2 everywhere. This point will be returned to in Section 5.6.3.

5.4   The Potential Vorticity Perspective

5.4.1   Basic Ideas

Hoskins et al. (1985) have produced an exhaustive (and exhausting!) review of the use of potential vorticity (PV) in meteorology; only a partial account will be given here.

PV, introduced by Rossby (1940) and Ertel (1942), is customarily used in the form (5.5) or, with the hydrostatic approximation,

$$P \simeq -g \zeta_{a\theta} \, \partial\theta/\partial p . \quad (5.20)$$

For a frictionless, adiabatic atmosphere P is materially conserved. Further, for balanced motion the distribution of P as well as lower boundary θ may be inverted to give a total (if approximate) description of the atmosphere at that instant. As discussed by Charney and Stern (1962), quasi-geostrophic potential vorticity, q, is a quantity whose behavior on a horizontal surface approximates that of P on an isentropic surface.

The climatological distribution of P and θ in the atmosphere below 100 mb is summarized in Fig. 5.5. Isentropic surfaces such as that with $\theta = 330$ K have PV values (in units specified in the caption) rising from 0 near the equator to slightly greater than 1 near the tropopause. There is then a rapid transition to stratospheric values. If the motion is adiabatic and frictionless the P contours will be advected on each isentropic surface. Equally, θ contours are advected on a P-surface. From the pole to about $25°$ the $P = 2$ surface corresponds to the tropopause. Thus the advection of θ contours on this surface shows the movement of the "dynamic" tropopause.

A positive P-anomaly or a positive lower boundary θ-anomaly both correspond in general to cyclonic circulation in the surrounding atmosphere. The static stability is enhanced at the level of the anomaly and reduced above and below. At an upper boundary a negative θ-anomaly has the same consequences.

Since, with approximations of balance, P is obtained by an elliptic operator acting on the pressure perturbation (or

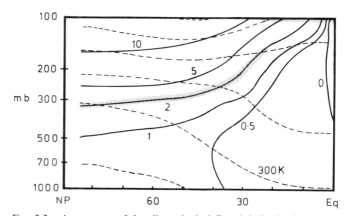

FIG. 5.5.   A summary of the climatological P and θ distribution below 100 mb in the Northern Hemisphere winter. The dashed contours are those of θ, drawn every 30 K. Values of P are given in terms of the unit PVU $= 10^{-6}$ K m^2 kg^{-1} s^{-1}, and contours are drawn at 0, 0.5, 1, 2, 5 and 10. The "dynamical" tropopause, specified by 2 PVU, is indicated by stippling.

geopotential) it is tempting, by analogy with the omega equation, to assume that they are negatively correlated. The derivation of (5.12), however, required the application of the simple boundary condition $w = 0$; such arguments are possible for this case only if the concept of PV is extended in the manner of Bretherton (1966) to include the θ boundary conditions.

5.4.2 Rossby Waves and Development

Neutral Rossby waves are possible on a P-gradient on a θ-surface or, equivalently, a θ-gradient on a P-surface. The tropopause is an example of such a region. Referring to Fig. 5.6a, the "meridional" displacement shown implies a cyclonic anomaly and the meridional velocities indicated. There is therefore a tendency to produce the same sign in meridional displacement upstream and the opposite sign downstream. This corresponds to the well-known properties of neutral Rossby waves, i.e., their phase speed is westward relative to the basic flow, $c < \bar{u}$, but their group velocity, c_g, is greater than c. For example, in the calculations shown by Hoskins and Jin (1990), equivalent barotropic Rossby waves propagate rapidly away from an initial perturbation, or a stationary source such as a diabatic heating region or a mountain, forming a new middle-latitude trough or ridge in about a day. Figure 5.7 gives an example of the day 2 and day 4 Northern Hemisphere upper tropospheric response to an initial vorticity perturbation in the tropics. The low-level response in middle latitudes is similar but weaker. There is almost zero vertical tilt up to day 4. It should be noted that the Rossby waves are essentially trapped by the tropopause, with only the very lowest wavenumbers propagating vertically as well as downstream (see, e.g., Held 1983).

Similarly, the "meridional" displacement in a region of surface baroclinity as shown in Fig. 5.6b implies a cyclonic anomaly and a tendency to produce the same sign in displacement downstream. Again, neutral Rossby waves are possible, but this time $c > \bar{u}$ and $c_g < c$. An example of the propagation of a neutral wave on a simple boundary temperature distribution is shown in Fig. 5.8. New troughs and ridges are produced on a time scale of a day moving with the surface flow, even though the flow is stable.

The two examples of neutral Rossby wave propagation show the possibilities for quite rapid development of downstream or upstream troughs and ridges. It is when the two situations coexist, however, that more impressive development is possible. Given the relative phases of Figs. 5.6a and 5.6b, the "poleward" velocity associated with the upper anomaly, extending downward through the atmosphere, will tend to reinforce the lower anomaly. Equally the equatorward velocity induced by the low-level anomaly will reinforce the upper anomaly. As long as the relative phases can be maintained this mutual reinforcement can continue. It should be noted that the phase speeds of the free modes are liable to be more similar than the flow speeds at the different levels. As described in Hoskins et al. (1985) the wave propagation mechanism tends to assist the phase-locking.

This process of mutual reinforcement of neutral Rossby waves is the essence of baroclinic instability and leads to a structure identical with that derived from our earlier arguments (Figs. 5.3 and 5.4). Even in situations where complete phase-locking is not possible, or where the upper anomaly is cut off so that immediate reinforcement is impossible, it is clear that important growth of the low-level cyclone is possible. The initial value problem studied by Simmons and Hoskins (1979) showed both the upstream and downstream development of essentially neutral Rossby waves and the mutual reinforcement process.

Farrell (1985) has recently emphasized the initial value problem and the growth that is possible even in stable flows simply by constructive interference without phase-

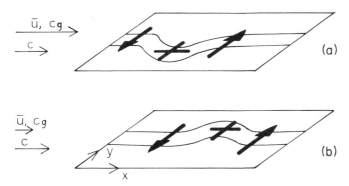

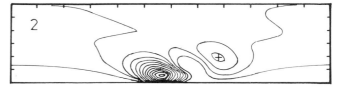

FIG. 5.6. A schematic showing neutral and interacting Rossby waves in the Northern Hemisphere. (a) At an upper level, PV contours on a θ-surface (or θ-contours on a PV surface) with values increasing (decreasing) with y. An equatorward displacement as shown corresponds to a positive (negative), "cyclonic" anomaly and meridional winds as indicated. These act to transfer the displacement upstream so that the phase speed (c) is less than the flow speed ($\bar{u}$). The group velocity (c_g), however, will be larger than the phase speed. These speeds are indicated on the left-hand side. (b) θ-contours on the lower boundary. The warm cyclonic anomaly leads to a tendency to transfer the displacement downstream but the group velocity will be less than this. The induced velocities will extend through some depth of the atmosphere. With the relative phases shown, the velocity field induced by each anomaly acts to increase the displacement and thus the size of the other anomaly.

FIG. 5.7 The perturbation resulting from adding an initial tropical vorticity dipole perturbation to a December–February climatological zonal flow. The model is T31 spectral with 15 layers, and has internal hyperdiffusion and low-level drag. Shown is the Northern Hemisphere streamfunction at level $\sigma = 0.34$, i.e., $p = 0.34\, p_{surface}$, at days 2 and 4. Tick marks are shown every 30° longitude and 15° latitude.

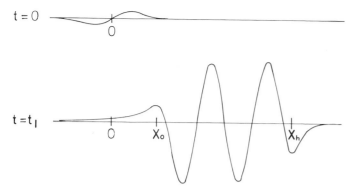

FIG. 5.8. Boundary Rossby waves in the 2-D Eady model (N, f, ρ, $\bar{u}_z$ all constant) with no lid and therefore no unstable modes. At $t = 0$ a PV anomaly, which is a δ-function in z, independent of y, and a dipole in x, is inserted at $z = h$. The boundary streamfunction corresponding to it is shown in the figure. The PV anomaly moves with the basic flow at $z = h$, its position being $x_h = \bar{u}(h)t_1$ at $t = t_1$. The group velocity (c_g) of neutral modes is the surface speed, reaching $x_0 = \bar{u}(0)t_1$ at $t = t_1$. Large amplitude waves which are almost steady in the frame moving with $\bar{u}(h)$ fill the region x_0 to x_h, with new systems being created in the region of the moving point x_0. If the dipole is removed, the region of waves moves with speed c_g, crests and troughs being created at the upstream end and destroyed at the downstream end. Using parameters $N = 10^{-2}$ s^{-1}, $f = 10^{-4}$ s^{-1}, $\bar{u}_z = 3$ m s^{-1} km^{-1}, $h = 5$ km and $\bar{u}(0) = 5$ m s^{-1}, the time t_1 shown here is $5 \cdot 10^5$ s ≈ 5.8 days and the wavelength is $\pi \times 1000$ km.

locking. For example (Emanuel, pers. comm.), consider that at initial time there are two identical quasi-geostrophic potential vorticity anomalies, q' (or, equivalently, boundary θ'), which are so distant that their associated streamfunction anomalies, ψ', are separated. Now suppose that the two anomalies are advected into close proximity by a shear flow. Then ψ' in the neighborhood of each q anomaly almost doubles and so, therefore, does the perturbation energy ($= -\int \rho \, \psi' q' \, dV$). In energetic terms there is transfer of energy from the shear flow associated with up-shear perturbation phase tilts. Of course this perturbation energy will subsequently decay back to its original value as the anomalies separate.

The importance of the phase speed matching of the

upper and lower Rossby waves is well illustrated by the calculations of Hoskins and Jin (1990) referred to above. Inspection of longitude-time plots of the upper tropospheric meridional velocity at 30°N (not shown) for the solution in Fig. 5.7 suggests that up to day 15 there are no characteristics of continuing growth through baroclinic instability in the equivalent barotropic waves with their essentially zero phase speed. For other cases in which the waves have a westward phase speed this period, with no evidence of baroclinic instability, is extended. Equivalent barotropic Rossby waves with an eastward phase speed, however, show westward tilts and baroclinic growth within a few days.

The Charney–Stern (1962) criterion for baroclinic instability of both signs in PV gradient, or the equivalent in boundary θ-gradient, may be interpreted as the condition that the two neutral Rossby waves are possible. The Fjørtoft condition that the westerly wind and the PV gradient are positively correlated means that the phase speeds are such that phase-locking is possible.

5.4.3 Early Theories

The Eady (1949) model had zero interior PV gradients and relied on upper- as well as lower-boundary θ-gradients. The normal mode structure with its "equivalent" PV anomaly is sketched in Fig. 5.9a. The pressure trough, being the solution of an elliptic problem, tilts westward with height but less than the line joining the two cyclonic PV anomalies. The Charney (1947) model has interior PV gradients independent of height rather than the localized values used in the simple discussion in the previous section. The normal mode structure (Fig. 5.9b) is, however, understandable as the interaction between the flow induced by the distributed interior PV anomaly, particularly that near the steering level (where $\bar{u} = c$), and that associated with the boundary anomaly.

In the Eady model for short horizontal wavelengths the smallness of the vertical penetration depth (H_R) of neutral

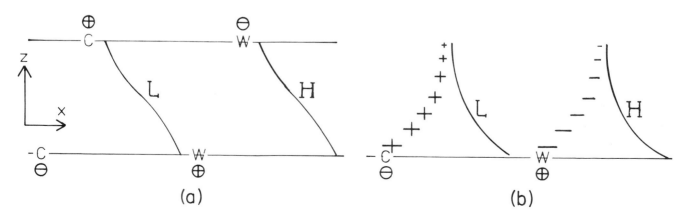

FIG. 5.9 Schematic PV pictures for (a) Eady and (b) Charney baroclinic instability modes. L and H indicate the axes of the pressure minima and maxima, and C and W the same for boundary temperature. In (b), interior PV anomalies are shown by plus and minus signs. The PV anomalies equivalent to the boundary temperature anomalies are shown in both (a) and (b) by plus and minus signs in circles.

modes on the two boundaries and the phase speed mismatch of the modes $((H - 2H_R)\bar{u}_z)$ mean that phase-locking is impossible. There is, therefore, a short wave cutoff to the instability. In the Charney model the shallow short wavelengths have amplitude in an interior region where Rossby waves are possible, and they are unstable.

The most unstable mode in the Eady model has a growth rate

$$\sigma \simeq 0.31 \, f\bar{u}_z/N . \qquad (5.21)$$

The parameter dependence is the same as that in (5.6) and the constant shows that the model's efficiency is not far below the optimum. With the same parameter values used in Section 5.2.2, the maximum growth rate is about $(1.2 \, \text{d})^{-1}$. Lindzen and Farrell (1980) showed that the same formula works remarkably well for the most unstable mode in the Charney and more complicated problems.

Whereas the Eady and Charney solutions were not originally couched in terms of PV, Kleinschmidt, in a series of papers summarized in Kleinschmidt (1957), gave PV a central position in his cyclone theory. Based on his observational analyses, he considered that every cyclone was associated with an internal positive PV anomaly. For larger scale cyclones this anomaly could be associated with undulations of the tropopause, though he wondered whether it could also be the product of an unknown torque. For frontal cyclones he considered that the PV anomaly was diabatically produced. Kleinschmidt's work appears to have been seen as totally at variance with the accepted baroclinic instability theory and to have received little recognition. Certainly he seems not to have been aware that boundary warmth could also be associated with cyclonic circulation. The middle or upper-tropospheric PV anomaly in his theory, however, is consistent with the tropospheric Rossby wave part of the present description of baroclinic instability. As will be discussed below, the diabatically created low-level PV maximum is also now thought to be an important ingredient in vigorous cyclones.

5.4.4 Some Extensions

Growth rates as high as (5.21) are not always attainable. James (1987) has shown that in baroclinic flows with horizontal shear at the lower boundary, baroclinic instability modal structure can be difficult to maintain against the horizontal shearing. For a simple two layer instability set-up, his calculation showed that the growth rate maximum of about $(1 \, \text{d})^{-1}$ was approximately halved by the addition of a weak barotropic horizontal shear of magnitude $5 \, \text{m s}^{-1}$ per 1000 km. When this shear is written as $(2.3 \, \text{d})^{-1}$ the dramatic reduction in growth rate is perhaps less surprising.

The approximation that the Lagrangian time scale, the characteristic time for the change in velocity following the motion, is much larger than f^{-1}, led Eliassen (1948) to the geostrophic momentum approximation. In this approximation, as shown in Hoskins (1975), an approximation to full PV is conserved following the 3-D motion. When

combined with a coordinate transformation, the resulting semigeostrophic equations were a modification of the quasi-geostrophic equations that allowed discussion of the growth of baroclinic waves into the nonlinear regime. Hoskins and West (1979) used them to show how unstable modes on a uniform PV flow between two rigid boundaries take on a more realistic appearance as the basic baroclinity is taken to be more localized in the meridional direction. In particular the nonlinear modes exhibited the following:

(i) more intense and smaller lows and broader, weaker highs;
(ii) poleward (equatorward) migration of surface lows (highs);
(iii) realistic cold frontal structures;
(iv) intense shear and baroclinity regions on the poleward side of the low;
(v) strong warm frontal development in cases of ambient low level cyclonic shear;
(vi) shrinkage of the region of warm air near the surface; and
(vii) in cases with a basic tropopause structure, the descent of a tongue of stratospheric air moving from the upper ridge to the trough (Hoskins and Heckley 1981).

5.5 Spherical, Primitive Equation Studies

5.5.1 Overview

Using modern computers it has been possible to extend the theory of baroclinic instability to the spherical domain, more realistic zonal flows, and the primitive equations and to determine nonlinear behavior. Generally the linear results such as those in Simmons and Hoskins (1976, 1977a) and Hoskins and Revell (1981) are in accord with those anticipated from the early models. The growth rate curve for a $47 \, \text{m s}^{-1}$ jet at $45°\text{N}$ given in the latter paper has a maximum at zonal wavenumber 8 with a value of about $(1.2 \, \text{d})^{-1}$. The structures are consistent with those discussed in earlier sections. The concentration of PV gradient at the tropopause is generally reflected in the existence of a secondary maximum in perturbation horizontal velocity in this region, for wavelengths longer than that of the growth rate maximum. For flows with increased low-level $f\bar{u}_z/N$ it is possible (Gall 1976; Gall and Blakeslee 1977; Simmons and Hoskins 1977b) for the growth rate maximum to occur at quite short wavelengths with their shallow vertical structure. Climatological zonally-averaged flows are probably less relevant as basic flows than are the intense baroclinic flows in the storm-track regions. They exhibit weaker instability with e-folding times about double those for the $47 \, \text{m s}^{-1}$ jet (Valdes and Hoskins 1988). The inclusion of reasonable surface damping reduces the growth rate maximum to about $(5 \, \text{d})^{-1}$ and stabilizes the short shallow waves. James (1987) showed that the subtropical portion of the Southern

Hemisphere winter zonal flow is almost rendered neutral by the barotropic shear in the region.

Nonlinear integrations using as initial conditions a zonal flow plus a small amplitude normal mode have been discussed in Simmons and Hoskins (1977a, 1980). The numerical model contained only a horizontal hyper-diffusion, this being necessary to balance the cascade to "grid"-scale occurring in frontal regions. Waves whose wavelengths are comparable to or shorter than those at which the growth-rate maximum occurs tend to attain a relatively small level of eddy energy, whereas the slightly longer waves proceed through periods of:

(i) quasi-exponential growth;
(ii) formation of surface frontal structures, the position and nature of which is determined by the deformation fields and trajectories associated with the basic state plus finite amplitude mode;
(iii) cessation of low-level growth but continued upper tropospheric growth which can be considered to be due to the upward propagation of wave activity; and

(iv) either anticyclonic wave-breaking or cyclonic cutoff at upper levels, the former leading to dynamical decay, and the latter to a finite amplitude, neutral, equivalent barotropic Rossby wave.

The short waves that do not "feel" the tropopause do not go through stages (iii) and (iv).

5.5.2 Two Life Cycles

The life cycles for two wavenumber six modes from particular flows will now be presented in some detail. Since the initial perturbations for the runs and the absence of physical processes are unrealistic, the life cycles are not considered total events that should be compared with observation. Rather they are presented as sequences of dynamical events, each providing a paradigm for observed cyclonic events.

The zonal flows to be discussed here are the basic flow and the WE flow used by Simmons and Hoskins (1980)

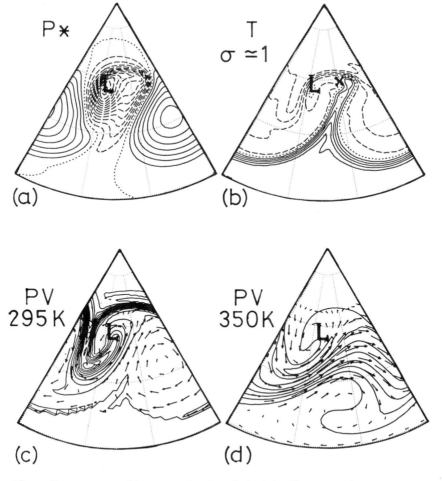

FIG. 5.10 Day 6 structure of the nonlinear most unstable wavenumber 6 on the basic jet. Shown on 60° longitude sectors north of 20°N are (a) surface pressure with contours every 4 mb, positive values continuous lines. The center of the low pressure is indicated here and on the other plots by an L. (b) Lowest model level temperature with contours every 4 K and the center of a small region of descent indicated by a cross. (c) 295 K PV with contours every 1/4 PVU. The contour on the equatorial flank is the intersection with the lower boundary. Flow vectors on the surface relative to the normal mode phase speed are also shown. (d) 350 K PV with contours every 1 PVU and relative flow vectors.

and shown in Hoskins (1983). The basic flow has a jet of 47 m s^{-1} on a sloping tropopause and zero flow at the surface. The WE flow has the same thermal structure but an added barotropic flow ranging from 10 m s^{-1} westerly at 20°N to 10 m s^{-1} easterly at 50°N. This was designed to give the low-level cyclonic shear in the region of cyclogenesis which semigeostrophic theory suggested would lead to strong warm frontal development. These cases have been rerun for wavenumber six normal modes with much higher resolution than used previously (Thorncroft 1988). The results to be shown here will be discussed in detail in a subsequent paper. The spectral numerical model has horizontal truncation at total wavenumber 95 (T95) and a ∇^6 horizontal hyperdiffusion acting on a time scale of 1 hour at the smallest scale. The number of levels in the vertical is 30 in one case and 15 in the other.

The structure of the basic flow wavenumber six mode at day 6 is summarized in Fig. 5.10. This is about at the end of stage (ii), as listed above. At this high resolution all the features noted for the semigeostrophic modes (except (v)) are apparent. The cold frontal temperature structure with its pressure trough is marked. The very strong shears and thermal gradients around the poleward edge of the system are separate from the almost meridional occlusion region.

In addition, the center of the low pressure contains a small secluded region of warmer air. Marked in Fig. 5.10b is the center of a small, isolated region of descent and from this region a wave-like feature appears toward the southwest along the baroclinic region. This wave appears in other fields also, and preliminary analysis of this case and others suggests that it could be an example of a Rossby wave on the surface baroclinity, generated by the strong circulations in the northeast portion of the system.

The PV on the 295 K surface (Fig. 5.10c) illustrates clearly the involvement of polar upper tropospheric–lower stratospheric air in the circulation around the low. Consistent with the relative flow vectors shown, it descends along the sloping isentropic surface and proceeds eastward and then northeastward behind the cold frontal region. PV on the 350 K surface (Fig. 5.10d) emphasizes the simple meandering of the westerly flow in the lower stratosphere at this time. There are indications of cyclonic "wrap-up" on the polar side and anticyclonic wrap-up of the tropopause region on the anticyclonic side.

As anticipated from semigeostrophic theory and emphasized in Hoskins (1983), the synoptic development in the WE case (Fig. 5.11) is in many ways very different. The frontal structure is now prominent ahead of the warm sec-

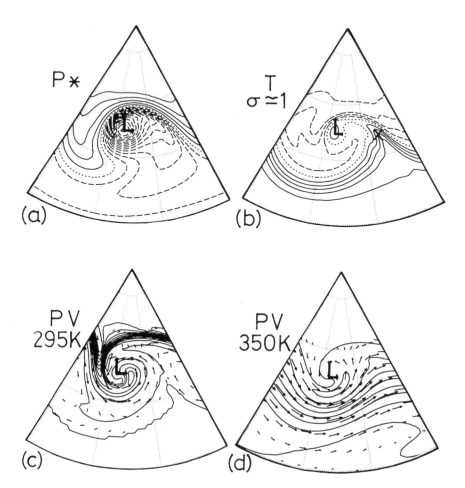

FIG. 5.11   Day 6 structure of the nonlinear most unstable wavenumber 6 on the WE flow. The convention is as in Fig. 5.10.

tor and merges into a region poleward of the low similar to that found before. Again warmer air is secluded in the center of the low, and there is an isolated region of descent. There is a very slight indication of a wave on the broad baroclinic region in the cold front region. The PV pictures are similar to those in Fig. 5.10, though the relative flow vectors tend to emphasize the cyclonic gyres in this case.

During the next days, as the upper-level amplitudes increase, the differences in the isentropic PV away from the earth's surface become marked. Examples are shown in Fig. 5.12. In the basic case (a) the anticyclonic gyres become dominant. The PV is advected southwestward behind the surface cold front, and at 350 K the contours indicate its motion around the base of the anticyclone and northeastward ahead of the following cold front. In contrast the WE mode (b) shows a dominance of the cyclonic wrap-up through the depth of the troposphere.

The subsequent behaviors depend crucially on these developments. The basic case exhibits a wave-breaking in PV and a decay in eddy kinetic energy comparable with its growth. The WE case forms a cyclonic, positive PV cutoff that loses its energy only very slowly.

In routine PV diagnosis of the atmosphere at Reading both modes of behavior are found; Fig. 5.13 shows exam-

ples. The cold front marked on standard synoptic charts ahead of each PV maximum and the subsequent developments of the systems may be expected to be rather different. This is the subject of current research.

The decline in eddy kinetic energy is arrested by a development summarized in Fig. 5.14 by 330 K PV and lowest-level temperature contours for days 8, 9 and 10. The PV "trough" behind the cold front pinches off to form an isolated maximum. This interacts with the low-level baroclinity in the manner discussed in Section 5.4.2 to form a frontal wave. The development does not continue because the isolated PV region cannot be reinforced.

5.5.3 Frontal Cyclones

It has not been clear over the years whether there is a real distinction between observed cyclogenesis on a baroclinic region and that on a frontal region. The Margules front at which two homogeneous fluids are separated by a sloping discontinuity has been analyzed in detail by Orlanski (1968). He found Rayleigh shear instability, Helmholtz shear instability, baroclinic instability and combinations of them in various parameter regimes. More recently, Moore and Peltier (1987) have examined the stability of a semigeostrophic front and given evidence of a

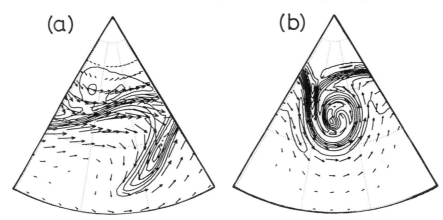

FIG. 5.12   PV pictures contrasting the nonlinear behavior of the two baroclinic waves: (a) Basic case, day 8, 330 K surface, contour increment 1 PVU. (b) WE case, day 7, 310 K contour increment ½ unit. In both cases the vectors show the velocities relative to the moving system.

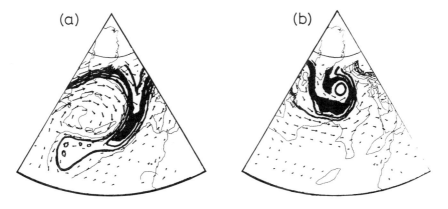

FIG. 5.13   315 K PV pictures for the sector 60°–0°W and poleward of 20°N for (a) 13 January 1983 and (b) 5 October 1985. Contours are at 0.5, 1, 1.5, 2–3 darkened, and 5 PVU. In both cases the vectors show the actual velocities.

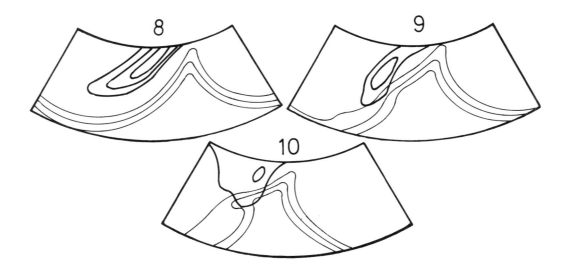

FIG. 5.14. The frontal wave development in the basic wavenumber 6 life cycle. Shown are the 330 K PV contours at 1, 3, . . . PVU (heavy) and the lowest-level temperature contours every 12 K (light) for days 8, 9 and 10. The sector is 60° in longitude and from 15–40°N. The normal mode phase speed has been removed from the motion of the system.

short wave instability, separate from the Eady branch. Since the PV with the geostrophic momentum approximation was uniform, semigeostrophic theory would have given only the Eady branch. Other investigators are currently using semigeostrophic models to study the instability of cold frontal regions associated with particular PV features. Schär and Davies (1990) consider cases with the warmest air ahead of the front and a reversal of boundary θ-gradient. Joly and Thorpe (1988) include an interior PV maximum that could have been generated by diabatic heating (see Section 5.6.2 below).

The life cycle experiments described in the previous section have shown two different frontal disturbances. The first appeared to be a Rossby wave ripple along the low-level baroclinity. The second was an interaction of a cutoff high PV region with the low-level baroclinity. Thorncroft (1988) investigated the stability of a zonal flow obtained by taking the mass distribution from a section across the cold front in the basic flow wave at day 6 (Fig. 5.10). As well as Eady-type waves he found a short wavelength branch with weak growth rates and energetics dominated by conversions from the kinetic energy of the zonal flow. Despite this instability, when a 1000 km wavelength sinusoidal disturbance was imposed upon the day 6 cold front and the life cycle was continued, the disturbance virtually disappeared within a day. It appears that the deformations in the evolving frontal region do not allow the unstable structures to be maintained, as suggested by the work of James (1987), discussed in Section 5.4.4, and Juckes and McIntyre (1987).

5.6 Diabatic Processes

5.6.1 Moist Symmetric Instability

The ellipticity of the omega equation is measured by

f^2N^2. In semigeostrophic theory the same role is played by fP, and in Hoskins (1974) it is shown that the maximum and minimum frequencies of symmetric disturbances have the property

$$\omega_{max}^2 \, \omega_{min}^2 \propto fP . \qquad (5.22)$$

Therefore P is in many ways a measure of the stiffness of the atmosphere. Also, since P is conserved in adiabatic motion, symmetric instability cannot be generated in an adiabatic atmosphere.

In the real atmosphere P is not conserved so that symmetric instability could be generated. Near-zero values of P, however, are generally found only in the upper troposphere in middle latitudes when subtropical air has been advected rapidly poleward and, as remarked in Section 5.2.1, dry symmetric instability probably does not occur. But in a saturated atmosphere it is the more steeply sloped, moist isentropes that are relevant for ascent, and in a cyclone it is possible for these surfaces to be more vertical than those of constant absolute momentum. In this case we must anticipate inertial instability along moist isentropic surfaces (Eliassen 1957, pp. 70–72; Bennetts and Hoskins 1979). Thus, although the energy in the basic latitudinal temperature contrast cannot be released in this manner, locally in a cyclone such a mechanism is possible. Emanuel (1988) has presented evidence that in regions of slantwise ascent in cyclones there is approximate neutrality: Absolute momentum and moist isentropic surfaces coincide.

A measure of the moist stiffness of the atmosphere is

$$P_e = \frac{1}{\rho} \vec{\zeta}_a \cdot \nabla \theta_e . \qquad (5.23)$$

The condition for moist symmetric instability is P_e negative. If θ_e is conserved and the atmosphere is frictionless, P_e

can be changed following the motion by gradients in moisture along the thermal wind. For a 2-D or saturated atmosphere this term is zero, but in general P_e does change and moist symmetric instability can be generated.

5.6.2 PV Sources and Sinks

Integrating PV over a mass of atmosphere with boundary S gives

$$\int_m P\,dm = \int_S C_\theta\,d\theta, \qquad (5.24)$$

where C_θ is the absolute circulation around an isentropic circuit on S. As stressed by Thorpe and Emanuel (1985) and Hoskins et al. (1985), this implies that the mass-weighted PV in a material region cannot be changed by diabatic heating or friction which are purely internal to the region. Now the material change of P is governed by

$$\frac{DP}{Dt} = \frac{1}{\rho}\,\vec{\zeta}_a \cdot \nabla\mathcal{H} + \frac{1}{\rho}\nabla\times\mathcal{F}\cdot\nabla\theta. \qquad (5.25)$$

Diabatic heating in a region must lead to material sources and sinks of the form sketched in Fig. 5.15, the mass-weighted values canceling. Heating at a lower boundary produces a negative source in the interior PV but a compensating equivalent positive source in the boundary warming.

Boundary friction does not necessarily lead to a damping of PV anomalies. For example, if $\mathcal{F} = -\lambda(z)\mathbf{V}$, then

(5.25) becomes

$$DP/Dt = -\lambda\rho^{-1}\,\zeta_a\,\partial\theta/\partial z + \rho^{-1}\,v_s|\nabla\theta|\,d\lambda/dz, \qquad (5.26)$$

where v_s is the component of wind in the direction s along the thermal wind. For a situation in which a warm boundary anomaly overcomes a low interior PV to produce a cyclonic low-level flow, the first term indicates a tendency to increase the magnitude of the interior PV anomaly. For $d\lambda/dz$ negative, the latter term has the opposite sign to v_s and can be significant (M. Blackburn, pers. comm.).

5.6.3 Effect on Cyclone Development

The effect of diabatic heating on the development of middle-latitude weather systems has been discussed in Section 5.3.4 from an omega equation perspective, but a complementary view is now possible. As remarked in Section 5.3.4, the simplest, though crude, approach is to model the reduced stability to moist ascent by a global reduction in static stability. The maximum growth rate of baroclinic instability (5.21) increases as N^{-1} and the wavenumber of this instability decreases with N: There is a shift to shorter wavelengths with larger growth rates. Emanuel et al.(1987) have carried this approach much further for an Eady wave independent of the meridional coordinate. They have used semigeostrophic theory and parameterized latent heat release only in the ascending air, the basic assumption underlying this parameterization being that the atmosphere adjusts itself to be almost neutral to moist slantwise ascent, i.e., $P_e = 0$. They found an increase in growth of about 2.5 and a large decrease in the breadth of the region of ascent. The total wavelength decreased by a factor of about 0.6.

As discussed above, latent heat release in the ascending air leads to an increase in PV below and a decrease above. Since the middle tropospheric ascent leads the surface low by less than a quarter wavelength, the PV source acts in the sense of increasing the low-level cyclonic circulation. Similarly it acts to increase the amplitude of the upper ridge. Emanuel et al. (1987) showed this process occurring in a numerical integration of a moist 2-D Eady wave. Convective heating in the cold air similarly tends to lead to a low-level positive PV source somewhat in phase with the surface cyclone, thereby reinforcing it. The upper-level sink, however, tends to act to damp the upper-level trough. The net effect is to act to transfer the upper PV maximum to the lower troposphere.

Surface fluxes of momentum generally do act to decrease the magnitude of the cyclonic circulation around a surface low. Surface fluxes of water vapor, however, act to increase the possibility of saturated ascent and thus to enhance the development of the system. Surface fluxes of heat can be considered as producing a warm cyclonic boundary anomaly with a compensating negative interior PV anomaly. Internal processes, however, can lead to the redistribution of the interior anomaly, e.g., by convection or advection, and the realization of the cyclonic circulation associated with the boundary warmth.

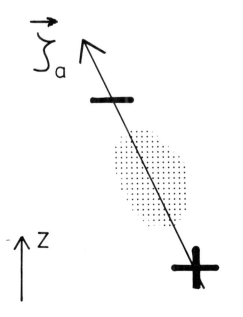

FIG. 5.15 PV sources (+ and −) for a diabatic heating region (stippled). The arrow shows the direction of the absolute vorticity vector.

5.7 A Case Study

5.7.1 Introduction

In the early morning of 16 October 1987 the winds associated with a cyclone caused great devastation in southeast England and northern France. (The lack of people able to reach the stock market on the following Monday could have contributed toward the crash!) The maximum hourly mean wind recorded on the south coast of England was 38 m s^{-1} and the maximum gust 51 m s^{-1}. In Normandy a gust of 60 m s^{-1} was recorded. Associated with the system was also a U.K. record frontal temperature rise of 9.1°C in 20 minutes and a record pressure rise of 12.1 mb in one hour.

Five days before, the forecast models had been predicting a severe event, though shifted from the real cyclogenesis; however, they generally weakened the intensity in forecasts from subsequent days. Because of this one must be cautious in the interpretation of diagnostics of the operational analyses produced at this time. The discussion here is mostly taken from the study of Berrisford (1988) and Hoskins and Berrisford (1988). The data used are from the routine initialized ECMWF analyses, and from a successful rerun of the U.K. Meteorological Office fine mesh (70 km) model starting from a modified analysis at 00 UTC 15 October.

5.7.2 The Situation at 00 UTC 16 October

At this time the cyclone is estimated to have had a central pressure of 952 mb, its center being between Brittany and southwest England. The topography of the tropopause is shown by the θ-contours on the 2 PVU surface (Fig. 5.16a) and the low-level structure by θ-contours on the 850 mb surface and P-contours on the 300 K surface (Fig. 5.16b). In the region of the storm the transition from a subtropical to a subpolar tropopause occurs in a quasi-two-dimensional region on the smallest resolved scale (the grid is 1.875°). The intense baroclinity shows a distinct wave and the 300 K PV is high.

A vertical section across the storm is shown in Fig. 5.17. The jet maximum at 65 m s^{-1} is strong but not extreme. The low-level maximum of more than 40 m s^{-1} on this scale is consistent with the observed low-level winds. The PV section shows the remarkable jump in the dynamic tropopause and very large values in low-level PV linked by the one contour to the tropopause in a "PV tower."

Given that the system is not very 3-D at this time, Berrisford (1988) has used a 2-D semigeostrophic model to show that if the PV and boundary θ distribution are known then the damaging wind field can be deduced. Using a schematic PV distribution based on Fig. 5.17b, the resulting wind and θ distribution is that shown in Fig. 5.17c. Given that no tuning was performed, the similarity with Fig. 5.17a provides convincing evidence that the development can be viewed in PV terms, and that the origin of the strong low-level winds is understood if the origin of the important features of the PV distribution can be determined. By experimentation it is found that the low-level PV distribution is crucial for the low-level winds but that the upper tropospheric structure is also important.

5.7.3 The Time Development

It is shown in Hoskins and Berrisford (1988) that the tropopause jump can be traced back 36 hours to an even more spectacular feature present in the west Atlantic. It appears that the intensity of this tropopause jump, and in particular the origin of the air on its equatorial flank, might be related to the outflow from a hurricane that had struck Florida two days previously. The tropopause jump with its associated 85 m s^{-1} jet moved steadily across the Atlantic at about 30 m s^{-1}.

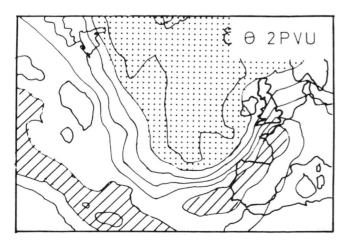
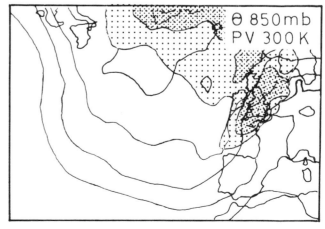

Fig. 5.16   The situation over the north Atlantic and west Europe at 00 UTC 16 October 1987. Shown on the left are the θ-contours on the 2-PVU surface. The θ-contours are drawn every 10 K, with the region less than 320 K stippled and that greater than 360 K hatched. On the right are 850 mb θ-contours every 5 K. Also indicated are the 300 K PV values between ³/₄ and 1 by light stippling and greater than this by heavy stippling. (Adapted from Hoskins and Berrisford 1988.)

It was also shown by Hoskins and Berrisford that a strong baroclinic region extended right across the Atlantic by 06 UTC 15 October, with extremely warm air moving into the Bay of Biscay region at the time of year when the water is at its warmest. The analysis suggested that high PV features existed at low levels in the baroclinic region before 12 UTC 15 October but the continuity was poor. It was clear, however, that there was a large rise in low-level PV values in the region of the developing storm in the 18 hours before midnight on 16 October.

An interesting, more detailed picture of the storm that was about to develop is given by the U.K. Meteorological Office rerun fine mesh forecast for 06 UTC 15 October, as summarized in Fig. 5.18. The 330 K PV shows an intense maximum located in a broad PV "trough" about 1000 km west of the nearest surface low, the one that became the record storm. Six hours later this separation had halved. The 700-mb temperature field shows the strong baroclinic region from the Atlantic to northwest Europe. A sequence of shallow depressions had developed in this region, caus-ing some confusion to forecasters trying to identify their movement from one synoptic map to the next. The temperature wave and *Q*-vector signature associated with the latest in the sequence, the low mentioned above, is clear. The *Q*-vector indicates warm frontogenesis and strong ascent ahead of the low. There is evidence also of the previous system to the east.

5.7.4 A Summary of the Development

The storm of October 1987 appears to have many of the ingredients discussed in this review. There was an intense low-level baroclinic region, and a succession of low-level disturbances developed and moved along it in the manner of surface Rossby waves. An intense upper air PV anomaly moved rapidly toward the baroclinic region and locked onto one of the surface waves. Corroborating evidence for the existence of the PV anomaly is given by the TOMS total ozone picture for mid-day on 15 October (L. Uccellini, pers. comm.) which shows a local maximum in the

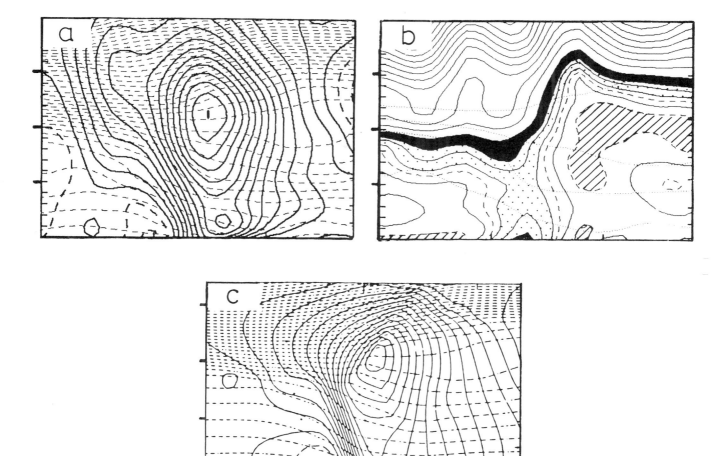

FIG. 5.17 Vertical cross sections across the storm at 00 UTC 16 October. (a) Velocity into the section with isotachs every 5 m s⁻¹ (negative heavy dashed) and θ-contours every 5 K. (b) PV with hatching for the region with values less than ¼, a dashed contour at ¾ and continuous contours at ½, 1, 2, 3 and then every 2 PVU. The region with values between 1 and 2 is stippled and that between 2 and 3 blackened. Also shown dotted are the 300, 315, 330 and 350 K isentropes. (c) As (a) but for a 2-D semigeostrophic inversion of an idealized PV distribution. (Berrisford 1988.) In each case the tick marks on the vertical axis are every 5 km and those on the horizontal axis every 1000 km.

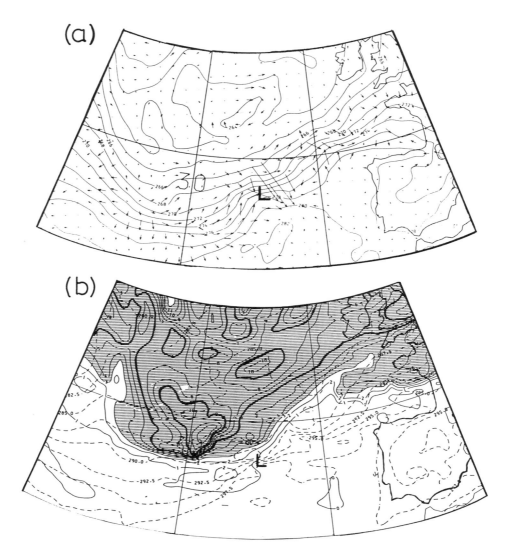

Fig. 5.18.   The situation at 06 UTC 15 October as given by a rerun of the U.K. Meteorological Office fine mesh (70 km) model, initiated 6 hours previously. The region shown is from 45°–0°W and 35°–55°N. (a) 700-mb temperature and Q-vectors. The temperature contours are drawn every 2 K from 258 K in the northwest to 282 K in the south. The Q-vector convergence was in good agreement with the model-generated ascent. The position of the surface low pressure which developed into the storm is indicated by an L both here and in (b). (b) PV on the 330 K θ-surface. The PV contours are drawn at intervals of 1 PVU, with hatching for the region greater than 3 and heavy contours at 6 and 9 PVU. Also shown are 900-mb potential temperature contours drawn every 2.5 K.

region. The ascending air ahead of the cyclone was very warm and moist, having traveled from the subtropics over warm water. The P_e was small and there was little stability for this ascent. There was large latent heat release, leading to a negative PV source above and positive source below. The upper tropospheric air passed through the region, probably leading to the streamer of very low or negative PV and high θ on the 2 PVU surface. The low-level air tended to remain much longer in the source region, leading to a large increase in PV and a low-level cyclone dominated by its PV anomaly much as envisaged by Kleinschmidt (1957). In the mature stage the upper PV maximum overran the lower tropospheric maximum to form the PV tower.

Most of these ingredients are found in other explosive developments investigated by Berrisford (1988), and by

Uccellini (Chapter 6 in this volume) and those referenced by him.

5.8   Concluding Remarks

The theory of extratropical cyclones has matured to the point that detailed analysis and interpretation of real developments, and sophisticated numerical models of them in terms of the theory, are possible and should lead to an extension of that theory. A major emphasis over the next few years must be in the interaction of the physical and dynamical processes. Latent heating effects can perhaps be added on to the dry dynamics for the large cyclone scale, but on the frontal cyclone scale this is less likely. This chapter has placed little emphasis on the subfrontal scale motions, on the decay of cyclones, and on the organization of storm tracks. Research is also occurring on these important problem areas but much remains for us to learn.

Acknowledgments

This paper is the result of collaboration and discussion with my colleagues at Reading over many years. Very useful comments on the paper have been made by them and by Arnt Eliassen, Kerry Emanuel, Eero Holopainen, Glenn Shutts and Michael McIntyre. Figures contributed by Jin Fei-Fei, Paul Berrisford, Chris Thorncroft and Glen Shutts are acknowledged with thanks.

REFERENCES

Bennetts, D. A., and B. J. Hoskins, 1979: Conditional symmetric instability — a possible explanation for frontal rainbands. *Quart. J. Roy. Meteor. Soc.,* **105**, 945-962.

Berrisford, P., 1988: Potential vorticity in extratropical cyclones. Ph.D. Thesis, Univ. of Reading, 168 pp.

Bretherton, F. P., 1966: Critical layer instability in baroclinic flows. *Quart. J. Roy. Meteor. Soc.,* **92**, 325-334.

Charney, J. G., 1947: The dynamics of long waves in a baroclinic westerly current. *J. Meteor.,* **4**, 135-162.

——, and M. E. Stern, 1962: On the stability of internal baroclinic jets in a rotating atmosphere. *J. Atmos. Sci.,* **19**, 159-172.

Eady, E. T., 1949: Long waves and cyclone waves. *Tellus,* **1**, No. 3, 33-52.

Eliassen, A., 1948: The quasi-static equations of motion. *Geofys. Publ.,* **17**, No. 3, 1-44.

——, 1957: Adiabatic and frictionless motions. Stability properties and the theory of small-amplitude oscillations and waves. Chap. II in *Dynamic Meteorology* by A. Eliassen and E. Kleinschmidt. *Handbuch der Physik,* **48**, S. Flügge, Ed. Springer-Verlag, 45-90.

Emanuel, K., 1988: Observational evidence of slantwise convective adjustment. *Mon. Wea. Rev.,* **116**, 1805-1816.

——, M. Fantini and A. J. Thorpe, 1987: Baroclinic instability in an environment of small stability to slantwise moist convection. Part I: Two-dimensional models. *J. Atmos. Sci.,* **44**, 1559-1573.

Ertel, H., 1942: Ein Neuer hydrodynamischer Wirbelsatz. *Meteor. Zeits.,* **59**, 271-281.

Farrell, B., 1985: Transient growth of damped baroclinic waves. *J. Atmos. Sci.,* **42**, 2718-2727.

Gall, R., 1976: A comparison of linear baroclinic instability theory with the eddy statistics of a general circulation model. *J. Atmos. Sci.,* **33**, 349-373.

——, and R. Blakeslee, 1977: Comments on "A note on the wavelength of maximum growth rate for baroclinic instability." *J. Atmos. Sci.,* **34**, 1479-1480.

Green, J. S. A., 1960: A problem in baroclinic instability. *Quart. J. Roy. Meteor. Soc.,* **86**, 237-251.

Held, I. M., 1983: Stationary and quasi-stationary eddies in the extratropical troposphere: Theory. *Large-Scale Dynamical Processes in the Atmosphere*, B. J. Hoskins and R. P. Pearce, Eds. Academic Press, 127-168.

Helmholtz, H. v., 1888: Über atmosphärische Bewegungen. *Sitz-Ber. Akad. Wiss. Berlin*, 647-663. English translation in Abbe, C., 1893: *The Mechanics of the Earth's Atmosphere*, Smithsonian Institution, 78-93.

Hoskins, B. J., 1974: The role of potential vorticity in symmetric stability and instability. *Quart. J. Roy. Meteor. Soc.,* **100**, 480-482.

——, 1975: The geostrophic momentum approximation and the semigeostrophic equations. *J. Atmos. Sci.,* **32**, 233-242.

——, 1983: Dynamical processes in the atmosphere and the use of models. *Quart. J. Roy. Meteor. Soc.,* **109**, 1-21.

——, and N. V. West, 1979: Baroclinic waves and frontogenesis. Part II: Uniform potential vorticity jet flows — cold and warm fronts. *J. Atmos. Sci.,* **36**, 1663-1680.

——, and W. A. Heckley, 1981: Cold and warm fronts in baroclinic waves. *Quart. J. Roy. Meteor. Soc.,* **107**, 79-90.

——, and M. J. Revell, 1981: The most unstable long wavelength baroclinic instability modes. *J. Atmos. Sci.,* **38**, 1498-1503.

——, and P. Berrisford, 1988: A potential vorticity perspective of the storm of 15-16 October 1987. *Weather,* **43**, 122-129.

——, and F.-F. Jin, 1990: The initial value problem for tropical perturbations to a baroclinic atmosphere. *Quart. J. Roy. Meteor. Soc.,* submitted.

——, I. Draghici and H. C. Davies, 1978: A new look at the ω-equation. *Quart. J. Roy. Meteor. Soc.,* **104**, 31-38.

——, M. E. McIntyre and A. Robertson, 1985: On the use and significance of isentropic potential vorticity maps. *Quart. J. Roy. Meteor. Soc.,* **111**, 877-946. (See also **113**, 401-404, comments by J. S. A. Green and reply by authors.)

James, I. N., 1987: Suppression of baroclinic instability in horizontally sheared flows. *J. Atmos. Sci.,* **44**, 3710-3720.

Joly, A., and A. J. Thorpe, 1988: The stability of two-dimensional fronts modified by latent heat release. Preprints, *Palmén Memorial Symposium on Extratropical Cyclones*, Helsinki. Amer. Meteor. Soc., 94-97.

Juckes, M. N., and M. E. McIntyre, 1987: A high resolution one-layer model of breaking planetary waves in the stratosphere. *Nature,* **328**, 590-596.

Kleinschmidt, E., Jr., 1957: Cyclones and anticyclones. Chap. IV in *Dynamic Meteorology* by A. Eliassen and E. Kleinschmidt. *Handbuch der Physik,* **48**, S. Flügge, Ed. Springer-Verlag, 112-154.

Lindzen, R. S., and B. Farrell, 1980: A simple approximate result for the maximum growth rate of baroclinic instability. *J. Atmos. Sci.,* **37**, 1648-1654.

Moore, G. W. K., and W. R. Peltier, 1987: Cyclogenesis in frontal zones. *J. Atmos. Sci.,* **44**, 384-409.

Orlanski, I., 1968: Instability of frontal waves. *J. Atmos. Sci.,* **25**, 178-200.

Petterssen, S., 1956: *Weather Analysis and Forecasting*, 2nd ed., Vol. 1. McGraw-Hill, 428 pp.

Rossby, C.-G., 1940: Planetary flow patterns in the atmosphere. *Quart. J. Roy. Meteor. Soc.,* **66**, Suppl., 68-87.

Schär, C., and H. C. Davies, 1990: An instability of mature cold fronts *J. Atmos. Sci.,* in press.

Simmons, A. J., and B. J. Hoskins, 1976: Baroclinic instability on the sphere — normal modes of the primitive and quasigeostrophic equations. *J. Atmos. Sci.,* **33**, 1454-1477.

——, and ——, 1977a: Baroclinic instability on the sphere: solutions with a more realistic tropopause. *J. Atmos. Sci.,* **34**, 581-588.

——, and ——, 1977b: A note on the wavelength of maximum growth rate for baroclinic instability. *J. Atmos. Sci.,* **34**, 1477-1478.

——, and ——, 1979: The downstream and upstream development of unstable baroclinic waves. *J. Atmos. Sci.,* **36**, 1239–1254.

——, and ——, 1980: Barotropic influences on the growth and decay of nonlinear baroclinic waves. *J. Atmos. Sci.,* **37**, 1679–1684.

Sutcliffe, R. C., 1947: A contribution to the problem of development. *Quart. J. Roy. Meteor. Soc.,* **73**, 370–383.

Thorncroft, C., 1988: Frontal cyclogenesis. Ph.D. Thesis, Univ. of Reading, 216 pp.

Thorpe, A. J., and K. Emanuel, 1985: Frontogenesis in the pres-ence of small stability to slantwise convection. *J. Atmos. Sci.,* **42**, 1809–1824.

——, B. J. Hoskins and V. Innocentini, 1989: On the applicability of the parcel method. *J. Atmos. Sci.,* **46**, 1274–1284.

Trenberth, K. E., 1978: On the interpretation of the diagnostic quasigeostrophic omega equation. *Mon. Wea. Rev.,* **106**, 131–137.

Valdes, P. J., and B. J. Hoskins, 1988: Baroclinic instability of the zonally averaged flow with boundary layer damping. *J. Atmos. Sci.,* **45**, 1584–1593.

Chapter 6

Processes Contributing to the Rapid Development of Extratropical Cyclones

Louis W. Uccellini

Laboratory for Atmospheres, NASA/Goddard Space Flight Center, Greenbelt, Maryland 20771

6.1 Introduction: Historical Perspective

The study of extratropical cyclones has provided the basis for vigorous scientific debates within the meteorological community for at least the past 150 years. In her monograph entitled *The Thermal Theory of Cyclones: A History of Meteorological Thought in the Nineteenth Century,* Kutzbach (1979) documents the interest of the leading European and American meteorologists of the 19th and early 20th centuries in providing a description of the weather and airflow associated with cyclones and identifying the physical processes that contribute to their development. In the 19th century, the emergence of the so-called "thermal theory of cyclones" (see Fig. 6.1) was based, to a large degree, on the work of Espy, who believed that the decrease of surface pressure in storms is related primarily to the release of latent heat in the ascending air near the storm center. By the early 20th century, the

theoretical work of Margules and V. Bjerknes and the observational studies by Dines (which indicated extratropical cyclones were cold core systems) led to a more dynamically based perspective on cyclogenesis. The energy conversions and low-level convergence associated with instabilities in regions marked by significant temperature gradients (especially in the lower troposphere) were recognized as important contributing factors in the development of extratropical storms.

The growing awareness of the importance of dynamical processes provided a basis for the polar front theory of cyclogenesis that was developed by the Bergen school in Norway (see, e.g., Bjerknes and Solberg 1922) and set the stage for vigorous discussions concerning the relative importance of dynamic and thermodynamic processes in extratropical storms. Kutzbach's (1979, pp. 125–128) discussion on the "controversial evidence" introduced through the synoptic studies of Hann and Loomis in the late 19th century, and Brunt's (1930) brief note on the origin of cyclones, in which he reviews the differences between the thermal (or "local heating") and dynamic (or

*Present affiliation: National Meteorological Center/NOAA, World Weather Building, 5200 Auth Road, Camp Springs, MD 20746

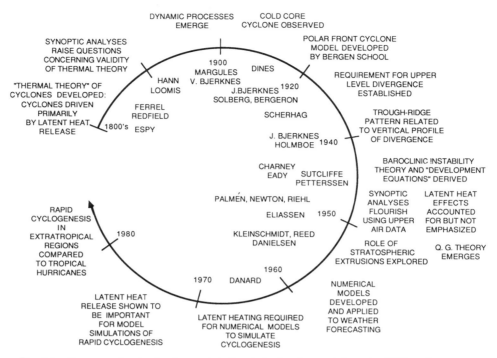

FIG. 6.1.   Summary of major developments in the study of cyclogenesis from the 1800s to the present.

"polar front") theories, provide evidence of the early debates on the relative importance of various physical processes in rapid cyclogenesis. Brunt concludes that observational studies in the 1920s tended to support the concept that dynamic processes associated with low-level fronts and the existence of a strong upper-level current are important for the development of cyclones, while not ruling out the importance of boundary layer heating and latent heat release.

From the 1920s to the 1950s, rapid advances in the understanding of cyclogenesis occurred over a relatively short period of time (Fig. 6.1). Upper-level trough/ridge systems were shown to provide the divergence required to reduce the surface pressure, while low-level convergence contributed to the vorticity increase that marked the rapid spin-up of cyclones (see, e.g., Bjerknes and Holmboe 1944). By the end of this period, the jet stream was discovered, the role of stratospheric extrusions in cyclogenesis was elucidated, and baroclinic instability theory became firmly established as a basis for describing the energy conversions associated with cyclogenesis. Furthermore, synopticians began to focus on vorticity advection and thermal advection patterns as key factors in cyclogenesis, as reflected by Petterssen's (1956, p. 337) hypothesis that "cyclone development at sea level occurs when and where an area of appreciable vorticity advection in the upper troposphere becomes superimposed upon a slowly moving quasi-stationary front at sea level." Therefore, an almost complete transition had occurred in that cyclones were now increasingly related to dynamic processes associated with upper-level troughs and jets and low-level

fronts rather than to thermodynamic processes associated with the release of latent heat.

Despite the emphasis on dynamics (especially with the emergence of baroclinic instability concepts in the late 1940s and early 1950s), synopticians continued to recognize the important role of diabatic processes in cyclogenesis. For example, the development equations derived by Sutcliffe (1947) and Petterssen (1956, p. 324) include a diabatic term that accounts for the effect that latent heat release has in offsetting the cooling associated with adiabatic ascent in a statically stable environment. In his *Compendium of Meteorology* article on extratropical cyclones, Palmén (1951) also discusses the importance of latent heat release in focusing the area of "principal ascent" in the precipitation region associated with cyclones. In separate diagnostic studies, Krishnamurti (1968) and Johnson and Downey (1976) emphasize the importance of latent heat release for its contribution to the rapid deepening of extratropical cyclones and the vertical extension of the vortex from the lower to middle troposphere.

The introduction of numerical weather prediction models in the 1950s based on the quasi-geostrophic framework, however, and their failure to simulate rapid cyclogenesis in many cases, set the stage for the reemergence of the concept that the impact of latent heat must be accounted for to describe and simulate cyclogenesis (Danard 1964). As discussed by Keyser and Uccellini (1987), the proliferation of model sensitivity studies from the 1960s to the present has had a major impact in focusing attention on the importance of latent heat release in the overall development of cyclones, perhaps contributing to an overemphasis of its importance at the expense of the dynamic processes. This trend has nearly brought us full circle to the position espoused by Espy in the 19th century (Fig. 6.1), with some recent work on rapid cyclogenesis drawing an analogy between extratropical cyclones and tropical hurricanes (e.g., Rasmussen 1979; Bosart 1981; Anthes et al. 1983; Gyakum 1983a,b). Nevertheless, current modeling systems and observations are far from perfect, and our understanding of the interaction among the various physical and dynamical processes is incomplete. Thus, the meteorological community still finds itself involved in a vigorous debate concerning the relative importance of latent heat release, boundary-layer processes and dynamical processes in the development of extratropical cyclones.

6.2 Recent Interest in Rapid Cyclogenesis

The recent interest in cyclogenesis has focused on cyclones that undergo a period of rapid development and are often marked by severe winds and heavy precipitation. In their study of "explosive" cyclogenesis in the Northern Hemisphere, Sanders and Gyakum (1980) found that the rapidly deepening storms occur primarily over the ocean above or just to the north of the warm ocean currents in the North Atlantic and North Pacific Oceans. This result is confirmed in follow-up studies by Roebber (1984; see Fig. 6.2), Rogers and Bosart (1986), and numerous case studies which include: analyses of the QE II storm in the North Atlantic (Anthes et al., 1983; Gyakum 1983a,b; Uccellini 1986); a study of a North Pacific cyclone which deepened 40 mb in a 12-hour period and attained a central pressure of 950 mb or less (Reed and Albright 1986; Kuo and Reed 1988); studies of cyclogenesis along the east coast of Australia (Holland et al. 1987; Leslie et al. 1987); a number of papers on major snowstorms along the east coast of the United States (e.g., Bosart 1981; Bosart and Lin 1984; Uccellini et al. 1984, 1985, 1987; Kocin et al. 1985; Sanders and Bosart 1985a,b; Bosart and Sanders 1986; Kocin and Uccellini 1990); and a growing number of studies on polar lows in the North Atlantic and Pacific Oceans (e.g., Rasmussen 1979; Sardie and Warner 1985; Shapiro et al. 1987; Businger and Reed 1989). There are always exceptions to the rule that rapid cyclogenesis occurs over the ocean or near a coastline. For example, several major cyclones occur over the central United States each winter that have deepening rates exceeding the criterion for explosive development. An example is the 25–26 January 1978 cyclone which deepened 40 mb in 24 hours over the east-central United States and southern Canada producing severe blizzard conditions over a large area as described by Burrows et al. (1979) and Salmon and Smith (1980).

In an extension of the Sanders and Gyakum study, Roebber (1984) presents a statistical analysis of the 24-hour deepening rates for a one-year sample of cyclones occurring in the Northern Hemisphere, and shows that the distribution is skewed toward the rapidly deepening

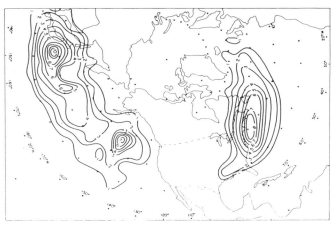

FIG. 6.2. Geographic distribution of maximum deepening positions for explosive cyclogenesis observed during 24-h periods from 1976 to 1982, smoothed over a 5° longitude by 5° latitude grid (Roebber 1984).

storms (Fig. 6.3). Roebber chose a normal distribution approach to argue that two normal curves can be used to classify cyclogenesis in two categories; one being "common" or "ordinary" and the other "explosive." An important aspect of this distinction (and a major practical reason for the growing interest in studying rapid cyclogenesis) is that in many instances numerical models continue to have problems simulating cyclones that exhibit an explosive development phase. In recent papers by Anthes et al. (1983) and Kuo and Reed (1988) which describe numerical simulations of rapid cyclogenesis, even the best simulations had central pressures in the storm center that were 15 to 19 mb above those observed. The rapid cyclogenesis that produced destructive winds in southern England on 15 October 1987 (see Section 5.7) was also poorly predicted by the best operational models in Great Britain (Morris and Gadd 1988).

The storms that are characterized by the most rapid deepening rates are marked by decreasing pressure for a longer period of time compared to ordinary cyclones (Roebber 1984). As noted by Roebber, however, the

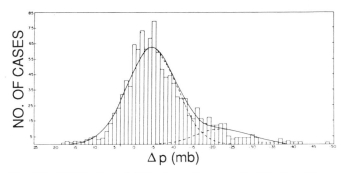

FIG. 6.3. Distribution of 24-h deepening rates for Northern Hemisphere cyclones observed for a 1-year period and adjusted for latitude dependence. The solid line indicates the sum of two normal curves; the dashed lines indicate the separate curves. The pressure difference (Δp) has been adjusted according to latitudinal position; negative deepening rates imply a net filling of the system during a 24-h period (Roebber 1984).

period of extreme rapid deepening occurs for only a fraction of the time encompassing the cyclogenetic event, a result which is consistent with Kocin and Uccellini's (1990) review of 23 major snowstorms along the east coast of the United States. An example of the rapid development phase of an extratropical cyclone is provided by Reed and Albright (1986) for the Pacific cyclone of 12–14 November 1981 (Fig. 6.4). Between 06 UTC 12 November and 03 UTC 14 November, the cyclone deepened from 1011 to 947 mb. However, within 12 hours of that 45-hour period, the cyclone deepened from 992 mb (06 UTC 13 November) to 981 mb (12 UTC 13 November) to 954 mb (18 UTC 13 November). Thus, 60 percent of the documented deepening of this storm occurred in only 26 percent of the time that deepening was observed.

The observations that many of these cyclones exhibit a short period of extreme rapid deepening lends support to the terminology of "explosive development" used by Sanders and Gyakum (1980) and Roebber (1984), among many others, in describing these storms. The separation of explosive and ordinary cyclogenesis by these authors, combined with the well-known fact that baroclinic instability theory yields development rates which are below those which are observed (e.g., Farrell 1984), have also led Roebber (1984, p. 1582) to suggest that "explosive cyclogenesis is produced by a mechanism or mechanisms that are distinct in some meaningful way from the baroclinic process" and that rapid cyclogenesis "develops differently from less intense storms." However, the observations might also suggest that these storms are a result of an interaction of various physical and dynamical processes that occurs over a relatively short period of time—an interaction that is common to some degree in all cyclones, but which might act more efficiently in the more intense storm systems.

These differing viewpoints have provided the scientific basis for field programs along the east coasts of Canada and the United States such as the Canadian Atlantic Storms Program (CASP) (Stewart et al. 1987), the Genesis of Atlantic Lows Experiment (GALE) conducted in 1986 (Dirks et al. 1988) and the Experiment on Rapidly Intensifying Cyclones over the Atlantic (ERICA) completed in the winter of 1988–1989 (Hadlock and Kreitzberg 1988). Given the ongoing research efforts, it is not possible, at this time, to resolve entirely the complex issues concerning the interaction of various physical processes and their role in rapid cyclogenesis.

6.3 Characteristics of Rapid Cyclogenesis

There are a number of characteristics that are common to rapid cyclogenesis, whether the storms are synoptic-scale systems (such as coastal storms) or smaller, mesoscale systems (such as polar lows). The common characteristics along with associated dynamical and physical processes are described in this section (see also Section 3.3.4). While these processes are treated separately in order to identify their possible contributions to the developing storm

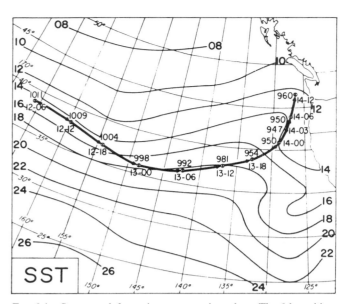

FIG. 6.4.   Storm track for an intense oceanic cyclone. The 6-h positions and corresponding central pressures are marked for the period from 06 UTC 12 November to 12 UTC 14 November. Light solid lines are sea-surface temperature (°C) (Reed and Albright 1986).

systems, the interaction among these various processes appears to be the critical factor for rapid cyclogenesis, an issue which is addressed in Section 6.4.

6.3.1   Upper-Level Processes

The study of upper-level conditions required for cyclogenesis dominated synoptic meteorological research during the first half of the 20th century in association with the introduction of techniques to monitor and measure atmospheric winds, temperature and moisture above the earth's surface. As described by Palmén and Newton (1969, Chap. 5), a basic principle which emerged during this period (largely due to the concepts promoted by Margules, Dines and Scherhag) is that the development of cyclonic disturbances at sea level requires upper-level divergence, so as to yield a net reduction of mass and a decrease in the sea-level pressure in a region where the low-level wind field is generally convergent. Bjerknes and Holmboe (1944) relate the vertical distribution of divergence required to sustain cyclogenesis to the presence of an upper-level trough-ridge pattern, with divergence aloft, convergence near the earth's surface and a level of non-divergence in the middle troposphere located downstream of the trough axis (Fig. 6.5a). The recognition that upper-level divergence is required for surface cyclogenesis has also been linked with an associated requirement for the existence of "longitudinal" or along-stream ageostrophic wind components that result from cyclonic or anticyclonic curvature (Sutcliffe 1939; Bjerknes and Holmboe 1944; Bjerknes 1951). Subgeostrophic flow at the base of a trough and supergeostrophic flow at the ridge crest are associated with the divergence (convergence) downstream (upstream) of the trough axis (Fig. 6.5a).

A

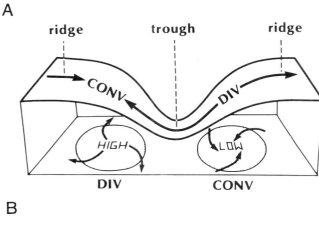

B

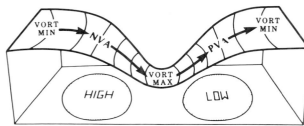

FIG. 6.5. (a) Schematic relating the along-stream ageostrophic wind at upper levels to patterns of divergence associated with an upper-level wave and surface high- and low-pressure couplets (based on Bjerknes and Holmboe 1944). (b) Schematic of maximum (cyclonic) and minimum (anticyclonic) relative vorticity centers and advections (NVA = negative or anticyclonic vorticity advection; PVA = positive or cyclonic vorticity advection) associated with an idealized upper-level wave (Kocin and Uccellini 1990).

Given the problem of diagnosing divergence aloft and the associated ageostrophic wind field, these processes have been inferred through the use of the vorticity and thermodynamic equations, forming the basis of the Sutcliffe (1947) and Petterssen (1956) development equations. Within this framework, the divergence in the upper levels is approximated by the vorticity advection fields (Fig. 6.5b), with cyclonic or positive vorticity advection (PVA) associated with the divergence required for surface cyclogenesis (see also Palmén and Newton 1969, pp. 318–319). Furthermore, as derived by Sutcliffe, the advection of absolute vorticity by thermal wind (typically at 500 mb) has been shown to be highly correlated with surface cyclogenesis, a relationship which provided a basis for the synoptic analyses and forecast procedures used before the advent and acceptance of numerical models. Recent climatological studies of rapid cyclogenesis confirm that the development of these storms commences as the trough/ridge system and its associated region of PVA propagate to within 500 km upstream of the cyclogenetic region (Sanders and Gyakum 1980; Sanders 1986, 1987).

In addition to the contribution of the longitudinal or along-stream ageostrophic components to divergence within trough/ridge patterns, Bjerknes (1951) and Reiter (1963, pp. 339–342) discuss the likely contribution of "transverse" (or cross-stream) ageostrophic components,

and associated divergence patterns, in the entrance and exit regions of jet streaks to surface cyclones and anticyclones. As described by Namias and Clapp (1949), Bjerknes (1951) and Murray and Daniels (1953), the entrance region of an *idealized* jet streak (with a maximum wind speed greater than the propagation rate of the jet) is marked by a transverse ageostrophic component directed toward the cyclonic-shear side of the jet (Fig. 6.6a). This component represents the upper branch of a direct transverse circulation that converts available potential energy into kinetic energy for parcels accelerating into the jet. The direct circulation is defined by the vertical ascent on the anticyclonic (or warm) and descent on the cyclonic (or cold) sides of the jet (Fig. 6.6b), a pattern that is consistent with vorticity advection concepts described by Riehl et al. (1952) and illustrated in Fig. 6.6c. Conversely, in the exit region, the ageostrophic components in the upper tropo-

A

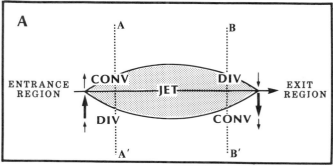

B

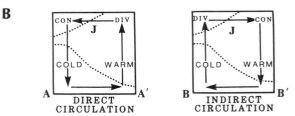

C

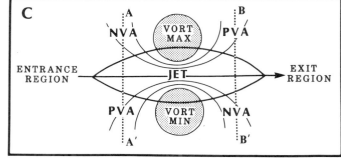

FIG. 6.6. (a) Schematic of transverse ageostrophic wind components and patterns of divergence (DIV) and convergence (CON) associated with the entrance and exit regions of a straight jet streak (based on Bjerknes 1951). (b) Vertical cross sections illustrate vertical motions and direct and indirect circulations in the entrance region (line A-A′) and exit region (line B-B′) of a jet streak. Cross sections include two representative isentropes (dotted), upper-level jet (J) location, upper-level divergence and horizontal ageostrophic wind components within the plane of each cross section. (c) Schematic of maximum and minimum relative vorticity centers, and associated PVA and NVA patterns, associated with a straight jet streak (after Riehl et al. 1952). Schematic is from Kocin and Uccellini (1990).

sphere are directed toward the anticyclonic-shear side of the jet (Fig. 6.6a), representing the upper branch of an indirect transverse circulation pattern (Fig. 6.6b) that converts kinetic energy to available potential energy as parcels decelerate upon exiting the jet. (See example in Fig. 12.18.) In conjunction with this circulation pattern is ascent (descent) on the cyclonic or cold (anticyclonic or warm) side of the jet, which again is in agreement with the vorticity advection patterns (Fig. 6.6c). As discussed by Uccellini and Johnson (1979), an important factor that determines the magnitude of the horizontal ageostrophic components of the transverse circulation and the associated vertical motion pattern is the along-stream variation of the wind speed in the exit and entrance region of the jet and not necessarily the magnitude of wind maximum in the jet core.

The influence of curvature effects in masking or distorting the contribution of jet streaks to upper-level ageostrophy, divergence and vertical motion is discussed by Beebe and Bates (1955), Reiter (1963, pp. 293–297, 354–355), Shapiro and Kennedy (1981), Newton and Trevisan (1984), Uccellini et al. (1984), Keyser and Shapiro (1986), Kocin et al. (1986) and Uccellini and Kocin (1987). The more recent studies indicate that although the transverse circulations are normally depicted on a two-dimensional vertical plane, the existence of indirect and direct circulations is a consequence of three-dimensional variations in the ageostrophic winds and upper-level divergence that cannot be fully described in terms of the idealized two-dimensional jet streak dynamics. Nevertheless, Uccellini (1984) and Wash et al. (1988) emphasize that the upper-level "forcing" related to the presence of jet streaks can be very large even for jets exhibiting little or no curvature. These results demonstrate that the lack of a trough and associated cyclonic curvature is not sufficient to infer weak upper-level divergence, especially for situations involving relatively straight jet streaks that have well-defined entrance and exit regions marked by large along-stream wind variations. Furthermore, these studies raise questions concerning the criterion for a "type A" storm system defined by Petterssen and Smebye (1971) as that which develops over the ocean in straight flow aloft without upper-level forcing (i.e., without "appreciable vorticity advection," p. 459). Since even minor observation gaps or analysis errors can have a significant impact on the analyses of jet streaks and their vorticity advection and related divergence fields over data-rich areas, the application of this criterion to rapid cyclogenesis in the data-void regions over the oceans should be discouraged.

Despite the complications related to curvature effects, and also to the influence of latent heat in enhancing the ascent patterns associated with jet streaks (Cahir 1971; Uccellini et al. 1987), there is growing recognition that jet-streak-induced circulations play a role in rapid cyclogenesis. For example, in climatological studies of cyclogenesis in the lee of the Rocky Mountains, Hovanec and Horn

(1975) and Achtor and Horn (1986) show that most of the cyclones from a 60-day sample form in the left-front exit region of jet streaks propagating across the western United States toward the lee-slope of the Rocky Mountains (Fig. 6.7a), a result which is consistent with Newton's (1956) case study of the 17 November 1948 rapid cyclogenesis event to the lee of the Rocky Mountains. Achtor and Horn also show that development of these storms occurs within an area marked by diverging along-stream ageostrophic wind fields downstream of a trough axis (Fig. 6.7b) and diverging transverse ageostrophic components within the exit region of the upper-level jet streak (Fig. 6.7c). Mattocks and Bleck (1986) emphasize the role of the indirect circulation pattern in the exit region of upper-level jet streaks in the development of cyclones in the lee of the Alps and the Gulf of Genoa. In an analysis of model-simulated polar lows in the northern Pacific, Sinclair and Elsberry (1986) conclude that the entrance and exit regions of jet streaks are important for providing the environment in which these particular storms can deepen rapidly. Kocin and Uccellini (1990) show that the rapid development phase of 23 cyclones along the East Coast of the United States commence as the exit region of an upper-level jet becomes collocated with the region marked by increasing diffluence in the geopotential height field immediately downstream of the trough axis. In a companion paper published earlier, Uccellini and Kocin (1987) conclude that the transverse ageostrophic components associated with jet streaks aloft appear to combine with the longitudinal components associated with the trough-ridge pattern to enhance and focus the upper-level divergence required for rapid cyclogenesis, a process that was originally envisioned by Bjerknes (1951).

6.3.2   Stratospheric Extrusions, Tropopause Folds and Related Potential Vorticity Contribution to Surface Cyclogenesis

Upper-level trough/ridge patterns and jet streaks not only provide the divergence aloft needed for deepening surface cyclones, but also contribute to the intensity of upper-level fronts and related distribution of potential vorticity which can, in turn, have a significant impact on the spin-up of these storms through the descent and horizontal advection of stratospheric air toward the cyclogenetic region. Attempts have been made to link the extrusion of stratospheric air into the upper and middle troposphere to cyclogenesis through the principle of conservation of isentropic potential vorticity (IPV), where IPV $= -(\zeta_\theta + f)\partial\theta/\partial p$. As stratospheric air descends into the troposphere, the air mass is stretched and the static stability $(-\partial\theta/\partial p)$ decreases significantly. Consequently, the absolute vorticity $(\zeta_\theta + f)$ increases with respect to parcel trajectories as long as the stratospheric values of IPV are preserved.

Kleinschmidt (1950) was apparently the first to relate the advection of a stratospheric reservoir of high IPV

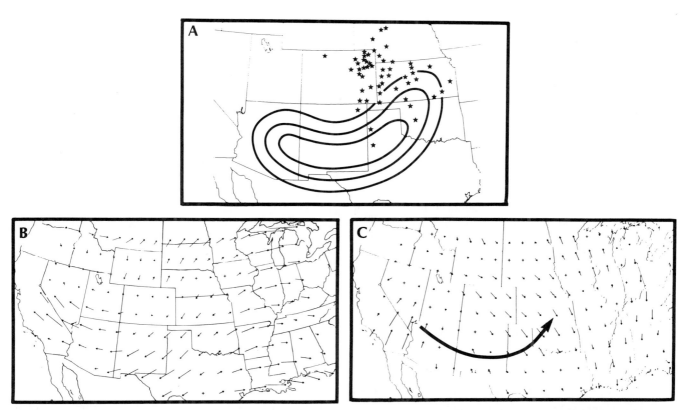

FIG. 6.7.   (a) Mean 300-mb isotach field superimposed on sites of cyclogenesis for cases during the spring season in Colorado (Hovanec and Horn 1975). (b) Longitudinal and (c) transverse ageostrophic components derived for a subsample of the spring season Colorado cyclones (Achtor and Horn 1986).

associated with a low tropopause to cyclogenesis, going so far as to state that the stratospheric reservoir "is essentially the producing mass of the cyclones" (Kleinschmidt 1957, p. 125). This emphasis on the stratosphere by Kleinschmidt reflects a long-term interest of German meteorologists in studying the association between warm-air advection above the tropopause and surface cyclogenesis, dating back to Wagner's work in the early part of the century (see Kutzbach 1979, p. 184). A recent review article by Hoskins et al. (1985) discusses the impact of stratospheric IPV anomalies on surface cyclogenesis (see Section 5.4). Through an "invertibility principle" expressed by Kleinschmidt (1950), Hoskins et al. show that a positive IPV anomaly that extends downward from the stratosphere into the middle troposphere provides an optimal situation for enhancing the IPV advection in the middle to upper troposphere, which acts to induce a cyclonic circulation that extends throughout the entire troposphere to the earth's surface (Fig. 6.8a).

Kleinschmidt (1957) also explores the means by which a stratospheric air mass is detached from the main reservoir and is subsequently displaced equatorward, hypothesizing that a disturbance associated with the jet stream is likely responsible for the equatorward displacement of the stratospheric air mass and its descent toward the middle troposphere during the period of cyclogenesis. It now appears that the transverse circulations associated with

"tropopause folding" (Section 3.3.2) along the axis of an upper-level jet/front system is the mechanism that acts to displace the stratospheric air down toward the 500 to 700 mb layer (Danielsen 1968; see Figs. 3.8 and 3.9). A tropopause fold is defined by Reed (1955) and Reed and Danielsen (1959) as the extrusion of stratospheric air within upper-tropospheric baroclinic zones downward from a normal tropopause level to the middle and lower troposphere. The concept of a tropopause fold complemented the studies of Reed and Sanders (1953) and Newton (1954), which pointed to a growing appreciation of the importance of subsidence in the upper and middle troposphere as a mechanism contributing to upper-level frontogenesis.

The work of Staley (1960), Bleck (1973, 1974), Boyle and Bosart (1983, 1986) and Bleck and Mattocks (1984) provides supporting evidence for the important role that tropopause folding can play in the development of surface cyclones. Staley discusses cyclogenesis in terms of a simultaneous strengthening of the vortex and tropopause folding. Bleck's analysis of numerical simulations of several cyclones, and Boyle and Bosart's case studies of an East Coast cyclone, also emphasize the simultaneous extrusion of stratospheric air into the middle and lower troposphere and surface cyclogenesis.

While the dominant theme has been to relate the *simultaneous development* of the tropopause fold and cyclogenesis, other studies indicate that a probable connection exists between upper-level frontogenesis and tropopause folding associated with jet-streak transverse circulation patterns and the subsequent development of surface cyclones. Dynamical processes that link jet systems and attending tropopause folds with the *subsequent* rapid surface cyclogenesis have been emphasized in recent case studies by Uccellini et al. (1985), Uccellini (1986) and Whitaker et al. (1988).

In the Uccellini et al. (1985) study of the Presidents' Day cyclone, which developed along the East Coast on 18–19 February 1979 (Fig. 6.9), an intensifying polar front jet (PFJ) and deepening trough were diagnosed in the central United States, 1500 km upstream of the cyclogenetic region (Fig. 6.10). A well-defined tropopause fold marked by the extrusion of stratospheric IPV values down to the 700-mb level (Fig. 6.11) could be isolated 1500 km upstream of the cyclogenetic region and 12 to 24 hours prior to the period of rapid surface development. Uccellini et al. show that subsidence along the axis of the PFJ contributed to the tropopause fold, and trace the stratospheric air mass to a position just upstream of the cyclogenetic region during the rapid development phase, using analyses based on the radiosonde network and ozone measurements by the Total Ozone Mapping Spectrometer (TOMS) aboard the Nimbus-7 polar-orbiting satellite.

Because of the data-void region off the East Coast, Whitaker et al. (1988) use a model-based diagnostic study of the same cyclone to analyze the stratospheric extrusion in the central United States and its subsequent eastward displacement toward the coastal region where rapid cyclogenesis occurred. A three-dimensional perspective of the model-simulated stratospheric extrusion and eastward displacement of this air mass was generated on the University of Wisconsin McIDAS system and is shown from a southern perspective in Fig. 6.12, with selected trajectories in Fig. 6.13 and from an eastern perspective in Fig. 6.14 at 6-hour intervals between 00 UTC and 18 UTC 19 February. The descent and horizontal advection of the 2×10^5 K mb^{-1} s^{-1} IPV surface that preceded and accompanied the intensification of the surface cyclone off the East Coast are clearly depicted in the three-dimensional illustrations. The detailed diagnostic computations that relate the stretching associated with the eastward displacement of the IPV anomaly and the associated increase in absolute vorticity, following the parcel trajectories shown in Figs. 6.13 and 6.14, can be found in the Whitaker et al. (1988) study. These results point to a more active role for the subsynoptic-scale processes associated with jet streaks and upper-level fronts in the extrusion of stratospheric air and subsequent evolution of a surface cyclone, in contrast to the concept that these processes are a passive consequence of frontogenesis or cyclogenesis, an issue discussed by Palmén and Newton (1969, pp. 256–258) and more recently by Keyser and Shapiro (1986, p. 493).

The model-simulated IPV fields depicted for the Presidents' Day storm (Figs. 6.12–6.14) also point to the importance of a separate region of high IPV confined to the lower troposphere. As discussed by Kleinschmidt (1957, pp. 134–136), Gyakum (1983b), Bosart and Lin (1984), Boyle and Bosart (1986) and Whitaker et al. (1988), diabatic processes (primarily associated with the vertical and horizontal distribution of latent heat release within a low-level baroclinic zone) contribute to the development of low-level IPV anomalies. The low-level trajectories in Figs. 6.13 and 6.14 that (1) approach the Presidents' Day storm from the east and wrap around the center, and (2) approach the storm center from the south and rise rapidly before turning anticyclonically, pass through the low-level 2×10^5 K mb^{-1} s^{-1} IPV surface

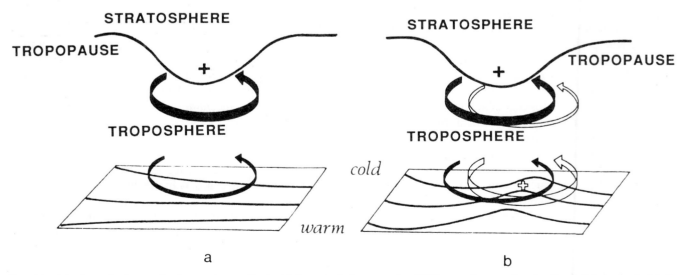

a   b

FIG. 6.8. "A schematic picture of cyclogenesis associated with the arrival of an upper-level IPV anomaly over a low-level baroclinic region. In (a), the upper-level IPV anomaly, indicated by a solid plus sign and associated with the low tropopause shown, has just arrived over a region of significant low-level baroclinicity. The circulation induced by the anomaly is indicated by solid arrows, and potential temperature contours are shown on the ground" (Hoskins et al. 1985). A low-level IPV anomaly can also induce a cyclonic circulation indicated by the open arrows in (b) that acts to reinforce the circulation pattern induced by the upper-level IPV anomaly.

along the East Coast. These parcel trajectories are influenced by the latent heat simulated by the model (Whitaker et al. 1988) and illustrate the nonconservative aspects of the low-level IPV maximum in a region of heavy precipitation. The low-level IPV maximum, and the associated thermal advection pattern, will also induce a cyclonic circulation extending upward throughout the entire troposphere (Fig. 6.8b) and add to the circulation induced by the upper-level IPV maximum, as long as the low-level anomaly remains downwind of the upper-level anomaly, maintaining a positive feedback between the two. The model results described by Whitaker et al. and illustrated in Figs. 6.12–6.14 basically confirm this hypothesis for the Presidents' Day cyclone.

6.3.3 Low-Level Processes

The previous discussion on the cyclogenetic processes as viewed from an IPV perspective provides a basis for linking upper- and lower-tropospheric processes in the evolution of a rapidly developing storm. This perspective is similar to the "type B" cyclogenesis described by Petterssen and Smebye (1971), which relates surface cyclogenesis to the superposition of cyclonic absolute vorticity advection ahead of an upper-level trough over a low-level baroclinic zone and associated thermal advection pattern as

depicted in Fig. 6.8b. Both perspectives account for not only the upper-tropospheric processes associated with troughs and jet streaks but also the influence of low-level baroclinic zones in the evolution of these storms (see also Farrell 1984, 1985).

At least four low-level processes appear to influence the deepening rates of extratropical cyclones: (1) the thermal advection pattern in the lower troposphere in conjunction with the presence of low-level baroclinic zones and strong low-level winds; (2) sensible and latent heat fluxes in the boundary layer (especially over the ocean) that act to fuel these systems; (3) the decrease of the static stability in the lower troposphere related, in part, to the boundary-layer heating noted above; and (4) mountain ranges.

Charney (1947) not only recognized the importance of Bjerknes and Holmboe's (1944) paper relating upper-level trough/ridge patterns to surface cyclogenesis, but also noted that many such features are observed without surface cyclogenesis. Charney (1947) and Eady (1949) introduced the concept of baroclinic instability, which defined preferred wavelengths for an atmospheric instability that is likely to produce surface cyclogenesis, and attempted to distinguish between those troughs which induce surface development and those that do not. As discussed by Eliassen (1956), even though the baroclinic instability

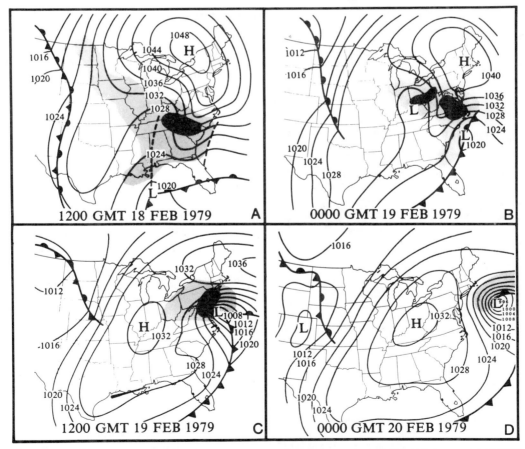

FIG. 6.9.   Sea-level pressure (mb) and surface frontal analyses for: (a) 12 UTC 18 February, (b) 00 UTC 19 February, (c) 12 UTC 19 February and (d) 00 UTC 20 February 1979. Shading indicates precipitation; dark shading, moderate to heavy precipitation. Dashed lines in (a) denote inverted and coastal troughs (Uccellini et al. 1985).

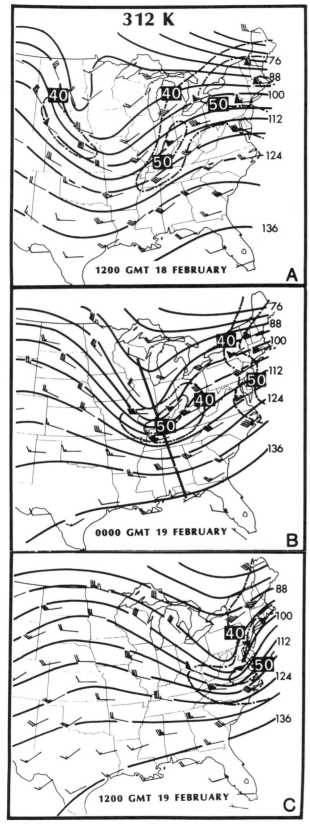

FIG. 6.10. The 312 K analyses of Montgomery streamfunction (solid, $124 = 3.124 \times 10^5$ m^2 s^{-2}) and isotachs (dot-dash, m s^{-1}) for: (a) 12 UTC 18 February, (b) 00 UTC 19 February and (c) 12 UTC 19 February 1979. Wind barbs represent observed wind speeds (whole barb 10 m s^{-1}, half barb 5 m s^{-1}) (Uccellini et al. 1985).

theories introduced by Charney and Eady do not properly account for the initial amplitude of observed trough/ridge patterns that precede cyclogenesis, these theories point to the low-level thermal structure and associated temperature advection patterns as important factors in the total evolution of cyclones. More recent theoretical work by Farrell (1984, 1985) indicates that, when treated as an initial value problem and accounting for the nonmodal aspects, baroclinic instability theory can account for a more rapid initial development when an upper-level perturbation is properly superimposed over a low-level thermal advection pattern.

As discussed as far back as Bjerknes and Solberg (1922), cyclogenesis is usually marked by a thermal field in the lower troposphere that evolves into an "S" shape pattern during the period of most rapid development. This pattern typifies the wide variety of cyclones ranging from the larger-scale storms along the east coast of the United States (Kocin and Uccellini 1990) to the meso-α-scale polar lows observed in the North Atlantic Ocean (see, e.g., Fig. 13 in Shapiro et al. 1987). This S-shaped isotherm pattern, combined with low-level winds ranging up to 40 m s^{-1} in many cases (usually taking the form of a low-level jet (LLJ)) and directed at a significant angle to the isotherms (Fig. 6.15), yields a favorable pattern for the Laplacian of the thermal advection and the well-known couplet of cold and warm air advection to the west and east of the storm center, respectively. The association between the thermal advection pattern and the relative vorticity and vertical motion patterns can be diagnosed from the "development equations" (Sutcliffe 1947; Petterssen 1955, 1956) and the quasi-geostrophic framework (see, e.g., Holton 1979, Chap. 7) that has been used in diagnostic studies of rapid cyclogenesis (see, e.g., Krishnamurti 1968).

The contribution of sensible and latent heat fluxes in the planetary boundary layer (PBL) to rapid cyclogenesis (involving the flow of relatively cold air over warm ocean currents toward the developing storm system) was assumed by some to be important for cyclogenesis in cold airstreams over the North Atlantic even in the 1920s (see, e.g., Brunt 1930). Diagnostic and model sensitivity studies of ten North Atlantic cyclones by Petterssen et al. (1962) indicate that sensible heat fluxes in the cold air stream behind the developing cyclone, combined with the release of latent heat, could "contribute significantly" to cyclone development. Bosart (1981) emphasizes that the sensible heating *prior to and during* the development of the Presidents' Day cyclone in the cold easterly air flow *ahead of the cyclone center* played a critical role in the rapid development phase of that particular cyclone, a result later supported by a model sensitivity study (Uccellini et al. 1987).

The preference for rapid cyclogenesis to occur over the ocean (Section 6.2) and recent model sensitivity and diagnostic studies by Nordeng (1988) for several polar lows, by Mailhot and Chouinard (1989) for three North Atlantic cyclones and by Mullen and Baumhefner (1988) for 11 cases of rapid cyclogenesis over the North Pacific all

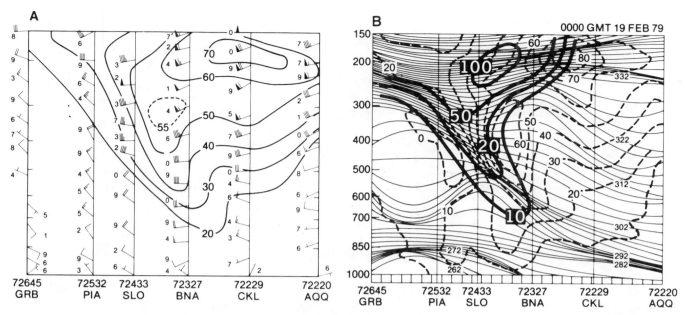

FIG. 6.11.   Vertical cross section from Green Bay, Wisconsin to Apalachicola, Florida, along heavy line in Fig. 6.10b, at 00 UTC 19 February 1979. (a) Isotach analysis for total wind speed (m s^{-1}); wind barbs plotted as in Fig. 6.10 with last digit of observed speed. (b) Isentropes (solid, K), geostrophic wind speed normal to plane of cross section (dashed, m s^{-1}) and potential vorticity (dark solid, 10 = 10 × 10^{-6} K mb^{-1} s^{-1}) (Uccellini et al. 1985).

indicate that the rate of cyclogenesis is enhanced by the sensible and latent heat fluxes within the ocean-influenced PBL. Mailhot and Chouinard emphasize that (for cyclones in the North Atlantic) the combination of (1) the large temperature differences between the colder air streaming off the North American continent to the north and east of the cyclone and the relatively warmer ocean, plus (2) the strong winds associated with the LLJs that develop in conjunction with the cyclone, yields large total heat fluxes that affect the airstreams which feed directly into the developing cyclones. Model-based trajectory diagnostics provided by Whitaker et al. (1988) for the Presidents' Day storm show that the potential temperature can increase by 1 K h^{-1} and the specific humidity by 0.5 to 1 g kg^{-1} h^{-1} for parcels in the cold low-level airstream approaching the cyclone from the east during its rapid development phase (i.e., the yellow-orange set of trajectories in Fig. 6.13). These results are consistent with those presented by Nordeng (1988) for model simulations of polar lows and provide supporting evidence that the sensible heat and moisture fluxes in the ocean-influenced PBL act to fuel the developing cyclone, especially through the enhanced moisture transport into the region of heavy precipitation associated with these storms (see also Uccellini et al. 1984).

Shapiro et al.'s (1987) measurements of the maximum total heat flux from the sea surface into the atmosphere of 1000 W m^{-2} for a polar low, combined with Emanuel and Rotunno's (1988) model-based study of the influences these fluxes have on deepening rates of polar lows, also provide supporting evidence that the sensible and latent heat fluxes contribute to rapidly developing cyclones. Yet the issue of the direct role of sensible and latent fluxes in

rapid cyclogenesis is not entirely resolved. Cases of major storms over land masses (such as the 25–26 January 1978 blizzard noted in Section 6.2) indicate that perhaps sensible and latent heat fluxes in the lower troposphere are not necessary for rapid cyclogenesis. Model sensitivity studies by Danard and Ellenton (1980), and more recently by Kuo and Reed (1988) and Kuo and Low-Nam (1989), show a minimal impact of the sensible and latent heat fluxes in the boundary layer on the rate of cyclogenesis. The contrasting nature of these results may be related to either (1) a large case-to-case variability where the temperature difference between the ocean and atmosphere in the precyclogenetic period has a direct bearing on the extent to which heat and moisture fluxes can influence a developing storm, or (2) the strengths and weaknesses of the various model boundary-layer parameterization schemes being employed in the various numerical experiments. Another factor is that the time at which the model is initialized with respect to the period of most rapid deepening can also influence the results of model sensitivity studies, in that the initial conditions of the model may include a thermal and wind structure that has already been significantly influenced by heating in the PBL.

Even if the degree to which sensible and latent heat fluxes in the lower troposphere act to fuel rapid cyclogenesis is still in debate, it is readily apparent that these same processes are acting to decrease the low-level static stability in the cyclogenetic region (see, e.g., Smith et al. 1988. As Eliassen (1962), Shapiro (1981), Bosart (1981) and Keyser and Carlson (1984) have pointed out, the static stability is an important factor in determining the nature of secondary circulations that result from large-scale forcing associated with fronts and jets. Staley and Gall (1977)

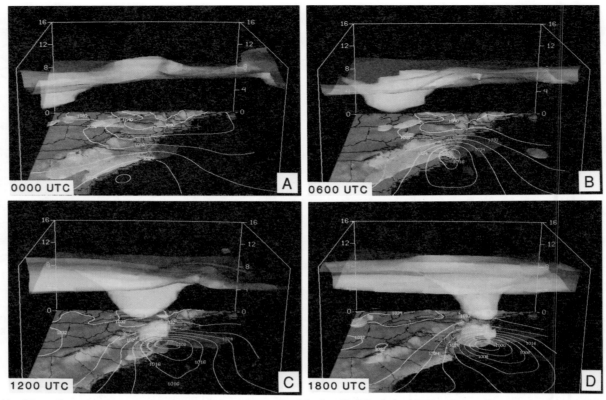

Fig. 6.12.   Three-dimensional perspectives, as viewed from the south, of the 2×10^{-5} K mb^{-1} s^{-1} IPV surface, and sea-level pressure isobar pattern (mb) derived from the numerical simulation of the Presidents' Day cyclone of Whitaker et al. (1988) for (a) 00 UTC, (b) 06 UTC, (c) 12 UTC and (d) 18 UTC 19 February 1979. The three-dimensional perspectives were derived by William Hibbard using the University of Wisconsin, Space Science and Engineering Center, three-dimensional McIDAS system.

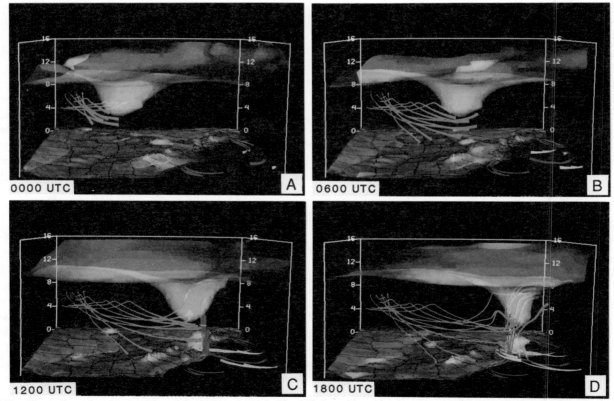

Fig. 6.13.   Three-dimensional potential vorticity perspective as in Fig. 6.12, but with sea-level pressure analyses removed and trajectories included, derived from 15-min model output as described by Whitaker et al. (1988). Blue trajectories originate within stratospheric extrusion west and north of the cyclone; yellow and red trajectories originate in the low levels within the ocean-influenced planetary boundary layer.

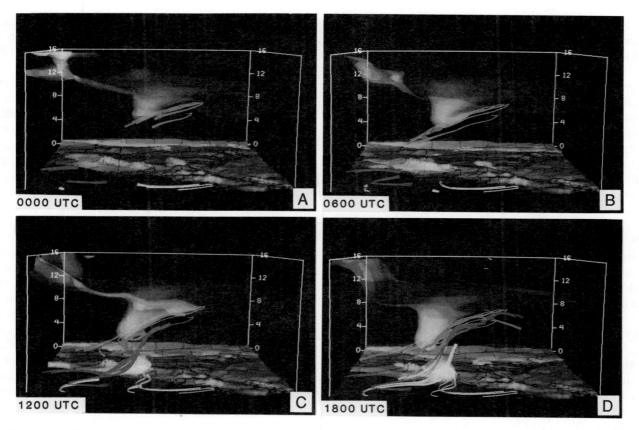

FIG. 6.14. Three-dimensional, model-generated potential vorticity perspective and trajectories as in Figs. 6.12 and 6.13, but as viewed from an eastern perspective, illustrating the slope nature of both the potential vorticity surface and the trajectories approaching the storm from the south.

conclude that the baroclinic growth rates are very sensitive to decreased static stability in the lower troposphere, again pointing to the important influence of PBL heating on rapid cyclogenesis. Wash et al. (1988) use model-based data sets to show that sensible heating of the atmosphere over the warmer ocean surface reduces the static stability prior to and during rapid cyclogenesis over the Pacific Ocean. They note that the decreased static stability effectively reduces the braking tendency of vertical motion on cyclogenesis, such that low-level convergence and upper-level divergence can more readily increase in magnitude during the rapid development phase of the storm. The increased sensible and latent heat fluxes also tend to decrease the symmetric stability (Sections 5.2.1, 5.6.1, 9.6), a process that tends to render the atmospheric conditionally unstable to "slantwise convection" (Emanuel 1983). Kuo and Reed (1988) use a model simulation of the November 1981 North Pacific cyclone (Fig. 6.4) to diagnose that the rapid sloped-ascent (and associated low-level convergence and increasing absolute vorticity) was focused within a region in which the model atmosphere has been affected by sensible and latent heat fluxes (and other processes as well), and which was marked by neutral (to slightly unstable) symmetric stability.

Finally, although the emphasis in this chapter has been on rapid cyclogenesis which occurs over the ocean, orographical features play an important role in enhancing

cyclogenesis in some areas. For example, case studies and numerical experiments demonstrate that the Alps exert a significant modifying influence on large-scale flow patterns and jet-streak circulation patterns that contribute to rapid cyclogenesis in the Ligurian Sea just to the west of Italy (Buzzi and Tibaldi 1978; Bleck and Mattocks 1984; Mattocks and Bleck 1986). As discussed by Newton (1956)

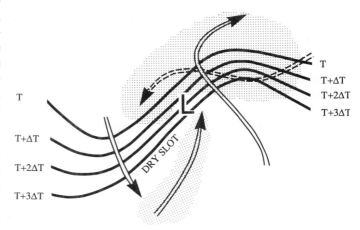

FIG. 6.15. Schematic illustration of the lower-tropospheric S-shaped isotherm pattern and asymmetric cloud distribution associated with rapid cyclogenesis. The "dry slot" indicates region where stratospheric air approaches cyclone. Areas of strong low-level wind maxima or low-level jets which act to enhance thermal advection pattern also indicated with arrows.

and Hovanec and Horn (1975), the Rocky Mountains also contribute to cyclogenesis through vortex tube stretching and the subsequent concentration of absolute vorticity to the lee of the mountains. The Appalachian Mountains play a significant role in influencing the low-level thermal fields (principally by the "damming" of the cold air along the coastal plain) which, along with coastal frontogenesis, provides a low-level baroclinic zone in the Carolinas which contributes to coastal cyclogenesis (see, e.g., Baker 1970; Richwien 1980; Bosart 1981; Stauffer and Warner 1987; Bell and Bosart 1988). The influence of orography on cyclones is covered by Tibaldi, Buzzi and Speranza in Chapter 7.

6.3.4 Latent Heat Release

Perhaps the most common feature of rapidly-developing extratropical cyclones is that these storms are characterized by an asymmetric distribution of clouds, precipitation and an associated vertical motion pattern with respect to the center of the developing surface low (see, e.g., Bjerknes 1919; Palmén and Newton 1969, p. 284). As depicted in Fig. 6.15, an extensive area of clouds and precipitation is located on the poleward side of the surface low. The area of clouds and precipitation is related to a relatively cold and moist easterly flow that is ascending and moving through the storm system, and to a warm airstream rising rapidly over the warm front associated with these storms (see Fig. 6.13). A clear dry slot extends from the west of the surface low toward the equatorward side, which is related to the descending stratospheric airstream discussed in the previous section (see Figs. 6.13 and 6.14). These "dry," "cold" and "warm" "conveyor belts" are described in detail by Carlson (1980), Young et al. (1987) and Browning, who presents a general review of airflow in cyclones in Chapter 8.

In all of the case studies reviewed for this paper, the onset of most rapid deepening of the surface cyclone coincides with the development of heavy precipitation in the area extending from the northeast to the north and west of the cyclone center (see, e.g., the case studies provided by Krishnamurti 1968; Johnson and Downey 1976; Kocin and Uccellini 1990). The diagnostic study by Johnson and Downey shows that latent heat release contributes to the intensification of the cyclone mass circulation and the associated angular momentum transport and redistribution required for the concurrent decrease of surface pressure, increase in the low-level circulation and vertical growth of the vortex from the lower to middle troposphere during the rapid development phase. The importance of latent heat release in enhancing development rates and perturbing the mass and wind fields throughout the entire troposphere is also demonstrated by idealized numerical experiments (Gall 1976) and numerous model sensitivity studies, most notably those of Danard (1964) and Chang et al. (1982). Model-based energy diagnostic studies, performed for wet and dry simulations of several cyclones in the central United

States, demonstrate that latent heat release provides an important energy source for these storms (Robertson and Smith 1983; Kenney and Smith 1983; Chang et al. 1984; Dare and Smith 1984).

Yet questions remain concerning the relative importance of latent heat release, which is difficult to assess given the interaction of this physical process with the boundary-layer and free-atmospheric processes discussed earlier. Several studies have pointed out the difficulty of treating sensible heat and moisture fluxes in the boundary layer and their subsequent influence on convective (subgrid-scale) or stable (grid-resolvable) precipitation processes as separate factors (Ooyama 1982; Danard 1983, 1986; Emanuel and Rotunno 1989). Latent heat release also can have a direct and immediate impact on the structure and dynamics of the upper-level trough/ridge systems and jet streaks which then act to enhance cyclogenesis, a point recently emphasized by Chang et al. (1982), Uccellini et al. (1987), Manobianco (1989) and discussed in Section 6.4. Latent heat release can focus the dynamic processes and associated vertical motion pattern on a smaller scale (Emanuel 1985), which may then act to enhance the baroclinic processes that affect the development rate of the storm system. A question that arises is whether the latent heat is directly responsible for the decrease in sea-level pressure through hydrostatic considerations, or contributes to a scale contraction of the baroclinic processes that is essential for the mesoscale dynamic processes that enhance deepening rates, or both. Given this range, it may not be possible to assign a specific percentage to a separate physical process while attempting to determine its relative impact on development rates of cyclones.

The role of convection in enhancing cyclogenesis also remains unresolved. Hypotheses have been presented that convective cells near the storm center play an active role in contributing to and even initiating rapid cyclogenesis (Tracton 1973; Bosart 1981; Gyakum 1983b). However, the evidence presented to support these hypotheses is still inconclusive. Model sensitivity studies using actual data (Danard 1986; Leslie et al. 1987); theoretical studies using axisymmetric models (Shutts et al. 1988); and linear CISK models (Økland 1987), demonstrate significant sensitivity of simulated surface low-pressure systems to latent heat release associated with convection. Other studies show little or no impact related to the inclusion of convective parameterization schemes in numerical model systems (see, e.g., Mullen and Baumhefner 1988; Reed et al. 1988; Mailhot and Chouinard 1989).

As noted for the boundary layer issues, these diverging results may point to model deficiencies, case-to-case variability, or both. In either event, the impact of convection on rapid cyclogenesis has not been clearly demonstrated, nor has the means by which convection may actually decrease the sea-level pressure over a large domain for an extended period of time been shown in a convincing manner. Indeed, even in the CISK-type papers that relate convection to cyclone development, there is a disagreement as to whether heating associated with the convection decreases the surface pressure (e.g., Rasmussen 1979; Danard 1983) or the warming related to compensating subsidence acts to decrease the surface pressure (Sardie and Warner 1985).

6.4 Feedback Between Diabatic and Dynamical Processes During Rapid Cyclogenesis

The various physical processes discussed in Section 6.3 and their potential for complex nonlinear interactions on the mesoscale (both space and time) have set the stage for the most recent debates concerning their relative importance during periods of rapid cyclogenesis. An increasing number of model-based sensitivity studies (see Sections 11.6 and 12.3.2) and diagnostic analyses of major cyclone events indicates that the individual dynamic and diabatic processes should be looked upon as necessary for rapid cyclogenesis, but not sufficient to produce these storm systems when acting alone. That is, the rapid development phase of extratropical cyclones is dependent not on the individual contribution of these physical processes, but on nonlinear synergistic interactions among them (see also Section 12.3.2g).

The problem in assessing the relative contributions of various physical processes to rapid cyclogenesis revolves around the rapid feedback that occurs among the processes within a relatively small domain and over a short period of time. For example, if sensible heat fluxes east or northeast of a surface low act to increase the temperature gradients (as shown in Figs. 6.16a,b), the developing low is affected by not only the increases of heat and moisture in the PBL but also the baroclinic processes associated with the increased temperature gradients and the resultant thermal advection pattern. The feedback does not stop there. A more intense low-level baroclinic zone depicted in Fig. 6.16b could be expected to contribute to stronger low-level wind speeds that could further enhance the warm-air advection pattern and deepening rate of the storm (Fig. 6.16c).

The increase of wind speed depicted in Fig. 6.16c is related to two factors: 1) an isallobaric contribution due to the change of the pressure gradient force associated with the deepening cyclone and 2) the vertical parcel displacement in a region where the pressure gradient force changes with height. As shown in Fig. 6.17, the vertical parcel displacement east and northeast of a developing surface cyclone (enhanced by the sensible and latent heat fluxes and latent heat release) can lead to a situation in which the parcel passes from one level, marked by a closed circulation (e.g., 850 mb) in which the parcel is in a relatively balanced state, to a level marked by an open wave (e.g., 700 mb) in which the parcel is now directed toward lower geopotential heights and accelerates rapidly. Model-based trajectory results described by Uccellini et al. (1987) and Whitaker et al. (1988) illustrate that this process operates over a very short period of time (2 to 4 hours) and contributes to ageostrophic wind speeds approaching 50 m s^{-1} and subsequent rapid parcel acceleration. Their results confirm Durst and Sutcliffe's (1938), Godson's (1950) and Newton and Palmén's (1963, p. 115) discussions on the

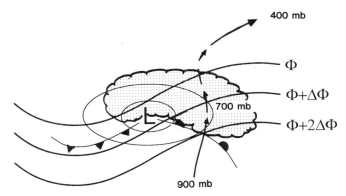

Fig. 6.17. Schematic illustration of the vertical displacement of a parcel trajectory approaching the cyclone from the south-southeast and passing through the area of precipitation associated with the cyclone and crossing the geopotential contours at the 700-mb level (marked by an open wave) at a significant angle.

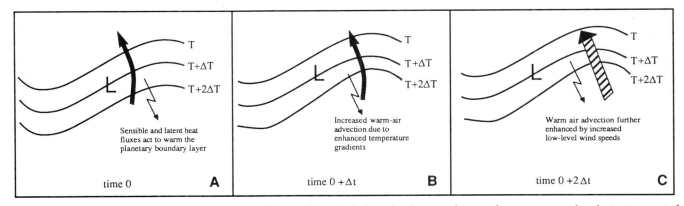

Fig. 6.16. Schematic illustration of the impact that sensible heat fluxes in the boundary layer can have on the temperature advection pattern east of the cyclone center (marked by an L): (a) at time 0, prior to sensible heat influence; (b) at time 0+Δt, when sensible heat flux has acted to increase temperature gradients and associated warm-air advection; (c) at time 0+2Δt, when increased wind speed associated with deepening surface low further enhances temperature advection pattern.

association between organized vertical motion patterns and the horizontal wind acceleration.

The acceleration of the east to southeasterly flow through the precipitation region near the 700- to 600-mb layer (Fig. 6.17) is generally located beneath the more southwesterly flow aloft associated with the upper-level trough/ridge system. Whitaker et al. (1988) show that, for the model simulation of the Presidents' Day cyclone, the transition layer between the accelerating southeasterly and southwesterly flow regimes marked the region in which the mass divergence increased to a maximum during the rapid development phase of that storm. These results indicate that the deepening rates of extratropical storms are related to a complex interaction between thermodynamic and dynamic processes, which is dependent on the spatial configuration of the pressure gradient force and the horizontal and vertical distributions of latent heat release (Fig. 6.16). From the perspective presented in Fig. 6.17, the release of latent heat poleward and east of a developing cyclone, within the transition layer between a closed circulation pattern in the lower troposphere and an open wave aloft, would be especially important for enhancing the parcel accelerations, divergent airflow and associated development rate of the cyclone. This process might explain the sensitivity of numerical simulations of extratropical cyclones to the vertical distribution of latent heat release as discussed by Anthes and Keyser (1979).

The parcel accelerations in the southeasterly flow depicted in Fig. 6.17 are consistent with Sechrist and Dutton's (1970) energetics study of a cyclone along the East Coast of the United States in which they diagnose a kinetic energy (KE) generation in the lower troposphere south and east of the cyclone center, in a region where the available potential energy (APE) is also increasing. Palmén (1951, p. 618) notes that a simultaneous increase of KE and APE accompanies the initial period of cyclogenesis, wherein the increase of APE is related to frontogenesis within the middle and upper troposphere and the increase in KE to increasing wind speeds in the lower troposphere. These energy changes are also consistent with the jet streak perspective discussed in Section 6.3.1 for cyclones developing in the exit region of the streak. The indirect transverse circulation in the exit region (Fig. 6.6a) is frontogenetic (as viewed from an Eulerian perspective) and acts to convert KE along the axis of the upper-level jet to APE as parcels exit the jet streak. In the lower branch of the indirect transverse circulation, parcels influenced by isallobaric and diabatic processes accelerate rapidly (Kocin et al. 1986; Uccellini et al. 1987) and contribute to the rapid development of low-level jets and an associated local increase of KE in the lower troposphere.

The possible feedback that sensible and latent heating can have on temperature gradients, parcel accelerations, energy transformations and the thermal and vorticity advection patterns is not confined to the lower troposphere. A model sensitivity study by Chang et al. (1982) shows the dramatic impact that latent heat release can have upon the temperature, geopotential height and wind fields throughout the entire troposphere. Similar results are obtained for a series of numerical simulations conducted for the Presidents' Day cyclone, which are presented below.

Three 24-hour model simulations, initialized at 12 UTC 18 February, were run to illustrate the sensitivity of the full-physics numerical simulation of the Presidents' Day cyclone (used to depict the IPV fields in Figs. 6.12–6.14) to the incorporation of boundary-layer physics and latent heat release. The 58-km grid, 32-level σ-coordinate numerical model, the initialization procedure and the full-physics simulation are described by Whitaker et al. (1988). The other three model runs include an adiabatic simulation, a simulation that includes the effect of latent heat release but no boundary-layer fluxes, and a simulation with the boundary-layer fluxes included but not the effects of latent heat release, following the experimental design described by Uccellini et al. (1987).

The sea-level pressure (SLP) maps derived from the four simulations are shown in Fig. 6.18. The adiabatic simulation produces only a weak inverted trough (Fig. 6.18a). Including either latent heat release (Fig. 6.18b) or boundary-layer fluxes (Fig. 6.18c) produces only a modest impact on the deepening rate. There is, however, a major impact on the simulated cyclone when both the boundary-layer fluxes and latent heat release are included (Fig. 6.18d). The 32-mb difference between the full-physics simulation and the adiabatic simulation (Fig. 6.19) illustrates the dramatic influence that the diabatic processes can exert upon an extratropical storm, when these processes are acting in a synergistic mode with the upper-level trough/ridge pattern and jet streaks, as described for the initial development phase of this storm by Uccellini et al. (1987).

The difference in the circulation pattern between the full-physics and adiabatic simulations extends throughout the entire troposphere. At 850 mb, the geopotential height difference of 160+ gpm (Fig. 6.20a) reflects the deeper cyclonic circulation in the full-physics run. The impact on the 850-mb wind field (Fig. 6.20b) is equally dramatic with 35 m s^{-1} differences in the wind field computed east and northwest of the developing storm system.

At 300 mb, the height difference between the full-physics and adiabatic simulations reverses sign and approaches 120+ gpm north-northeast of the surface cyclone (Fig. 6.21a). This increase in geopotential height reflects a tendency for the downstream upper-level ridge to remain locked in place in the full-physics simulation (as the trough approaches from the west), rather than to continue to move eastward as occurs in the adiabatic simulation. This result is in agreement with the Chang et al. (1982) study for a Midwest cyclone and Atlas' (1987) model sensitivity study of the Presidents' Day cyclone using a global model. Associated with the maintenance of the ridge axis aloft is the maintenance and enhancement of the 300-mb jet as depicted by the 40 m s^{-1} difference between the

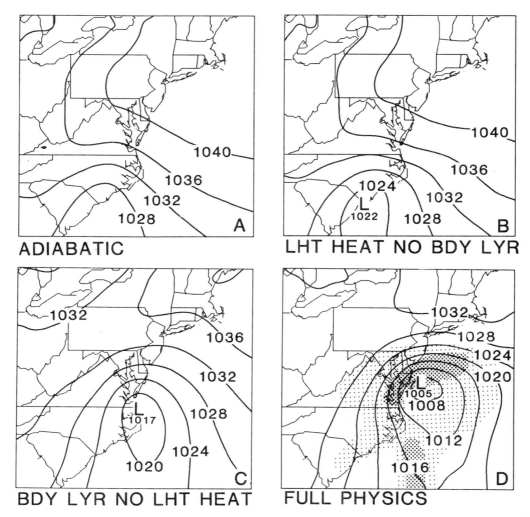

FIG. 6.18.   Sea-level pressure analyses from 24-h model simulations of the Presidents' Day cyclone valid at 12 UTC 19 February 1979: (a) adiabatic simulation; (b) simulation with latent heat included but no boundary-layer fluxes; (c) simulation with boundary-layer fluxes but no latent heat release; and (d) full-physics simulation. Total precipitation greater than 2.0 cm for full-physics run indicated by light shading; greater than 4.0 cm, darker shading. See also Fig. 12.14.

full-physics and adiabatic simulations (Fig. 6.21b), which takes the form of an anticyclonic "outflow jet" similar to that isolated for a Midwest cyclone by Chang et al. (1982) and for a spring convective complex by Maddox et al. (1981). Comparison of Figs. 6.21 and 6.19 reveals that the area of maximum difference in the SLP between the adiabatic and full-physics simulations does not lie directly beneath the region marked by enhanced ridging aloft, but beneath the entrance region of this outflow jet. It appears from the difference maps in Figs. 6.19 and 6.21 that the acceleration of the flow into this jet is acting to evacuate mass from the column located over the developing storm system.

The 300-mb difference fields for the geopotential height (Fig. 6.21a) and wind (Fig. 6.21b) attest to the major influence that diabatic processes have throughout the entire troposphere during cyclogenesis. There is no doubt that the latent and sensible heat fluxes are acting to enhance the upper-level ridge and subsequently increase

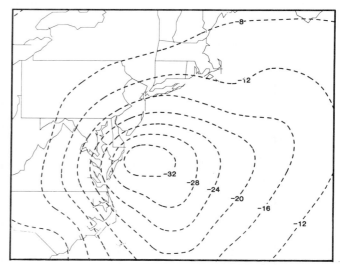

FIG. 6.19.   Difference in the sea-level pressure (mb) between the 24-h full-physics and adiabatic model simulations of the Presidents' Day storm valid at 12 UTC 19 February as shown in Fig. 6.18.

the wind speeds aloft for this case. It appears from this experiment, however, that attempts to place the upper-level ridge directly above the developing surface low or directly above the region of maximum precipitation (Rasmussen 1979; Danard 1983) are not appropriate to describe the impact that latent heat release has on the upper-level height and wind fields during extratropical cyclogenesis. The region of maximum precipitation and latent heat release (Fig. 6.18d) and largest SLP difference between the adiabatic and full-physics run (Fig. 6.19) is 350 km upstream of the region marked by the largest positive geopotential height differences at 300 mb (Fig. 6.21a). The ridging aloft is located directly over the region where the 850-mb warm-air advection pattern is enhanced due to the increased wind speeds and cyclonic circulation pattern in the low levels (Fig. 6.20). These characteristics in the 300- and 850-mb difference fields indicate that the enhanced warm-air advection pattern in the lower troposphere is also an important factor in maintaining and enhancing the upper-level ridge and associated upper-level jet northeast of the surface low. The asymmetry in the difference fields between the adiabatic and full-physics simulations and associated downwind displacement of enhanced ridging aloft from the center of the surface low is in agreement with Palmén's (1951, pp. 610–611) discussion on the asymmetric nature of extratropical cyclones. Palmén emphasized that this factor is critical for describing the vertical distribution of vorticity and divergence required for the simultaneous decrease in the SLP and convergent cyclonic air flow in the lower troposphere, and the divergent anticyclonic air flow in the middle troposphere immediately downstream of the low-pressure center.

6.4.1 Sutcliffe's Self-Development Concept

While the problem of defining necessary conditions that are applicable to all rapidly developing cyclones remains a contested issue, the "self-development" concept defined

by Sutcliffe and Forsdyke (1950) and discussed by Palmén and Newton (1969, pp. 324–326) does provide a basis for describing the interactions of dynamical and diabatic processes that contribute to rapid cyclogenesis. The self-development concept has been recently applied to major cyclones along the east coast of the United States (Kocin and Uccellini 1990) and is depicted schematically in Fig. 6.22. The approach of an upper-level trough and/or jet streak toward a low-level baroclinic zone and a pre-existing, relatively weak surface cyclone act to focus and enhance the effects of warm-air advection, sensible heat flux and moisture fluxes in the PBL, and latent heat release above 850 mb north and east of the surface low. The net effect is to warm the lower to middle troposphere near the axis of the upper-level ridge (Fig. 6.22a) and to increase the divergence aloft between the ridge and trough axes, a process discussed in detail by Bjerknes (1951, p. 599).

The increased temperature associated with these processes affects the divergence aloft in the following manner. The increased warming acts to slow the eastward progression of the upper-level ridge and to increase the ridge amplitude as the trough moves eastward and amplifies (partly in response to an amplification in the cold-air advection pattern to the west of the surface low-pressure center). The decrease in the wavelength between the trough and ridge axes, an increase in the diffluence corresponding to the spread of geopotential height lines downstream of the trough axis, and the increase in the maximum wind speeds of the upper-level jet streaks all combine to enhance the divergence in the middle to upper troposphere above the surface low. The increased upper-level divergence (represented by an enhancement of the cyclonic vorticity advection in Fig. 6.22b) acts to deepen the cyclone even further.

As the surface low deepens, the lower-tropospheric wind field surrounding the storm increases in intensity, especially to the north and east of the low, where the contribution of isallobaric effects and vertical motions to the

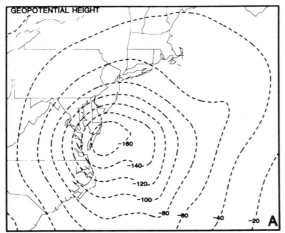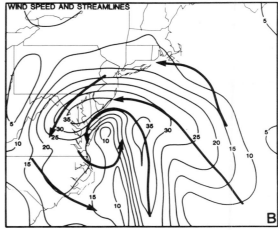

FIG. 6.20.   (a) Difference in the 850-mb geopotential height field (gpm) and (b) isotachs (m s⁻¹) and streamlines of the wind field difference between the 24-h full-physics and adiabatic model simulations of the Presidents' Day storm valid at 12 UTC 19 February.

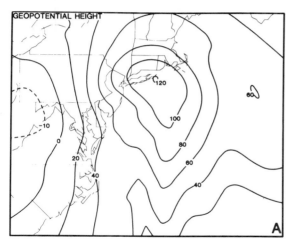
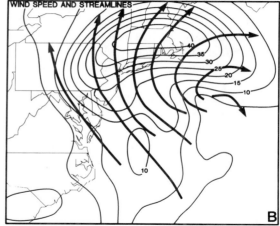

FIG. 6.21. Same as Fig. 6.20, but for the 300-mb level.

acceleration of air parcels is large. Often, a low-level jet develops to the north and/or east of the storm center, enhancing the moisture and heat fluxes within the oceanic PBL, the moisture transport toward the region of heavy precipitation and the warm-air advection east of the developing cyclone (Fig. 6.22b). Thus, the development of the LLJ further contributes to the self-development process that continues until the cyclone occludes and the heating is effectively cut off.

Self-development depends on the following conditions: (1) the existence of the upper-level features (such as trough/ridge systems and jet streaks) that focus the divergence aloft, conducive for maximum mass divergence and ascent immediately downstream of the developing surface low; and (2) warming (poleward and east of the surface low) due to diabatic processes and an enhanced thermal advection pattern associated with a lower-tropospheric baroclinic zone and strong low-level winds. The concept accounts for not only the adiabatic quasi-geostrophic framework that has been applied to cyclogenesis (Holton 1979, Chap. 7) but also the various interactions among the dynamic and diabatic processes discussed earlier. The asymmetric character of extratropical cyclones depicted in Fig. 6.15 and emphasized by Palmén (1951), and the convergence of the distinctly different airstreams illustrated in Figs. 6.13 and 6.14 and described by Carlson (1980), are also accounted for. As such, Sutcliffe's self-development concept represents a basis upon which the contribution of the various physical processes to rapid cyclogenesis can be described.

6.5 Summary and Issues

The study of extratropical cyclogenesis has been a focus of active meteorological research for at least the past 150 years, marked by alternating emphasis on the thermodynamic and dynamic processes that contribute to these systems. Upper-level trough/ridge systems, jet streaks, low-level fronts and jets, latent heat release, sensible and latent heat fluxes in the planetary boundary layer,

sea surface temperatures and (in some areas) mountain ranges have been shown to be important factors in cyclogenesis. However, recent diagnostic analyses (based to a

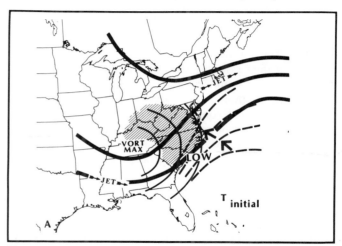
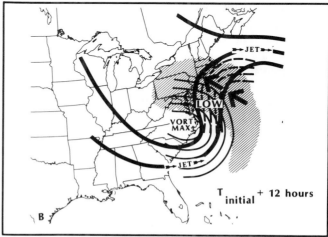

FIG. 6.22. Schematic illustration of the self-development concept postulated by Sutcliffe and Forsdyke (1950), illustrating how the temperature advections, sensible heat and moisture fluxes in the PBL, and latent heat release associated with cyclogenesis, enhance the amplitude and decrease the wavelength of the upper-level trough/ridge system which contributes to an increase in upper-level divergence (increased PVA) that further enhances cyclogenesis (Kocin and Uccellini 1990).

growing extent on numerical simulations of rapid cyclogenesis) are leading to the recognition that the individual processes may be necessary for the development of extratropical cyclones but are not sufficient when acting alone to produce rapid cyclogenesis. The nonlinear interaction among the various dynamic and thermodynamic processes within relatively small space and temporal domains is crucial for the rapid evolution of these storms.

Although cyclones which undergo a period of rapid development seem to have common characteristics, the review of 23 snowstorms along the East Coast of the United States by Kocin and Uccellini (1990) and the recent model sensitivity studies for a large number of cyclones by Mullen and Baumhefner (1988) and Kuo and Low-Nam (1989) provide an important reminder that cyclones display remarkable case-to-case variability, especially during the initial development phase. This issue was often discussed by S. Pettersen during his visits to the University of Wisconsin–Madison in the early 1970s, where he stated: "Extratropical cyclones are born in a variety of ways, but their appearance at death is remarkably similar" (quote provided by D. R. Johnson). Given the degrees of freedom involved with the nonlinear interactions among the various physical processes, it is not surprising that the sensitivity of model-simulated cyclones to latent heat and boundary-layer processes covers a large spectrum in the numerical experiments cited above, indicating perhaps that some processes are more important than others in individual storms. Nevertheless, there is a growing consensus that 1) a superposition of upper- and lower-tropospheric dynamic processes is required for rapid cyclogenesis (whether it be described in terms of the IPV concepts, the development equation derived by Sutcliffe and by Pettersen or the more theoretical initial-value baroclinic approach presented by Farrell (1984, 1985)); and 2) the development rates are significantly enhanced by the interaction of diabatic and dynamic processes, especially those that are related to the release of latent heat and those that act to reduce the static and symmetric stability of the lower troposphere.

Numerous research topics remain with respect to rapid cyclogenesis. As noted in Section 6.3, the role of convection in either initiating or enhancing cyclogenesis needs to be investigated further. As part of this effort, the issue concerning the "slantwise" nature of the convective heat flux and its impact on the development rate of extratropical cyclogenesis needs to be addressed. Bjerknes (1951, p. 595) anticipated the importance of moist slantwise ascent along an inertially neutral θ_e surface, and provides an example of a vertical lapse rate that is less than the moist adiabatic but possesses moist slantwise neutrality in the precipitation region ahead of a developing cyclone. Emanuel (1983, 1988) provides additional examples where the atmosphere is conditionally stable for vertical convection but neutral for parcel displacement along a slanted surface of constant absolute momentum, and supporting evidence that the slantwise convection is a fundamental part of the precipitation regime associated with extratropical cyclones. This concept appears to be relevant for both resolving the nature of the airflow through the principal ascent regions associated with extratropical storms, where the region of ascent takes on the appearance of a narrow sloping band, and accounting for the vertical and horizontal redistribution of heat associated with convective elements that may feed back upon the development rate of the cyclone. Nordeng's (1987) recent attempt to parameterize slantwise convection, comparing it to parameterization schemes based on vertical convective heat fluxes and applying it to several polar low cases, should be extended to the simulation of a larger number of cases of rapid cyclogenesis in different geographical locations. The assessment of the impact of convection upon rapid cyclogenesis should also involve the study concerning the extent to which boundary-layer heat and moisture fluxes merely precondition the cyclone environment, or actively fuel the convective systems and enhance development rates.

Another issue concerns the growing evidence that mesoscale flow regimes that are not properly described by either quasi-geostrophic and geostrophic momentum concepts or the balance equation, and thus appear to be unbalanced in nature, may be an important factor in cyclogenesis. A diagnostic case study of the Presidents' Day storm (Uccellini et al. 1984) indicates that the precyclogenetic environment was marked by a region in which the Rossby number approaches unity and the divergence tendency following air parcels exceeds 10^{-9} s^{-2} (indications that balance constraints are not being met). In the model simulations of this case, ageostrophic wind components approaching 40 to 50 m s^{-1} were diagnosed in the lower to middle troposphere (Uccellini et al. 1987; Whitaker et al. 1988). These large ageostrophic wind speeds occur near regions of heavy precipitation, latent heat release, and vertical ascent and precede the rapid accelerations that mark the development of low-level jets and rapid decrease of SLP.

Another indication of the unbalanced nature of these storms is the increasing number of observational studies that have documented the existence of large-amplitude gravity-inertia waves before and during cyclogenetic events (Uccellini 1975; Bosart and Sanders 1986; Uccellini and Koch 1987; Bosart and Seimon 1988). The recent 15 December 1987 blizzard in the central United States described by Schneider (1990) was associated with a rapidly developing cyclone (Figs. 6.23a,b) and a superimposed, large-amplitude (~12 mb) gravity wave (Figs. 6.23c,d). The barograph traces from north and west of the cyclone reveal that 10-mb pressure falls occurred during a 10-minute period with the passage of the gravity-inertia wave. The gravity-inertia wave could be clearly identified at individual stations, given the strong, gusty east to northeast winds at the wave trough (as expected from gravity wave considerations), in contrast to the weaker, slowly rotating winds near the storm center, as illustrated by the pressure trace from Chicago O'Hare Airport (where

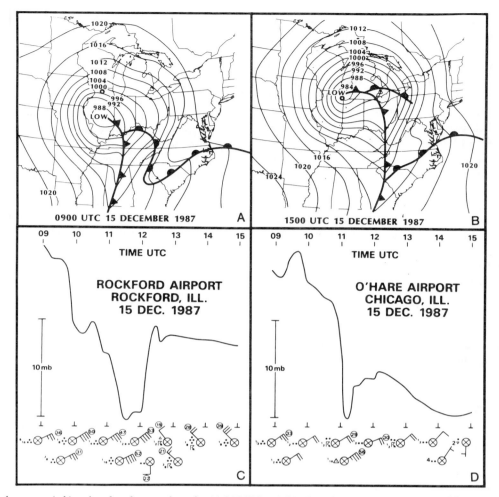

FIG. 6.23. Sea-level pressure (mb) and surface front analyses for (a) 09 UTC and (b) 15 UTC 15 December 1987. Pressure traces and hourly surface observations for (c) Rockford, Illinois and (d) Chicago O'Hare International Airport; locations indicated by circles in (a) and (b), respectively. Surface observations include wind direction and speed, gusts (kn) encircled, visibility (miles) and weather (symbols standard). (Figure derived from Schneider 1990.)

the SLP was lower during the gravity wave passage near 11 UTC than during the passage of the low center between 14 and 15 UTC (Fig. 6.23d)). The important issue is not only the effect this wave had on the weather (heavy snow plus strong gusty winds created "white-out" conditions during the wave passage (Figs. 6.23c,d)) but also the fact that the wave passed through the storm center (from south to north) during the rapid cyclogenetic period, when the central pressure of the cyclone decreased 5 to 7 mb in 1 hour (Schneider 1990). If this type of mesoscale adjustment is representative of other explosively developing storms, it would indicate that rapid cyclogenesis represents a mixed mode of dynamic processes that cannot be totally resolved through the use of the hydrostatic, quasi-geostrophic theory or other approaches based on larger-scale, balanced-flow considerations.

Resolving these issues and advancing our understanding of the nonlinear interactions among the numerous physical processes that contribute to rapid cyclogenesis requires improved models and enhanced data sets. Palmén (1951) ended his *Compendium* article on cyclones by calling for upper-air data with 2- to 3-hour temporal resolution to resolve the means by which the various processes contribute to cyclogenesis. This call is often repeated, seldom heeded and is still relevant to today's research requirements. Indeed, recent model-based diagnostic studies indicate that hourly data is necessary for studying certain aspects of rapid cyclogenesis. Future research efforts that address the issues discussed above and are based on enhanced data sets and well-designed numerical model experiments will not only advance our understanding of rapid cyclogenesis but also enhance our ability to predict the occurrence of these storms with acceptable reliability.

Acknowledgments

This paper is based to a large degree on research efforts during the past 10 years in collaboration with numerous people, including Keith F. Brill, Daniel Keyser, Paul J. Kocin, Ralph A. Petersen, James J. Tuccillo, Carlyle H. Wash and Jeffrey S. Whitaker. Donald R. Johnson (University of Wisconsin) and Lance F. Bosart (SUNY-

Albany) also are acknowledged for their numerous discussions with me, which have had an important influence on the perspective of cyclones presented in this paper. Reviews of the original manuscript provided by Lance F. Bosart, Chester W. Newton, Richard J. Reed, Russel S. Schneider and Carlyle H. Wash helped to clarify portions of the manuscript and are much appreciated. The three-dimensional displays of the potential vorticity and trajectories in Figs. 6.12–6.14 were derived from a video representation of a model simulation of the Presidents' Day cyclone produced at the Space Science and Engineering Center under the direction of William Hibbard and with the help of David Santek and Keith F. Brill. I also thank Kelly Pecnick and Patty Golden for typing the numerous versions of this paper and Lafayette Long, Paul J. Kocin, and Keith F. Brill for their assistance in the preparation of the manuscript.

REFERENCES

Achtor, T. H., and L. H. Horn, 1986: Spring season Colorado cyclones. Part 1: Use of composites to relate upper and lower tropospheric wind fields. *J. Clim. Appl. Meteor.*, **25**, 732–743.

Anthes, R. A., and D. Keyser, 1979: Tests of a fine-mesh model over Europe and the United States. *Mon. Wea. Rev.*, **107**, 963–984.

——, Y.-H. Kuo and J. R. Gyakum, 1983: Numerical simulations of a case of explosive marine cyclogenesis. *Mon. Wea. Rev.*, **111**, 1174–1188.

Atlas, R., 1987: The role of oceanic fluxes and initial data in the numerical prediction of an intense coastal storm. *Dyn. Atmos. and Oceans,* **10**, 359–388.

Baker, D. G., 1970: A study of high pressure ridges to the east of Appalachian Mountains. Ph.D. Dissertation, MIT, 127 pp.

Beebe, R. G., and F. C. Bates, 1955: A mechanism for assisting in the release of convective instability. *Mon. Wea. Rev.*, **83**, 1–10.

Bell, G. P., and L. F. Bosart, 1988: Appalachian cold-air damming. *Mon. Wea. Rev.*, **116**, 137–161.

Bjerknes, J., 1919: On the structure of moving cyclones. *Geofys. Publ.,* **1**, No. 2, 1–8.

——, 1951: Extratropical cyclones. *Compendium of Meteorology,* T. F. Malone, Ed. American Meteorological Society, 577–598.

——, and H. Solberg, 1922: Life cycle of cyclones and the polar front theory of atmospheric circulation. *Geofys. Publ.,* **3**, No. 1, 30–45.

——, and J. Holmboe, 1944: On the theory of cyclones. *J. Meteor.,* **1**, 1–22.

Bleck, R., 1973: Numerical forecasting experiments based on the conservation of potential vorticity on isentropic surfaces. *J. Appl. Meteor.,* **12**, 737–752.

——, 1974: Short-range prediction in isentropic coordinates with filtered and unfiltered numerical models. *Mon. Wea. Rev.*, **102**, 813–829.

——, and C. Mattocks, 1984: A preliminary analysis of the role of potential vorticity in Alpine lee cyclogenesis. *Beitr. Phys. Atmos.,* **57**, 357–368.

Bosart, L. F., 1981: The Presidents' Day snowstorm of 18-19 February 1979: A subsynoptic-scale event. *Mon. Wea. Rev.*, **109**, 1542–1566.

——, and S. C. Lin, 1984: A diagnostic analysis of the Presidents' Day storm of February 1979. *Mon. Wea. Rev.*, **112**, 2148–2177.

——, and F. Sanders, 1986: Mesoscale structure in the megalopolitan snowstorm of 11–12 February 1983. Part III: A large amplitude gravity wave. *J. Atmos. Sci.,* **43**, 924–939.

——, and A. Seimon, 1988: A case study of an unusually intense atmospheric gravity wave. *Mon. Wea. Rev.*, **116**, 1857–1886.

Boyle, J. S., and L. F. Bosart, 1983: A cyclone/anticyclone couplet over North America: An example of anticyclone evolution. *Mon. Wea. Rev.*, **111**, 1025–1045.

——, and ——, 1986: Cyclone-anticyclone couplets over North America. Part II: Analysis of a major cyclone event over the eastern United States. *Mon. Wea. Rev.*, **114**, 2432–2465.

Brunt, D., 1930: The present position of theories of the origin of cyclonic depressions. *Quart. J. Roy. Meteor. Soc.,* **56**, 345–350.

Burrows, W. R., R. A. Treidl and R. G. Lawford, 1979: The southern Ontario blizzard of January 26 and 27, 1978. *Atmos.-Ocean,* **17**, 306–320.

Businger, S., and R. J. Reed, 1989: Cyclogenesis in cold air masses. *Weather and Forecasting,* **4**, 133–156.

Buzzi, A., and S. Tibaldi, 1978: Cyclogenesis in the lee of the Alps: A case study. *Quart. J. Roy. Meteor. Soc.,* **104**, 271–287.

Cahir, J. J., 1971: Implications of circulations in the vicinity of jet streaks at subsynoptic scales. Ph.D. Thesis, Pennsylvania State University, 170 pp.

Carlson, T. N., 1980: Airflow through midlatitude cyclones and the comma cloud pattern. *Mon. Wea. Rev.*, **108**, 1498–1509.

Chang, C. B., D. J. Perkey and C. W. Kreitzberg, 1982: A numerical case study of the effects of latent heating on a developing wave cyclone. *J. Atmos. Sci.,* **39**, 1555–1570.

——, —— and ——, 1984: Latent heat induced energy transformations during cyclogenesis. *Mon. Wea. Rev.*, **112**, 357–367.

Charney, J. G., 1947: The dynamics of long waves in a baroclinic westerly current. *J. Meteor.,* **4**, 135–162.

Danard, M. B., 1964: On the influence of released latent heat on cyclone development. *J. Appl. Meteor.,* **3**, 27–37.

——, 1983: On the role of the planetary boundary layer in cyclogenesis over the ocean. *Atmos.-Ocean,* **21**, 466–470.

——, 1986: On the sensitivity of predictions of maritime cyclogenesis to convective precipitation and sea temperature. *Atmos.-Ocean,* **24**, 52–72.

——, and G. E. Ellenton, 1980: Physical influences on East Coast cyclogenesis. *Atmos.-Ocean,* **18**, 65–82.

Danielsen, E. F., 1968: Stratospheric-tropospheric exchange based upon radioactivity, ozone and potential vorticity. *J. Atmos. Sci.,* **25**, 502–518.

Dare, P. M., and P. J. Smith, 1984: A comparison of observed and model energy balance for an extratropical cyclone system. *Mon. Wea. Rev.*, **112**, 1289–1308.

Dirks, R. A., J. P. Kuettner and J. A. Moore, 1988: Genesis of Atlantic Lows Experiment (GALE): An overview. *Bull. Amer. Meteor. Soc.,* **69**, 148–160.

Durst, C. S., and R. C. Sutcliffe, 1938: The importance of vertical motion in the development of tropical revolving storms. *Quart. J. Roy. Meteor. Soc.,* **64**, 75–84.

Eady, E. T., 1949: Long waves and cyclone waves. *Tellus,* **1** (3), 33–52.

Eliassen, A., 1956: Instability theories of cyclone formation. In: S. Petterssen, *Weather Analysis and Forecasting,* Chap. 15.

——, 1962: On the vertical circulation in frontal zones. *Geofys. Publ.,* **24**, 147–160.

Emanuel, K. A., 1983: On assessing local conditional symmetric instability from atmospheric soundings. *Mon. Wea. Rev.,* **111**, 2016–2033.

——, 1985: Frontal circulations in the presence of small moist symmetric instability. *J. Atmos. Sci.,* **42**, 1062–1071.

——, 1988: Observational evidence of slantwise convective adjustment. *Mon. Wea. Rev.,* **116**, 1805–1816.

——, and R. Rotunno, 1989: Polar lows or arctic hurricanes. *Tellus,* **41A**, 1–17.

Farrell, B., 1984: Modal and non-modal baroclinic waves. *J. Atmos. Sci.,* **41**, 668–673.

——, 1985: Transient growth of damped baroclinic waves. *J. Atmos. Sci.,* **42**, 2718–2727.

Gall, R., 1976: The effects of released latent heat in growing baroclinic waves. *J. Atmos. Sci.,* **33**, 1686–1701.

Godson, W. L., 1950: A study of the deviation of wind speeds and directions from geostrophic values. *Quart. J. Roy. Meteor. Soc.,* **76**, 3–15.

Gyakum, J. R., 1983a: On the evolution of the QE II storm. I: Synoptic aspects. *Mon. Wea. Rev.,* **111**, 1137–1155.

——, 1983b: On the evolution of the QE II storm. II: Dynamic and thermodynamic structure. *Mon. Wea. Rev.,* **111**, 1156–1173.

Hadlock, R., and C. W. Kreitzberg, 1988: The Experiment on Rapidly Intensifying Cyclones over the Atlantic (ERICA) field study: Objectives and plans. *Bull. Amer. Meteor. Soc.,* **69**, 1309–1320.

Holland, G. J., A. H. Lynch and L. M. Leslie, 1987: Australian east-coast cyclones: Synoptic overview and case study. *Mon. Wea. Rev.,* **115**, 3024–3036.

Holton, J. R., 1979: *An Introduction to Dynamic Meteorology,* 2nd ed. Academic Press, 391 pp.

Hoskins, B. J., M. E. McIntyre and A. W. Robertson, 1985: On the use and significance of isentropic potential vorticity maps. *Quart. J. Roy. Meteor. Soc.,* **111**, 877–946.

Hovanec, R. D., and L. H. Horn, 1975: Static stability and the 300 mb isotach field in the Colorado cyclogenetic area. *Mon. Wea. Rev.,* **103**, 628–638.

Johnson, D. R., and W. K. Downey, 1976: The absolute angular momentum budget of an extratropical cyclone: Quasi-Lagrangian diagnostics 3. *Mon. Wea. Rev.,* **104**, 3–14.

Kenney, S. E., and P. J. Smith, 1983: On the release of eddy available potential energy in an extratropical cyclone system. *Mon. Wea. Rev.,* **111**, 745–755.

Keyser, D., and T. N. Carlson, 1984: Transverse ageostrophic circulations associated with elevated mixed layers. *Mon. Wea. Rev.,* **112**, 2465–2478.

——, and M. A. Shapiro, 1986: A review of the structure and dynamics of upper-level frontal zones. *Mon. Wea. Rev.,* **114**, 452–499.

——, and L. W. Uccellini, 1987: Regional models: Emerging research tools for synoptic meteorologists. *Bull. Amer. Meteor. Soc.,* **68**, 306–320.

Kleinschmidt, E., 1950: On the structure and origin of cyclones (Part 1). *Meteor. Rundsch.,* **3**, 1–6.

——, 1957: Cyclones and anticyclones. Chap. IV in *Dynamic Meteorology,* by A. Eliassen and E. Kleinschmidt. *Handbuch der Physik,* **48**, S. Flügge, Ed. Springer-Verlag, 1–154.

Kocin, P. J., and L. W. Uccellini, 1990: *Snowstorms Along the Northeastern Coast of the United States: 1955 to 1985. Meteor. Monogr.,* **22**, No. 44, 280 pp.

——, ——, J. W. Zack and M. L. Kaplan, 1985: A mesoscale numerical forecast of an intense convective snowburst along the East Coast. *Bull. Amer. Meteor. Soc.,* **66**, 1412–1424.

——, —— and R. A. Petersen, 1986: Rapid evolution of a jet streak circulation in a pre-convective environment. *Meteor. Atmos. Phys.,* **35**, 103–138.

Krishnamurti, T. N., 1968: A study of a developing wave cyclone. *Mon. Wea. Rev.,* **96**, 208–217.

Kuo, Y.-H., and R. J. Reed, 1988: Numerical simulation of an explosively deepening cyclone in the eastern Pacific. *Mon. Wea. Rev.,* **116**, 2081–2105.

——, and S. Low-Nam, 1990: Prediction of nine explosive cyclones over the western Atlantic Ocean with a regional model. *Mon. Wea. Rev.,* **118**, 3–25.

Kutzbach, G., 1979: *The Thermal Theory of Cyclones. A History of Meteorological Thought in the Nineteenth Century.* American Meteorological Society, 254 pp.

Leslie, L. M., G. J. Holland and A. H. Lynch, 1987: Australian east-coast cyclones: Numerical modeling study. *Mon. Wea. Rev.,* **115**, 3037–3053.

Maddox, R. A., D. J. Perkey and J. M. Fritsch, 1981: Evolution of upper tropospheric features during the development of a mesoscale convective complex. *J. Atmos. Sci.,* **38**, 1664–1674.

Mailhot, J., and C. Chouinard, 1989: Numerical forecasts of explosive winter storms: Sensitivity experiments with a meso-α scale model. *Mon. Wea. Rev.,* **117**, 1311–1343.

Manobianco, J. T., 1989: Explosive East Coast cyclogenesis: Numerical experimentation and model-based diagnosis. *Mon. Wea. Rev.,* **117**, 2384–2405.

Mattocks, C., and R. Bleck, 1986: Jet streak dynamics and geostrophic adjustment processes during the initial stages of lee cyclogenesis. *Mon. Wea. Rev.,* **114**, 2033–2056.

Morris, R. M., and A. J. Gadd, 1988: Forecasting the storm. *Weather,* **43**, 70–89.

Mullen, S. L., and D. P. Baumhefner, 1988: Sensitivity of numerical simulations of explosive oceanic cyclogenesis to changes in physical parameterizations. *Mon. Wea. Rev.,* **116**, 2289–2329.

Murray, R., and S. M. Daniels, 1953: Transverse flow at entrance and exit to jet streams. *Quart. J. Roy. Meteor. Soc.,* **79**, 236–241.

Namias, J., and P. F. Clapp, 1949: Confluence theory of the high tropospheric jet stream. *J. Meteor.,* **6**, 330–336.

Newton, C. W., 1954: Frontogenesis and frontolysis as a three-dimensional process. *J. Meteor.,* **11**, 449–461.

——, 1956: Mechanisms of circulation change during lee cyclogenesis. *J. Meteor.,* **13**, 528–539.

——, and E. Palmén, 1963: Kinematic and thermal properties of a large-amplitude wave in the westerlies. *Tellus,* **15**, 99–119.

——, and A. Trevisan, 1984: Clinogenesis and frontogenesis in jet-stream waves. Part I: Analytical relations to wave structure. *J. Atmos. Sci.,* **41**, 2717–2734 .

Nordeng, T. E., 1987: The effect of vertical and slantwise convection on the simulation of polar lows. *Tellus,* **39A**, 354–375.

——, 1990: A model-based diagnostic study of the development and maintenance mechanism of two polar lows. *Tellus*, **42A**, 92–108.

Økland, H., 1987: Heating by organized convection as a source of polar low intensification. *Tellus*, **39A**, 397–407.

Ooyama, K. V., 1982: Conceptual evolution of the theory and modeling of the tropical cyclone. *J. Meteor. Soc. Japan*, **60**, 369–379.

Palmén, E., 1951: The aerology of extratropical disturbances. *Compendium of Meteorology*, T. F. Malone, Ed. American Meteorological Society, 599–620.

——, and C. W. Newton, 1969: *Atmospheric Circulation Systems. Their Structure and Physical Interpretation*. Academic Press, 603 pp.

Petterssen, S., 1955: A general survey of factors influencing development at sea-level. *J. Meteor.*, **12**, 36–42.

——, 1956: *Weather Analysis and Forecasting*, 2nd ed., Vol. 1. McGraw-Hill, 428 pp.

——, and S. J. Smebye, 1971: On the development of extratropical cyclones. *Quart. J. Roy. Meteor. Soc.*, **97**, 457–482.

——, D. L. Bradbury and K. Pedersen, 1962: The Norwegian cyclone models in relation to heat and cold sources. *Geofys. Publ.*, **24**, 243–280.

Rasmussen, E., 1979: The polar low as an extratropical CISK disturbance. *Quart. J. Roy. Meteor. Soc.*, **105**, 531–549.

Reed, R. J., 1955: A study of a characteristic type of upper-level frontogenesis. *J. Meteor.*, **12**, 226–237.

——, and F. Sanders, 1953: An investigation of the development of a mid-tropospheric frontal zone and its associated vorticity field. *J. Meteor.*, **10**, 338–349.

——, and E. F. Danielsen, 1959: Fronts in the vicinity of the tropopause. *Arch. Meteor. Geophys. Bioklim.*, **A11**, 1–17.

——, and M. D. Albright, 1986: A case study of explosive cyclogenesis in the eastern Pacific. *Mon. Wea. Rev.*, **114**, 2297–2319.

——, A. J. Simmons, M. D. Albright and P. Undén, 1988: The role of latent heat release in explosive cyclogenesis: Three examples based on ECMWF operational forecasts. *Weather and Forecasting*, **3**, 217–229.

Reiter, E. R., 1963: *Jet Stream Meteorology*. University of Chicago Press, 515 pp.

Richwien, B. A., 1980: The damming effect of the southern Appalachians. *Nat. Wea. Dig.*, **5**, 2–12.

Riehl, H., and Collaborators, 1952: *Forecasting in Middle Latitudes. Meteor. Monogr.*, **1**, No. 5, 80 pp.

Robertson, F. R., and P. J. Smith, 1983: The impact of model moist processes on the energetics of extratropical cyclones. *Mon. Wea. Rev.*, **111**, 723–744.

Roebber, P. J., 1984: Statistical analysis and updated climatology of explosive cyclones. *Mon. Wea. Rev.*, **112**, 1577–1589.

Rogers, E., and L. F. Bosart, 1986: An investigation of explosively deepening oceanic cyclones. *Mon. Wea. Rev.*, **114**, 702–718.

Salmon, E. M., and P. J. Smith, 1980: A synoptic analysis of the 25–26 January 1978 blizzard in the central United States. *Bull. Amer. Meteor. Soc.*, **61**, 453–460.

Sanders, F., 1986: Explosive cyclogenesis in the west-central North Atlantic Ocean, 1981–1984. Part I: Composite structure and mean behavior. *Mon. Wea. Rev.*, **114**, 1781–1794.

——, 1987: Skill of NMC operational models in prediction of explosive cyclogenesis. *Weather and Forecasting*, **2**, 322–336.

——, and J. R. Gyakum, 1980: Synoptic-dynamic climatology of the "bomb." *Mon. Wea. Rev.*, **108**, 1589–1606.

——, and L. F. Bosart, 1985a: Mesoscale structure in the megalopolitan snowstorm of 11–12 February 1983. Part I: Frontogenetical forcing and symmetric instability. *J. Atmos. Sci.*, **42**, 1050–1061.

——, and ——, 1985b: Mesoscale structure in the megalopolitan snowstorm of 11–12 February 1983. Part II: Doppler radar study of the New England snowband. *J. Atmos. Sci.*, **42**, 1398–1407.

Sardie, J. M., and T. T. Warner, 1985: On the mechanism for the development of polar lows. *J. Atmos. Sci.*, **40**, 869–881.

Schneider, R. S., 1990: Large amplitude mesoscale wave disturbances within the intense midwest extratropical cyclone of 15 December 1987. *Weather and Forecasting*, **5**, submitted.

Sechrist, F. S., and J. A. Dutton, 1970: Energy conversions in a developing cyclone. *Mon. Wea. Rev.*, **98**, 354–362.

Shapiro, M. A., 1981: Frontogenesis and geostrophically forced secondary circulations in the vicinity of jet stream-frontal zone systems. *J. Atmos. Sci.*, **38**, 954–973.

——, and P. J. Kennedy, 1981: Research aircraft measurements of jet stream geostrophic and ageostrophic winds. *J. Atmos. Sci.*, **38**, 2642–2652.

——, L. S. Fedor and T. Hampel, 1987: Research aircraft measurements of a polar low over the Norwegian Sea. *Tellus*, **39A**, 272–306.

Shutts, G. J., M. Booth and J. Norbury, 1988: A geometric model of balanced axisymmetric flows with embedded penetrative convection. *J. Atmos. Sci.*, **45**, 2609–2621.

Sinclair, M. R., and R. L. Elsberry, 1986: A diagnostic study of baroclinic disturbances in polar air streams. *Mon. Wea. Rev.*, **114**, 1957–1983.

Smith, P. J., C. H. Tsou and M. N. Baker, 1988: Static stability variations during a winter marine cyclone development. Preprints, *Palmén Memorial Symposium on Extratropical Cyclones.* Amer. Meteor. Soc., 132–135.

Staley, D. O., 1960: Evaluation of potential-vorticity changes near the tropopause and related vertical motions, vertical advection of vorticity, and transfer of radioactive debris from stratosphere to troposphere. *J. Meteor.*, **17**, 591–620.

——, and R. L. Gall, 1977: On the wavelength of maximum baroclinic instability. *J. Atmos. Sci.*, **34**, 1679–1688.

Stauffer, D. R., and T. T. Warner, 1987: A numerical study of Appalachian cold-air damming and coastal frontogenesis. *J. Appl. Meteor.*, **115**, 799–821.

Stewart, R. E., R. W. Shaw and G. A. Isaac, 1987: Canadian Atlantic Storms Program: The meteorological field project. *Bull. Amer. Meteor. Soc.*, **68**, 338–345.

Sutcliffe, R. C., 1939: Cyclonic and anticyclonic development. *Quart. J. Roy. Meteor. Soc.*, **65**, 518–524.

——, 1947: A contribution to the problem of development. *Quart. J. Roy. Meteor. Soc.*, **73**, 370–383.

——, and A. G. Forsdyke, 1950: The theory and use of upper air thickness patterns in forecasting. *Quart. J. Roy. Meteor. Soc.*, **76**, 189–217.

Tracton, M. S., 1973: The role of cumulus convection in the development of extratropical cyclones. *Mon. Wea. Rev.*, **101**, 573–592.

Uccellini, L. W., 1975: A case study of apparent gravity wave initiation of severe convective storms. *Mon. Wea. Rev.*, **103**, 497–513.

——, 1984: Comments on "Comparative diagnostic case study of East Coast secondary cyclogenesis under weak versus strong synoptic-scale forcing." *Mon. Wea. Rev.,* **112,** 2540–2541.

——, 1986: The possible influence of upstream upper-level baroclinic processes on the development of the QE II storm. *Mon. Wea. Rev.,* **114,** 1019–1027.

——, and D. R. Johnson, 1979: The coupling of upper and lower tropospheric jet streaks and implications for the development of severe convective storms. *Mon. Wea. Rev.,* **107,** 682–703.

——, and S. E. Koch, 1987: The synoptic setting and possible energy sources for mesoscale wave disturbances. *Mon. Wea. Rev.,* **115,** 721–729.

——, and P. J. Kocin, 1987: The interaction of jet streak circulations during heavy snow events along the East Coast of the United States. *Weather and Forecasting,* **2,** 289–308.

——, ——, R. A. Petersen, C. H. Wash and K. F. Brill, 1984: The Presidents' Day cyclone of 18–19 February 1979: Synoptic overview and analysis of the subtropical jet streak in-fluencing the pre-cyclogenetic period. *Mon. Wea. Rev.,* **112,** 31–55.

——, D. Keyser, K. F. Brill and C. H. Wash, 1985: The Presidents' Day cyclone of 1–19 February 1979: Influence of upstream trough amplification and associated tropopause folding on rapid cyclogenesis. *Mon. Wea. Rev.,* **113,** 962–988.

——, R. A. Petersen, K. F. Brill, P. J. Kocin and J. J. Tuccillo, 1987: Synergistic interactions between an upper-level jet streak and diabatic processes that influence the development of a low-level jet and a secondary coastal cyclone. *Mon. Wea. Rev.,* **115,** 2227–2261.

Wash, C. H., J. E. Peak, W. F. Calland and W. A. Cook, 1988: Diagnostic study of explosive cyclogenesis during FGGE. *Mon. Wea. Rev.,* **116,** 431–451.

Whitaker, J. S., L. W. Uccellini and K. F. Brill, 1988: A model-based diagnostic study of the rapid development phase of the Presidents' Day cyclone. *Mon. Wea. Rev.,* **116,** 2337–2365.

Young, M. V., G. A. Monk and K. A. Browning, 1987: Interpreta-tion of satellite imagery of a rapidly deepening cyclone. *Quart. J. Roy. Meteor. Soc.,* **11,** 1089–1115.

Chapter 7

Orographic Cyclogenesis

Stefano Tibaldi, Andrea Buzzi* and Antonio Speranza*

Department of Physics, University of Bologna, Via Irnerio 46, 40126 Bologna, Italy

7.1 Introduction

The idea that extratropical atmospheric variability on time scales of the order of several days is due to an intrinsic instability of the atmospheric circulation is widely accepted in dynamic meteorology. The most evident manifestation of this variability is the development and movement of cyclones and anticyclones (Blackmon et al. 1984). The leading process has been identified, after Charney (1947) and Eady (1949), in the baroclinic instability of a vertically sheared current. The basic formulation of the theory has been substantially improved over the past thirty years. While the linear problem has been generalized to more "realistic" basic state flows, the nonlinear problem has been tackled with an increasing degree of complexity, including dynamical analysis of chaotic regimes (Malguzzi et al. 1988; Buzzi et al. 1990). Baroclinic instability depends in an essential way upon boundary conditions, and orography enters the problem as a lower boundary condition. We shall see that orographic cyclogenesis is a phenomenological manifestation of the sensitivity of the baroclinic atmosphere to surface relief.

That terrain characteristics are important in determining cyclogenesis and cyclone paths has long been recognized in synoptic meteorology (see, e.g., Ficker 1920), but progress in the understanding of the different processes associated with orography (flow blocking or diversion, roughness variations, elevated heat sources and sinks, etc.) has been rather slow. Mountains and ocean-continent contrasts induce quasi-stationary planetary waves that destroy the zonal symmetry of the time-averaged flow. This asymmetry, in turn, affects the spatial distribution of cyclogenesis frequency and of cyclone tracks (see, e.g., Manabe and Terpstra 1974). This is not, however, the sole effect of mountains on cyclonic scale disturbances. Mountains also have a strong direct influence on baroclinic transient eddies, in the sense that they locally affect, through flow diversion and blocking, the spatial structure, rate of growth and propagation of these synoptic scale disturbances (Hsu 1987; Buzzi and Tosi 1989) and these, in turn, affect the time-averaged flow (Speranza 1988; Malguzzi et al. 1988).

Forecasting orographic cyclogenesis has always been a difficult task probably due, among other causes, to lack

---

* FISBAT-CNR, c/o Department of Physics, University of Bologna, Via Irnerio 46, 40126 Bologna, Italy

of dynamical understanding. The advent of numerical forecasting models did not (until recently) substantially alleviate this problem, largely as a result of resolution limitations and of the related difficulties encountered in properly representing orography (e.g., Mesinger 1985).

An impressive indication of the impact of orography on cyclogenesis comes from Petterssen's (1956) classical map of cyclogenesis frequency in the Northern Hemisphere during wintertime, reproduced in Fig. 7.1. While the frequency of cyclogenesis over the mid-latitude oceans is relatively high but rather uniformly distributed, definite peaks of limited spatial extent occur in proximity of many mountain ranges, generally to the east and south of them. Examples of frequency maxima to the south of orography are evident in the Mediterranean and in the Gulf of Alaska. The similarity between these two types of cyclogenesis will be discussed below. Maxima of cyclogenesis tend to occur to the east of mountain complexes when these extend mainly in the meridional direction, as is the case for the Rockies. Orographic influence cannot be excluded (although other factors, such as enhanced baroclinicity and oceanic heat source, are likely to be much more important) for the cyclogenetic areas off the east coasts of Asia and North America, where mountain ranges of moderate height are aligned from northeast to southwest. Other authors have extended and refined Petterssen's hemispheric statistics (Klein 1957; Whittaker and Horn 1982). For more detailed statistics of cyclogenesis on the regional scale, see also Radinović and Lalić (1959; also summarized in Kuettner 1982) and Radinović (1965a) for the Mediterranean; Chung et al. (1976) for the East Asia region (where Petterssen's analysis suffers from data scarcity) and North America; and Chung (1977) for South America.

It is worth noting that the above-mentioned statistics should be taken with some caution, because of the uncertainty and subjectivity in the definition of lee cyclogenesis itself (see Speranza 1975). This definition is usually based on the appearance of closed isobars at the surface, with different limits and criteria chosen by different authors. Such criteria appear, in some cases, so broad that shallow thermal lows not evolving into active cyclones might be mistakenly included in the cyclogenic count. Other more recent statistics of high-frequency atmospheric variability in the vicinity of mountains (Hsu 1987; Buzzi and Tosi 1989) provide an estimate of the distribution of cyclone paths and characteristics that is not biased by the slowly varying components of the flow (see also Wallace et al. 1988). Nevertheless, a firm conclusion that can be derived from all the above analyses is that the spatial distribution of cyclogenetic frequency is very unevenly distributed near mountains. This is equivalent to saying that mountains strongly influence the place (if not the time) of development.

The highest frequency of cyclogenesis is observed "in the lee," where this is usually defined with respect to some prevailing flow. The word "lee," however, needs further clarification in dynamical terms: for the moment, the term "lee cyclogenesis" will be used simply as a synonym for orographic cyclogenesis. The implication is that the neighboring orography is essential in determining the location and/or timing of cyclone formation. With this definition, we choose to include cases of cyclonic reintensification, as when a system passes over or near mountains. As will be discussed below, lee cyclogenesis is often manifested as a secondary cyclogenesis. Obviously, confirmation of such a definition would require the use of numerical models capable of running twin experiments with and without mountains.

Figure 7.1 shows that the most prominent and best-isolated Northern Hemisphere maximum of cyclogenetic frequency corresponds to the area where Alpine lee cyclogenesis takes place. Observing and understanding this particular phenomenon, together with the study of related orographic effects, were the main objectives of ALPEX, whose field phase took place in 1982. The observational, numerical and theoretical work related to ALPEX has led to substantial progress over the past few years. For this reason Alpine cyclogenesis is the main subject of this review, with particular attention given to the post-ALPEX results (see also Mesinger and Pierrehumbert 1986). Earlier reviews by Speranza (1975), Tibaldi (1980) and Buzzi and Speranza (1983) provide a good summary of the pre-ALPEX work (see also Kuettner 1982). Other types of orographic cyclogenesis also will be discussed, although more briefly, emphasizing similarities with and differences from Alpine cyclogenesis.

One important point about this paper should be clear from the outset: the review nature of this work applies to the description of the observational and numerical modeling results. As far as theory of orographic cyclogenesis is

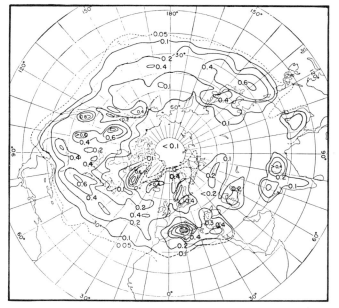

FIG. 7.1. Percentage frequency of cyclogenesis during winter in the Northern Hemisphere in squares of 100,000 km² (Petterssen 1956).

concerned, we have limited ourselves to the description of what could be called the "Bologna school theory." This, admittedly, is not because this theory is the only available or because other theories have nothing interesting to contribute (e.g., Pierrehumbert 1985; Smith 1984, 1986; Mattocks and Bleck 1986). Rather, in view of the natural bias of the authors, we leave it to other, possibly more objective, judges to compare the relative merits of alternative theories (see, e.g., Egger 1988).

Section 7.2 describes the basic phenomenology of the process, while Section 7.3 outlines the theory. Section 7.4 discusses, in light of the theory, the more recently acquired observational facts. Section 7.5 deals with some of the more recent numerical modeling results, although extensive reference to modeling work is made throughout the paper. Section 7.6 attempts to describe lee cyclogenesis in many different locations in a unified way, and Section 7.7 contains some concluding remarks.

7.2 The Basic Phenomenology of Alpine Cyclogenesis

A considerable number of depressions form each year near the surface in the region south or southeast of the Alps. As mentioned above, not all cases should be classified as "true" lee cyclogenesis. For the 13 months of the extended ALPEX observing period, Pichler and Steinacker (1987) have counted 40 cases they consider, on an empirical basis, as orographically induced cyclogenesis, having excluded thermally induced shallow lows and lows moving from the southwest or the south toward the Alps. Weak cases are included in this classification. During the ALPEX special observing period (SOP) (March–April 1982), six to eight cases of orographically induced cyclones (an objective evaluation of the orographic effects is not yet available for all cases) occurred in the Alpine area (Radinović 1986; Buzzi 1986). On average, about ten to twenty cases that can be arbitrarily considered as moderate or strong lee cyclones occur in a typical year. Explosive events ("bombs" in the definition of Sanders and Gyakum 1980) are rare in the Mediterranean and will not be discussed here explicitly.

The mobility of lee cyclones is variable, but usually those that move slowly attain the greatest strength and vertical extent (Illari et al. 1981), as occurred in the ALPEX event of 4–5 March 1982 (Fig. 7.2). In these as in other similar cases (see Illari et al. 1981; Tibaldi and Buzzi 1983), the mature stage is associated with the establishment of a split westerly flow over Europe. In the initial stage of growth, the apparent movement of lee cyclones near the surface tends to be small in almost all cases (Radinović 1986).

As observed by earlier investigators, the initial depression appears in the lee of the Alps ahead of, rather than on, a cold front which reaches the mountain range from a direction between west and north. The first stage of growth is also not associated with extensive cloud and precipitation systems. Usually, these gradually develop during the

cyclone growth. As noted by Buzzi and Tibaldi (1978) and Mesinger and Pierrehumbert (1986), these factors seem to eliminate sensible heat flux, frontal instability and latent heat release as main factors in initiating the development.

A feature that does seem to be important in the initiation of the lee cyclone is the interaction of the cold front with orography, resulting in cold air "damming" on the windward side of the Alps, retardation of the cold advection in the lee and distortion of the frontal structure, with frontogenesis above the mountain and a positive thermal anomaly forming in the lee at low levels (Radinović 1965b; Buzzi and Tibaldi 1978). A deepening trough aloft, associated with an upper-level jet maximum pointing toward the western Mediterranean, was also identified as another key feature conducive to deep lee cyclones (Reiter 1963; Danielsen 1973; Buzzi and Tibaldi 1978; Mattocks and Bleck 1986). Rapid pressure falls near the surface occur when the front-left quadrant of the advancing jet streak is located above the region between the Alps and the Pyrenees. The upper-level flow is altered, in turn, by the orographic influence: In the growth stage, jet splitting tends to occur northwest of the Alps, even at high tropospheric levels. This splitting is induced, or at least enhanced, by the orographic perturbation superimposing on the undisturbed flow. This tends to fill the upper-level wave north of the Alps and to deepen it to the south (see Tibaldi et al. 1980 and the discussion in Section 7.3 below). A cutoff low over the Mediterranean and extending throughout the troposphere is often the end product of strong Alpine lee cyclogenesis.

It is significant that both the cold front and the upper jet are usually part of the same preexisting synoptic-scale system: an approaching, often growing, cyclonic disturbance (the so-called parent low or parent cyclone). That is, Alpine lee cyclogenesis appears almost invariably as a secondary cyclogenesis, requiring the existence of a primary disturbance interacting with the Alps (Buzzi and Tibaldi 1978; Buzzi and Speranza 1983). In this respect, lee cyclones are more attributable to a wave-scattering process than to lee-wave or vortex generation created by an obstacle in an incident parallel flow. This notion forms the basis for the recent progress in the physical understanding of the process. Lee cyclogenesis should not be confused with quasi-stationary, mesoscale disturbances of the "lee wave" type which are frequently observed when the basic low-level flow is mainly perpendicular to the mountain range (Buzzi and Tibaldi 1978).

Buzzi and Tibaldi, with simple scale evaluations, found two different stages in the growing process of the particular lee cyclone they analyzed. In the first, more rapid stage, the process is associated with frontal deformation and is mesoscale in character with strong orographic influence. In the second, they recognized a more conventional process of baroclinic instability, during which a coherent cyclone develops on the synoptic scale. Buzzi and Tibaldi acknowledged the importance of the latter baroclinic stage in characterizing well-developed lee cyclones, as opposed

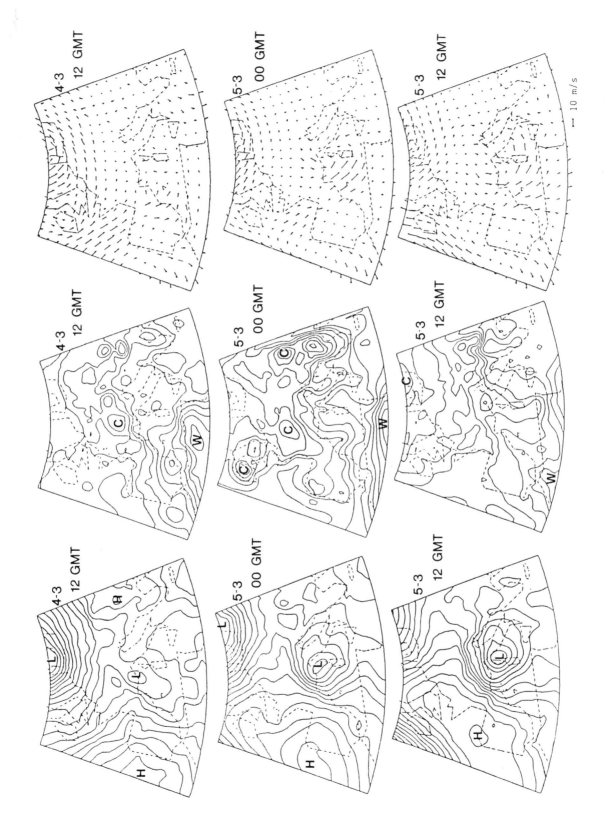

Fig. 7.2.　Sea level pressure (2.5 hPa interval, left), sea level potential temperature (2 K interval, middle) and surface wind arrows (right) for the ALPEX cyclogenesis case of 4–5 March 1982. See also Figs. 7.12–7.14.

to shallow and short-lived depressions. Note that the total pressure fall in the Buzzi–Tibaldi case was almost equally distributed between the two stages, although the growth rate was apparently faster in the first one. The important role played by orography in the second stage was first investigated by Tibaldi et al. (1980) and then clearly demonstrated by Tosi et al. (1983) as a result of extensive numerical experimentation in idealized conditions: The mountain was shown to be essential in determining location and strength of cyclone formation even after the initial stage.

It is worth noting here that, starting from the pioneering work of Egger (1972), the contribution made to our understanding of Alpine cyclogenesis by numerical experimentation is intimately related to that of observational studies. For example, the identification of lee cyclogenesis with an essentially baroclinic process was already empirically noted by Egger (1972) and Trevisan (1976) in their numerical simulations. The importance of baroclinic conversion was then quantitatively demonstrated, also by means of numerical experiments, by Tibaldi et al. (1980) and further confirmed by McGinley (1982) and Michaelides (1987), diagnosing real data.

Another important result obtained by the numerical experiments is the identification of the scale and shape of the mountain-induced disturbance in cases of cyclogenesis. This disturbance appears in the geopotential field as a relatively simply structured dipolar feature, with high pressure north or northeast of the mountain and low pressure on the opposite side (see, e.g., Tibaldi and Buzzi 1983; Tosi et al. 1983; Tibaldi and Dell'Osso 1986; McGinley and Goerss 1986). This is an example of a typical result which could not be entirely derived from observations and which has allowed substantial theoretical advances. This difficulty of separating contributions from observational studies and numerical modeling work is reflected throughout this review. We have referred and will continue to refer to numerical modeling results whenever this is made necessary by the discussion within a section, without attempting to confine all references to modeling in a separate section. The purpose of Section 7.5 is only to condense the most significant and the most recent modeling results in a single place, for ease of reference and consultation.

7.3 A Theory of Lee Cyclogenesis

We summarize here first some general properties of lee cyclogenesis that we consider theoretically important in the sense that they seem to hold for different types of lee cyclogenesis around the world, and in the sense that they are connected with some essential symmetries of the physical process in question. The properties are listed below.

(a) Lee cyclogenesis occurs in association with a preexisting synoptic-scale trough or cyclone (the "parent low") that interacts with the orography.
(b) The development of the lee cyclone starts before the strong thermal contrasts associated with cold frontal penetration take place in the lee.
(c) The mature, deep lee cyclone scales on the Rossby deformation radius (based on the tropospheric depth), and the influence of orography takes the form of a high-low dipole that scales on the same horizontal and vertical length as the cyclone itself (see Fig. 7.3).

A physical process displaying all the above properties is baroclinic instability in the presence of orography. In order to isolate the essential physics we shall consider cases in which the basic flow, homogeneous and parallel, does not

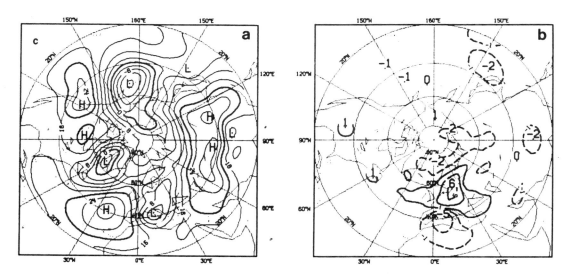

FIG. 7.3. (a) 1000 hPa geopotential height, 5-day mean forecast for the Northern Hemisphere (day 0 to day 5), using the ECMWF N48 global grid-point model with realistic Alps; (b) 1000 hPa geopotential height 5-day mean difference between realistic Alps experiment and no Alps experiment. Isolines every 4 and 2 dam respectively (Tibaldi and Buzzi 1983).

itself interact with orography (orography of infinitesimal height and/or parallel to the basic flow). Thermal properties of the atmosphere enter the problem only through the parameters characterizing the basic baroclinicity. Properties (a) and (b) are therefore reasonably represented. The primary (parent) cyclone is to be interpreted as the baroclinic disturbance that would develop on the same basic flow in the absence of bottom orography. This orography distorts the flow, producing secondary cyclogenesis.

Property (c) is more critical. The presence near the ground of two opposite signs of the orographic pressure deformation on the two sides of the mountain requires an antisymmetry in the equations of motion. Such antisymmetry is associated with the opposite sign of the mountain slopes with respect to the incident meridional flow of the primary wave.

Now that the problem of baroclinic instability in the presence of orography has been analyzed in many aspects (Speranza et al. 1985; Buzzi and Speranza 1986; Malguzzi et al. 1987; Buzzi et al. 1987; Trevisan et al. 1988), it has become evident that the main physics of the process relevant to Alpine cyclogenesis is described by the simplest case: that of an infinite ridge elongated in the direction of the basic flow. Subsection 7.3.1 is devoted to the analysis of this problem, while subsection 7.3.2 contains an overview of the principal results obtained with obstacles of finite horizontal extent.

7.3.1 Baroclinic Instability of a Basic Flow Parallel to an Infinite Ridge

a) *Quasi-Geostrophic Flow*

We consider here the modifications induced on the baroclinic instability of a plane-parallel basic flow by an infinite orographic ridge. The ridge is chosen parallel to the basic flow so as not to interact with it.

Following Speranza et al. (1985), we shall start our analysis from the simplest case: shallow orography in a quasi-geostrophic, two-layer atmosphere (Pedlosky 1964). The basic equations are, in standard notation:

$$\partial_t q_{1,2} + J(\psi_{1,2}, q_{1,2}) = 0$$
$$q_1 = \nabla^2 \psi_1 + F(\psi_2 - \psi_1) + \beta y \qquad (7.1)$$
$$q_2 = \nabla^2 \psi_2 + F(\psi_1 - \psi_2) + \beta y + h'(y)/Ro,$$

where $F = (f_o^2 L^2)/(N^2 H^2)$ is the internal Froude number, $Ro = U/f_o L$ is the Rossby number and we assume orography as an infinite east-west ridge $h'(y)$ (scaled with half of the tropospheric depth $H/2$). Any stationary zonal flow is consistent with the boundary conditions imposed by such orography; for simplicity we consider $\bar{u}_1 = \text{const} = \bar{u}$; $\bar{u}_2 = 0$. The set of equations resulting from a linearization of (7.1) under the above conditions is:

$$\begin{cases} \partial_t[\nabla^2 \psi_1' + F(\psi_2' - \psi_1')] - \partial_x \psi_1'(F\bar{u} - \beta) \\ \qquad + \bar{u}\partial_x[\nabla^2 \psi_1' + F(\psi_2' - \psi_1')] = 0 \\ \partial_t[\nabla^2 \psi_2' + F(\psi_1' - \psi_2')] - \partial_x \psi_2'(F\bar{u} - \beta) \\ \qquad + \partial_x \psi_2 \partial_y(h'/Ro) = 0 . \end{cases} \qquad (7.2)$$

By introducing solutions of the form:

$$\psi_{1,2}' = \phi_{1,2}(y)e^{i(kx - \omega t)} \qquad (7.3)$$

the linear set (7.2) can be transformed into the eigenvalue problem:

$$\begin{cases} (-i\omega + \bar{u}\partial_x)(\nabla^2 - F)\phi_1 \\ \qquad + (\beta + F\bar{u})\partial_x\phi_1 + (-i\omega + \bar{u}\partial_x)F\phi_2 = 0 \\ (-i\omega F)\phi_1 - i\omega(\nabla^2 - F)\phi_2 \\ \qquad + (\beta - F\bar{u})\partial_x\phi_2 + \partial_x \phi_2 \partial_y(h'/Ro) = 0 . \end{cases} \qquad (7.4)$$

The parametric dependence on the y-coordinate of this problem makes its solution not straightforward. We need to have recourse to either numerical or perturbation techniques. Outlined here is the perturbation approach since, in some of its aspects, it is physically instructive. If orography is small, we can expand the eigenvalues and eigenfunctions of (7.4) in terms of the small parameter ε (we pose $h'/Ro = \varepsilon h$):

$$\phi_{1,2} = \phi_{1,2}^{(0)} + \varepsilon \phi_{1,2}^{(1)} + \ldots$$
$$\omega = \omega^{(0)} + \varepsilon \omega^{(1)} + \ldots \qquad (7.5)$$

By substituting (7.5) into (7.4), reordering terms in powers of ε and assuming that different orders of expansion vanish independently, we obtain a sequence of linear problems. The 0th order expansion gives (with $c = \omega/k$):

$$\phi_{1yy}^{(0)} - k^2 \phi_1^{(0)} + F(\phi_2^{(0)} - \phi_1^{(0)}) + \frac{\beta + F\bar{u}}{\bar{u} - c^{(0)}} \phi_1^{(0)} = 0 \qquad (7.6)$$

$$\phi_{2yy}^{(0)} - k^2 \phi_2^{(0)} + F(\phi_1^{(0)} - \phi_2^{(0)}) + \frac{\beta - F\bar{u}}{-c^{(0)}} \phi_2^{(0)} = 0$$

which is the classical baroclinic instability problem on a flat bottom boundary. The eigenvalue problem (7.6) has solutions of the form (see, e.g., Pedlosky 1979):

$$\phi_1^{(0)} = A \cos \lambda y$$

$$\phi_2^{(0)} = \cos \lambda y$$

$$c^{(0)} = \frac{\bar{u}}{2} - \frac{\beta(k^2 + \lambda^2 + F)}{(k^2 + \lambda^2)(k^2 + \lambda^2 + 2F)} \pm$$

$$\left(\frac{\beta^2 F^2}{(k^2 + \lambda^2)^2 (k^2 + \lambda^2 + 2F)^2} - \frac{\bar{u}^2(2F - k^2 - \lambda^2)}{(k^2 + \lambda^2 + 2F)} \right)^{1/2} \qquad (7.7)$$

$$A = \frac{F(\bar{u} - c^{(0)})}{(\lambda^2 + k^2)(\bar{u} - c^{(0)}) - \beta - Fc^{(0)}} .$$

We interpret this solution as the "primary" baroclinic wave (although it should be borne in mind that, from a synoptic point of view, the "parent cyclone" is not what it would be without the mountain except sufficiently far upstream).

Orographic effects appear in the first-order expansion:

$$\begin{cases} \phi_{1yy}^{(1)} - k^2\phi_1^{(1)} + F(\phi_2^{(1)} - \phi_1^{(1)}) + \dfrac{\beta + F\bar{u}}{\bar{u} - c^{(0)}}\ \phi_1^{(1)} = \\[2mm] \qquad -\dfrac{c^{(1)}(\beta + F\bar{u})}{(\bar{u} - c^{(0)})^2}\ \phi_1^{(0)} \\[4mm] \phi_{2yy}^{(1)} - k^2\phi_2^{(1)} + F(\phi_1^{(1)} - \phi_2^{(1)}) + \dfrac{\beta - F\bar{u}}{-c^{(0)}}\phi_2^{(1)} = \\[2mm] \qquad \dfrac{h_y}{c^{(0)}}\ \phi_2^{(0)} - \dfrac{c^{(1)}}{c^{(0)2}}(\beta - F\bar{u})\ \phi_2^{(0)}\ . \end{cases} \tag{7.8}$$

From the solvability condition of (7.8) we obtain the first-order "orographic" correction to the eigenvalue:

$$c^{(1)} = \frac{1}{D}\int_{-L_y/2}^{+L_y/2} \left| \phi_2^{(0)} \right|^2 h_y\, dy \tag{7.9}$$

wherein

$$D = \left[\frac{(\beta + F\bar{u})\, c^{(0)}}{(\bar{u} - c^{(0)})^2}\ \int_{-L_y/2}^{+L_y/2} \left| \phi_1^{(0)} \right|^2 dy \right. \\ \left. + \frac{\beta - F\bar{u}}{c^{(0)}}\int_{-L_y/2}^{+L_y/2} \left| \phi_2^{(0)} \right|^2 dy \right].$$

The first-order correction vanishes if orography is symmetric in latitude. It is only at the second order that we obtain a correction of the eigenvalue for a symmetric ridge:

$$c^{(2)} = \frac{1}{D}\int_{-L_y/2}^{+L_y/2} \phi_2^{(0)*}\, \phi_2^{(1)}\, h_y\, dy. \tag{7.10}$$

This indicates that, even for an infinite ridge, the effect of orography on the growth rate and speed of the unstable modes is generally small. What is more relevant for lee cyclogenesis is the modification induced by the orography on the spatial structure of the eigenfunctions.

The field of orographic distortion can be shown to possess a "far-field" of large scale (Rossby deformation

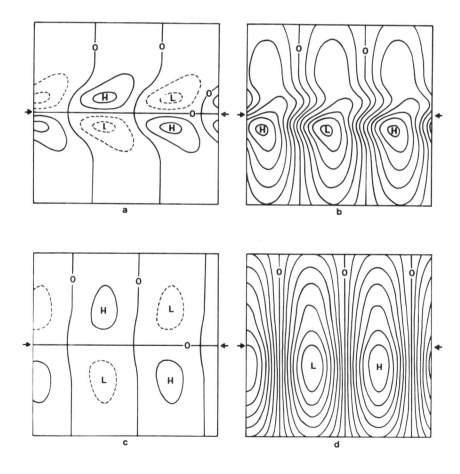

a **b** **c** **d**

FIG. 7.4.   Analytical solution for a baroclinic wave in the infinite beta-plane two-layer model, with an east-west ridge mountain. The arrows mark the position of the ridge crest. The parameter values are: $\bar{u}_1 = 1.5$, $F = 2.0$, $\beta = 1.6$, $k = 1.1$, $\lambda = 0.3$, $h_o = 1.0$, $\bar{\lambda} = 3.0$. The contour interval is arbitrary. A portion of the domain of 8×8 nondimensional length units is shown. (a) Streamfunction of orographic perturbation only, in the lower layer; (b) total streamfunction of modified baroclinic wave in the lower layer; (c) and (d) as in (a) and (b), respectively, but in the upper layer, and with a doubled contour interval. The basic zonal wind is not added. (Speranza et al. 1985; see for more details.)

radius) and the asymmetry dictated by the h_y term in (7.8). (See Speranza et al. 1985 for details.) Figure 7.4 shows the streamfunction pattern obtained in the specific case of a ridge of cosine form in a limited latitudinal strip, in a β-plane infinite domain. It can be noticed how the orographic correction, besides displaying the required high-low symmetry, possesses a large-scale structure, both in the horizontal and vertical directions.

b) Nongeostrophic Flow

Real orography is often "steep" in the sense that the slope of its surface exceeds the basic stratification limit f/N (for the middle-latitude atmosphere, about $1/100$). As a consequence, vertical velocities incompatible with the quasi-geostrophic approximation tend to be forced near orographic slopes. It is interesting to examine how the breakdown of quasi-geostrophy takes place and what are the consequences of this breakdown on the far field. One possibility is that nongeostrophic effects are important only near steep orography and the global solution remains essentially unaltered. Another, more critical, possibility is that the whole field is modified and the global properties of the solutions of the baroclinic eigenvalue problem are upset by the presence of steep orography.

This problem has been analysed in detail by Malguzzi et al. (1987) using the primitive equations. Let us consider the equations of motion in the hydrostatic and Boussinesq approximation:

$$\begin{cases} u_t + uu_x + vu_y + wu_z - f_o v = -\Phi_x \\ v_t + uv_x + vv_y + wv_z + f_o u = -\Phi_y \\ g\,\theta/\theta_s = \Phi_z \\ \theta_t + u\theta_x + v\theta_y + w\theta_{sz} = 0 \\ u_x + v_y + w_z = 0 \end{cases} \quad (7.11)$$

where the following definitions have been made:
f_o is the Coriolis parameter, assumed constant;
$\Phi = p/\rho_o$, with ρ_o a constant density;
$\Theta = \theta_s(z) + \theta(x,y,z,t)$
with Θ indicating potential temperature and θ_s indicating the background stratification.

Let us introduce the basic state $\bar{u}(y,z) = m^*(y)z$ which is a generalization of the basic profile of the Eady problem, so that

$$\begin{cases} u = \bar{u} + u' \\ v = v' \\ w = w' \\ \theta = -\theta_s \dfrac{f_o}{g} \int \bar{u}_z\, dy + \dfrac{\theta_s}{g}\,\theta' \\ \Phi_z = -f_o \int \bar{u}_z\, dy + \Phi'_z. \end{cases} \quad (7.12)$$

Substituting (7.12) into (7.11) and linearizing:

$$u'_t + \bar{u}u'_x + \bar{u}_y v' + m^* w' - f_o v' = -\Phi'_x$$
$$v'_t + \bar{u}v'_x + f_o u' = -\Phi'_y$$
$$\Phi'_z = \theta'$$
$$\theta'_t + \bar{u}\theta'_x - f_o m^* v' + N^2 w' = 0$$
$$u'_x + v'_y + w'_z = 0$$

where $N^2 = g\theta_{sz}/\theta_s$ is the Brunt–Väisälä frequency, which is assumed to be constant. By introducing the following scales:
U horizontal velocity scale,
H vertical space scale equal to the depth of the atmosphere,
U/f_o horizontal space scale,
Hf_o vertical velocity scale,
f_o^{-1} time scale,
the only relevant dimensionless number for the resulting adimensional system of equations is the Richardson number $Ri = N^2 H^2/U^2$, which is large if "bulk" values for U and N are taken. The dimensionless vertical shear becomes $m = m^* H/U$.

The solution of (7.13) is written in normal mode form:

$$\Phi' = \hat{\Phi}(y,z)e^{ik(x-ct)}$$

with similar equations for u', v' and w'. A single equation for $\hat{\Phi}$ can be obtained by using the momentum and thermodynamic equations to substitute for $\hat{u}$, $\hat{v}$ and $\hat{w}$ in the continuity equation.

The lower boundary condition is $\hat{w} = \hat{v}h_y$ computed at $z = h(y)$ and the upper condition is $\hat{w} = 0$ at $z = 1$. As lateral boundary conditions, we will impose $\hat{v} = 0$ at $y = \pm L_y/2$ (channel with lateral walls). In order to transform the $y - z$ domain into a rectangle, the vertical coordinate $\eta = (z - h)/(1 - h)$ is introduced.

The meridional structure of the streamfunction is governed by the following equations and boundary conditions:

$$\hat{\Phi}_{\eta\eta} + C_1\hat{\Phi}_{yy} + C_2\hat{\Phi}_{y\eta} + C_3\hat{\Phi}_y + C_4\hat{\Phi}_\eta + C_5\hat{\Phi} = 0$$
$$\hat{\Phi}_\eta + \alpha_{0,1}\hat{\Phi}_y + \beta_{0,1}\hat{\Phi} = 0 \qquad \text{at } \eta = 0, 1$$
$$\hspace{9cm}(7.14)$$
$$\hat{\Phi}_y + \frac{m}{Ri}\hat{\Phi}_\eta - \frac{1}{mz-c}\hat{\Phi} = 0 \qquad \text{at } y = L_y/2$$

where the coefficients C_n, $\alpha_{0,1}$ and $\beta_{0,1}$ are expressions involving y, η, k, Ri, $m(y)$, $h(y)$ and the eigenvalue c. These equations were solved numerically by Malguzzi et al. (1987) by defining $\hat{\Phi}$ and the coefficients over a two-dimensional grid on the y, η domain. The problem was thus reduced to that of finding the values of c which cancel the determinant of the matrix obtained from the discretization of (7.14). The algorithm used to find the eigenvalues is described in Malguzzi et al. (1987).

Figure 7.5 illustrates one solution along with the corresponding quasi-geostrophic solution. It is clear that for

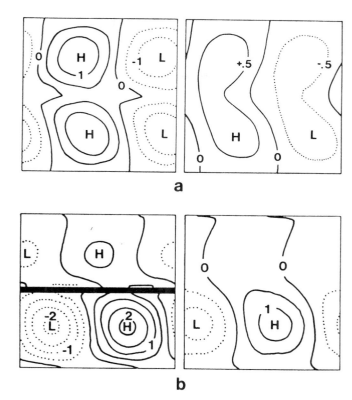

FIG. 7.5. (a) Quasi-geostrophic and (b) primitive equation solutions of the eigenvalue problem (7.14) for the following parameter values: $f_o = 10^{-4}$ s^{-1}, vertical scale $H = 10$ km, $U = 30$ m s^{-1}, $Ri = 10$ (corresponding to a Brunt–Väisälä frequency $N^2 = 0.9 \cdot 10^{-4}$ s^{-2}), mountain width $y_o = 1.0$ (300 km), mountain height $h_o = 0.2$ (2 km), domain width $L_y = 16.666$ (5,000 km). The value of U represents the mean zonal wind at $z = H$. The panels on the left are for $z = 0$, those on the right for $z = H$ (Malguzzi et al. 1987).

steep orography the eigenvalue problem is globally sensitive to nongeostrophic effects. The qualitative properties of the solution (e.g., dipolar structure) are, however, not changed with respect to those discussed for the quasi-geostrophic case with a smooth orography. This means that the quasi-geostrophic approximation gives qualitatively correct results with smooth orography, while, as expected, the steep orography case must be dealt with in the framework of the primitive equations.

7.3.2 Three-Dimensional Orography

An extension of the simple formulation of Section 7.3.1 consists in considering orography that is also limited in the direction of the basic flow. This extension obviously constitutes an improvement in realism although, as we will see, it adds little to the basic physics.

The problem, outlined in Speranza et al. (1985), is discussed exhaustively in Buzzi and Speranza (1986) and applied to various real cyclogenetic processes in Buzzi et al. (1987).

Let us ignore, for the time being, the complications induced by finite height and/or slope of orography. If

orography is small and the zonal wind vanishes at $z = 0$, the basic flow is not deformed from plane-parallel flow so again we can treat orographic effects as perturbations. Let us therefore analyze the Eady problem for a fluid of constant density and stratification, confined within a zonally periodic f-plane of length L_x, with lateral walls at $y \pm = L_y/2$ and bounded by $z = 0$ and $z = H$. The equations governing the evolution of a small perturbation superimposed on the mean zonal wind $\overline{u} = Uz/H$ are:

$$\nabla^2\psi + \psi_{zz} = 0$$
$$\psi_{zt} - \psi_x = -J(\psi, h'/Ro) \text{ at } z = 0$$
$$\psi_{zt} - \psi_x + \psi_{xz} = 0 \qquad \text{at } z = 1 \qquad (7.15)$$
$$\psi = 0 \qquad\qquad \text{at } y = \pm L_y/2$$

As in Section 7.3.1, orography is assumed such that $h'/Ro = \varepsilon h$, where ε is a small parameter.

With the usual expansion (see Section 3 of Speranza et al. 1985 for details) and assuming $\psi = \phi(x,y,z)e^{-i\omega t}$, we obtain at 0th order the unperturbed solution:

$$\phi^{(0)} = A(\sinh K_z + B \cosh K_z) \cos(\pi y/L_y)e^{i2\pi\overline{m}x/L_x} \quad (7.16)$$

where:

$$K^2 = \frac{\pi^2}{L_y^2} + \frac{4\pi^2\overline{m}^2}{L_x^2}$$

$$c^{(0)} \equiv \frac{\omega^{(0)}}{2\pi\overline{m}/L_x} = \frac{1}{2} \pm \left(\frac{1}{4} + K^{-2} - K^{-1}\coth K\right)^{1/2}$$

$$B = -c^{(0)}K.$$

An approach that proves useful, within limits to be carefully determined (see Buzzi and Speranza 1986), consists in representing orographic corrections in terms of the 0th order solutions (7.16):

$$\phi^{(1)} = \sum_{n=1}^{+\infty}\sum_{m=-\infty}^{+\infty}(a_{m,n}\sinh K_{m,n}z + b_{m,n}\cosh K_{m,n}z) \cdot$$

$$\sin\frac{n\pi(y+L_y/2)}{L_y} e^{2\pi imx/L_x},$$

$$K^2_{m,n} = \frac{4\pi^2 m^2}{L_x^2} + \frac{n^2\pi^2}{L_y^2}. \qquad (7.17)$$

A similar decomposition is introduced for the orographic forcing:

$$J(\phi^{(0)},h)\Big|_{z=0} = i\sum_{n=1}^{+\infty}\sum_{m=-\infty}^{+\infty}\alpha_{m,n}\sin\frac{n\pi(y+L_y/2)}{L_y} e^{2\pi imx/L_x}$$

$$\qquad (7.18)$$

$$\alpha_{m,n} = \frac{AB\pi^2}{L_xL_y}\left[(\overline{m}n-m)h_{m-\overline{m},n-1} - (\overline{m}n+m)h_{m-\overline{m},n+1}\right].$$

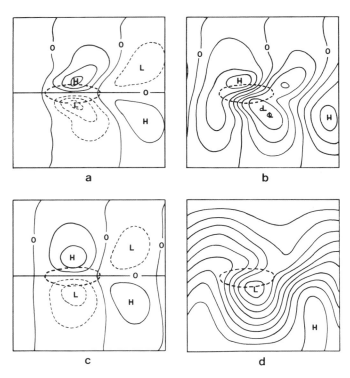

Fig. 7.6. Solution for a baroclinic wave in the continuous Eady model in a long periodic channel with isolated orography. The thick dashed ovals mark the orographic contour of e^{-1} of the maximum height. The parameter values are: $U = 2.0$, $\overline{m} = 5.0$, $\varepsilon = 1.0$, $\overline{x} = 1.5$, $\overline{y} = 0.5$, $L_x = 30.0$, $L_y = 8.0$. A portion of the channel of 8×8 nondimensional length units is shown. (a) Streamfunction of orographic perturbation only at $z = 0$; (b) total streamfunction of modified baroclinic wave at $z = 0$; (c) and (d) as in (a) and (b) respectively, but at $z = 0.5$ and with half contouring interval. The basic zonal wind is added in (d) (Speranza et al. 1985).

With this expansion (7.15) reduces to the algebraic system:

$$\begin{cases} \omega^{(0)} K_{m,n} a_{m,n} + \dfrac{2\pi m}{L_x} b_{m,n} = \alpha_{m,n} + \omega^{(1)} KAB\delta_{m,\overline{m}}\, \delta_{n,1}\,, \\[2mm] \left[\left(\omega^{(0)} - \dfrac{2\pi m}{L_x}\right) K_{m,n} \cosh K_{m,n} + \dfrac{2\pi m}{L_x} \sinh K_{m,n}\right] a_{m,n} + \\[2mm] \hspace{6cm} (7.19) \\[2mm] \left[\left(\omega^{(0)} - \dfrac{2\pi m}{L_x}\right) K_{m,n} \sinh K_{m,n} + \dfrac{2\pi m}{L_x} \cosh K_{m,n}\right] b_{m,n} = \\[2mm] A\omega^{(1)} K(\cosh K + B \sinh K)\, \delta_{n,1}\, \delta_{m,\overline{m}}\,. \end{cases}$$

A solution obtained for a bi-Gaussian mountain is shown in Fig. 7.6. There is a clear improvement in realism with respect to the ridge case (see, for example, Fig. 7.4); the physics, however, appears to be essentially the same.

Regarding the case of a three-dimensional mountain of finite height, we just show the results obtained by semi-numerical means for orography of arbitrary slope in a quasi-geostrophic model atmosphere, without discussing the mathematical procedure which can be found in Buzzi and Speranza (1986).

Figure 7.7 shows the orographic deformation induced on baroclinic instability by a finite mountain oriented in the east-west direction, such as the Alps. The corresponding results for a mountain similar to the Rockies (north-south) are shown in Fig. 7.8. Comparison with observations shows that these results capture many aspects of the local cyclogenetic phenomenology.

The case of an isolated steep orography (Alps), but with use of the primitive equations, has been recently considered by Trevisan et al. (1988). In this work, the normal mode structure with a realistic basic state has been computed using a primitive equation model in isentropic coordinates and removing the limiting assumptions made in earlier analytical studies.

In this section, attention has been concentrated on the process of growth of baroclinic disturbances in the presence of bottom orography. Particular attention has been given to the qualitative properties (symmetries) of the process. Although many details still have to be investigated, there is considerable evidence that the orographic modification of baroclinic instability provides a theoretical model to understand the basic properties of lee cyclogenesis. Important aspects of the problem still to be clarified are the rapid initial stage, the growth to finite amplitude of the lee cyclone and the interaction between scales in the mature phase.

7.4 Discussion of Recent Observational Results

ALPEX has recently provided an extensive database suitable, in principle, for quantitative analysis and diagnostics of lee cyclogenesis. In order to extract meaningful information from it, it is necessary to employ appropriate analysis schemes that can provide a consistent three- or possibly four-dimensional description of the atmospheric states on scales at least of the order of the meso-α. Particular care is required to ensure an accurate evaluation of the effects of orography in the mass and wind fields. The development of suitable analysis schemes is part of the research connected to ALPEX. A brief summary of different analysis characteristics and methods is given here.

Isentropic analysis has been adopted by several researchers (see, e.g., Steinacker 1984; Bleck and Mattocks 1984; Buzzi et al. 1985; Reimer 1986; Johnson and Hill 1987; Pichler and Steinacker 1987) in view of its advantages in describing mesoscale structures such as fronts and jets and allowing direct computation of trajectories and potential vorticity. Bleck and Mattocks (1984), Reimer (1986) and Steinacker et al. (1988) apply an optimum interpolation scheme. Steinacker et al. use strongly anisotropic structure functions across the Alps, as indicated by cross-correlation analysis at radiosonde stations in the mountain region. Buzzi et al. (1985) and Trevisan et al. (1985) use a simple univariate variational method, concentrating their efforts on producing an accurate description of wind and mass fields near steep mountains.

Some degree of readjustment between mass and wind is generally applied, but no specific "initialization" proce-

FIG. 7.7.   Streamfunction of the fastest-growing mode in the lower layer of a two-layer, periodic channel model with an isolated east-west oriented mountain of finite amplitude. The mountain is bi-Gaussian, with maximum height $\bar{H} = 5$ (corresponding in dimensional units to about 2.5 km); the contour H/e is dotted. (a) through (f) represent phases corresponding to different times of evolution without including amplitude growth. The basic state zonal velocity is zero in the lower layer. In the upper layer, the westerly sheared flow is $\bar{u}_1(y) = 1.7 + 0.3 \cos [\pi(2y/L_y - 1)]$. Other nondimensional parameters are: $\beta = 1.6$; $F = 2.0$; $L_x = 10.0$; $L_y = 5.0$. (Buzzi and Speranza 1986).

FIG. 7.8.   As Fig. 7.7, but with a mountain oriented north-south, representing an idealization of the Rockies (Buzzi et al. 1987).

dure has been attempted so far to provide dynamically consistent analyses. An exception is the variational analysis scheme proposed by McGinley (1986a; see also McGinley 1984), which constrains the interpolated variables using a nearly complete set of dynamical equations. This scheme utilizes pressure coordinates and, in the latest formulation, "step mountain" representation (Mesinger 1984, 1985). The large imbalances shown by McGinley (1986a) to be present in the fields before the adjustment procedure is applied indicate the danger of attaching stringent physical significance to fields derived from univariate methods. Additional research effort is needed to test multivariate methods that include "initialization" procedures on the mesoscale. At present, quantitative diagnostics derived from objective (and subjective) analysis methods suffer from serious uncertainties when higher-order quantities are evaluated on subsynoptic scales. As a consequence, a well-established and physically consistent observational picture of lee cyclogenesis has not yet emerged from post-ALPEX diagnostics, though some confirmation of previous results and some new findings have come out.

The case-to-case variability, well represented also in the limited ALPEX sample of lee cyclones (Frenzen and Speth 1986; Buzzi 1986), tends to obscure the common characteristics and to hinder the construction of a phenomenological model of general validity, particularly if the interpretation does not rely upon a theoretical scheme to be validated. For all these reasons we will examine critically the most significant observational results in light of the theoretical framework outlined in the previous section, in the hope that the loss in objectivity will be compensated by a more rational treatment.

As regards typological differences, Pichler and Steinacker (1987) identify two basic types of Alpine lee cyclogenesis according to the direction of the (local) upper-level wind: a "southwesterly" type and a "northwesterly" type (see Fig. 7.9). The first case has an upper-level trough moving to the east in a large-scale mean westerly flow. The orographic action on cyclogenesis is particularly evident if the trough is slow moving as, for example, in the case of 4–5 March 1982 (Fig. 7.2; see also Dell'Osso and Tibaldi 1982). In the second case, we have an upper disturbance traveling in a northerly or northwesterly, large-scale mean flow. Several ALPEX cases were of this latter type.

In light of the theory, these two types may be interpreted essentially by changing the direction of the mean large-scale flow (or more properly, thermal wind) with respect to the orientation of the mountain chain. The strongest orographic modification is predicted when the wind component associated with the baroclinic wave is nearly perpendicular to the principal axis of the mountain, that is in the southwesterly type, in agreement with the observations. This is the type for which the theory of Speranza et al. (1985) seems most relevant, also because the primary wave moves rather slowly and, therefore, is under the orographic influence (not only of the Alps, but also of the Pyrenees: see Jansa and Ramis 1982) for a longer time. At the opposite extreme, in a case of a wave embedded in an almost northerly basic flow (and northerly thermal wind; a situation typically associated with North Atlantic blocking), the disturbance is not expected to have strong interaction with the Alps, which are oriented essentially in the zonal direction. Such a case occurred during ALPEX SOP (24–25 April). Though a cyclone formed in the Gulf of Genoa, the role played by orography on its development, in agreement with the experiments performed by McGinley and Goerss (1986), appears to be marginal.

Radinović (1986), using composite diagnostics based on eight cases of cyclogenesis that occurred during the ALPEX SOP, has identified the following typical characteristics of these cyclones:

(a) convergence in the lowest layers and upward motion dominate near the cyclone center in the developing stage;
(b) at the beginning, cold advection is obstructed below the mountain level. Warm air is drawn into the forward side of the cyclone, but a warm front can hardly be identified; the cold front, on the contrary, intensifies over the Alps, creating regions of large thermal gradients; later, however, baroclinicity decreases;
(c) the pressure tendency near the surface is opposite north and south of the Alps, exhibiting a strong tendency gradient across the relief (Fig. 7.10);
(d) kinetic energy increases in a fixed volume embracing the cyclone, the main contribution being the net influx across the boundaries; and
(e) the low-level vorticity increase starts when cold air deflection around the obstacle, and augmentation of baroclinicity, produce negative thermal vorticity below mountain top level; the vorticity advection aloft is small initially but rapidly increases when the upper trough moves over the region of the low-level cyclone.

Some of these features, (b) and (e) in particular, are identified by Radinović as being distinctive of orographic cyclogenesis with respect to types A and B of mid-latitude cyclogenesis of Petterssen and Smebye (1971). Point (d) (see also Frenzen and Speth 1984) might seem problematic for the theory of Speranza et al. (1985), which implies that the kinetic energy of the disturbance comes from the mean available potential energy. The energy budget in a limited volume extending to the upper troposphere, however, is largely dominated by the passage through this volume of the upper-level jet, representing a large influx of kinetic energy which can mask other conversion processes. This kind of spatial inhomogeneity is not described by the normal mode theory, except for the local deformation induced by an isolated orography. Features (b) and (c), on the other hand, are in agreement with the theory. In particular, the pressure tendency exhibits the same dipolar structure identified in the numerical models as charac-

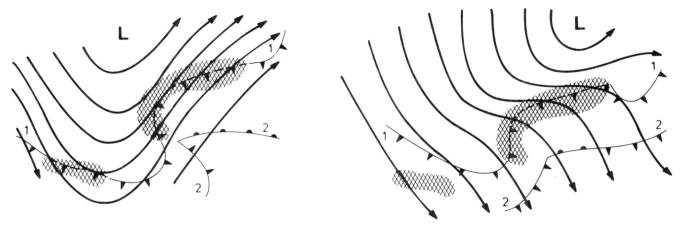

FIG. 7.9. Schematic patterns of upper-level contours for the "southwesterly" (left) and "northwesterly" (right) types of Alpine cyclogenesis; Alps and Pyrenees high ground regions are shaded (Pichler and Steinacker 1987).

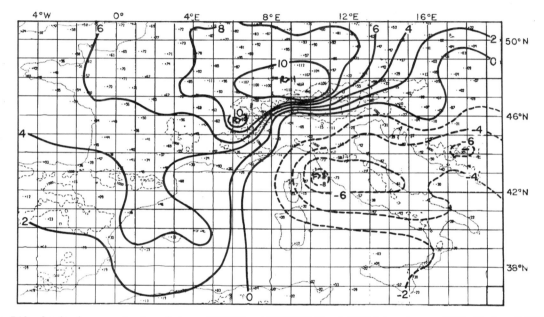

FIG. 7.10. Sea-level pressure tendency between 06 UTC and 12 UTC 2 March 1982. Intervals every 2 hPa (Radinović 1986).

teristic of the orographic perturbation. The pressure tendency maintains the structure of the "orographic perturbation" while this grows on the preexisting "undisturbed" wave.

In any case, it is difficult to extract from the observations those features that are specific to the orographic action (see, e.g., Johnson and Hill 1987). Theoretical results are illuminating in this respect, showing that, even in a very idealized case, the action of the orography does not remain confined to the orographic scale alone but affects the spatial structures on the synoptic scale on which the baroclinic instability manifests itself. The lee cyclogenetic process is viewed as a readjustment of the free-mode atmospheric growing disturbance (the parent cyclone) to a change of the lower boundary condition (the orography) along its path. A spatial rearrangement of fields is predicted, but without a dramatic change of the basic internal conversion

processes from the no-mountain balance. For instance, vorticity and energy budgets within the cyclone volume are not expected to differ markedly from those of other extratropical cyclones, with all their complications and variability.

As examples, we consider budgets of vorticity, an appropriate indicator of low-level cyclogenesis, for individual cases. ALPEX studies focusing on vorticity and related quantities have been presented, among others, by Mattocks (1982), Bleck and Mattocks (1984), Frenzen and Speth (1984, 1986), Reimer (1986), McGinley (1986b), Pichler and Steinacker (1987) and Johnson and Hill (1987). Frenzen and Speth (1984) analyzed individual terms of the vorticity equation in isobaric coordinates for the case of 4–5 March 1982, using Reimer's isentropic analysis interpolated on pressure surfaces. Positive advection of relative vorticity is found at all levels, peaking at

300 hPa, throughout the growing stage. Vorticity production by convergence is observed to peak also at upper levels (in agreement with Buzzi and Tibaldi's earlier observational study, 1978), but to become more important at lower levels in the later stages of vorticity increase. Budgets were made over a fixed large area. In a second paper, Frenzen and Speth (1986) compared various ALPEX cases, trying to identify common and different features in the vorticity (and kinetic energy) budgets. The positive vorticity advection into the developing cyclone and mass convergence at mid levels, preceding cutoff formation, are noted as common features, although not very distinctive of orographic action. An indication of the latter is found in the pattern of relative vorticity near the Alps, positive to the west (or southwest) and negative to the east (or northeast), consistent with normal mode theory in the case of a finite-amplitude, three-dimensional mountain (Buzzi and Speranza 1986).

McGinley (1986b) presented similar budgets but for smaller areas following the movement of the surface cyclone ("quasi-Lagrangian"), for three ALPEX cases (one of them is shown in Fig. 7.11). Individual terms are evaluated at four isobaric levels, using a flux form of the vorticity equation. Two of the three cases are similar to each other because both were characterized by short traveling upper waves embedded in a general northwesterly stream, accompanied by a jet streak penetrating over the western Mediterranean. Vorticity budgets also appear similar in the developing stages, being dominated by relative vorticity advection in the upper layers and by absolute vorticity convergence in the lower layers. Tilting and vertical transport seem to play a secondary role. This kind of vorticity budget is reminiscent of the type-B cyclogenesis identified by Petterssen and Smebye (1971); the orographic effect, on the other hand, is not easily appreciated, though the sensitivity of the budget to the presence of the orographic barrier in the analysis scheme is evaluated by McGinley and appears to be quite strong.

Steinacker (1984) and Pichler and Steinacker (1987) adopted a different approach to vorticity diagnostics, considering the evolution of absolute vorticity on isentropic surfaces. They considered total vorticity as being split into shear vorticity and curvature vorticity, having noted, after accurate wind and trajectory analyses, that substantial exchanges between shear and curvature vorticity take place along trajectories passing near the Alps (Fig. 7.12). Pichler and Steinacker showed that, while the total vorticity increases in the cyclone core over the western Mediterranean (because of flux convergence), the shear vorticity along trajectories passing west of the Alps initially increases and is then transformed into curvature vorticity when air parcels enter the cyclonic vortex. This result emphasizes the strong mesoscale deformation induced by orography and its role in producing vorticity in a preferred location.

Recalling the theory of Section 7.3, we can safely state that this is not inconsistent with the existence of strong shear and deformation near the mountain (shown, for instance, in the three-dimensional mountain cases in Fig. 7.7), but that nongeostrophic dynamics are required (as in the extension by Trevisan et al. 1988) for internal consistency. Even in the quasi-geostrophic case, however, the large-scale features of the flow deformation are realistically represented.

Bleck and Mattocks (1984) approach the diagnostic problem more synthetically, looking at the Ertel potential vorticity fields near the tropopause. They emphasize the correlation between cyclogenesis and positive potential vorticity advection in the upper layers, showing that lee cyclogenesis is preceded by a southward displacement of a nucleus of high potential vorticity from the low polar stratosphere, moving toward the Alpine region (see also Tibaldi and Trevisan 1973). Minor or transient developments were found to be associated with "streamers" of potential vorticity injected into the Alpine region from troughs passing north of the Alps, while intense cyclogenesis occurred when potential vorticity maxima moved directly over the barrier. The use of potential vorticity as a powerful diagnostic quantity has also been illustrated by Hoskins et al. (1985). What needs further investigation, in cases of Alpine cyclogenesis, is the role of orography in modifying the evolution of the potential vorticity field itself. The tendency of deep lee cyclogenesis to produce upper cutoff lows seems to indicate that the associated cutoff of potential vorticity maxima could be one aspect of the same process.

Johnson and Hill (1987) present quasi-Lagrangian diagnostics of mass and angular momentum balances in cylindrical, isentropic coordinates following the motion of the cyclone. They identify two stages of growth of the cyclone of 4–5 March 1982. The first phase is characterized by large-scale forcing through the asymmetric baroclinic and barotropic structure, while during the second stage the forcing due to latent heat release dominates.

Other diagnostic studies have concentrated upon particular aspects of Alpine lee cyclogenesis on the subsynoptic scale, such as frontogenesis (Buzzi et al. 1985); stratospheric ozone descent (Buzzi et al. 1984; Tosi et al. 1987); fluxes of latent and sensible heat (Emeis and Hantel 1984); vorticity components and ageostrophic motions in isobaric layers (Reimer 1986); and mountain drag (Hafner and Smith 1985; Davies and Phillips 1985; Tibaldi and Dell'Osso 1986). Again, some of these features are qualitatively accounted for by the theory (frontogenesis, form drag) and some are not, but an assessment of their relative physical importance at the various scales is still needed.

7.5   Results of Numerical Modeling

The earlier numerical simulations of lee cyclogenesis were based on idealized initial conditions and simple orographic representations. Using vertical-wall mountains in a low-resolution, primitive-equation model, Egger was able to produce a secondary cyclone not only in the Alpine

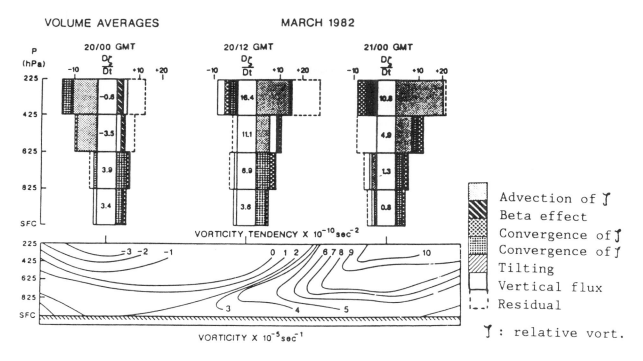

FIG. 7.11. Vorticity budgets for three different times, labeled at the top of the figure. Budgets are computed for a small volume, moving with the low-level cyclone from north France to the Tyrrenian Sea. 12-h observed vorticity changes are plotted in the middle of each block; terms contributing to vorticity increases (decreases) are plotted to the right (left). The bottom panel shows a pressure-time cross section of the volume-averaged vorticity (McGinley 1986b).

region but also in the lee of north-south barriers like Greenland and the Rocky Mountains (Egger 1972, 1974). The importance of a baroclinic mean flow and of the direct interaction of the preexisting low with orography were clearly stated in Egger's works. Subsequent experiments (Trevisan 1976) showed that more conventional, finite-slope mountains of sufficiently large volume could also induce simulated lee cyclogenesis. Bleck (1977), introducing simulations based on observed initial conditions

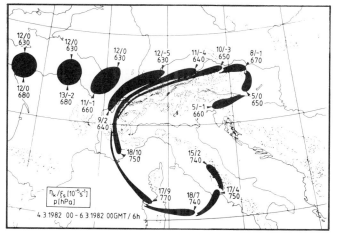

FIG. 7.12. Deformation of an isentropic surface, during a case of Alpine cyclogenesis, plotted every 6 h, between 00 UTC 4 March and 00 UTC 6 March 1982. At the northern and southern sides of the area, curvature vorticity, shear vorticity and pressure are plotted (key in box at lower left) (Pichler and Steinacker 1987).

and realistic orography, showed that acceptable results could be obtained only with high resolution (85-km grid spacing) and mountain enhancement with respect to the grid average. Bleck's experiments were comparatively more successful in simulating the low-level, initial development stage rather than the baroclinic stage leading to full upper-level development. Similar difficulties were experienced by other real-data modelers, as for instance Mesinger and Strickler (1982; see Section 12.3.2f), who firstly presented a systematic comparison between experiments made with and without mountains. They showed that, together with "true" orographic cases, there are others in which the modification introduced by the model orography is only minor.

In the meantime, controlled experimentation continued, with the objective of testing theoretical hypotheses and diagnosing dynamical fields rather than evaluating different numerical schemes and parameterizations (Tibaldi et al. 1980; Tosi et al. 1983). As should have become evident from the above discussion, these experiments were at least as important as the real observations for the subsequent theoretical developments and dynamical understanding. Concepts related to the role exerted by orography in energy conversions at various development stages, to absolute versus convective instability (Illari et al. 1981) as a function of the initial state characteristics, and to the dipolar nature of the "mountain-induced disturbance" (Tibaldi and Buzzi 1983) received clarification from controlled experiments. A more comprehensive review including these, as well as other numerical experiments, is given in Buzzi and Speranza (1983).

Recent numerical works have been devoted to integration tests based mainly on ALPEX cases. One exception is the case study presented by Mesinger (1985) and by Mesinger and Pierrehumbert (1986), simulating the "refractory" case (3–4 April 1973) analyzed by Buzzi and Tibaldi (1978). A new mountain representation ("step" or "eta") was compared with the more conventional sigma representation. Results indicate less noisy fields and better simulation of the 500 hPa cutoff low in the new version, stressing the sensitivity to mountain specification at moderate model resolution.

Sensitivity to orographic representation, in terms of different terrain definitions at different resolutions and using a limited-area version of the ECMWF grid-point model, has been tested in a series of papers by Dell'Osso and Tibaldi (1982), Dell'Osso and Radinović (1984), Dell'Osso (1984) and Tibaldi and Dell'Osso (1986). The introduction of an "envelope orography" (Wallace et al. 1983; Tibaldi 1986; see also Section 11.3.2c) has been found to have a positive impact on the forecast not only of the planetary waves but also of some transient features like lee cyclones, as shown by Jarraud et al. (1986). They confirm Tibaldi and Buzzi's (1983) observation that errors in forecasting Alpine cyclogenesis tend to propagate downstream over large areas of the Northern Hemisphere and grow because of mid-latitude dynamical instabilities. With respect to mountain representation, a result of the aforementioned experiments conducted on different ALPEX cases is that subgrid mountain parameterization with envelope orography is beneficial at low resolution. As stated by Dell'Osso (1984), "the requirement of an envelope-like parameterization decreases with increasing (model) resolution." This had been postulated in the original work by Wallace et al. (1983). Two- and three-day forecast experiments with a nested limited-area model at resolutions up to about 50 km of grid distance (N192), with slight or no enhancement of terrain height, gave good results when applied to ALPEX cases. This was not only with respect to cyclone intensity and position but also to mesoscale temperature, wind (Fig. 7.13) and even to some extent precipitation structures.

The role of condensation processes has been tested by Dell'Osso and Radinović (1984) in a high resolution experiment on the ALPEX case of 18–19 March (a "true" orographic case, according to their experiments). Latent heat release was found to be more important in upper levels and at later stages of development, while the initiation of the lee cyclone was almost unaffected by it. Additional experiments reported by Tibaldi and Dell'Osso (1986) confirm this general view, though the latent heat release may have different effects in different cases (see also Johnson and Hill 1987; Hantel 1987; Rasmussen and Zick 1987).

Progress in model performance in forecasting Alpine cyclogenesis, when sufficient resolution is employed, is also reported by a number of investigators, e.g., Pham (1982, 1986) Tafferner (1986), McGinley and Goerss (1986) and Hortal et al. (1985). It is too early to draw more general conclusions regarding model performance in simulating lee cyclogenesis in terms of coordinates (sigma, pressure and theta have been used), resolution, mountain representation, initial conditions, etc. More systematic experimentation and evaluation work is needed.

Returning to theoretical considerations, we recall that the dipolar nature of the orographic perturbation in the geopotential field near the mountain is ubiquitous, having been found in high-resolution experiments with real data (Hortal et al. 1985; Tibaldi and Dell'Osso 1986; McGinley and Goerss 1986); see also Fig. 7.14. Though capable of accounting for the basic characteristics of lee cyclogenesis, the simple Eady-type model of instability, modified by the orography, does not seem to be fully adequate to represent those cases of lee cyclogenesis that more closely resemble, in the initial conditions, type-B of Petterssen and Smebye. Idealized controlled experiments, such as those recently performed by Mattocks and Bleck (1986) which stress the role of potential vorticity "anomalies," are useful to clarify this aspect.

7.6   Other Types of Lee Cyclogenesis

In accordance with the above discussion it is an obvious step to look for other types of lee cyclogenesis in different parts of the world, where mid- or high-latitude mountain complexes extend mainly in the zonal direction. In the Mediterranean area, we find that the Pyrenees, the Atlas and the Anatolian mountains present this characteristic. Cases of secondary cyclogenesis occurring "in the lee" of these mountains are well documented (see U.K. Met. Office 1962).

The normal mode theory, however, predicts that the strongest response in the interaction of baroclinic waves with mountain chains occurs when the "basic" thermal wind is aligned more or less parallel to the main axis of the ridge. This means that nonzonal mountains under conditions of nonzonal flow are expected to produce cyclogenetic effects similar to those of the Alps. This has been shown by Buzzi et al. (1987), in a paper dealing with the generalization of the above theory to different types of orographic cyclogenesis. Again, on the basis of numerical modeling results obtained in this case with the ECMWF global spectral model, cyclogenesis in the Gulf of Alaska, occurring under local northwesterly sheared mean flow, displays basic features very similar to Alpine cyclogenesis (see Fig. 7.15). The Rocky Mountains play a crucial role in focusing the cyclonic development over the Gulf of Alaska and in maintaining the cyclone on their western side until the mature stage is reached.

A typical example of this development is described by Winston (1955): In a general situation of dipolar blocking over the Pacific Ocean, a developing baroclinic trough

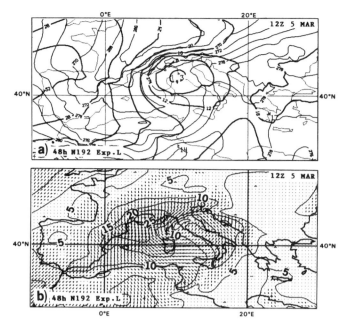

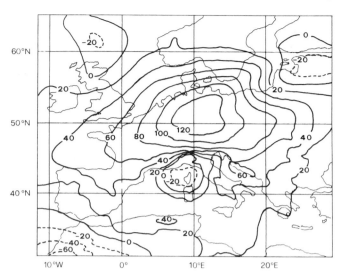

FIG. 7.13. Geopotential height and 850 hPa temperature (a) and 1000 hPa wind arrows and isolines of wind speed (b) for a high resolution, 48 h forecast experiment valid 12 UTC 5 March 1982, and performed using the ECMWF grid-point limited area model (Dell'Osso and Tibaldi 1982).

FIG. 7.14. Mean orography experiment minus zero orography experiment difference map for 1000 hPa geopotential height, for the same 48-h high resolution experiment of Fig. 7.13.

moves along the northwesterly branch of the jet which flows parallel to the northern portion of the Rocky Mountains. In the course of a few days the cyclone grows in horizontal size and depth, becoming a major perturbation on the synoptic scale. Winston stressed the importance of heat exchange between the atmosphere and the sea, but the effect of orography was apparently overlooked.

Buzzi et al. (1987) also considered classical cyclogenesis in the lee of the Rockies, in the more usual meaning of cyclonic development on the continental side of the Cordillera in the presence of westerly mean flow. Also on the basis of previous synoptic studies (see Section 6.3.1), they identified the following typical characteristics:

(a) the existence of a precursor low in the Pacific;

(b) the deceleration, northward curve and filling of this low near the surface as it approaches the American coast, just prior to lee cyclogenesis;

(c) the disappearance of the parent low above the Rockies, associated with the growth of a distinct trough in the lee, already initiated before the Pacific low center reaches the west coast;

(d) the development of the lee cyclone further south of the region of incidence of the parent low, most frequently over Colorado but also in the lee of the highest ranges of the Canadian Rockies; and

(e) the slow southeastward movement of the lee cyclone, as long as it remains close to the mountainous region, and its subsequent northeastward acceleration as it drifts away from the mountain, possibly associated with reintensification.

These characteristics are captured by simply considering a baroclinic wave interacting with a north-south oriented large-scale mountain (see Fig. 7.8). These results indicate that, despite the apparent differences, dynamical analogies exist among the various types of orographic cyclogenesis.

Recently Hsu (1987) has investigated the propagation of high-frequency disturbances near mountain ranges, using composites and one-point correlation maps. This technique reveals the shape and path of the eddies, as they tend to follow anticyclonically the large-scale mountain contours, in a way that closely resembles the above description based on individual events. In the case of the Rockies (but also true for Greenland and the Tibetan Plateau), Hsu shows that anticyclonic disturbances behave very similarly to cyclonic disturbances, the differences in synoptic maps being essentially due to the superposition of the low-frequency components of the flow.

Buzzi and Tosi (1989) have recently extended Hsu's analysis using ECMWF archive data. They have presented various statistical indicators of high-frequency eddy activity near the Alps and the Rocky Mountains. They have also compared these observational results with different theories of lee cyclogenesis and eddy propagation near mountains, showing that the normal mode theory of lee cyclogenesis accounts for most of the observed statistical properties.

Concerning in particular Rocky Mountain cyclogenesis, a theory proposed by Hayes et al. (1987) tries to explain the generation of the lee cyclone in terms of superposition of Eady modes upon a basic state represented by a steady flow over a ridge. This model may account for some of the apparent decay and subsequent reinforcement of the disturbances passing over the Rocky Mountains. This theoretical model, however, neglects the direct interaction

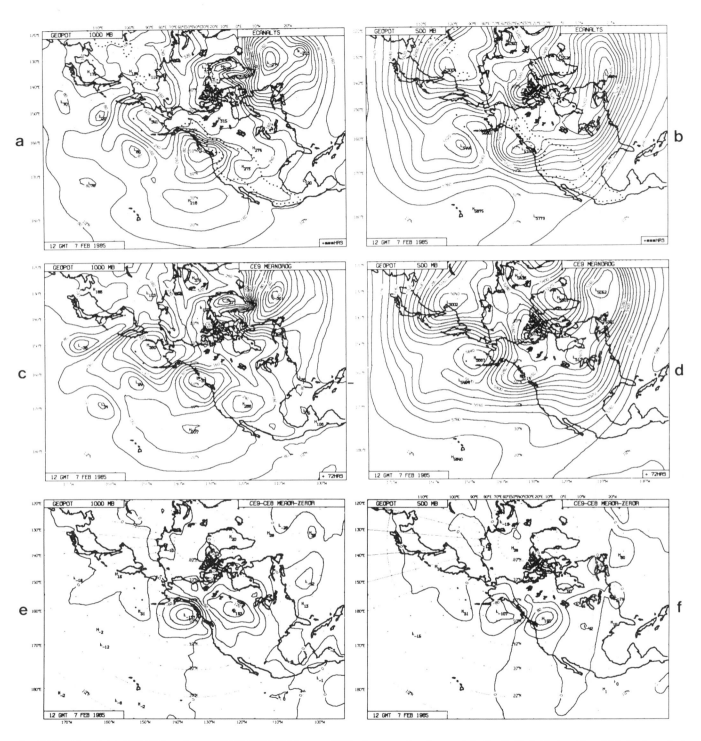

Fig. 7.15.   (a) and (b): ECMWF analyses valid 12 UTC 7 February 1985, of a case of cyclogenesis in the Gulf of Alaska; (c) and (d): 72-h control forecasts (ECMWF T106, mean orography, global spectral model) verifying on the same date and time; (e) and (f): difference maps between control run and zero orography run at 72 h. Left panels: 1000 hPa height, 40 m contour interval (30 m for difference map); right panels: 500 hPa height, 60 m contour interval (40 m for difference map) (Buzzi et al. 1987).

between the eddies and the orography. Only this direct interaction may account for the observed uneven distribution of high-pass filtered variance (including a pronounced maximum over the Colorado-Oklahoma region) and other properties of the eddies per se.

On the basis of the results of Buzzi et al. (1987) and of Buzzi and Tosi (1989), we therefore propose to interpret both lee cyclogenesis and propagation of disturbances of either sign near different mountains as distinct aspects of the same dynamical phenomenon, that is, the interaction of synoptic-scale baroclinic eddies with orography. Theory based on this simple model appears to account for the basic symmetries of the process, in particular explaining the climatological properties of lee cyclones. Observed differences in the details of cyclone evolution in various geographical regions can be related essentially to differences in mountain geometry and mean flow characteristics.

7.7 Summary and Conclusions

Lee cyclogenesis in various parts of the world shows different characteristics that can, to a large extent, be interpreted as orographic modifications induced on baroclinic cyclonic transients under different flow conditions and mountain geometries. Alpine cyclogenesis has received much attention in recent years as one of the most striking and frequent examples of orographic cyclogenesis. Peculiar characteristics have been identified in many observational studies, but controlled numerical experiments have been of invaluable help in identifying and isolating the basic features of the orographic disturbance, which is not confined to the mesoscale.

The normal mode theory of lee cyclogenesis developed by the Bologna school is capable of reproducing the essential observational features of the process actually occurring in nature by modeling it as the growth of baroclinic instability in the presence of an appropriate bottom orography. The results of this theoretical model compare well with data diagnosed both from observations (e.g., from the ALPEX campaign) and idealized controlled numerical experimentation.

There are, however, problems that need further investigation. One of these is related to the initial fast growth rate that is observed in many cases and seems to be associated with upper and lower frontal interaction with the orography. The solution of initial-value problems rather than the normal mode approach may enlighten this aspect. Other aspects that remain to be clarified are related to the finite-amplitude effects of both the "primary low" and subsynoptic contributions (latent heat release, convection, heat fluxes from the Mediterranean Sea, etc.).

Numerical forecasts of Alpine cyclogenesis have been shown, both in the literature and in day-to-day operational practice, to improve dramatically with better mountain representation and increased resolution. More systematic investigation, however, is still needed in terms of analysis and initialization schemes (for both diagnostic and modeling purposes) and of intercomparison of different models and numerical schemes.

The knowledge and understanding gained in working on the problem of lee cyclogenesis has important implications for the representation of orographic effects in climate models. This subject has never been explored with the necessary care, but see Speranza (1988) for an introductory discussion.

Acknowledgments

S. Tibaldi is grateful to the organizers of the Palmén Memorial Symposium for the invitation to deliver this lead paper and for the excellent organization of the meeting. We are also grateful to P. Malguzzi, E. Tosi and A. Trevisan for having read the manuscript and provided comments and advice. Both referees also contributed to making the text more readable.

REFERENCES

Blackmon, M. L., Y.-H. Lee and J. M. Wallace, 1984: Horizontal structure of 500 mb height fluctuations with long, intermediate and short time scales. *J. Atmos. Sci.,* **41**, 961–979.

Bleck, R., 1977: Numerical simulation of lee cyclogenesis in the Gulf of Genoa. *Mon. Wea. Rev.,* **105**, 428–445.

——, and C. Mattocks, 1984: A preliminary analysis of the role of potential vorticity in Alpine lee cyclogenesis. *Beitr. Phys. Atmos.,* **57**, 357–368.

Buzzi, A., 1986: Review of the weather phenomena observed during the ALPEX Special Observing Period. Sci. Conf. on the Results of the Alpine Experiment, Venice, 1985. WMO, Geneva, 15–27.

——, and S. Tibaldi, 1978: Cyclogenesis in the lee of the Alps: A case study. *Quart. J. Roy. Meteor. Soc.,* **104**, 271–287.

——, and A. Speranza, 1983: Cyclogenesis in the lee of the Alps. *Mesoscale Meteorology: Theories, Observations and Models,* D. K. Lilly and T. Gal-Chen, Eds. NATO ASI Series, Reidel, 55–142.

——, and A. Speranza, 1986: A theory of deep cyclogenesis in the lee of the Alps. Part II: Effects of finite topographic slope and height. *J. Atmos. Sci.,* **43**, 2826–2837.

——, and E. Tosi, 1989: Statistical behavior of transient eddies near mountains and implications for theories of lee cyclogenesis. *J. Atmos. Sci.,* **46**, 1233–1249.

——, G. Giovanelli, T. Nanni and M. Tagliazucca, 1984: Study of high ozone concentrations in the troposphere associated with lee cyclogenesis during ALPEX. *Beitr. Phys. Atmos.,* **57**, 380–392.

——, A. Trevisan and E. Tosi, 1985: Isentropic analysis of a case of Alpine cyclogenesis. *Beitr. Phys. Atmos.,* **58**, 273–284.

——, ——, S. Tibaldi and E. Tosi, 1987: A unified theory of orographic influences upon cyclogenesis. *Meteor. Atmos. Phys.,* **36**, 91–107.

——, P. Malguzzi and A. Trevisan, 1990: The statistical properties of the interaction of high-frequency eddies with mountains in a two-layer model. *Tellus,* **42A**, 28–40.

Charney, J. G., 1947: The dynamics of long waves in a baroclinic westerly current. *J. Meteor.,* **4**, 125–162.

Chung, Y. S., 1977: On the orographic influence and lee cyclogenesis in the Andes, the Rockies and the East Asian mountains. *Arch. Meteor. Geophys. Bioklim.*, **A26**, 1–12.

____, K. D. Hage and E. R. Reinelt, 1976: On lee cyclogenesis and
air flow in the Canadian Rocky mountains and the East
Asian mountains. *Mon. Wea. Rev.*, **104**, 879–891.

Danielsen, E. F., 1973: Cyclogenesis in the Gulf of Genoa. *Mesoscale Meteorological Phenomena.* CNR–UNESCO, Venice,
189–192.

Davies, H. C., and P. D. Phillips, 1985: Mountain drag along the
Gotthard section during ALPEX. *J. Atmos. Sci.*, **42**,
2093–2109.

Dell'Osso, L., 1984: High-resolution experiments with the
ECMWF model: A case study. *Mon. Wea. Rev.*, **112**,
1853–1883.

____, and S. Tibaldi, 1982: Some preliminary modeling results on
an ALPEX case of lee cyclogenesis. ALPEX Preliminary
Scientific Results. GARP-ALPEX No. 7, WMO, Geneva,
3–19.

____, and D. Radinović, 1984: A case study of cyclone develop-
ment in the lee of the Alps on 18 March 1982. *Beitr. Phys.
Atmos.*, **57**, 369–379.

Eady, E. T., 1949: Long waves and cyclone waves. *Tellus*, **1**, No. 3,
33–52.

Egger, J., 1972: Numerical experiments on the cyclogenesis in the
Gulf of Genoa. *Beitr. Phys. Atmos.*, **45**, 320–346.

____, 1974: Numerical experiments on lee cyclogenesis. *Mon.
Wea. Rev.*, **102**, 847–860.

____, 1988: Alpine lee cyclogenesis: Verification of theories. *J.
Atmos. Sci.*, **45**, 2176–2186.

Emeis, S., and M. Hantel, 1984: ALPEX diagnostics: Subsynoptic
heat fluxes. *Beitr. Phys. Atmos.*, **57**, 495–511.

Ficker, H. v., 1920: Der Einfluss der Alpen auf Fallgebiete des
Luftdruckes und die Entstehung von Depressionen über
dem Mittelmeer. *Meteor. Zeits.*, **37**, 350–363.

Frenzen, G., and P. Speth, 1984: ALPEX diagnostics: Kinetic
energy and vorticity budgets for a case of lee cyclogenesis.
Beitr. Phys. Atmos., **57**, 512–526.

____, and ____, 1986: Comparative study of several cases of
Alpine lee cyclogenesis: Kinetic energy and vorticity. *Beitr.
Phys. Atmos.*, **59**, 216–230.

Hafner, T. A., and R. B. Smith, 1985: Pressure drag on the European Alps in relation to synoptic events. *J. Atmos. Sci.*, **42**,
562–575.

Hantel, M., 1987: Subsynoptic vertical heat fluxes from high-
resolution synoptic budgets. *Meteor. Atmos. Phys.*, **36**,
24–44.

Hayes, J. L., R. T. Williams and M. A. Rennick, 1987: Lee cyclogenesis. Part I: Analytic studies. *J. Atmos. Sci.*, **44**, 432–442.

Hortal, M., A. Jansa and C. Gimeno, 1985: Spanish LAM behavior in two cases of Mediterranean cyclogenesis. Sci. Conf.
on the Results of the Alpine Experiment, Venice, 1985.
WMO, Geneva, 195–206.

Hoskins, B. J., M. E. McIntyre and A. W. Robertson, 1985: On the
use and significance of isentropic potential vorticity maps.
Quart. J. Roy. Meteor. Soc., **111**, 877–946.

Hsu, H.-H., 1987: Propagation of low-level circulation features in
the vicinity of mountain ranges. *Mon. Wea. Rev.*, **115**,
1864–1892.

Illari, L., P. Malguzzi and A. Speranza, 1981: On the breakdown
of the Westerlies. *Geophys. Astrophys. Fluid Dyn.*, **17**, 27–49.

Jansa, A., and C. Ramis, 1982: Catalonian-Balearic sea cyclogenesis. ALPEX Preliminary Scientific Results. GARP-
ALPEX No. 7, WMO, Geneva, 49–61.

Jarraud, M., A. J. Simmons and M. Kanamitsu, 1986: Impact of
an envelope orography in the ECMWF model. ECMWF
Seminar 1985, Vol. 2, 199–250.

Johnson, D. R., and D. K. Hill, 1987: Quasi-Lagrangian diagnostics of a Mediterranean cyclone: Isentropic results. *Meteor.
Atmos. Phys.*, **36**, 118–140.

Klein, W. H., 1957: Principal tracks and mean frequencies of
cyclones and anticyclones in the Northern Hemisphere. Res.
Pap. No. 40, U.S. Weather Bureau. U.S. Government Printing Office, Washington D.C., 60 pp.

Kuettner, J., 1982: ALPEX Experiment Design. GARP-ALPEX
No. 1, WMO, Geneva, 99 pp.

Malguzzi, P., A. Trevisan and A. Speranza, 1987: Effects of finite
height topography on nongeostrophic baroclinic instability:
Implications to theories of lee cyclogenesis. *J. Atmos. Sci.*,
44, 1475–1482.

____, ____, U. Giostra and A. Speranza, 1988: Recent develop-
ments in the theory of orographic cyclogenesis: Impact of
orographic modifications on statistical properties. *Il Nuovo
Cimento*, **11C**, 703–714.

Manabe, S., and T. B. Terpstra, 1974: The effects of mountains on
the general circulation of the atmosphere as identified by
numerical experiments. *J. Atmos. Sci.*, **31**, 3–42.

Mattocks, C., 1982: A precursory case study of lee cyclogenesis.
ALPEX Preliminary Scientific Results. GARP-ALPEX
No. 7, WMO, Geneva, 62–76.

____, and R. Bleck, 1986: Jet streak dynamics and geostrophic
adjustment processes during the initial stages of lee cyclogenesis. *Mon. Wea. Rev.*, **114**, 2033–2056.

McGinley, J. A., 1982: A diagnosis of Alpine lee cyclogenesis.
Mon. Wea. Rev., **110**, 1271–1287.

____, 1984: Analysis of flow blocking during ALPEX by imposi-
tion of mass continuity. *Rivista Meteor. Aeron.*, **44**, 95–102.

____, 1986a: A variational objective analysis scheme for analysis
of the ALPEX data set. Sci. Conf. on the Results of the
Alpine Experiment, Venice, 1985. WMO, Geneva, 59–72.

____, 1986b: Vorticity budgets for Alpine Cyclogenesis with and
without the forcing of terrain. Sci. Conf. on the Results of the
Alpine Experiment, Venice, 1985. WMO, Geneva, 265–280.

____, and J. S. Goerss, 1986: Effects of terrain height and block-
ing initialization on numerical simulation of Alpine lee
cyclogenesis. *Mon. Wea. Rev.*, **114**, 1578–1590.

Mesinger, F., 1984: A blocking technique for representation of
mountains in atmospheric models. *Rivista Meteor. Aeron.*,
44, 195–202.

____, 1985: The sigma system problem. Preprints, Seventh Conf.
on Numerical Weather Prediction, Montreal. Amer. Meteor.
Soc., 340–347.

____, and F. Strickler, 1982: Effects of mountains on Genoa
cyclogenesis. *J. Meteor. Soc. Japan*, **60**, 326–338.

____, and R. T. Pierrehumbert, 1986: Alpine lee cyclogenesis:
Numerical simulation and theory. Sci. Conf. on the Results of
the Alpine Experiment, Venice, 1985. WMO, Geneva,
141–164.

Michaelides, S. C., 1987: Limited area energetics of Genoa cyclogenesis. *Mon. Wea. Rev.*, **115**, 13–26.

Pedlosky, J., 1964: The stability of currents in the atmosphere and
the ocean. *J. Atmos. Sci.*, **21**, 201–219.

——, 1979: *Geophysical Fluid Dynamics.* Springer-Verlag, 624 pp.

Petterssen, S., 1956: *Weather Analysis and Forecasting,* 2nd ed., Vol. I. McGraw-Hill, 428 pp.

——, and S. J. Smebye, 1971: On the development of extratropical cyclones. *Quart. J. Roy. Meteor. Soc.,* **97,** 457–482.

Pham, H. L., 1982: Numerical simulation of a case of cyclogenesis during ALPEX. ALPEX Preliminary Scientific Results. GARP-ALPEX No. 7, WMO, Geneva, 36–40.

——, 1986: The role of Alpine mountains representation in the lee cyclogenesis simulation. Sci. Conf. on the Results of the Alpine Experiment, Venice, 1985. WMO, Geneva, 231–241.

Pichler, H., and R. Steinacker, 1987: On the synoptics and dynamics of orographically induced cyclones in the Mediterranean. *Meteor. Atmos. Phys.,* **36,** 108–117.

Pierrehumbert, R. T., 1985: A theoretical model of orographically modified cyclogenesis. *J. Atmos. Sci.,* **42,** 1244–1258.

Radinović, D., 1965a: Cyclonic activity in Yugoslavia and surrounding areas. *Arch. Meteor. Geophys. Bioklim.,* **A14,** 391–408.

——, 1965b: On the forecasting of cyclogenesis in the west Mediterranean and other areas bounded by mountain ranges by baroclinic model. *Arch. Meteor. Geophys. Bioklim.,* **A14,** 279–299.

——, 1986: On the development of orographic cyclones. *Quart. J. Roy. Meteor. Soc.,* **112,** 927–951.

——, and D. Lalić, 1959: Cyclonic activity in the western Mediterranean. Fed. Hydromet. Institute, Belgrade. Memoirs No. 7, 57 pp.

Rasmussen, E., and C. Zick, 1987: A subsynoptic vortex over the Mediterranean with some resemblance to Polar Lows. *Tellus,* **39A,** 408–425.

Reimer, E., 1986: Analysis of ALPEX data. ECMWF Workshop: High resolution analysis. ECMWF, June 1985, 155–181.

Reiter, E. R., 1963: *Jet Stream Meteorology.* University of Chicago Press, 515 pp.

Sanders, F., and J. R. Gyakum, 1980: Synoptic-dynamic climatology of the "bomb." *Mon. Wea. Rev.,* **108,** 1589–1606.

Smith, R. B., 1984: A theory of lee cyclogenesis. *J. Atmos. Sci.,* **41,** 1159–1168.

——, 1986: Further development of a theory of lee cyclogenesis. *J. Atmos. Sci.,* **43,** 1582–1602.

Speranza, A., 1975: The formation of baric depressions near the Alps. *Annali di Geofis.,* **28,** 177–217.

——, 1988: Orographic modification of cyclogenesis and blocking. ECMWF Seminar on the Nature and Prediction of Extratropical Weather Systems, September 1987. ECMWF, Reading, U.K., 175–192.

——, A. Buzzi, A. Trevisan and P. Malguzzi, 1985: A theory of deep cyclogenesis in the lee of the Alps. Part I: Modifications of baroclinic instability by localized topography. *J. Atmos. Sci.,* **42,** 1521–1535.

Steinacker, R., 1984: The isentropic vorticity and flow over and around the Alps. *Rivista Meteor. Aeron.,* **44,** 79–84.

——, A. Lanzinger and G. Mayr, 1988: Fine mesh analysis in the Alpine region. Proc. 20th Intl. Conf. on Alpine Meteorology. Servizio Meteorologico Italiano, in press.

Tafferner, A., 1986: Numerical simulation of lee cyclogenesis during ALPEX with an isentropic coordinate model. Sci. Conf. on the Results of the Alpine Experiment, Venice, 1985. WMO, Geneva, 215–230.

Tibaldi, S., 1980: Cyclogenesis in the lee of orography and its numerical modeling with special reference to the Alps. Orographic effects in planetary flows. GARP Pub. Ser. No. 23, R. Hide and P. W. White, Eds. WMO, Geneva, 207–232.

——, 1986: Envelope orography and maintenance of the quasi-stationary circulation in the ECMWF global models. *Advances in Geophysics,* **29,** 339–374.

——, and A. Trevisan, 1973: Application of a geostrophic NWP model. *Mesoscale Meteorological Phenomena.* CNR-UNESCO, Venice, 274–281.

——, and A. Buzzi, 1983: Effects of orography on Mediterranean lee cyclogenesis and its relationship to European blocking. *Tellus,* **35A,** 269–286.

——, and L. Dell'Osso, 1986: Representation of pressure drag effects in numerical modeling of Alpine cyclogenesis. Sci. Conf. on the Results of the Alpine Experiment, Venice, 1985. WMO, Geneva, 207–214.

——, A. Buzzi and P. Malguzzi, 1980: Orographically induced cyclogenesis: Analysis of numerical experiments. *Mon. Wea. Rev.,* **108,** 1302–1314.

Tosi, E., M. Fantini and A. Trevisan, 1983: Numerical experiments on orographic cyclogenesis: Relationship between the development of the lee cyclone and the basic flow characteristics. *Mon. Wea. Rev.,* **111,** 799–814.

——, R. B. Smith and L. Bradford, 1987: Aerial observations of stratospheric descent in a Gulf of Genoa cyclone. *Meteor. Atmos. Phys.,* **36,** 141–160.

Trevisan, A., 1976: Numerical experiments on the influence of orography on cyclone formation with an isentropic primitive equation model. *J. Atmos. Sci.,* **33,** 768–780.

——, A. Buzzi, E. Tosi and S. Rambaldi, 1985: A fine-mesh objective analysis scheme in isentropic coordinates. *Il Nuovo Cimento,* **8C,** 805–821.

——, L. Ferranti and P. Malguzzi, 1988: Further developments of normal mode theory of lee cyclogenesis: Isentropic coordinate model. *J. Atmos. Sci.,* **45,** 3880–3888.

U. K. Meteorological Office, 1962: *Weather in the Mediterranean,* Vol. 1. Her Majesty's Stationery Office, London, 362 pp.

Wallace, J. M., S. Tibaldi and A. Simmons, 1983: Reduction of systematic forecast errors in the ECMWF model through the introduction of an envelope orography. *Quart. J. Roy. Meteor. Soc.,* **109,** 683–718.

——, G. H. Lim and M. L. Blackmon, 1988: Relationship between cyclone tracks, anticyclone tracks and baroclinic waveguides. *J. Atmos. Sci.,* **45,** 439–462.

Whittaker, L. M., and L. H. Horn, 1982: Atlas of Northern Hemisphere extratropical cyclone activity, 1958–1977. University of Wisconsin Press, Madison, 40 pp.

Winston, J. S., 1955: Physical aspects of rapid cyclogenesis in the Gulf of Alaska. *Tellus,* **7,** 481–500.

Chapter 8

Organization of Clouds and Precipitation in Extratropical Cyclones

K. A. Browning

Meteorological Office, Bracknell, Berkshire RG12 2SZ, U.K.

8.1 Introduction

A number of models accounting for the distribution of cloud and precipitation in extratropical cyclones were proposed during the 19th and early 20th centuries. A history of these has been recounted by Bergeron (1959, abridged version in Bergeron 1981) and also by Ludlam (1966) in his inaugural lecture as professor of meteorology. These models culminated in the classical Norwegian polar-front cyclone model of the Bergen school (Bjerknes and Solberg 1922) in which the patterns of cloud and precipitation were related to vertical air motions resulting from the relative movement of different air masses along inclined frontal surfaces. This model is still widely used today. During the past quarter-century, however, the availability of imagery from satellites and radars has revolutionized the capability to observe cloud and precipitation. The imagery has drawn attention to many synoptic-scale and mesoscale features not explained by the classical model, as discussed by Reed in Section 3.3.3. It is now clear that the Norwegian model, despite its popularity, is a broad-brush model that fails to explain many important variations in structure among cyclones. In this chapter a different paradigm is presented which stresses not large-scale air masses but smaller-scale concentrated flows from within the air masses that come together and interact in the cyclone. The geometry and dynamics of these flows determine the cloud and precipitation distributions as well as the structure and evolution of the cyclone.

The emphasis in this chapter is on the concentrated flows within cyclones and how they can be related to other phenomena and to variations in structure observed from one cyclone to the next. To reveal these concentrated flows and to understand the resulting patterns of cloud and precipitation, it is helpful to carry out analyses of airflow within isentropic surfaces; these may be either moist (θ_w) or dry (θ) isentropic surfaces according to whether the flow is saturated. To a useful approximation θ_w (or θ) is conserved for moist (or dry) flow within extratropical cyclones. Thus cloud formation (dissipation) can be associated with regions of ascent (descent) of air within the sloping portions of these surfaces. Analyses for appropriate sets of θ_w (or θ) surfaces are able to identify well-defined belts of cloud-producing airflows having continuity over long distances, whereas the more traditional isobaric charts suffer from the fact that constant pressure surfaces intersect the flows as they ascend or descend through them.

An important aspect of using isentropic analysis to interpret the cloud- and precipitation-bearing systems is that the analysis should be carried out within a coordinate frame traveling with the weather system of interest. Thus, for example, whereas an earth-relative analysis either on an isentropic surface or on a 500-mb isobaric surface (Fig. 8.1a) might show an airflow apparently meandering around a trough-ridge system in a generally west-east direction, a relative flow analysis on an isentropic surface would be capable of revealing the trough-ridge system as characterized by two distinct airstreams separated by a confluent asymptote (Fig. 8.1b).

Vertical motion and the formation and dissipation of areas of cloud and precipitation can be inferred quantitatively from the component of relative upslope motion within the isentropic surface only if the isentropic structure of the overall system translates without change of shape and intensity. When a system is undergoing development this assumption is invalid but, even so, such an analysis often gives a useful visualization of the qualitative features of the organization. Indeed this approach is invaluable for making sense of the patterns of clouds and precipitation in extratropical cyclones as revealed in satellite and radar imagery. When analyzed relative to the ground, flows that appear to cross sharply defined features of the imagery such as cloud edges take on a more easily intelligible relationship to the imagery when viewed in a coordinate system tied to the imagery.

Recognition of the utility of relative-flow isentropic analysis is not new. It was recognized in the 1930s by the Rossby school (see, e.g., Fig. 8.2) and was subsequently a major theme in the work of R. J. Reed and E. F. Danielsen during the '50s and '60s. Isentropic analysis is getting a new lease of life now partly because it is the natural way of interpreting the increasingly widely-used imagery. Together with the imagery it is the cornerstone of the analyses of cloud and precipitation described in this review, which is written from an observational perspective.

8.2 The Warm Conveyor Belt and its Associated Cloud System

Figure 8.3 is an elaboration of Fig. 8.1b showing the airflow relative to a major trough-ridge system in middle latitudes as derived by Green et al. (1966; see also Ludlam 1966). The dominant feature of such a disturbance is

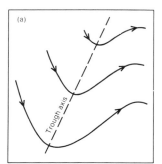
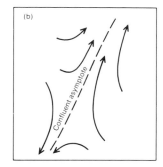

FIG. 8.1. Schematic representation of flow in a trough depicted (a) relative to the ground in the 500-mb isobaric surface and (b) relative to the moving trough on a surface of constant potential temperature (θ). No scale is shown in the diagram: The same ideas apply whether it is a major trough extending thousands of kilometers north-south or a short-wave trough hundreds of kilometers long associated with a polar air disturbance.

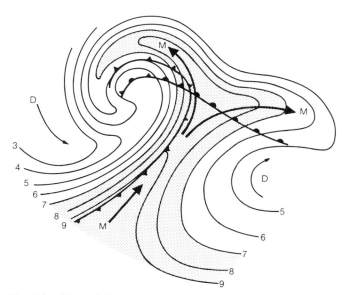

FIG. 8.2. Schematic isentropic analysis of moist and dry tongues around an occluded cyclone (Namias 1939). Arrows denote system-relative flow of ascending moist air (M) and descending dry air (D). This diagram contains elements of the models, presented later in this article, that account for the synoptic-scale distribution of cloud within an extratropical cyclone.

baroclinic slantwise motion, and Fig. 8.3 shows how such motions are organized on the large scale. A key feature is the elongated band of cloud (hatched) that forms along the boundary of a major confluence zone at the leading edge of the trough. In the frame of reference moving with the trough-ridge system, warm air enters the cloud belt from the convective boundary layer at its southern end. As this air travels along the axis of the cloud belt it ascends into the middle and upper troposphere, producing low- and medium-level cloud and then a belt of upper-level cirrus that dissipates at the leading edge of the system. Following Harrold (1973), this airflow is referred to as the *warm conveyor belt* (WCB); large quantities of heat, moisture and westerly momentum are conveyed poleward and upward within this relatively narrow flow.

The WCB is not, as we shall show, the only important well-defined flow within an extratropical disturbance; it is, however, the primary cloud-producing flow. As such it has been found to be a particularly useful concept in practice to account for aspects of the cloud and precipitation distribution, not only in northwestern Europe where the idea was first crystallized but also in the U.S. (Carlson

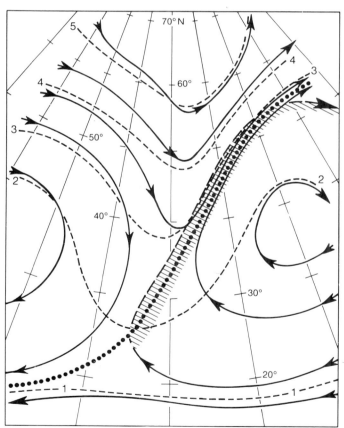

FIG. 8.3. Model of flow relative to a major middle-latitude trough within an isentropic surface sloping generally upward toward the north (heights indicated by dashed lines labeled in km). A sea-level cyclone is centered beneath this surface in the northern part of the diagram. A confluence line (dotted) in the flow aloft separates two distinct airstreams. The northward-moving stream ahead of the confluence line ascends above the dry isentropic surface and produces a cloud-belt (hatched) (Ludlam 1966).

1980) and Australia (Ryan and Wilson 1985). An example of a well-defined cloud belt associated with a long WCB is given in Fig. 8.4. Cloud elements tracked within this WCB showed that the air within it was traveling rapidly along its length relative to the overall synoptic pattern. A distinctive feature of the cloud belts associated with WCBs is that the western and poleward edge (i.e., in the Northern Hemisphere, the left side looking along the flow) tends to be quite sharp and to consist of high cloud. These sharp cloud edges constitute asymptotes which air does not cross in the relative system. Most of the cloud on the right edge is at middle and low levels and this edge is often less well defined. There is a general increase in the height of the cloud top along the length of the WCB. Toward its northern end the WCB flow in Fig. 8.4 turns to the right as in Fig. 8.3. This behavior, although evident from the infrared picture in Fig. 8.4a, is not so obvious from the visible picture (Fig. 8.4b) in which the WCB cloud is hard to distinguish from a separate belt of cloud labeled PP.

WCBs vary greatly in length and are certainly not always as long as the one in Fig. 8.4. Sometimes a shorter cloud belt can be seen just ahead of a short-wave trough, with the characteristically sharp western cloud edge having a slightly S-shaped curvature. Such cloud areas are referred to by Weldon (1979) as baroclinic cloud leaves. They occur in the early stages of cyclone development when there is no identifiable surface cyclone (see also Section 8.7).

Vertical sections derived from radiosonde ascents along the axis of WCBs confirm that the WCBs are mainly saturated flows of high wet-bulb potential temperature, rising from the lower troposphere at their southern end into the upper troposphere at their northern end. Figure 8.5 is an example from Carlson (1987) in which the WCB is characterized by a 3-km deep layer with θ_w about 16°C. The WCB air is nearly everywhere close to neutral static stability, i.e., saturated, with $\partial \theta_w / \partial z \approx 0$. Considerable precipitation is generated in the WCB flow especially where it ascends rapidly in the low-to-middle troposphere. In cases such as Fig. 8.5 where there is a pronounced warm frontal zone, the WCB ascends most rapidly just after it encounters this strongly baroclinic region; in other cases significant baroclinicity may extend into the so-called warm sector and the ascent begins correspondingly earlier.

Cahir et al. (1985) have carried out a composite analysis of a large number of WCBs and shown that they are characterized by a relative-wind jet stream within and closely parallel to the left-hand cloud edge viewed along the direction of flow. Recent detailed analyses using wind profiler data (Hemler 1987) have confirmed that the WCB generally corresponds to a belt of relatively strong winds. The left-hand edge of the cloud associated with the WCB lies close to the wind maximum in the upper troposphere. At middle levels the strongest winds lie closer to the axis of the WCB, some distance to the right of the position of the left-hand cloud edge aloft.

Carlson (1980) identified the left-hand edge of the WCB

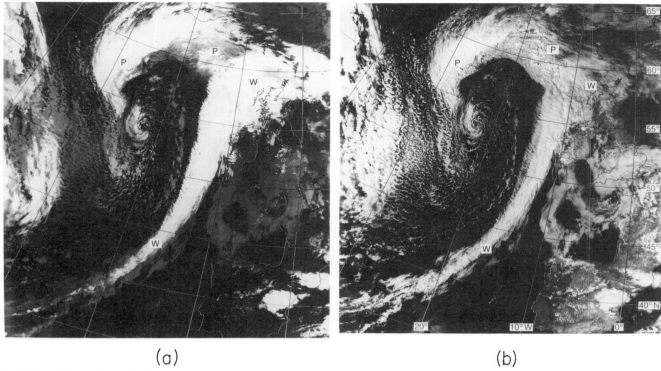

FIG. 8.4.   (a) Infrared and (b) visible pictures from a NOAA satellite at 1550 UTC 2 September 1987, showing an elongated belt of cloud (WW) associated with a major warm conveyor belt. The belt of cloud labeled PP is a separate feature of the kind discussed later in Section 8.5. (Courtesy of University of Dundee.)

cloud as being associated with a limiting streamline or confluent asymptote corresponding to a more or less well-defined frontal zone separating air masses on either side of the trough axis. Usually there is a marked contrast in relative humidity across this zone, with ascending WCB air of high θ_w on one side and recently descended dry air of low θ_w on the other. The term "recently descended" is used because, although the dry air in this region has a history of

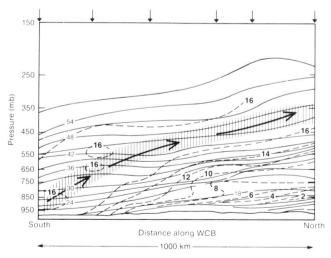

FIG. 8.5.   Cross section along the axis of a warm conveyor belt derived from a chain of six radiosondes over a distance of 1000 km in the eastern U.S., showing potential temperature θ (solid lines labeled in °C) and wet-bulb potential temperature θ_w (dashed lines labeled in °C) at 12 UTC 27 February 1984. Hatching represents the axis of maximum relative humidity (>90 percent). Arrows parallel to the sloping layer of high-θ_w suggest motion of air within the warm conveyor belt (Carlson 1987).

descent, by the time it is traveling alongside the confluent asymptote it is likely to have begun ascending again (Durran and Weber 1988). In the case of a well-developed frontal system the left-hand edge of the upper cloud lies roughly parallel to the surface cold front, but it may be located either ahead of or behind the surface cold front, depending on whether the air in the WCB (whose main component of motion is parallel to the front) has a tendency to upglide with a component rearward or forward relative to the advancing cold front. This distinction is discussed in Section 8.3.

Vertical sections across the southern parts of a WCB, where it is still in contact with the earth's surface, usually (in the U.K.) show the WCB to be characterized by a low-level jet immediately ahead of a surface cold front (Fig. 8.6). Browning and Pardoe (1973) found that these low-level jets tend to have maximum velocities from 25 to 30 m s^{-1}, and to occur at heights from 900 to 850 mb. In extreme cases they can be as strong as 40 m s^{-1}. The vertical and lateral extents of the low-level jets, expressed in terms of the water vapor half-width, are typically 2 to 3 km and 200 to 500 km, respectively. Within the half-width points the total water-vapor flux is typically 3 to 10×10^5 t s^{-1}. The decrease in wind speed with height just above the low-level jet is due to a reverse thermal wind associated with a locally poleward increase in temperature. This in turn is caused by the limiting streamline on the extreme left-hand edge of the WCB originating farthest south and bringing the warmest air northwards close to the surface cold front.

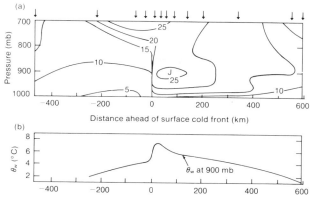

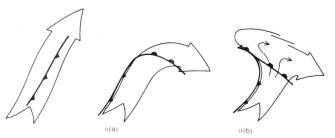

Fig. 8.7. Configurations of the warm conveyor belt (WCB): (i) WCB undergoing rearward-sloping ascent above the cold frontal zone; (iia and b) WCB undergoing forward-sloping ascent in the warm baroclinic region ahead of the cold frontal zone. The distinction between (iia) and (iib) is discussed in Section 8.4.

Fig. 8.6. (a) Vertical section normal to the axis of a warm conveyor belt in the U.K. on 27 November 1972 showing the along-axis wind component in m s^{-1}. The section is through the southern end of the WCB where it is still in contact with the surface. (Some of the air in the WCB was being extruded upwards and to the left above the advancing surface cold front, but this is not germane to the main theme of Section 8.2, and so the cross section is terminated at 700 mb.) (b) Wet-bulb potential temperature at the 900-mb level, showing the θ_w-maximum in the core of the low-level jet just ahead of the surface cold front (Browning and Pardoe 1973).

8.3 Rearward-Sloping and Forward-Sloping Configurations of the Warm Conveyor Belt and the Associated Patterns of Cloud and Precipitation

The concept of the WCB was introduced in Section 8.2 in broad terms, simply as a stream of high-θ_w air flowing along the length of a cold front. Although the main component of motion within the WCB is indeed parallel to the cold front, the relatively small and partly ageostrophic component perpendicular to the front has an important bearing on the frontal structure. Also the situation becomes more complex where the WCB encounters the warm frontal zone. Browning (1986) has suggested that it is useful to distinguish two situations that lead to contrasting organizations of cloud and precipitation:

(i) A "rearward-sloping ascent" configuration of the WCB, in which the air in the WCB has a component of motion rearward relative to the movement of the cold front, and in which the slantwise ascent occurs in the vicinity of and above the cold frontal zone; see the schematic depiction in Fig. 8.7(i).

(ii) A "forward-sloping ascent" configuration of the WCB, in which the air in and above the WCB has a component of motion forward relative to the movement of the cold front, with its main region of slantwise ascent occurring farther downwind in regions of warm frontal baroclinicity; see the schematic depictions in Fig. 8.7(ii, a and b). The WCB eventually turns to the right in Fig. 8.7(ii, a and b); however, the flow in the latter case undergoes considerable deformation with parts of it initially making a leftward excursion.

Transitions between rearward-sloping ascent and forward-sloping ascent can, as we shall show, occur both in time and in space (along the length of a cold front).

8.3.1 The Warm Conveyor Belt with Rearward-Sloping Ascent

The rearward-sloping ascent configuration (Fig. 8.8), in which some of or all the WCB air rises with a component rearwards above an advancing wedge of cold air, corresponds to the classical ana-cold frontal situation (Bergeron 1937; Sansom 1951). Such fronts tend to occur ahead of confluent troughs in the upper air pattern (i.e., troughs that are confluent on their east side). In contrast to situations of forward-sloping ascent (see Section 8.3.2), the surface cold front in cases of rearward-sloping ascent tends to be sharp. The warm air in the boundary layer ahead of the surface cold front is lifted abruptly at up to several meters per second within a narrow strip adjacent to the surface cold front. This is a region of intense cyclonic shear (10^{-2} s^{-1}) on the western boundary of the pre-cold-frontal low-level jet, and the vertical air velocity is consistent with the Ekman-layer convergence.

The air rises through only 2 to 3 km during its abrupt ascent at the surface cold front; it then undergoes further ascent in slantwise fashion, at a few tens of centimeters per second, above the wedge of cold air (Browning and Harrold 1970). These two regions produce two distinct patterns of precipitation: (i) a narrow band of very heavy rain associated with the upright line convection at the surface cold front; (ii) a broad belt of light-to-moderate rain associated with mainly stratiform cloud extending behind and often to some extent ahead of the surface cold front. These features are discussed further in later sections.

8.3.2 The Warm Conveyor Belt with Forward-Sloping Ascent

The forward-sloping ascent configuration, shown in Fig. 8.9, corresponds to a kata-cold front situation (usually with an ana-warm front ahead of it) (Bergeron 1937; Sansom 1951). Such frontal systems tend to occur ahead of diffluent troughs in the upper air pattern. Unlike in the ana-cold frontal situation in Section 8.3.1, the upper winds have a component overtaking the frontal system. The term "forward-sloping," which we use to describe this common frontal archetype, refers to the ascending WCB; it does not refer to the orientation of the cold frontal zone. The main

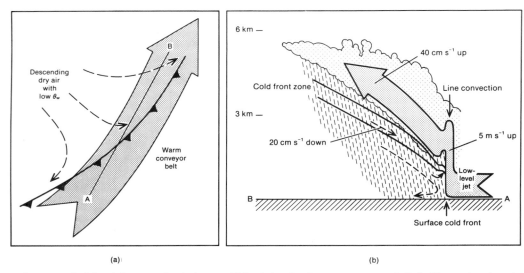

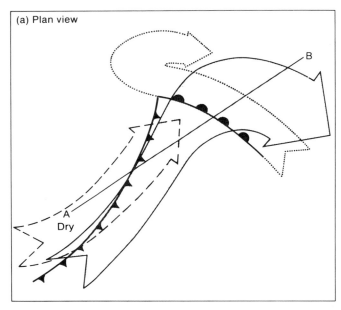

Fig. 8.8.   Schematic portrayal of the airflow at a classical ana-cold front showing the warm conveyor belt (bold arrow) undergoing rearward-sloping ascent above the cold frontal zone, with the cold air (dashed lines) descending beneath it: (a) plan view; (b) vertical section along AB in (a). Flows are shown relative to the moving frontal system.

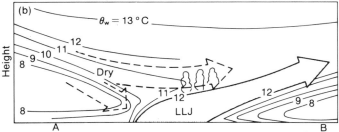

Fig. 8.9.   Schematic portrayal of the airflow in an extratropical cyclone in which the warm conveyor belt (solid arrow with stippled shading) is undergoing forward-sloping ascent ahead of a kata-cold front, before rising above a flow of cold air ahead of the warm front (dotted arrow referred to in Section 8.4 as the cold conveyor belt). Middle-tropospheric air with low θ_w (dashed arrow) is shown overrunning the cold front and generating potential instability in the upper portions of the warm conveyor belt. Plan view and vertical section are shown in (a) and (b), respectively, the section in (b) being along the line AB in (a). Flows are shown relative to the moving frontal system.

ascent of the WCB occurs ahead of the surface cold front, beneath where recently-descended air with low θ_w in the middle troposphere overruns the WCB as described by Miles (1962). This leads to the generation of potential instability, which is realized as convection once the general flow has been lifted sufficiently. This convection sometimes occurs as deep convection from the surface, especially in the daytime (Carr and Millard 1985), but more usually, in the U.K. at least, it occurs as shallow middle-level convection. Eventually the cloudy WCB flow turns anticyclonically, i.e., to the right in the Northern Hemisphere, as it overtakes and ascends over the cold air ahead of the surface warm front. As discussed later, this flow can take different forms as depicted in Fig. 8.7(ii, a and b). The convex-poleward boundary to this flow where it ascends and turns anticyclonically may be detectable in satellite infrared imagery (Fig. 8.4a), and also sometimes in visible imagery from the shadow the upper cloud casts on the cloud below.

The leading edge of the overrunning dry low-θ_w air advancing ahead of the surface "cold front" often appears as a well-defined upper "cold front" (UU in Fig. 8.10). Because of the separate existence of the upper front ahead of the surface front, Fig. 8.10 is referred to as a split-front model (Browning and Monk 1982). Both the upper and the surface "cold fronts" in this kind of situation are better defined in the humidity and θ_w fields than in the temperature fields. Indeed the temperature sometimes actually rises with the arrival of the lower-θ_w air at the surface "cold front." Thus Browning and Monk suggest that these fronts might be better regarded as "humidity fronts." Nevertheless they can be referred to simply as cold fronts so long as it is kept in mind that the term refers to the change of θ_w rather than θ. Of course, given the onset of large-scale ascent that accompanies rapid development, such a θ_w front quickly transforms into a real temperature front. In

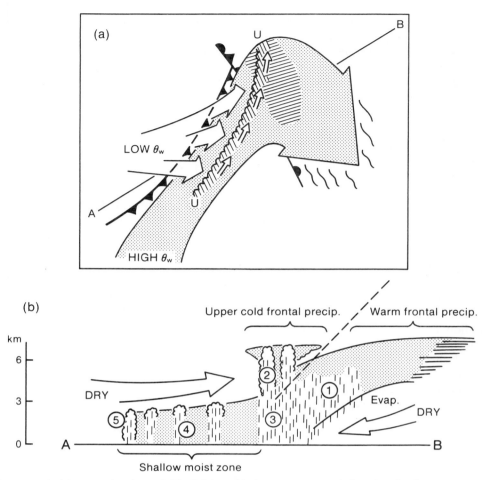

FIG. 8.10.   Schematic portrayal of the same situation as in Fig. 8.9, i.e., with the warm conveyor belt undergoing forward-sloping ascent, but drawing attention to the split-front characteristic and the overall distribution of precipitation: (a) plan view; (b) vertical section along AB in (a). In (a) UU represents the upper "cold" front. The hatched shading along UU and ahead of the warm front represents precipitation associated with the upper "cold" front and warm front, respectively. Numbers in (b) represent precipitation type as follows: (1) warm frontal precipitation; (2) convective precipitation-generating cells associated with the upper "cold" front; (3) precipitation from the upper "cold" frontal convection descending through an area of warm advection; (4) shallow moist zone (SMZ) between the upper and surface "cold" fronts, characterized by warm advection and scattered outbreaks of mainly light rain and drizzle; and (5) shallow precipitation at the surface "cold" front itself (Browning and Monk 1982).

general, however, the fact that the upper θ_w front runs ahead of the surface θ_w front does not imply a forward slope to the overall temperature front.

Split cold fronts exhibit a characteristic sequence of cloud and precipitation. Just ahead of the upper cold front is a deep layer of warm moist air associated with an organized band of convection which gives a wide band of moderate-to-heavy rain. This band is often located at the trailing edge of a region of rather lighter and more stratiform warm frontal precipitation, much of which may evaporate before reaching the ground. The passage of the upper cold front is followed by what we refer to as a *shallow moist zone* (SMZ) (Fig. 8.10b) with scattered outbreaks of weakly convective rain and drizzle, perhaps with some outbreaks of deeper convection especially close to the cyclone center. The surface cold front itself is a weak feature characterized by a clearance or partial clearance of cloud and an end to the scattered outbreaks of light precipitation. Split "cold" fronts with this kind of weather sequence are very common in the U.K. and there is confu-

sion in their analysis when forecasters attempt to apply the simple classical frontal model.

8.4 The Cold Conveyor Belt and its Associated Cloud System

Although the WCB has been identified as the dominant cloud- and precipitation-producing flow in extratropical systems, it is not the only important flow of this kind. Another well-defined cloud- and precipitation-producing flow, shown by the dotted arrow in Fig. 8.9, is the *cold conveyor belt* (CCB) (Carlson 1980; see also Fig. 9.28 on p. 344 of Ludlam 1980, although the term "CCB" is not used by him). Originating in the anticyclonic low-level flow to the northeast of a cyclone, the air in the CCB travels westward (relative to an eastward-moving cyclone) just ahead of the surface warm front, undercutting the WCB. Thus the interface between the CCB and WCB corresponds to the warm frontal zone. At first the air in the CCB subsides and is very dry; precipitation from the WCB evaporates on falling into it. As it travels westward toward the cyclone center, the CCB begins to ascend, reaching into the middle troposphere near the apex of the warm sector. Air on the cyclonically sheared edge of the CCB, near the surface warm front, experiences enhanced ascent owing to frictional convergence. If and when the CCB emerges beneath the western edge of the WCB, it may ascend anticyclonically and merge with the WCB as sketched in Fig. 8.9. Part of the CCB flow emerging beneath the western edge of the WCB may also descend cyclonically around the cyclone center. The area of cloud associated with the emerging CCB constitutes the head of a comma cloud pattern.

An analysis by Carlson (1987) of the *comma cloud pattern* associated with an emerging CCB is shown in Fig. 8.11. The western boundary of the WCB is demarcated by a hatched double line labeled LSW, LSW. The double-shafted arrow represents the relative flow within the WCB as it ascends from 600 to 300 mb (isobars shown dashed). In the cold air behind the WCB solid streamlines depict descending flow on a dry isentropic surface (dot-dashed isobars). The CCB flow protruding into this region is represented by dashed streamlines ascending from 700 mb (isobars shown dotted where the flow is beneath the WCB) to 400 mb (dashed isobar). The CCB cloud (F), where it protrudes to the west of the WCB, is demarcated

by a hatched double line labeled CC, CC, CC. (A separate area of boundary layer stratus is denoted by the unshaded scalloped boundary.) The cloud associated with the CCB is mainly confined to low and medium levels, with tops significantly lower than those associated with the WCB; the cloud tops, however, become higher in the cross-hatched western part of the CCB where the ascending cloudy air flow approaches a confluent asymptote.

8.5 Instant Occlusion and the Associated Cloud and Precipitation

The process known as *instant occlusion,* leading to a characteristic lambda-shaped cloud pattern, is a common occurrence that takes place when a cloud band associated with a polar air trough approaches and interacts at a large angle with the cloud band associated with the WCB (Zillman and Price 1972; Weldon 1975; Reed 1979; Thepenier and Cruette 1981). See also Section 3.3.3. An example of the resulting cloud pattern was shown earlier in Fig. 8.4, in which the cloud band associated with the polar air trough was labeled PP and that associated with the WCB was labeled WW. The mature cloud pattern accompanying instant occlusion is interpreted by Browning and Hill (1985) in terms of a dual-conveyor-belt configuration, with the two conveyor belt flows intersecting as shown in

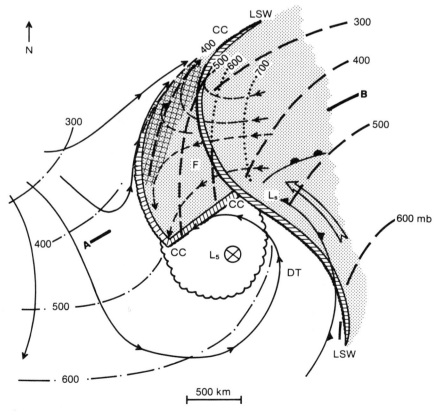

FIG. 8.11.   Partially schematic isentropic relative flow analysis for an extratropical cyclone over the central United States on 22 October 1979, showing a cold conveyor belt (CCB) flow emerging beneath the western boundary of a warm conveyor belt (WCB) (Carlson 1987). The symbols L_s and L_5 denote the locations of the cyclone center at the surface and 500-mb, respectively, and the encircled cross shows the location of the 500 mb vorticity maximum. Surface fronts are shown conventionally. Other details in text.

Fig. 8.12. The feature labeled "polar-front conveyor belt" corresponds to the WCB and it manifests itself as an upper-tropospheric jet streak. The feature labeled "polar-trough conveyor belt" manifests itself as a low-level jet with an associated convective cloud band extending above it on the poleward side of the polar front. This low-level jet is situated beneath the left exit of the upper jet streak and may be part of an ageostrophic circulation forced by the latter (Uccellini and Johnson 1979).

The polar-trough conveyor belt, although having a location similar to the cold conveyor belt in Fig. 8.9a, tends to extend over a much greater distance into the cold air mass (e.g., PP in Fig. 8.4). Also the air in the polar-trough conveyor belt is characterized by a positive rather than negative anomaly in θ_w, the air being drawn poleward at low altitude seemingly from the tip of an ill-defined warm sector. The name "instant occlusion" arises because the mature cloud system resembles that associated with a classical occlusion; however, far from being associated with a classical occlusion process with the warm air being occluded from the surface, the air within the polar-trough conveyor belt often has its greatest positive anomaly of temperature and θ_w in the lowest kilometer or two. Cooler, drier air circulating around the cyclone center overruns the polar-trough conveyor belt leading to outbreaks of convective precipitation along it. Very dry air, associated with earlier descent in the region of the tropopause fold, tends to overrun the polar-trough conveyor belt close to where it emerges from beneath the often well defined poleward edge of the polar front conveyor belt (WCB) (Fig. 8.12). This sometimes suppresses the precipitation in this region; however, although this air has had a history of descent, it is once again rising in this location and outbreaks of intense precipitation can occur here if and when the potential instability is finally realized.

McGinnigle et al. (1988) have derived a three-stage life cycle model of the process of instant occlusion in terms of a region of vorticity and warm-air advection on the cold side of a preexisting polar frontal cloud belt (Fig. 8.13):

Stage 1: The cold-air cloud feature C, coincident with a positive vorticity advection maximum aloft, approaches the cloud belt associated with a cold frontal zone F. At this stage C is composed of a series of convective cells generated at its rear edge with anvils combining to produce the upper cloud shield. At low levels, air of low θ_w follows the surface trough at the rear of C. At middle and upper levels, dry air moves around the base of the trough within the strong upper flow, overrunning the tail of C, then travelling parallel to the sharp edge of F. At low levels, warm moist air is advected ahead of C, weakening the thermal contrast associated with F and generating potential instability within a new shallow moist zone (SMZ) between C and F.

Stage 2: Cloud band C appears to rotate rapidly, leaving behind a trailing low-level θ_w boundary. Convective cells continue to be generated along the southern edge of C, with a series of anvils carried forward and dissipating upon encountering the dry air to the rear of F. The potential instability already created in the gap between C and F may be released with the onset of ascending motion associated with warm air advection and positive vorticity advection. Rapid cloud growth may then proceed in the gap. Warm advection ahead of C generates a thermal gradient on its northern side and a low-level flow is established from F towards C within this nascent frontal zone.

Stage 3 (the mature stage): Cloud bands C and F have linked, thus completing the instant occlusion process as traditionally interpreted. The new front has been analyzed along the inside edge of the hook-shaped cloud C on the warm side of the 850 mb θ_w gradient. The edge of the cold frontal cloud band F may still be apparent above C. Warm, moist boundary-layer air from the SMZ ascends along the new frontal slope, producing a band of rain along the inside of the hook-shaped cloud C. Since this region is overrun by dry low-θ_w air, some convective cells will also be generated.

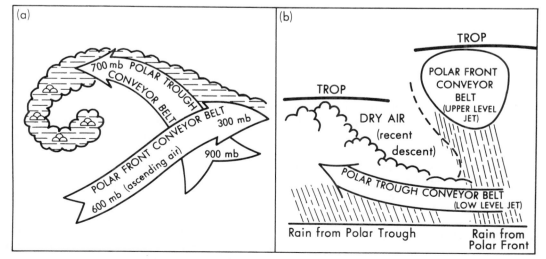

FIG. 8.12.   Schematic model of a mature instant occlusion, showing intersecting polar-trough conveyor belt (in the location of a CCB) and polar-front conveyor belt (corresponding to the WCB): (a) plan view, (b) vertical section along the axis of the polar trough (Browning and Hill 1985).

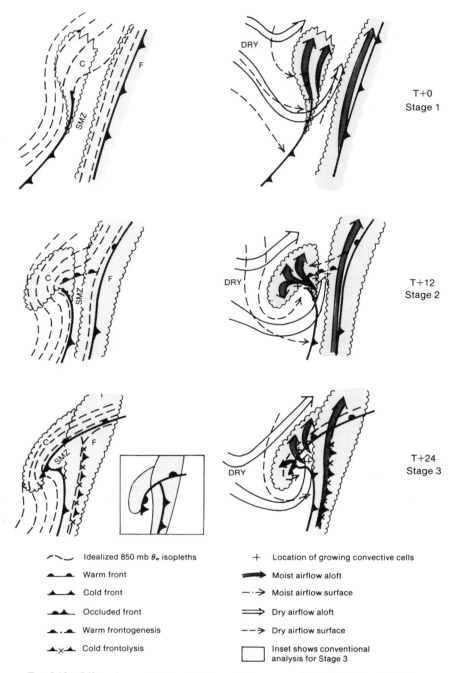

FIG. 8.13. Life cycle model of the instant occlusion process (McGinnigle et al. 1988).

Continued but less rapid ascent associated with the newly-formed baroclinic zone produces progressively colder cloud tops towards the outside of C but with lighter rainfall. Deep convection may occur (in areas marked +) where strong positive vorticity advection is acting upon an environment that is destabilizing due to cold advection aloft. The mature instant occlusion corresponding to Stage 3 differs from that represented in Fig. 8.12, in that the cloud band C is fed by high-θ_w air from a shallow moist zone behind it rather than by a flow oriented predominantly along its axis.

The cloud pattern associated with the instant occlusion process can be thought of as part of a spectrum of types (Figs. 8.14 and 8.15), in which the form of disturbance depends on the position of the advancing vorticity maximum with respect to the polar front (Zillman and Price 1972). When the vorticity maximum and its associated short-wave trough are well within the cold air and not interacting significantly with the main polar front and WCB (Fig. 8.15a), a simple comma cloud pattern is formed (Fig. 8.14a); although similar in shape to the comma cloud formed when a CCB emerges from beneath a WCB (Section 8.4), the comma cloud is much smaller and lacks the cloud-top discontinuity characteristic of the latter. In contrast, when the vorticity maximum is at the

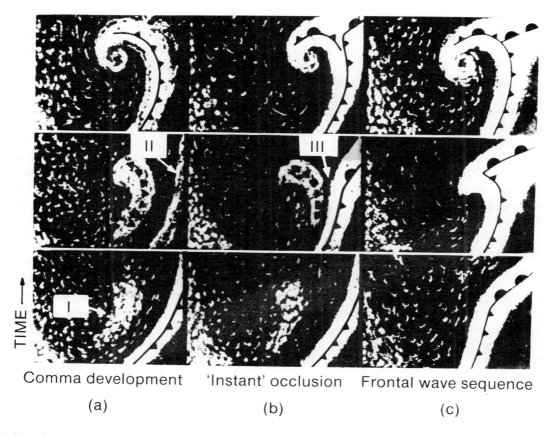

Comma development   'Instant' occlusion   Frontal wave sequence

(a)   (b)   (c)

FIG. 8.14. Schematic depiction of three basic sequences of vortex development evident in satellite imagery: (a) development of a simple comma cloud entirely within the cold air, (b) development of an instant occlusion, (c) development of a frontal wave. The figure (adapted from Zillman and Price 1972) was derived from observations over the Southern Ocean but is printed vertically inverted so as to apply to the Northern Hemisphere. Frontal symbols represent the original authors' way of representing the various evolution sequences using the tools of conventional frontal analysis. The labels I, II and III, respectively, indicate a region of enhanced convection, a decaying cloud band and a convective cloud band merging with the polar-front cloud band. See also Figs. 3.13 and 3.15.

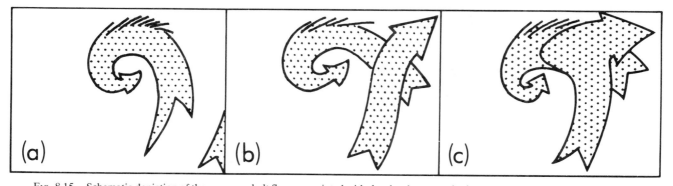

FIG. 8.15. Schematic depiction of the conveyor belt flows associated with the cloud patterns in the upper panels of Fig. 8.14(a, b and c).

latitude of the polar front (Fig. 8.15c), a frontal wave forms in which the main WCB associated with the polar front gets involved in the circulation and dominates the cloud pattern (Fig. 8.14c). In the intermediate situation of the instant occlusion (Figs. 8.14b and 8.15b), there are two distinct cloud belts, one associated with the polar trough and the other with the polar front (i.e., the WCB). The instant occlusion occurs as shown in Fig. 8.14b when the polar trough catches up with the polar front.

8.6 The Classical Occlusion

There is much confusion in the analysis of occlusions: Often instant occlusions and also the upper cold fronts of split-front systems (Section 8.3.2) are wrongly analyzed as classical occlusions. In fact split fronts and instant occlusions are very common events and some authors (e.g., Wallace and Hobbs 1977, p. 127) have been led to wonder whether occlusions conforming to the classical model actually exist. An interpretation of actual occlusions in terms of the conveyor belt paradigm is hinted at in Figs. 8.7(iib) and 8.15c, and made more explicit in Fig. 8.16. In situations where the cyclonic circulation is sufficiently deep and extensive, it will cause part of the WCB flow to become involved in its circulation (Kurz 1988) such that a vertical section along AB in Fig. 8.16a will show the high-θ_w air of the WCB (solid arrow) having been lifted above the CCB (dashed arrow), with no sign of high-θ_w air at the surface.

A classical occlusion is distinctly different from a split (kata) cold front, as described in Section 8.3.2, in which an upper cold front overruns the WCB and leaves a shallow moist zone (i.e, warm sector) in contact with high-θ_w air at the earth's surface (see also Fig. 8.16b$_2$). Of course a split cold frontal system could itself become occluded, and in this circumstance a structure similar to that in Fig. 8.16b$_1$ develops in which the upper cold front (scalloped) appears to correspond to the prefrontal cold surges referred to by Kreitzberg and Brown (1970), Matejka et al. (1980) and Parsons and Hobbs (1983a). The multiple structure of many prefrontal cold surges suggests that the leading edge of the cold air aloft often advances as a series of pulses, rather than continuously as shown here. It is possible also for an instant occlusion (Section 8.5) to evolve into a classical occlusion. This happened in the case shown in

Fig. 8.4; soon after the time of Fig. 8.4 the WCB (labeled WW) became involved in the cyclone circulation with part of it turning to the left and overrunning a large portion of the polar trough conveyor belt (PP).

8.7 The Dry Intrusion and its Influence on Cloud Patterns During Cyclogenesis

During the previous discussion of the patterns of cloud and precipitation generated by warm and cold conveyor belts (see Section 8.3.2, for example), it has been necessary to refer to the role of another major flow system, namely the cold dry air approaching from behind the cloud system. Going back to Fig. 8.3 and the isentropic analysis of Green et al. (1966) as well as the studies of Danielsen (1966), it is clear that much of the cold air that enters the cyclonic cloud system from the rear has had a history of descent, some of the air having descended from the lower stratosphere. We have already emphasized that the cloud-producing conveyor belt flows are notable for being narrow and belt-like; similarly the cold dry air flow often takes on a concentrated belt-like form which we refer to as a *dry intrusion*. The dry intrusion, although not itself a cloud-producing flow, nevertheless has an important influence on the pattern of cloud. It also plays a major role

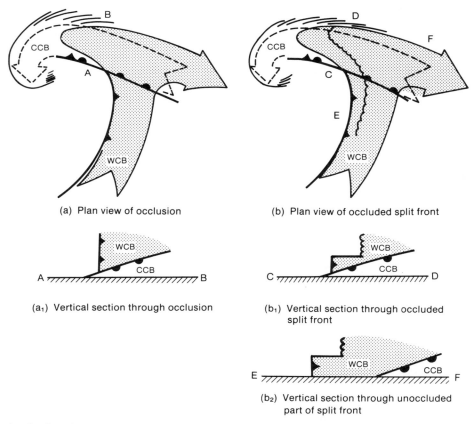

(a) Plan view of occlusion

(a$_1$) Vertical section through occlusion

(b) Plan view of occluded split front

(b$_1$) Vertical section through occluded split front

(b$_2$) Vertical section through unoccluded part of split front

FIG. 8.16. Schematic visualization of an occlusion in terms of the conveyor belt paradigm, in plan and vertical view: (a) portrays a classical occlusion with the warm conveyor belt air fully occluded within the section along AB; (b) portrays a similar situation for an occluded split front. The section along CD(b$_1$) shows the occluded part of the split front and the section along EF(b$_2$) shows the unoccluded part of the split front. The (scalloped) upper cold front in (b$_1$) is sometimes referred to as a prefrontal cold surge. (Note the similarity in the configuration of the warm conveyor belt to the distribution of moist air revealed in the early isentropic analysis shown in Fig. 8.2.)

in cyclogenesis and in the changes in cloud and precipitation patterns accompanying cyclogenesis (Uccellini et al. 1985).

The dry intrusion can be identified in several ways (Young et al. 1987): (i) its dryness; (ii) its association with a tongue of high potential vorticity (PV) brought down from levels where the ambient PV is high; and (iii) its close association with (the folded tropopause region on the left flank of) an upper tropospheric jet streak.

An example of a dry intrusion is given in Fig. 8.17. Figure 8.17a, derived using output from the Meteorological Office fine-mesh numerical prediction model, shows the tongue of dry air at 300 mb (hatched) on the left flank of the jet streak axis (bold arrow) with its leading edge splayed out in characteristic hammer-headed fashion just behind a region of high humidity (densely stippled) corresponding to the WCB and its associated cloud band. Output from the same numerical model (Fig. 8.17b) illustrates the corresponding tongue of high PV on the 315 K isentropic surface. It shows that the dry intrusion is associated with values of PV (hatched) characteristic of the upper troposphere and lower stratosphere from which this tongue of air has been extruded. Such events associated with tropopause folds were diagnosed long ago by Reed and Danielsen (1959). The resulting dry intrusion within the troposphere can nowadays be routinely monitored using not only model output as in Fig. 8.17, but also using time sequences of the 6.7-μm water vapor satellite imagery which is sensitive to the humidity over a deep layer in the upper troposphere.

The dry air encroaching upon the WCB influences the associated distributions of cloud and precipitation in the ways already alluded to in earlier sections. Thus, if dry air undercuts the WCB, either beneath a warm frontal zone, or a cold frontal zone in the case of a rearward-sloping WCB (Section 8.3.1), it leads to evaporation of some of the precipitation falling into it; whereas if it overruns the WCB, as in the case of a forward-sloping WCB (Section 8.3.2), it leads to the generation of a shallow moist zone with potential instability at its top. When the dry high-PV air encroaches in the form of a well-defined and fast-moving dry intrusion, these effects are augmented by more far-reaching effects. Hoskins et al. (1985) have described how the arrival of such a positive PV anomaly aloft is often accompanied by surface cyclogenesis, which can be particularly marked when it overruns a warm anomaly and may be further accentuated if the low-level air is moist. Thus a dry intrusion overrunning a high-θ_w WCB is the archetypal situation for rapid development.

The onset of rapid development is accompanied by a characteristic evolution in the cloud pattern. As mentioned in Section 8.2, Weldon (1979) introduced the term "baroclinic leaf" to refer to the characteristic leaf-shaped cloud pattern associated with the WCB during the early stages in the development of an extratropical cyclone. Weldon's schematic portrayal of the evolution of a baroclinic leaf cloud system is shown in Fig. 8.18. The term "baroclinic leaf" refers to the early stages shown in Fig. 8.18a-b; after

the onset of cyclogenesis the baroclinic leaf may evolve into a comma shape (Fig. 8.18d-e; see also Fig. 3.12). A baroclinic leaf is often distinctive in satellite imagery: its poleward boundary is sharply defined and, though it may be convex, straight or even concave, it more usually has an S-shape of shallow amplitude as shown in Fig. 8.18a. With the passage of time, the trailing part of the left-hand boundary is eroded by the approaching dry intrusion as shown in Fig. 8.18b-c and a relatively cloud-free region, dry slot or dry wedge, penetrates into the cloud system. This, together with the emergence of cloud associated with the

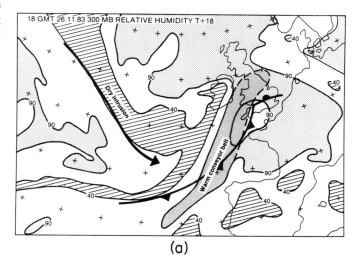

(a)

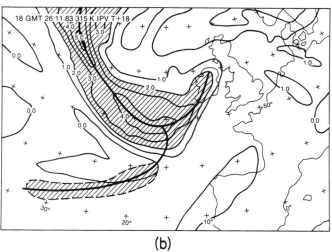

(b)

FIG. 8.17. The hammer-head shaped dry intrusion and associated jet streak and potential vorticity (PV) maximum in relation to the warm conveyor belt (WCB) as shown by model forecast output at 18 UTC 26 November 1983 just before a period of rapid cyclogenesis (Young et al. 1987). (a) Shows relative humidity at 300 mb, with areas less than 40 percent hatched and greater than 90 percent stippled. The area corresponding to the WCB is densely stippled. The axis of the upper jet streak is represented by a bold arrow. Surface fronts as inferred from the model are shown conventionally. (b) PV on the 315 K isentropic surface, with values greater than 2 PV units being hatched. The units used are those suggested by Hoskins et al. (1985) for which values less than 1.5 and more than 4.0, respectively, represent air of tropospheric and stratospheric origin. Intermediate values characterize a transitional zone. Also shown is a region where PV exceeds 2 on the 330 K surface (dashed line) to draw attention to a zone of high-PV air at the right exit of the upper jet which matches that occurring at the left exit on the 315 K surface.

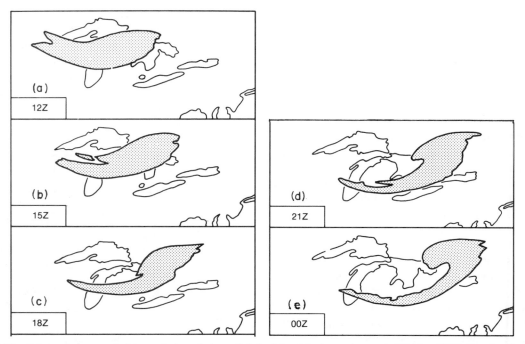

FIG. 8.18.   Schematic portrayal of the evolution of a baroclinic leaf cloud during cyclogenesis (Weldon 1979). See also Fig. 3.12.

CCB as described in Section 8.4, gives rise to the comma cloud pattern in Fig. 8.18e.

Figure 8.19 gives a closer look at the evolution in cloud structure at the critical stage when the dry intrusion begins to overtake the surface cold front. Initially in this example upper cloud is seen to have existed fairly extensively ahead of the surface cold front, but as the leading edge of the dry intrusion (double line) advanced so too the rear edge of the upper cloud, corresponding to the upper cold front, advanced ahead of the surface cold front. During the 3-hour period depicted in Fig. 8.19 the dry intrusion overrunning the WCB flow created an increasingly extensive shallow moist zone in the lowest 3 km between the upper and surface cold fronts. The high-θ_w air within the SMZ was traveling northward and feeding the slantwise ascent in the baroclinic leaf cloud. To the south of the southern tip of the leaf, where the dry air was overrunning it, the cold front was a kata-front, but to the north of the tip of the leaf cloud the front was an ana-front and WCB air was rising as line convection at the surface front before ascending within the leaf cloud. Toward the leading edge of the dry intrusion the large-scale ascent was releasing potential instability and growing convective tops could be seen within the dry slot. The dry slot is a favored region for deep convection (Carr and Millard 1985). The maximum hourly pressure falls also occurred in this region.

8.8   Wide Mesoscale Rainbands

The broad zone of gentle ascent within the WCB often contains one or more organized bands of stronger ascent giving moderate-to-heavy rain over regions several tens of kilometers wide (Fig. 8.20). These are referred to as wide mesoscale rainbands in contrast to the narrow rainbands, only a few kilometers wide, which are a rather distinct kind of dynamical feature discussed separately in Section 8.9. The wide rainbands are associated with mesoscale circulations within the conveyor belt about an axis parallel to the mean relative flow. Theories to account for them include propagating gravity waves (Uccellini 1975) and ducted gravity waves (Lindzen and Tung 1976), but the most promising theory is that they are associated with slantwise moist convection driven by conditional symmetric instability (Bennetts and Hoskins 1979; Emanuel 1983). Observational studies support this view (Bennetts and Sharp 1982; Parsons and Hobbs 1983b; Lemaitre and Testud 1988).

In a dry atmosphere, symmetric instability is a two-dimensional instability (see Sections 5.2.1 and 9.6) that manifests itself as helical roll perturbations with the axis of the rolls parallel to the baroclinic zone. Most frontal zones are in fact stable to symmetric instability. In saturated frontal regions, however, the latent heat released within rising air assists the symmetric instability, leading to the condition known as conditional symmetric instability (CSI). Bennetts and Hoskins (1979) show that the growth rate of CSI in a saturated atmosphere is given approximately by $-q_w/N_w^2$, where N_w^2 is the Brunt–Väisälä frequency of moist air and q_w is the vorticity on a θ_w-surface. They envisage the generation of rainbands by CSI as a three-stage process. First, as air moves poleward and rises through a baroclinic wave, its q_w becomes negative because of humidity gradients in the direction of the thermal wind. Second, when the air has been lifted sufficiently to become saturated, the CSI leads to roll circulations and bands of cloud. Third, the roll circulations generate

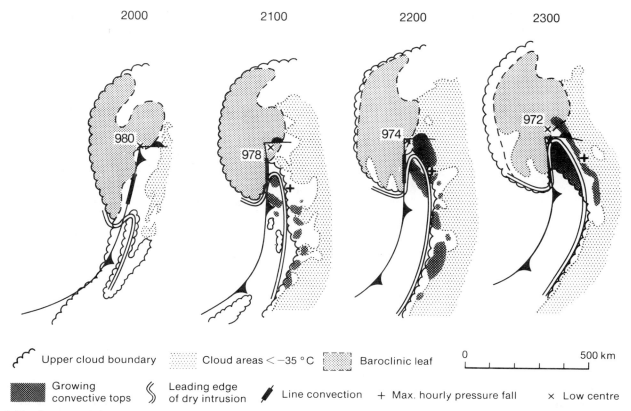

FIG. 8.19.   Sequence of sketches showing the overrunning process during the period of rapid cyclogenesis from 20 to 23 UTC 26 November 1983 (immediately following the time of Fig. 8.17). The central pressure at the location × is given in mb. The greatest pressure falls occurred at the location +. See key for further explanation (Young et al. 1987).

regions of conditional gravitational instability in the middle troposphere and the resulting convective cells lead to banded rainfall.

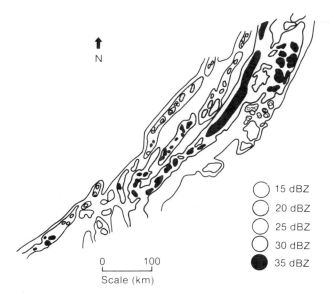

FIG. 8.20.   Composite horizontal radar reflectivity pattern showing a series of wide mesoscale rainbands over Washington state. The bands are oriented along the length of a warm conveyor belt, roughly parallel to the cold front. The bands at the leading edge are in the warm sector; the other bands are cold frontal (Hobbs et al. 1980).

The types of wide rainband that are produced include deep convective rainbands with convection originating near the surface and upper (or middle) tropospheric convective rainbands in which the convective updrafts originate at middle levels. The deep convective rainbands tend to occur away from the main frontal zones, as post-frontal (or cold sector) bands or as prefrontal (warm sector) bands. Prefrontal squall lines (not discussed here) are within this latter category. The most common type of wide rainband within extratropical cyclones, however, is the upper-tropospheric rainband.

As shown in Table 8.1, these rainbands may be manifested as warm frontal rainbands (e.g., Browning and Harrold 1969; Heymsfield 1979; Herzegh and Hobbs 1980), prefrontal cold surge rainbands (e.g., Kreitzberg 1964; Kreitzberg and Brown 1970; Browning et al. 1973; Matejka et al. 1980) or cold frontal rainbands (e.g., Hobbs et al. 1980; Parsons and Hobbs 1983a), depending on the frontal archetype (see Section 8.3) with which they are associated and their location with respect to the overall system. Nevertheless all the rainbands in Table 8.1 may conveniently be considered as essentially one dynamical type, sharing the characteristics listed below.

(1) They are associated with the ascending parts of the WCB where its top reaches into the middle troposphere.

TABLE 8.1
Types of wide upper-tropospheric convective rainbands.

Detailed classification (after Houze et al. 1976 and Hobbs 1978)	Frontal archetype with which associated	Location and orientation
Warm frontal rainband	forward-sloping ascent	parallel to the warm front and either on or ahead of it
Pre-frontal cold surge rainband	forward-sloping ascent	parallel to and just ahead of an overrunning upper cold front (often at an angle to the underlying warm front)
Cold frontal rainband	rearward-sloping ascent	parallel to and either behind or straddling an active surface cold front

(2) They contain clusters of middle- or upper-level convective cells which are generated within a shallow layer of potential instability where low-θ_w air overruns the WCB. The underlying air is generally statically stable, occasionally markedly so at some levels.

(3) They are 50 km wide (± factor of 2) and typically a few hundred kilometers long with an orientation parallel to the baroclinicity at their level. The baroclinicity at lower levels not only is often stronger but also may be oriented differently.

Kreitzberg and Brown (1970), in their study of upper-tropospheric rainbands, use the term "leafed hyperbaroclinic structures" to describe the wrinkling of the θ_w-surfaces in the WCB above a frontal zone caused by the mesoscale circulations. Each major wrinkle, or warm tongue, in the WCB gives rise to a separate rainband. The wrinkles locally enhance the potential instability and lead to the upper-level convective generating cells. The precipitation-generating cells, and the inclined trails or streamers of precipitation descending beneath them, have

a characteristic appearance when viewed by a vertically scanning radar (Marshall and Gordon 1957).

One of the first detailed observational data sets showing the mesoscale circulations associated with wide upper tropospheric rainbands was obtained by Heymsfield (1979). His observations apply to warm frontal rainbands and he summarized his results as in Fig. 8.21. Each rainband was associated with a transverse circulation 100 km wide and 3 km deep situated in the WCB above the warm frontal zone. Vertical velocities in each band reached 30 to 40 cm s^{-1}. Below the frontal zone were other circulations apparently produced by pressure perturbations set up by melting-induced cooling, as suggested by Atlas et al. (1969). In another study of a wide precipitation band, Sanders and Bosart (1985) showed that the band was associated with a shallow layer of strong transverse-band velocity components, evidently due to large-scale frontogenetic forcing separating ascending air with small hydrostatic and symmetric stability above from descending air with large stability below.

8.9 Narrow Mesoscale Rainbands Associated with Line Convection

Narrow rainbands, about 3 km across, are an important boundary-layer phenomenon. Although feeble bands of light rain and drizzle, probably generated by helical vortex circulations, sometimes occur within the SMZ ahead of the surface cold front, the most significant narrow bands are those that occur at the sharp surface cold front in the situations of rearward-sloping ascent described in Section 8.3.1. They tend to occur in the cold seasons when the air ahead of the surface cold front is not unstable. (The presence of convective instability leads to lines of broader, more distinctly three-dimensional convective cells.) Immediately ahead of the surface cold front the strong low-level flow in the boundary layer commonly gives rise

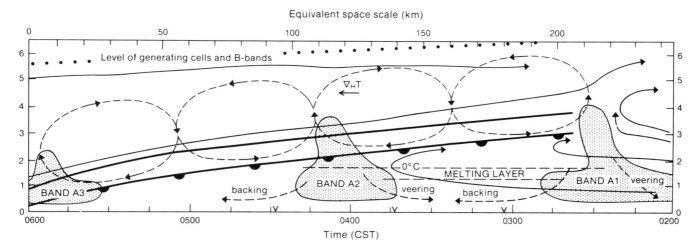

FIG. 8.21. Schematic cross section through a warm front containing three warm frontal rainbands (A1, A2, A3). The top and bottom of the warm frontal zone are represented by thick solid lines. The large-scale flow relative to the front is represented by thin solid streamlines. The secondary circulations associated with the rainbands (axes of bands are normal to the plane of the diagram) are represented by dashed streamlines (Heymsfield 1979).

to a neutrally-stratified boundary layer, typically 2 km deep and capped by a stable layer. The narrow rainband that occurs here is aligned along the surface cold front. Even though seldom more than 3 km keep in the U.K., such bands produce a burst of very heavy rain and sometimes even small hail.

The band of almost vertical convection that gives rise to a narrow cold frontal rainband is referred to as *line convection* (Browning and Harrold 1970). Figure 8.22 shows the relative flow pattern for a case of line convection in California. Although uncharacteristically intense, this example is given because of the exceptional quality of the triple-Doppler radar data that were used. In fact the depth of the inflow, the intensity of the updraft and the height to which it ascends are about twice the values typical for such fronts in the U.K. Carbone (1982) has pointed out that the (stippled) region of forward relative flow in Fig. 8.22b has the characteristic shape of a density or gravity current with an elevated nose at its leading edge. According to Parsons et al. (1987), the pressure field at the leading edge is locally nonhydrostatic and nonsemigeostrophic. Carbone (1982) and Hobbs and Persson (1982) have demonstrated that the movement of such fronts is not inconsistent with the expected propagation velocity calculated on the assumption that they are density currents. Smith and Reeder (1988) have stressed that, although density current theory provides a speed of propagation, the formula is difficult to apply because of uncertainties in determining appropriate values for the variables involved from the observations. Thus an apparently consistent propagation velocity cannot by itself be used as firm proof that the front is indeed a density current.

Figure 8.23 shows the distributions of the updraft velocity and front-parallel wind component for an example of line convection over the Gulf of Alaska derived by Bond and Fleagle (1985). The region at the surface front where the boundary layer peels off to form the 6 m s^{-1} updraft of the line convection is seen to be associated with a strong horizontal gradient of the front-parallel wind component, corresponding to a cyclonic shear of about 10^{-2} s^{-1} over 1 km, at the boundary of a pre-cold frontal low-level jet which reaches 40 m s^{-1}. The two-dimensional mass convergence within the friction layer in a region of cyclonic shear can be calculated from a relationship given by Eliassen (1959). (See Sections 3.3.3 and 9.2.) For two cases of line convection Browning and Harrold (1970) showed that the frictional convergence calculated in this way was comparable with the convergence inferred from the measured transverse-front velocities assuming two-dimensional continuity. On the basis of the direct aircraft measurements in Fig. 8.23 Bond and Fleagle (1985) showed that frictional convergence in the boundary layer accounted for 80 percent of the observed updraft in the line convection.

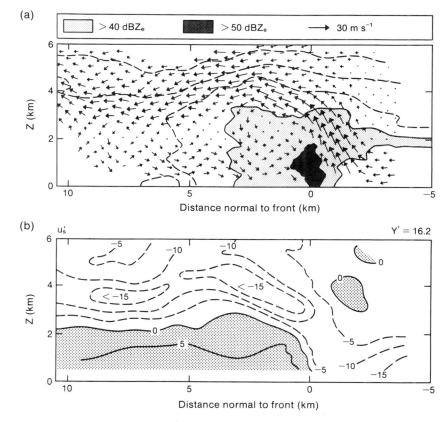

FIG. 8.22. (a) Relative flow and radar reflectivity, and (b) component of the wind normal to the front, in a vertical section perpendicular to an element of intense line convection. Isotachs in (b) are at 5 m s^{-1} intervals, being shown dashed where the flow relative to the front is from right to left (Carbone 1982).

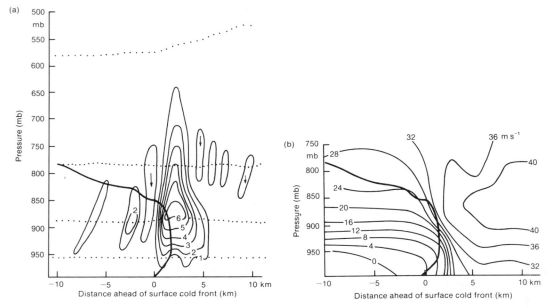

FIG. 8.23.   (a) Updraft velocity and (b) front-parallel component of the wind within a vertical section perpendicular to the axis of a sharp surface cold front with line convection. Isotachs are labeled in m s^{-1}. The position of the cold-front nose is represented by the 307 K equivalent potential temperature isopleth (thick line). Measurements were obtained from aircraft traverses along the dotted lines in (a) (Bond and Fleagle 1985). See also Fig. 10.10.

The linear character of the line convection is due to the surface cold front propagating into a neutrally- rather than unstably-stratified air mass, thereby generating convection that is forced rather than free. Line convection can, on occasion, extend as an unbroken line for a hundred kilometers. More usually, it is broken into a series of line elements leading to precipitation cores each of the order of tens of kilometers in length (Fig. 8.24) (James and Browning 1979; Hobbs and Biswas 1979). Moore (1985) has suggested that the formation of these line elements is associated with a horizontal shearing instability at the strongly sheared edge of the prefrontal low-level jet. Thorpe and Emanuel (1985) have suggested that the line elements are due to an internal baroclinic/barotropic instability. The sharpest transitions of pressure, wind, temperature and humidity occur in association with the line elements. In the gaps between the elements the transitions are more gradual.

The shallow cumulonimbus associated with line convection tends to occur toward the leading edge of stratiform cloud associated with the rearward-sloping ascent (Fig. 8.24). Sometimes it occurs right at the leading edge, in which case it may be easily detected in satellite imagery. More often it is embedded within the main mass of stratiform cloud (Fig. 8.24b); it then may not be evident at all in infrared cloud imagery (Fig. 8.25a) but the associated narrow rainband can be easily detected by radar (Fig. 8.25b). Narrow rainbands often coexist with the wide mesoscale rainbands; according to Parsons and Hobbs (1983a), the wide bands tend to travel independently of the narrow rainband, typically forming behind it and sometimes overtaking it.

8.10   The Mesoscale Structure and Mechanisms of Ana-Cold Fronts

Ana-cold fronts associated with the rearward-sloping ascent of the WCB (Section 8.3.1) exhibit a combination of the mesoscale features which have been described individually in preceding sections. The various ingredients are summarized in the list below.

(1)   A WCB with its main component of flow parallel to the cold front and a smaller ageostrophic component ascending rearward above the cold frontal zone.

(2)   A low-level jet within the WCB just in advance of the surface cold front.

(3)   Line convection and an associated narrow rainband at the surface cold front, along the cyclonically sheared boundary of the low-level jet, where the WCB air is abruptly peeled away from the boundary layer by the advancing cold air, probably acting as a density current.

(4)   A broad band of slantwise ascent and associated light rain, where the WCB ascends with a rearward component above the advancing cold frontal zone. Within this region, perhaps caused by conditional symmetric instability, there may be one or more wide mesoscale bands of enhanced slantwise ascent with associated mid-level convective cells giving moderate rain.

(5)   A rear inflow of cold dry air undergoing slantwise descent within and beneath the cold frontal zone, leading to evaporative cooling as precipitation falls into it.

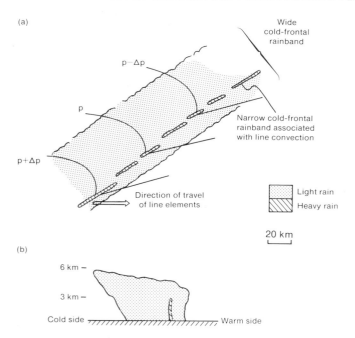

FIG. 8.24. Schematic depiction of the precipitation distribution at a sharp ana-cold front (a) in plan view and (b) in a vertical cross section normal to the front.

Matejka et al. (1980) have put these ingredients together from the point of view of the precipitation structure to give the model in Fig. 8.26. A corresponding model from a kinematic point of view is shown in Fig. 8.27a-b, the two

parts of which show complementary features derived for an archetypal ana-cold front using Doppler radar measurements of wind velocity, divergence and deformation (Browning and Harrold 1970). The two major extrusions identified in Fig. 8.27b are separated by a region of strong deformation whose maximum lies close to the zero vertical velocity contour ($w=0$ in Fig. 8.27a). The $w=0$ contour corresponds to the main cloud base which characteristically inclines upward rather more steeply than the frontal zone in this kind of front (although not in Fig. 8.26). Virtually the entire region of cold air in Fig. 8.27 is descending, but the strongest descent occurs within the cold frontal zone. The closeness of the relationship between this descending flow and the frontal zone suggests that it may be a downward extension of the phenomenon observed by Danielsen (1968) and Shapiro et al. (1982) who found extrusions of high potential vorticity, radioactivity and ozone within upper frontal zones which form initially on the west side of the upper trough (see also Reed 1955): hence the label "stratospheric extrusion" in Fig. 8.27b. This feature may correspond to the deep fronts analyzed by Newton (1958) and Palmén and Newton (1969, pp. 335–338) ahead of well-developed upper troughs. Stratospheric air probably does not descend all the way to the ground on isentropic surfaces; however, some stratospheric air, having penetrated to lower-middle levels, may be mixed convectively to the surface through the boundary layer (Reiter and Mahlman 1965).

Ferris (1989) has conducted a diagnostic study of an

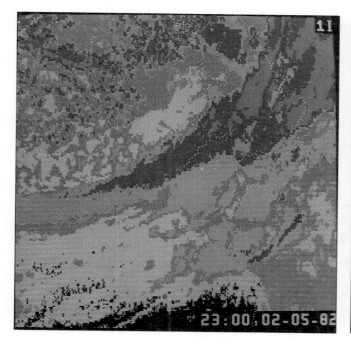

(a)

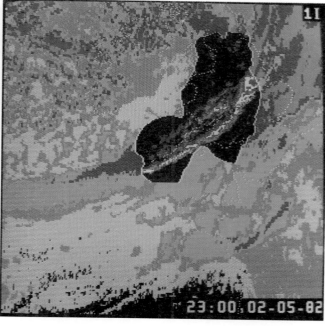

(b)

FIG. 8.25. (a) False-color infrared satellite image from Meteosat showing a cold-frontal cloud band oriented southwest-northeast across England and Wales. Red and pink, high cloud tops; dark blue, medium cloud; pale blue, low cloud and cold land; green, yellow and black, sea and warm land. (b) Same as (a) but with rainfall data from a network of weather radars embedded within it, on the same scale and projection. White corresponds to very heavy rain; red, heavy; pink, moderate; blue, light; black, no rain.

archetypal ana-cold front using the semioperational Meteorological Office mesoscale model. This is a nonhydrostatic primitive equation model covering the British Isles with a horizontal grid length of 15 km. The model has sixteen irregularly spaced levels below 12 km, and cloud water is represented explicitly. Ferris was able to identify most of the features referred to above: in particular, a strong transverse circulation, with rearward-sloping ascent in the warm air overlying a rear-to-front inflow maximum of dry air that extended from the tropopause fold, down along the base of the cold frontal zone, all the way to the nose of cold air just behind the surface cold front, as implied by Fig. 8.27b.

Ferris ran the model with and without moisture to investigate the effects of latent heat of condensation, the wet runs being repeated with and without evaporation to isolate the specific effects of the heat sinks. He demonstrated the effects on the dynamics listed below.

(1) The diabatic effects strengthened the low-level jet and greatly tightened the temperature gradient and wind shear across the surface front.

(2) Latent heat sources led to the updraft being greatly intensified within the model's representation of line convection and within the slantwise ascent behind, but with a region of slight subsidence and lighter precipitation in between, perhaps due to the updraft within the line convection overshooting its equilibrium level, as implied by Fig. 8.27a. The formation of this zone of subsidence thus made the region of precipitation farther behind the front appear as if it were a distinct mesoscale rainband.

(3) Upper-tropospheric air, identified by its high potential vorticity, was brought down into the middle troposphere in both moist and dry simulations but it penetrated a little farther in the moist run as a result of the intensification of the transverse circulation caused by the latent heat effects.

(4) Latent heat sinks due to evaporation led to the downdraft in the cold air being somewhat intensified, mainly at 900 mb just behind the surface cold front.

The above study suggested that the propagation velocity of the surface cold front was not much affected by the evaporative heat sink. At first sight, assuming the surface front to behave as a density current, one might expect the chilling of the cold air by evaporation (and melting) of precipitation, together with differential precipitation loading, to increase the propagation velocity (Cox 1988). If, however, the velocity were to increase without any increase in the larger-scale influx of cold air, then the depth of the density current would tend to decrease, thereby retarding its velocity. This points to the possible importance of the rear inflow maximum, identified as the stratospheric extrusion in Fig. 8.27b, in controlling the propagation velocity of the front. A rear inflow maximum is also a feature of some midlatitude squall line systems with rearward sloping anvils (Newton 1950; Smull and Houze 1985; Srivastava et al. 1986) and of tropical mesoscale convective systems (e.g., Testud 1982). According to Smull and Houze (1987), however, squall lines also exist in which no such inflow enters the rear edge of the system, yet a rear-to-front flow nevertheless develops within the system

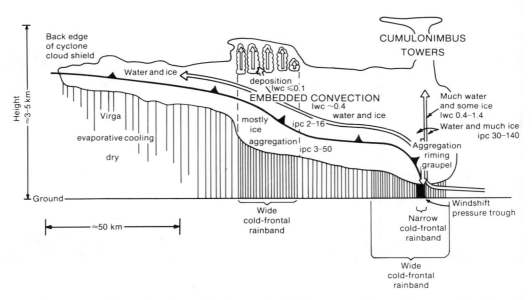

Fig. 8.26. Idealized cross section of the clouds and precipitation associated with an ana-cold front with rearward-sloping ascent (Matejka et al. 1980). Vertical hatching below cloud base represents precipitation; the density of the hatching corresponds qualitatively to the precipitation rate. Open arrows depict airflow relative to the front: a strong convective updraft and downdraft above the surface front and broader gentle ascent over the cold front aloft. Ice particle concentrations (ipc) are given in numbers per liter; cloud liquid water contents (lwc) are in g m^{-3}. Motion of the system is from left to right.

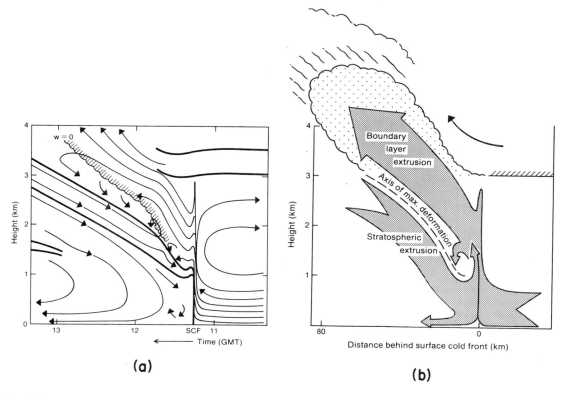

(a)   **(b)**

Fig. 8.27.   Time-height section during the passage of an ana-cold front with rearward-sloping ascent, showing (a) streamlines (thin lines) in relation to the cold frontal zone and other stable layers (delineated by thick lines) and (b) a simplified depiction of the main transverse flows. The stratospheric extrusion shown in (b) experiences considerable mixing during its descent and therefore much of the air in the lower part of this circulation is not of stratospheric origin. The shaded boundary in (a), of the region of upward air motion, happens to correspond rather closely with the axis of maximum deformation plotted in (b). The transverse components of the flow are superimposed on a strong component of motion into the plane of the diagram, especially in the warm air. Equivalent distance scale: 1 hour = 40 km (Browning and Harrold 1970).

owing to processes such as latent heat effects internal to the squall line itself.

The above considerations suggest that the speed of a cold front is governed by processes that occur on different scales, not necessarily cooperatively. First, on the large scale, there is a supply of cold air which must in the long term determine the advance of the cold air mass. Second, the leading edge of the cold air may act in the shorter term as a density current, with its own propagation speed which may or may not be matched at any given time to the large-scale advance of the cold air mass. The cold front is a multiscale phenomenon: Only when it is examined on the small scale will it resemble a density current; only when it is examined on a large scale will it relate to the advance of the cold air mass as a whole.

An ana-cold front with rearward-sloping ascent of the warm air has also been modeled by Hsie et al. (1984). They too used a primitive equation model with an explicit scheme for calculating cloud water and precipitation to investigate the effects of latent heating on frontal circulation, but the model was restricted to a two-dimensional section normal to the front. Their study, like that of Ferris, involved the comparison of moist and dry simulations. In addition to showing that the effect of moisture was to strengthen the ageostrophic circulation, and the low-level

and upper-tropospheric jets, together with the associated horizontal wind shears, Hsie et al. showed that mesoscale bands were formed which were not present in the dry simulation. In particular they found that these bands formed in regions of CSI characterized by negative equivalent potential vorticity (q_e) (see also Baldwin et al. 1984). Similar effects due to moisture were also reproduced in two-dimensional numerical simulations carried out by Knight and Hobbs (1988). They derived a conceptual model (Fig. 8.28) of the processes by which the mesoscale rainbands developed. Wide mesoscale bands with a wavelength of 70 km formed in a convectively stable region above the cold frontal zone and moved toward the surface cold front. The first band that appeared in Knight and Hobbs' numerical simulation formed and intensified in a region of negative q_e. Subsequent bands formed behind the first and intensified as they moved into the region of negative q_e. The spacing of the bands, the slope of their updrafts, and the fact that they disappeared when q_e was everywhere positive, are consistent with the theory of CSI.

Two-dimensional simulations can be highly instructive; Hsie et al. (1984), however, have stressed the importance of using full three-dimensional models in the future to address the following kinds of problems:

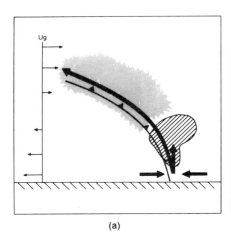
(a)

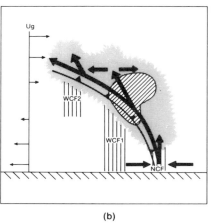
(b)

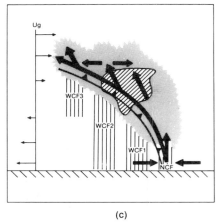
(c)

FIG. 8.28. Schematic diagram showing stages in the formation of mesoscale rainbands at an ana-cold front (Knight and Hobbs 1988). The slanted hatching shows a region of negative equivalent potential vorticity; stippled shading shows the region containing cloud water. Vertical hatching below cloud base represents precipitation. The geostrophic wind in the plane of the cross section (U_g) is indicated on the left-hand side of the figures. Broad arrows show ageostrophic air motions in the plane of the cross section. All winds shown are relative to the motion of the frontal system. (a) A region of negative equivalent potential vorticity, which forms in the warm air, is advected toward, then up along, the frontal surface by the ageostrophic motions. (b) When the region of conditional symmetric instability (CSI) becomes saturated the instability is realized, resulting in a wide mesoscale rainband (WCF1). A second wide mesoscale rainband (WCF2) is forced by convergence behind WCF1. This convergence is a result of divergent outflow at the top of the unstable region in WCF1. Convergence in the planetary boundary layer forces line convection, giving a narrow cold-frontal rainband (NCF) at the surface front. (c) WCF1 moves with the winds at the top of the rainband, i.e., toward the warm air. Meanwhile WCF2 moves in the same direction into the region of CSI and intensifies, and a third wide mesoscale rainband (WCF3) is forced by convergence behind WCF2.

(1) The interaction of shearing and stretching deformation and other physical processes such as diabatic heating in forming fronts and producing the difference in the vertical structure of warm and cold fronts (Hoskins and Heckley 1981).

(2) The interaction of jet streaks and frontal circulations (Uccellini and Johnson 1979).

(3) The different origins of the airstreams forming the frontal systems (Carlson et al. 1980).

(4) The nature of circulations in fronts embedded within synoptic-scale waves where curvature effects may be significant (Shapiro and Kennedy 1981).

8.11 Conclusions

During the past quarter-century the availability of imagery from satellites and radars has transformed our ability to observe clouds and precipitation. The patterns of cloud and precipitation in extratropical cyclones can be interpreted dynamically using relative-flow isentropic analysis and conceptual models. Conceptual models have been presented in this review for a wide variety of the synoptic and mesoscale features seen in the imagery.

The most important cloud- and precipitation-generating flows are the well defined moist flows referred to as the warm conveyor belt and cold conveyor belt. The warm conveyor belt is particularly important, and two contrasting frontal archetypes have been distinguished according to whether this flow ascends with a rearward or forward slope relative to the cold front. The two archetypes correspond to the well-known categories of ana- and kata-cold fronts. Each has a characteristic pattern of cloud and precipitation. The kata-cold front has a split frontal

structure in which upper frontal cloud runs ahead of the surface cold front.

Dry air with low wet-bulb potential temperature originating behind the cold front also plays an important role in determining the pattern of cloud and precipitation. It often overruns the warm conveyor belt to form a shallow moist zone and potential instability. Sometimes the low-θ_w air occurs as a well-defined dry intrusion of high-potential vorticity air extruded from the stratosphere, and this leads to rapid cyclogenesis when it overruns the high-θ_w air in the warm conveyor belt.

When a vorticity maximum in the polar air approaches a cold front, a variety of cloud systems may develop. Depending on how close it approaches, it may generate a comma cloud pattern entirely within the cold air or a wave on the cold frontal cloud band. Between these two extremes, a cloud system may form which is referred to as an instant occlusion. An instant occlusion has features in common with split kata-cold fronts and with true occlusions, and models have been presented that clarify the distinction between them.

The broad zones of frontal precipitation usually contain mesoscale banded features embedded within them. Two categories have been described: wide rainbands with shallow convective cells in the middle or upper troposphere and narrow rainbands confined to the lower troposphere. The former, typically 50 km wide, are associated with enhanced slantwise ascent perhaps due to conditional symmetric instability. The latter, only about 3 km across, are associated with upright line convection at the sharp surface cold front, probably forced by a density current. Latent heat plays an important role in intensifying these circulations.

REFERENCES

Atlas, D., R. Tatehira, R. C. Srivastava, W. Marker and R. E. Carbone, 1969: Precipitation-induced mesoscale wind perturbations in the melting layer. *Quart. J. Roy. Meteor. Soc.*, **95**, 544–560.

Baldwin, D., E.-Y. Hsie and R. A. Anthes, 1984: Diagnostic studies of a two-dimensional simulation of frontogenesis in a moist atmosphere. *J. Atmos. Sci.*, **41**, 2686–2700.

Bennetts, D. A., and B. J. Hoskins, 1979: Conditional symmetric instability — a possible explanation for frontal rainbands. *Quart. J. Roy. Meteor. Soc.*, **105**, 945–962.

——, and J. C. Sharp, 1982: The relevance of conditional symmetric instability to the prediction of mesoscale frontal rainbands. *Quart. J. Roy. Meteor. Soc.*, **108**, 595–602.

Bergeron, T., 1937: On the physics of fronts. *Bull. Amer. Meteor. Soc.*, **18**, 265–275.

——, 1959: Methods in scientific weather analysis and forecasting. An outline in the history of ideas and hints at a program. *The Atmosphere and the Sea in Motion* (Rossby Memorial Volume), B. Bolin, Ed. Rockefeller Institute Press, 440–474.

——, 1981: Synoptic meteorology: an historical review. *Pure Appl. Geophys.*, **119**, 443–473. Reprinted in *Weather and Weather Maps*, G. H. Liljequist, Ed. Birkhäuser Verlag.

Bjerknes, J., and H. Solberg, 1922: Life cycle of cyclones and the polar front theory of atmospheric circulation. *Geofys. Publ.*, **3**, No. 1, 1–18.

Bond, N. A., and R. G. Fleagle, 1985: Structure of a cold front over the ocean. *Quart. J. Roy. Meteor. Soc.*, **111**, 739–759.

Browning, K. A., 1986: Conceptual models of precipitation systems. *Weather and Forecasting*, **1**, 23–41.

——, and T. W. Harrold, 1969: Air motion and precipitation growth in a wave depression. *Quart. J. Roy. Meteor. Soc.*, **95**, 288–309.

——, and ——, 1970: Air motion and precipitation growth at a cold front. *Quart. J. Roy. Meteor. Soc.*, **96**, 369–389.

——, and C. W. Pardoe, 1973: Structure of low-level jet streams ahead of mid-latitude cold fronts. *Quart. J. Roy. Meteor. Soc.*, **99**, 619–638.

——, and G. A. Monk, 1982: A simple model for the synoptic analysis of cold fronts. *Quart. J. Roy. Meteor. Soc.*, **108**, 435–452.

——, and F. F. Hill, 1985: Mesoscale analysis of a polar trough intersecting with a polar front. *Quart. J. Roy. Meteor. Soc.*, **111**, 445–462.

——, M. E. Hardman, T. W. Harrold and C. W. Pardoe, 1973: The structure of rainbands within a mid-latitude depression. *Quart. J. Roy. Meteor. Soc.*, **99**, 215–231.

Cahir, J. J., G. S. Forbes, W. D. Lottes and T. Staskiewicz, 1985: Structural aspects of the warm conveyor belt. Unpublished manuscript, Department of Meteorology, Pennsylvania State University.

Carbone, R. E., 1982: A severe frontal rainband. Part I: Stormwide hydrodynamic structure. *J. Atmos. Sci.*, **39**, 258–279.

Carlson, T. N., 1980: Airflow through midlatitude cyclones and the comma cloud pattern. *Mon. Wea. Rev.*, **108**, 1498–1509.

——, 1987: Cloud configuration in relation to relative isentropic motion. *Satellite and Radar Imagery Interpretation* (preprint vol., workshop at U.K. Meteorological Office), M. Bader and T. Waters, Eds. EUMETSAT, Darmstadt, FRG, 43–61.

——, R. A. Anthes, M. Schwartz, S. G. Benjamin and D. G. Baldwin, 1980: Analysis and prediction of severe storms environment. *Bull. Amer. Meteor. Soc.,*, **61**, 1018–1032.

Carr, F. H., and J. P. Millard, 1985: A composite study of comma clouds and their association with severe weather over the Great Plains. *Mon. Wea. Rev.*, **113**, 370–387.

Cox, G. P., 1988: Modelling precipitation in frontal rainbands. *Quart. J. Roy. Meteor. Soc.*, **114**, 115–127.

Danielsen, E. F., 1966: Research in four-dimensional diagnosis of cyclonic storm cloud systems. Sci. Rep. No. 1, Contract AF 19(628)–4762, Pennsylvania State University, 53 pp.

——, 1968: Stratospheric-tropospheric exchange based on radioactivity, ozone and potential vorticity. *J. Atmos. Sci.*, **25**, 502–518.

Durran, D. R., and D. B. Weber, 1988: An investigation of the poleward edges of cirrus clouds associated with midlatitude jet streams. *Mon. Wea. Rev.*, **116**, 702–714.

Eliassen, A., 1959: On the formation of fronts in the atmosphere. *The Atmosphere and the Sea in Motion* (Rossby Memorial Volume), B. Bolin, Ed. Rockefeller Institute Press, 277–287.

Emanuel, K. A., 1983: On assessing local conditional symmetric instability from atmospheric soundings. *Mon. Wea. Rev.*, **111**, 2016–2033.

Ferris, P. D., 1989: Frontal structure in a mesoscale model. Ph.D. thesis, University of Reading.

Green, J. S. A., F. H. Ludlam and J. F. R. McIlveen, 1966: Isentropic relative-flow analysis and the parcel theory. *Quart. J. Roy. Meteor. Soc.*, **92**, 210–219.

Harrold, T. W., 1973: Mechanisms influencing the distribution of precipitation within baroclinic disturbances. *Quart. J. Roy. Meteor. Soc.*, **99**, 232–251.

Hemler, M. G., 1987: Doppler wind profiler examination of cloud edges. M.S. thesis, Dept. of Meteor., Pennsylvania State University.

Herzegh, P. H., and P. V. Hobbs, 1980: The mesoscale and microscale structure and organization of clouds and precipitation in mid-latitude cyclones. II: Warm-frontal clouds. *J. Atmos. Sci.*, **37**, 597–611.

Heymsfield, G. M., 1979: Doppler radar study of a warm frontal region. *J. Atmos. Sci.*, **36**, 2093–2107.

Hobbs, P. V., 1978: Organization and structure of clouds and precipitation on the mesoscale and microscale in cyclonic storms. *Rev. Geophys. Space Phys.*, **16**, 741–755.

——, and K. R. Biswas, 1979: The cellular structure of narrow cold-frontal rainbands. *Quart. J. Roy. Meteor. Soc.*, **105**, 723–727.

——, and P. O. G. Persson, 1982: The mesoscale and microscale structure and organization of clouds and precipitation in midlatitude cyclones. Part V: The substructure of narrow cold-frontal rainbands. *J. Atmos. Sci.*, **39**, 280–295.

——, T. J. Matejka, P. H. Herzegh, J. D. Locatelli and R. A. Houze, Jr., 1980: The mesoscale and microscale structure and organization of clouds and precipitation in midlatitude cyclones. I: A case study of a cold front. *J. Atmos. Sci.*, **37**, 568–596.

Hoskins, B. J., and W. A. Heckley, 1981: Cold and warm fronts in baroclinic waves. *Quart. J. Roy. Meteor. Soc.*, **107**, 79–90.

——, M. E. McIntyre and A. W. Robertson, 1985: On the use and significance of isentropic potential vorticity maps. *Quart. J. Roy. Meteor. Soc.*, **111**, 877–946.

Houze, R. A., P. V. Hobbs, K. R. Biswas and W. M. Davis, 1976:

Mesoscale rainbands in extratropical cyclones. *Mon. Wea. Rev.,* **104**, 868–878.

Hsie, E.-Y., R. A. Anthes and D. Keyser, 1984: Numerical simulation of frontogenesis in a moist atmosphere. *J. Atmos. Sci.,* **41**, 2581–2594.

James, P. K., and K. A. Browning, 1979: Mesoscale structure of line convection at surface cold fronts. *Quart. J. Roy. Meteor. Soc.,* **105**, 371–382.

Knight, D. J., and P. V. Hobbs, 1988: The mesoscale and microscale structure and organization of clouds and precipitation in midlatitude cyclones. XV: A numerical modeling study of frontogenesis and cold-frontal rainbands. *J. Atmos. Sci.,* **45**, 915–930.

Kreitzberg, C. W., 1964: The structure of occlusions as determined from serial ascents and vertically-directed radar. Rep. AFCRL-64-26, Air Force Cambridge Res. Lab., Bedford, Mass., 121 pp.

——, and H. A. Brown, 1970: Mesoscale weather systems within an occlusion. *J. Appl. Meteor.,* **9**, 417–432.

Kurz, M., 1988: Development of cloud distribution and relative motions during the mature and occlusion stage of a typical cyclone development. Preprints, *Palmén Memorial Symposium on Extratropical Cyclones,* Helsinki. Amer. Meteor. Soc., 201–204.

Lemaitre, Y., and J. Testud, 1988: Relevance of conditional symmetric instability in the interpretation of wide cold frontal rainbands. A case study: 20 May 1976. *Quart. J. Roy. Meteor. Soc.,* **114**, 259–269.

Lindzen, R. S., and K. K. Tung, 1976: Banded convective activity and ducted gravity waves. *Mon. Wea. Rev.,* **104**, 1602–1607.

Ludlam, F. H., 1966: The cyclone problem: A history of models of the cyclonic storm. Inaugural lecture as professor of meteorology, 8 November 1966, published by Imperial College of Science and Technology, London, 49 pp.

——, 1980: *Clouds and Storms.* Pennsylvania State University Press, 405 pp.

Marshall, J. S., and W. E. Gordon, 1957: Radiometeorology. *Meteor. Monogr.,* **3**, 73–113.

Matejka, T. J., R. A. Houze, Jr. and P. V. Hobbs, 1980: Microphysics and dynamics of clouds associated with mesoscale rainbands in extratropical cyclones. *Quart. J. Roy. Meteor. Soc.,* **106**, 29–56.

McGinnigle, J. B., M. V. Young and M. J. Bader, 1988: The development of instant occlusions in the North Atlantic. *Meteor. Mag.,* **117**, 325–341.

Miles, M. K., 1962: Wind, temperature and humidity distribution at some cold fronts over SE. England. *Quart. J. Roy. Meteor. Soc.,* **88**, 286–300.

Moore, G. W. K., 1985: The organization of convection in narrow cold-frontal rainbands. *J. Atmos. Sci.,* **42**, 1777–1791.

Namias, J., 1939: The use of isentropic analysis in short term forecasting. *J. Aeronaut. Sci.,* **6**, 295–298.

Newton, C. W., 1950: Structure and mechanism of the prefrontal squall line. *J. Meteor.,* **7**, 210–222.

——, 1958: Variations in frontal structure of upper level troughs. *Geophysica,* **6**, 357–375.

Palmén, E., and C. W. Newton, 1969: *Atmospheric Circulation Systems: Their Structure and Physical Interpretation.* Academic Press, 603 pp.

Parsons, D. B., and P. V. Hobbs, 1983a: The mesoscale and microscale structure and organization of clouds and precipitation in midlatitude cyclones. VII: Formation, development, interaction and dissipation of rainbands. *J. Atmos. Sci.,* **40**, 559–579.

——, and ——, 1983b: The mesoscale and microscale structure and organization of clouds and precipitation in midlatitude cyclones. XI: Comparisons between observational and theoretical aspects of rainbands. *J. Atmos. Sci.,* **40**, 2377–2397.

——, C. G. Mohr and T. Gal-Chen, 1987: A severe frontal rainband. Part III. Derived thermodynamic structure. *J. Atmos. Sci.,* **44**, 1615–1631.

Reed, R. J., 1955: A study of a characteristic type of upper level frontogenesis. *J. Meteor.,* **12**, 226–237.

——, 1979: Cyclogenesis in polar air streams. *Mon. Wea. Rev.,* **107**, 38–52.

——, and E. F. Danielsen, 1959: Fronts in the vicinity of the tropopause. *Arch. Meteor. Geophys. Bioklim.,* **A11**, 1–17.

Reiter, E. R., and J. D. Mahlman, 1965: Heavy radioactive fallout over the southern United States, November 1962. *J. Geophys. Res.,* **70**, 4501–4520.

Ryan, B. F., and K. J. Wilson, 1985: The Australian summertime cool change. Part III: Subsynoptic and mesoscale model. *Mon. Wea. Rev.,* **113**, 224–240.

Sanders, F., and L. F. Bosart, 1985: Mesoscale structure in the megalopolitan snowstorm, 11–12 February 1983. Part II: Doppler radar study of the New England snowband. *J. Atmos. Sci.,* **42**, 1398–1407.

Sansom, H. W., 1951: A study of cold fronts over the British Isles. *Quart. J. Roy. Meteor. Soc.,* **77**, 96–120.

Shapiro, M. A., and P. J. Kennedy, 1981: Research aircraft measurements of jet stream geostrophic and ageostrophic winds. *J. Atmos. Sci.,* **38**, 2642–2652.

——, A. J. Krueger and P. J. Kennedy, 1982: Nowcasting the position and intensity of jet streams using a satellite-borne total ozone mapping spectrometer. *Nowcasting,* K. A. Browning, Ed. Academic Press, 137–145.

Smith, R. K., and M. J. Reeder, 1988: On the movement and low-level structure of cold fronts. *Mon. Wea. Rev.,* **116**, 1927–1944.

Smull, B. F., and R. A. Houze, Jr., 1985: A midlatitude squall line with a trailing region of stratiform rain: Radar and satellite observations. *Mon. Wea. Rev.,* **113**, 117–133.

——, and ——, 1987: Rear inflow in squall lines with trailing stratiform precipitation. *Mon. Wea. Rev.,* **115**, 2869–2889.

Srivastava, R. C., T. J. Matejka and T. J. Lorello, 1986: Doppler radar study of the trailing anvil region associated with a squall line. *J. Atmos. Sci.,* **43**, 356–377.

Testud, J., 1982: Three-dimensional wind field analysis from Doppler radar data. *Mesoscale Meteorology — Theories, Observations and Models,* D. K. Lilly and T. Gal-Chen, Eds. Reidel, 711–753.

Thepenier, T. M., and D. Cruette, 1981: Formation of cloud bands associated with the American subtropical jet stream and their interaction with midlatitude synoptic disturbances reaching Europe. *Mon. Wea. Rev.,* **109**, 2209–2220.

Thorpe, A. J., and K. A. Emanuel, 1985: Frontogenesis in the presence of small stability to slantwise convection. *J. Atmos. Sci.,* **42**, 1809–1824.

Uccellini, L. W., 1975: A case study of apparent gravity wave initiation of severe convective storms. *Mon. Wea. Rev.,* **103,** 497–513.

——, and D. R. Johnson, 1979: The coupling of upper and lower tropospheric jet streaks and implications for the development of severe convective storms. *Mon. Wea. Rev.,* **107,** 682–703.

——, D. Keyser, K. F. Brill and C. H. Wash, 1985: The Presidents' Day cyclone of 18–19 February 1979: Influence of upstream trough amplification and associated tropopause folding on rapid cyclogenesis. *Mon. Wea. Rev.,* **113,** 962–988.

Wallace, J. M., and P. V. Hobbs, 1977: *Atmospheric Science; An Introductory Survey.* Academic Press, 467 pp.

Weldon, R. B., 1975: Satellite training course notes. Part II: The structure and evolution of winter storms. Unpublished lecture notes, Applications Division, National Environmental Satellite Service, NOAA, U.S. Dept. of Commerce.

——, 1979: Satellite training course notes. Part IV. Cloud patterns and upper air wind field. United States Air Force, AWS/TR-79/003.

Young, M. V., G. A. Monk and K. A. Browning, 1987: Interpretation of satellite imagery of a rapidly deepening cyclone. *Quart. J. Roy. Meteor. Soc.,* **113,** 1089–1115.

Zillman, J. W., and P. G. Price, 1972: On the thermal structure of mature Southern Ocean cyclones. *Austral. Meteor. Mag.,* **20,** 34–48.

Chapter 9

Transverse Circulations in Frontal Zones

Arnt Eliassen

University of Oslo, Institute of Geophysics, P. O. Box 1022, Blindern, 0315 Oslo 3, Norway

9.1 Introduction

Today, seventy years after the concept of fronts was introduced by the Bergen school, the nature of fronts and their connection with cyclones are still under intense investigation and debate in the meteorological community. New sophisticated observation techniques developed during the past decades and elaborate model simulations have made it possible to analyze the three-dimensional structure of fronts in great detail. Numerous studies published in recent years have increased our knowledge of the formation of fronts and jet streams. The classic textbook by Palmén and Newton (1969) has formed a solid basis for this research and has been of immense importance for the recent theoretical advances.

The present paper does not aim at a complete review of this extensive research activity, but deals mainly with the development of the semi-geostrophic two-dimensional theory. For more complete reviews of the field, the reader is referred to recent papers by Hoskins (1982), Orlanski et al. (1985), Keyser and Shapiro (1986), Bluestein (1986) and Keyser (1986). Additional aspects, with emphasis on recently observed three-dimensional frontal structures in cyclones, are reviewed by Shapiro and Keyser in Chapter 10.

In the years after World War I, Jack Bjerknes and his coworkers had to rely on surface observations and what they could see in the sky. Bjerknes (1919) arrived at his model of the polar front cyclone through a study of con-

vergence lines on the surface map. He inferred the existence of circulations in vertical planes normal to the front. Such transverse circulations were thus part of the frontal concept right from the beginning. Bjerknes assumed that the surface front would continue upward as a surface of discontinuity in velocity and temperature, sloping in accordance with Margules' formula.

As aerological observations became available in the late 1920s and 1930s, Jack Bjerknes could begin to study the three-dimensional structure of the frontal cyclones. Much of this work he did in close cooperation with Erik Palmén, and they wrote three joint papers on the subject. They dissected fronts in the troposphere and found that they were sloping baroclinic layers of transition, about a kilometer deep (Fig. 9.1).

In the early Bergen school, the polar front was considered the prime mover of weather systems in middle and high latitudes. Preexisting fronts were held responsible for the formation of new cyclones, and clouds and continuous precipitation were considered to be the result of warm air ascending over the sloping frontal surface. Two crucial questions, however, remained: How are fronts formed, and what causes the vertical motion that produces frontal clouds and precipitation?

Tor Bergeron (1928) gave at least a partial answer to the first question. He suggested that fronts could be formed as a result of advective concentration of isotherms along the dilatation axes in hyperbolic fields of horizontal flow. Such confluent advection, which is frequently seen to take place

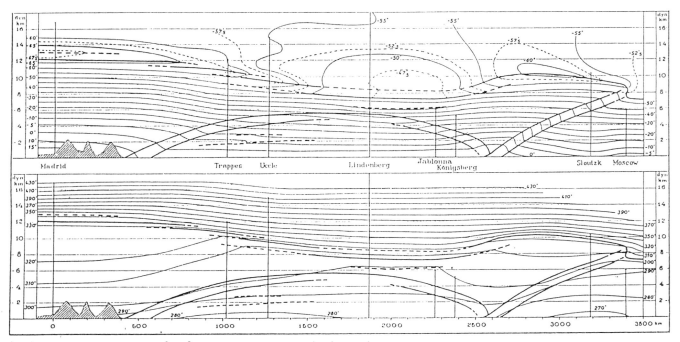

FIG. 9.1.   Vertical cross section Madrid–Moscow, morning of 17 February 1935. Top: Isotherms. Bottom: Isentropes (Bjerknes and Palmén 1937).

on synoptic maps, doubtless contributes to frontogenesis; but it cannot be the full explanation. In the first place, this process cannot explain the formation of the cyclonic wind shear at the front; that would require convergence, and hence vertical motion. Second, large-scale horizontal confluence can hardly produce temperature contrasts as sharp as we often observe them near the ground. The typical rate of contraction in a synoptic-scale confluence field is of the order $(12 \text{ h})^{-1}$. This would suffice to produce a temperature contrast of the order 10 K in a zone a few hundred kilometers wide in a day or so, starting with a normal meridional temperature gradient; but surface fronts are often as narrow as ten kilometers, or less.

A rational theory of synoptic-scale vertical motion did not emerge until after World War II. It was based on the assumption of immediate geostrophic adjustment through quick dispersal of gravity-inertia waves. It follows that the vertical circulation must be such as to preserve the thermal wind balance.

Namias and Clapp (1949) were among the first to apply this principle to explain the formation of upper-tropospheric jets as a result of confluence of warm and cold air currents. They argued that the increase of the horizontal temperature gradient caused by the confluent motion must be accompanied by a direct vertical circulation in planes normal to the flow, in order to form the corresponding increase in vertical wind shear, so as to preserve the thermal wind balance. This principle also forms the basis of the ω-equation.

It took several years before this theory was applied to fronts in general. The reason may have been that the geostrophic or thermal wind approximation was thought to be inapplicable to fronts because of their small width, with

Rossby numbers of the order 1 to 10. This cross-frontal Rossby number, however, is hardly relevant to the validity of the geostrophic approximation because air particles do not cross the frontal layer. They may move normally to the front, but then the front moves also.

9.2   Sawyer's Analysis

A pioneering study of transverse circulations in fronts, in response to confluence, was made by J. S. Sawyer (1956). He applied the geostrophic momentum approximation, assuming the along-front velocity to be geostrophic, but taking into account the advection by nongeostrophic and vertical motion in the cross-frontal direction, in which the gradients of momentum and potential temperature are strong. This nongeostrophic advection has proved to be essential to frontogenesis; in this problem quasi-geostrophic dynamics in its usual formulation, with only geostrophic advection, is inadequate. In fact, R. T. Williams (1967) pointed out that conservation of quasi-geostrophic potential vorticity prohibits the formation of strong frontal cyclonic shear unless the air becomes statically unstable.

Sawyer considered the case of an incompressible fluid, but we may here translate his analysis to apply to an adiabatic, non-Boussinesq gas. Using pressure coordinates (x,y,p) on the f-plane (with constant Coriolis parameter f), Sawyer considered a situation with straight isotherms in the x-direction, the potential temperature being $\theta(y,p,t)$. The velocity field was assumed to consist of three parts: (i) a barotropic, geostrophic confluent flow $(kx, -ky)$, where the constant k was taken to be about $^1/_3 f$; (ii) a geostrophic velocity $U(y,p,t)$ in the x-direction; and (iii) an ageostrophic transverse motion $v'(y,p,t)$, $\omega(y,p,t)$. Thus,

$$\theta = \theta(y,p,t)$$
$$u = u_g = kx + U(y,p,t)$$
$$v = -ky + v'(y,p,t)$$
$$\omega = \omega(y,p,t).$$
(9.1)

Figure 9.2 shows schematically the isotherms and the confluent geostrophic streamlines in an isobaric surface.

It is convenient to introduce the "absolute momentum"

$$M(y,p,t) = U - fy.$$
(9.2)

This quantity is conserved when $k=0$ and plays the same role in the dynamics of a straight current on the f-plane, as the absolute angular momentum in a circular vortex. In particular, the lines $M = $ constant in the yp-plane are the absolute vortex lines. The vertical absolute vorticity measured in isobaric surfaces is $-M_y$.

Since $u = M + kx + fy$ is assumed to be geostrophic, it satisfies the thermal wind equation

$$fM_p = \gamma\theta_y$$
(9.3)

where subscripts denote partial derivatives, and

$$\gamma(p) = \frac{1}{\rho\theta} = \frac{R}{p_o}\left(\frac{p_o}{p}\right)^{c_v/c_p}.$$
(9.4)

Here R is the gas constant, c_p and c_v the specific heats, $p_o = 1$ bar and ρ is density.

To satisfy conservation of mass, Sawyer expressed the transverse motion in terms of a streamfunction $\psi(y,p,t)$:

$$v' = -\psi_p, \quad \omega = \psi_y$$
(9.5)

The lines $\psi = $ constant in the yp-plane are the streamlines of the transverse circulation.

Since v' and ω are assumed independent of x, all particles situated on a straight line parallel to the x-axis will remain on such a line. The material time derivative following the total motion may be written

$$\frac{D}{Dt} = \frac{D'}{Dt} + u\frac{\partial}{\partial x}$$
(9.6)

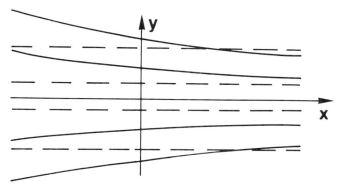

Fig. 9.2. Schematic map showing parallel isotherms (dashed) and confluent geostrophic streamlines. (For inferred transverse circulation, see also Fig. 3.6.)

where

$$\frac{D'}{Dt} = \frac{\partial}{\partial t} - (ky + \psi_p)\frac{\partial}{\partial y} + \psi_y\frac{\partial}{\partial p}$$
(9.7)

is the time derivative following the projection of a particle in the yp-plane.

Assuming dry-adiabatic changes of state, we have

$$\frac{D'\theta}{Dt} = 0$$
(9.8)

since θ is independent of x. Sawyer wrote the equation of the x-component of motion as

$$\frac{Du}{Dt} = fv'$$
(9.9)

since he assumed v' to be the ageostrophic part of v. In terms of M this becomes

$$\frac{D'M}{Dt} = -kM - k^2x.$$
(9.10)

Clearly, this equation is strictly not compatible with the assumption that M is independent of x at all times; this complication will be considered later in this article.

Assuming thermal wind balance to persist, time differentiation of (9.3) gives

$$\frac{\partial}{\partial p}(fM_t) = \frac{\partial}{\partial y}(\gamma\theta_t).$$
(9.11)

Eliminating M_t and θ_t between (9.8), (9.10) and (9.11), Sawyer obtained the following second-order differential equation in ψ:

$$L[\psi] = Q = -2k\gamma\theta_y,$$
(9.12)

where L is the linear operator,

$$L[\psi] = \gamma\frac{\partial}{\partial y}(\theta_y\psi_p - \theta_p\psi_y) - f\frac{\partial}{\partial p}(M_y\psi_p - M_p\psi_y).$$
(9.13)

Equation (9.12) was also dealt with by the author (1959, 1962) and is often referred to as the Sawyer–Eliassen (S–E) equation. When the fields of θ and M are known the S–E equation, supplemented by a boundary condition, will determine ψ, and hence the cross-frontal circulation. The simplest way to formulate the boundary condition is to define a closed curve S surrounding the region of interest in the yp-plane, and assume it to be impervious to the transverse motion. The boundary condition then is

$$\psi = 0 \text{ on } S.$$
(9.14)

Sawyer chose a rectangular curve consisting of an isobar near the ground, another isobar near the tropopause and two vertical lateral boundaries. The latter should be sufficiently far away, of the order a Rossby radius from the front, to avoid materially disturbing the solution in the central area.

Equation (9.12) is elliptic when

$$fq > 0$$
(9.15)

(i.e., $q > 0$ in the Northern Hemisphere), where

$$q(y,p,t) = g(M_y\theta_p - M_p\theta_y) = g\frac{\partial(M,\theta)}{\partial(y,p)}$$
(9.16)

is the geostrophic potential vorticity (with g denoting the acceleration of gravity). It follows from (9.8) and (9.10) that

$$\frac{D'q}{Dt} = 0. \qquad (9.17)$$

Consequently, the S-E equation (9.12) cannot change type in dry-adiabatic and frictionless motion.

On account of the thermal wind equation (9.3), (9.16) may be written

$$q = g(-M_y)(-\theta_p) - \frac{g\gamma}{f}(\theta_y)^2. \qquad (9.18)$$

In a frontogenetic situation, the last, baroclinic term will increase. In order for q to be conserved, either the absolute vorticity $(-M_y)$ or the static stability $(-\theta_p)$, or both, must also increase. In sharp fronts near the ground, the magnitude of each of the two terms on the right of (9.18) may be much larger than q.

With z denoting height, q may also be expressed in yz-coordinates as

$$q = \frac{1}{\rho}\frac{\partial(\theta,M)}{\partial(y,z)} = \frac{1}{\rho}\frac{\partial U}{\partial z}\frac{\partial \theta}{\partial z}(\vartheta_M - \vartheta_\theta). \qquad (9.19)$$

Here ϑ_M and ϑ_θ are the slopes $\partial z/\partial y$ of the M- and θ-surfaces, respectively. When the air is statically stable with positive absolute vorticity, the condition (9.15) implies that the absolute vortex lines $M = $ constant are steeper than the isentropes.

As noted by Sawyer, (9.15) is nearly always satisfied in the atmosphere. We shall therefore assume that $L[\psi]$ is elliptic; the nonhomogeneous problem (9.12), (9.14) has then a unique solution. With the y-axis pointing toward the cold side in the troposphere, θ_y is negative, and the forcing Q in (9.12) is positive. The elliptic operator $L[\psi]$ has the character of a distorted Laplacian, and its value at a point measures the deficit of ψ at that point compared with a certain mean of ψ in its surroundings. Positive values of Q in the area require negative values of ψ inside S, with at least one minimum. The streamlines $\psi = $ constant are closed curves around a minimum point, and according to (9.5) they represent a circulation in the thermodynamically direct sense, with ascending motion in the warm air and descent in the cold air, as shown in Fig. 9.3.

The transverse circulation will in turn produce advective changes in the fields of θ and M according to (9.8) and (9.10). A circulation in the direct sense will reduce the slope of the isentropes and hence counteract the increasing baroclinicity imposed by the confluence. In this sense, a direct transverse circulation has a frontolytic effect. In places, however, it will cause the gradients of θ and M to steepen. In particular, the transverse motion will cause the isentropes and M-lines near the ground to be pushed toward the warm side of the baroclinic zone (point A in Fig. 9.3), producing there a sharp temperature gradient and strong cyclonic shear. This agrees well with the synoptic experience, that the warm air on the surface

map is nearly homogeneous right up to the front, whereas there is considerable temperature gradient in the cold air. At the upper boundary, the M-lines will be advected towards the cold side, producing a front-parallel jet with strong cyclonic shear on its polar flank (near point B in Fig. 9.3). A striking example of the (M, θ) and potential vorticity structures of the jet stream is shown in Fig. 10.4.

9.3 Forcing by Confluence and Shear

Bergeron's confluent motion is not the only geostrophic wind field that can sharpen the horizontal temperature gradient by differential advection. As shown in Fig. 9.4, which is meant to illustrate the situation near the ground in a typical cold front, front-parallel winds with cyclonic shear will also contribute if a temperature gradient exists along the front. This effect is typically operating in many cold fronts, with warm air advection ahead of the front and cold advection in its rear. By taking this effect also into account, Eliassen (1962) obtained a more general form of the forcing term Q in (9.12):

$$Q = -2\gamma\left(\frac{\partial u_g}{\partial x}\frac{\partial \theta}{\partial y} - \frac{\partial u_g}{\partial y}\frac{\partial \theta}{\partial x}\right). \qquad (9.20)$$

Here the first term within the parentheses is Sawyer's confluence term, while the second is due to shear. The two effects, however, are not fundamentally different; they both depend on a geostrophic stretching of the isotherms. As pointed out by Hoskins (1982), Q represents 2γ times the material rate of change of $(-\theta_y)$ that would result in the absence of ageostrophic motion.

Using the thermal wind equation, (9.20) may also be written

$$Q = -2f\left(\frac{\partial u_g}{\partial y}\frac{\partial v_g}{\partial p} - \frac{\partial u_g}{\partial p}\frac{\partial v_g}{\partial y}\right) = -2f\frac{\partial(u_g, v_g)}{\partial(y, p)} \qquad (9.21)$$

and Q is thus measured by the Jacobian of the geostrophic wind components u_g and v_g in the yp-plane. If u_g- and v_g-isotachs are drawn in the yp-plane, Q is given by the

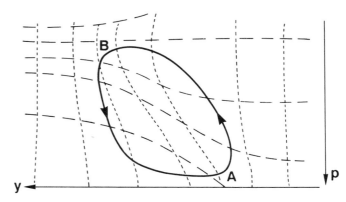

FIG. 9.3. Schematic cross section through a frontal zone showing absolute vortex lines $M = $ const. (dotted), isentropes (dashed) and streamlines of a direct transverse circulation.

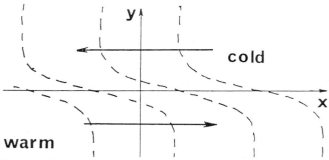

FIG. 9.4. Schematic map showing isotherms (dashed) deformed advectively by a geostrophic wind field with cyclonic shear.

density of their intersection points, reckoned with appropriate sign.

In a situation like the one pictured in Fig. 9.4, the shear effect alone will be operating, with $Q = -2f(\partial u_g/\partial y)(\partial v_g/\partial p)$. Figure 9.5 shows the cross section of an idealized frontal zone in this case. With the distribution of u_g and v_g in Fig. 9.5a, Q is positive in the frontal zone, producing a direct ageostrophic circulation. When this is added to the geostrophic flow in the cross-frontal direction, a picture of the total cross-frontal motion emerges. This is shown in Fig. 9.5b, in a frame of reference moving with the front. In this idealized case, warm air approaches the front at low levels, rises in the frontal zone and leaves at higher levels. The cold air behaves in the opposite way, approaching at high levels, descending in the frontal zone and leaving at low levels. Thus the ageostrophic circulation causes a radical change in the total streamline pattern, and prevents the front from being tipped over by the cross-frontal thermal wind.

If (9.21) is integrated over an area A inside a closed curve C, one obtains

$$\int\limits_A \int Q\,dy\,dp = -2f \oint\limits_C u_g\,dv_g \qquad (9.22)$$

where the integral along C is taken in the direction that

corresponds to rotating the vector ∇y toward ∇p. In particular, if C is taken as the closed u_g-isotach surrounding a jet, the right-hand side of (9.22) vanishes. Thus the forcing in a confluent jet core has the character of a doublet, producing circulations with opposite directions. Figure 9.6 shows schematically the resulting streamlines in a jet subject to confluence only, i.e., $\partial v_g/\partial y < 0$, $\partial v_g/\partial p = 0$. In this case, the circulations are opposite in the upper and lower parts of the jet, with flow toward the polar side through the jet maximum. Both circulations are direct, however, because the sign of θ_y reverses at the level of maximum wind.

Shapiro (1981) has analyzed the circulation in an observed intense jet where the upper frontal region below and on the polar side of the jet was subject to both confluence and shear forcing, i.e., $\partial v_g/\partial y < 0$, $\partial v_g/\partial p < 0$, as shown in Fig. 9.7a. The resulting transverse streamlines obtained by Shapiro are shown in Fig. 9.7b. In this case the indirect circulation forcing by strong lateral shear with cold advection, in the uppermost part of the frontal layer, dominates the direct circulation forcing by confluence. Compared to the situation in Fig. 9.6 the upper cell has now been moved down and poleward to give a pronounced indirect circulation in the upper part of the front. By advection this circulation will increase the baroclinicity in the area.

Studies of the frontogenetic circulation in upper-air fronts have also been made by Keyser and Pecnick (1985) and Reeder and Keyser (1988); see simulated circulations in Figs. 3.11 and 10.7. The relative importance of confluence and shear on surface frontogenesis has been studied by Keyser and Pecnick (1987).

9.4 Modifications in Frontal Clouds

Inside a cloud, (9.8) must be replaced by

$$\frac{D'\theta_e}{Dt} = 0 \qquad (9.23)$$

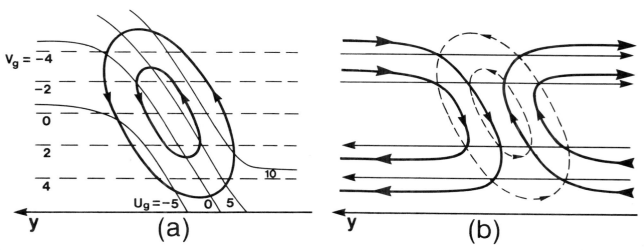

FIG. 9.5. Schematic frontal cross section illustrating pure shear forcing. (a) u_g-isotachs (thin), v_g-isotachs (dashed), ageostrophic circulation (thick). (b) Projection in the yp-plane of geostrophic streamlines (thin), ageostrophic circulation (dashed), and streamlines of total geostrophic plus ageostrophic flow (thick), in a frame following the motion of the front.

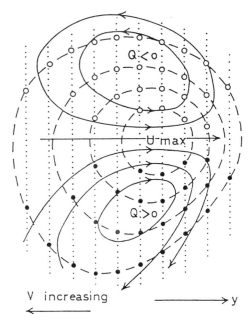

FIG. 9.6. Transverse circulation in the vicinity of an idealized jet core deformed by confluence only. Geostrophic isotachs of u_g (dashed) and v_g (dotted) (Eliassen 1962).

where θ_e is the equivalent potential temperature. The analysis leading up to (9.12) may be carried through with θ_e everywhere replacing θ. In this case, however, γ in the thermal wind equation (9.3) will not only be a function of pressure but will depend upon temperature as well. As a consequence, the resulting equation in ψ will differ from (9.12) in that it contains some additional first-order terms in ψ. This does not materially change the equation, however, and the ellipticity condition is still given by (9.15), except that q is now replaced by the moist potential vorticity

$$q_e = g \frac{\partial(M, \theta_e)}{\partial(y, p)} = \frac{1}{\rho} U_z \theta_{ez} (\vartheta_M - \vartheta_{\theta e}) \qquad (9.24)$$

where $\vartheta_{\theta e}$ is the slope of the moist isentropic surfaces. Since in a baroclinic zone the moist isentropic surfaces are steeper than the dry isentropic surfaces, it follows that q_e is considerably reduced compared to q and may even be negative.

As stressed by Bennetts and Hoskins (1979), q_e is conserved in saturated air, where θ_e is a function of θ and p only. Indeed, from (9.10) and (9.23) it follows that

$$\frac{D'q_e}{Dt} = 0 \qquad (9.25)$$

in saturated air.

9.5 Forcing by Ekman-Layer Convergence

A possible forcing mechanism for transverse ageostrophic motion is the upward flow from the Ekman layer in a region of low-level cyclonic shear. In the absence of other forcing effects ($Q = 0$), the streamfunction of the transverse flow above the Ekman layer must satisfy the homogeneous equation $L[\psi] = 0$. This gives a rising and diverging frontolytic flow in the yp-plane above the region of low-level cyclonic shear. This transverse motion, however, is modified if latent heat is released in the rising current. This effect was studied by the author (Eliassen 1959), who conjectured that latent heat release could even change the transverse flow into a convergent, frontogenetic one. He did not realize, however, that this would imply the occurrence of closed streamlines, which are incompatible with a homogeneous, elliptic equation. In order that the Ekman-condensation process shall have a frontogenetic effect, the stratification along the absolute vortex lines must be conditionally unstable so that the equation is hyperbolic inside clouds. Observational and simulation studies of the enhancement of vertical circulations associated with surface fronts, by friction and condensation heat release, are reviewed in Section 3.3.1.

9.6 "Symmetric" Inertial Stability

Sawyer noted that the ellipticity criterion (9.15) coincides with Solberg's (1936) stability criterion for a baroclinic current with respect to "symmetric" disturbances, i.e., disturbances independent of x. Solberg's analysis concerned the stability of a circular vortex, but it applies equally well to a straight current, with M replacing the angular momentum. There is indeed a close connection between the forced transverse circulations described by (9.12) and the free transverse oscillations in the absence of forcing. In the latter case, a horizontal acceleration $-\psi_{pt}$ in the y direction must be taken into account, leading to the homogeneous equation $\psi_{pptt} + L[\psi] = 0$. When (9.15) is fulfilled, the current is symmetrically stable and can sustain stable symmetric wave motions and oscillations in the yp-plane, under conservation of θ and M. Transverse displacements will produce restoring forces which depend on the direction of the displacements (see Fig. 5.1). In the hydrostatic approximation, the restoring force is weakest for displacements along the isentropes. Oscillations along streamlines shaped as flat cells along the isentropes have the smallest possible frequency

$$\nu_{min} = \left[f \left(f - \left(\frac{\partial U}{\partial y} \right)_\theta \right) \right]^{1/2} = \frac{1}{N\theta} \left(\frac{gfq}{\gamma} \right)^{1/2} \qquad (9.26)$$

where the derivative is taken along the isentrope. The direction of strongest stability is nearly vertical, and the highest frequency ν_{max} in a nonhydrostatic model is very close to the buoyancy frequency N.

The dependence of stability on direction strongly influences the solution of the nonhomogeneous equation (9.12). The forced transverse motion prefers to follow the directions of weak stability; as a result, the streamlines tend to stretch out along the isentropes. A rough measure of the ratio of the vertical depth of forced circulation cells to their

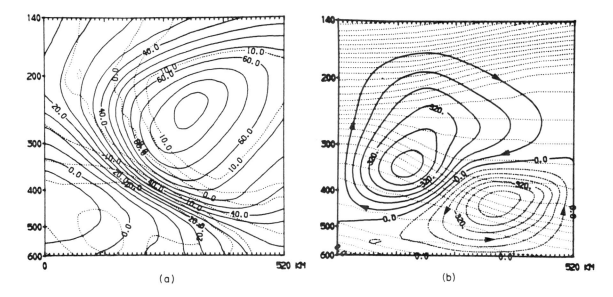

FIG. 9.7. Cross section through an upper-tropospheric jet stream over the midwestern United States, 11 April 1978. (a) Geostrophic isotachs (m s^{-1}) of alongfront (solid) and crossfront wind (dotted, positive for wind component toward left). (b) Circulation streamfunction (m s^{-1} mb, solid lines) and isentropes (dotted) (Shapiro 1981).

extent along the isentropes is provided by the ratio

$$\frac{v_{min}}{v_{max}} = \frac{f}{N}\left[1 - \frac{1}{f}\left(\frac{\partial U}{\partial y}\right)_\theta\right]^{1/2} = \frac{1}{\theta_z}\left(\frac{fq}{g\gamma}\right)^{1/2}. \quad (9.27)$$

Also the strength of the forced transverse circulation depends upon q. From an analysis of an equation equivalent to (9.12), Eliassen (1952) found that the Green's function, representing the solution when the forcing (Q) is a point source, contains a factor $q^{-1/2}$. Thus for a given forcing $Q(y,p)$, the solution will become particularly intense in regions of small q.

Inside frontal clouds θ must be replaced by θ_e and q by q_e, which is much smaller than q and may be nearly vanishing. In such regions there is little or no stability against motions along the moist isentropes, and forced circulations would be expected to be strong, with concentrated upward currents along the slanting θ_e-surfaces inside the cloud. Thorpe and Emanuel (1985) have computed the development due to confluence of a frontal zone, assuming saturation with a small value of q_e in the ascending branch. They found that condensation heating speeds up the circulation and concentrates the upward branch. An example of the M-θ_e distribution, in a cross section through a warm front, is given in Fig. 12.13.

In the case of negative q_e, the air inside clouds is symmetrically unstable and may sustain growing transverse circulations even in the absence of forcing. Bennetts and Hoskins (1979) have performed model calculations of such unstable circulations, assuming moist-adiabatic temperature changes in the ascending, and dry-adiabatic changes in the descending, branches. They found that the saturated air would become statically unstable in certain regions and suggested this mechanism as an explanation of frontal rainbands.

9.7 Geostrophic Momentum as Coordinate

$L[\psi]$ assumes a simpler form when M and p are used as independent variables instead of y and p:

$$L[\psi] = -\frac{1}{y_M}\left[\left(\frac{\gamma}{g}q\,\psi_M\right)_M + f\psi_{pp}\right]. \quad (9.28)$$

Here the subscripts denote partial differentiation of functions of M and p. In these variables, the forcing term (9.21) becomes

$$Q = -\frac{2}{y_M}\frac{\partial(u_g, v_g)}{\partial(M,p)}. \quad (9.29)$$

When substituted into (9.12), the factor $-y_M^{-1}$, which is the absolute vorticity measured in isobaric surfaces, drops out and the equation becomes

$$\left(\frac{\gamma q}{gf}\psi_M\right)_M + \psi_{pp} = 2\frac{\partial(u_g, v_g)}{\partial(M,p)} \quad (9.30)$$

where, from (9.16),

$$q = g\frac{\partial(M,\theta)}{\partial(M,p)}\bigg/\frac{\partial(y,p)}{\partial(M,p)} = g\frac{\theta_p}{y_M}. \quad (9.31)$$

M. Todsen (1964; also reported in Eliassen 1966) used (9.30) to calculate the transverse circulation in a cold front over western Europe from synoptic data. The synoptic situation of 12 UTC 8 April 1962 is shown in Fig. 9.8a. Figure 9.8b shows the M-p grid in a vertical cross section of the front. The resulting streamlines of the transverse ageostrophic circulation, assuming dry-adiabatic changes of state, are shown in Fig. 9.8c.

Todsen also computed the transverse circulation under the assumption that condensation would take place in that part of the upward branch where the measured dewpoint depression was less than 6 K. In that area he assumed that the moist isentropes would coincide with the *M*-lines, so that $q_e = 0$. Figure 9.9a shows the resulting moist circulation. As would be expected, and was also demonstrated by Sawyer (1956), the ascending motion in the moist case is stronger and more concentrated compared to the dry case. The streamlines of the total geostrophic plus ageostrophic transverse motion relative to the moving front are shown for the moist case in Fig. 9.9b. From the computed vertical motion and the observed frontal movement, Todsen calculated a total rainfall of 5 mm during the frontal passage, in fair agreement with measured values.

9.8 Temporal Development of Frontal Structure

R. T. Williams (1967, 1972) calculated the time evolution of a straight frontal zone with superimposed geostrophic

shear or confluence from a model based on the primitive equations. As in the geostrophic momentum theory, he obtained a direct transverse circulation which produced pronounced frontogenesis near the ground. In particular, he obtained the significant result that in the absence of diffusion, a frontal discontinuity at the ground would form in a finite time.

As mentioned previously, (9.10), which follows from Sawyer's (1956) analysis, is not strictly compatible with the assumption that U and M are independent of x at all times. Williams (1972) and also Hoskins and Bretherton (1972) noted that for consistency, $v'(y,p,t)$ in (9.1) must be assumed to have a geostrophic part $-k^2x/f$. This gives instead of (9.10) the momentum equation

$$\frac{D'M}{Dt} = -kM. \tag{9.32}$$

Based on this equation, Hoskins and Bretherton (1972) devised an ingenious method to calculate directly the change of frontal structure produced by confluence after an arbitrary time. From (9.32) they concluded that

$$\frac{D'm}{Dt} = 0, \quad \text{where} \quad m = Me^{kt} \tag{9.33}$$

is the initial value of M for a particle. Recalling (9.8) and (9.17), it is seen that in dry-adiabatic motion the three quantities m, θ and q are conserved following the projection of the motion in the yp-plane, and it follows that a functional relation

$$q = F(m,\theta) \tag{9.34}$$

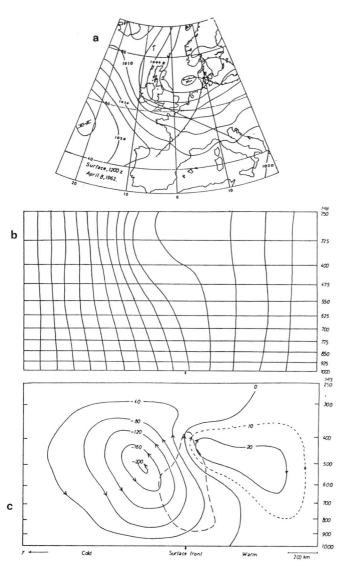

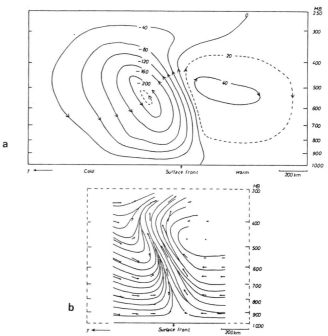

Fig. 9.8. Dry calculation of transverse circulation in a cold front over western Europe on 8 April 1962. (a) Surface map showing the position of the cross section used. (b) The *M-p* grid in the cross section. (c) Circulation streamfunction (10 m s^{-1} mb). The dashed curve is the outline of assumed cloud in the moist calculation (Todsen 1964).

Fig. 9.9. Moist calculation of transverse circulation for the same case as in Fig. 9.8. (a) Circulation streamfunction. (b) Total (geostrophic + ageostrophic) transverse motion relative to the moving surface front. Arrows indicate 1.5-h particle displacements (Todsen 1964).

must hold at all times. The function F can be determined from the known initial state.

In the coordinates M and p, with y and θ as dependent variables, the thermal wind equation (9.3) takes the form

$$fy_p + \gamma\theta_M = 0 . \tag{9.35}$$

Eliminating y by means of (9.31), the following equation in θ is obtained:

$$\gamma\theta_{MM} + \left(\frac{gf\theta_p}{F(Me^{kt},\theta)}\right)_p = 0 . \tag{9.36}$$

Hoskins and Bretherton derived this equation in a slightly different form, using the Exner function of pressure and the geostrophic coordinate $Y = -M/f$ as coordinates.

One might also use m and p as coordinates and write (9.36) in the form

$$\gamma e^{2kt}\theta_{mm} + \left(\frac{gf\theta_p}{F(m,\theta)}\right)_p = 0 . \tag{9.37}$$

In any case, time appears only as a parameter, and the equation may be solved for any value of t, provided that the solution exists. Equation (9.36) or (9.37) is almost a linear differential equation in θ, except that θ appears also as argument of the function F. The equation is elliptic when (9.15) is fulfilled, and the solution is then uniquely determined from values of θ on a closed boundary curve. Hoskins and Bretherton chose two isobars as the upper and lower material boundaries, where θ is known as a function of m from the initial conditions. At the two lateral boundaries far away from the front, θ may be considered as known functions of p.

Having determined $\theta(M,p,t)$, the function $y(M,p,t)$ follows from integration of (9.31) and (9.35), apart from an insignificant constant. The latter function may finally be inverted to give $M(y,p,t)$, and hence, the distributions of U and θ in physical space.

From their theory, Hoskins and Bretherton confirmed Williams' (1967, 1972) hypothesis that a frontal discontinuity can form at the ground in a finite time in the absence of diffusion. This would not be possible if the transverse circulation remained stationary during the frontogenetic development. It can be seen from (9.12), however, that the forcing increases in proportion to the frontal temperature gradient, giving a feedback on the transverse circulation that speeds up the frontogenesis.

Several numerical solutions based on Hoskins and Bretherton's theory have been presented by Hoskins (1971, 1972). Of particular interest are the cases where the initial atmosphere had a distinct tropopause separating the troposphere from the stratosphere, with much higher values of potential vorticity in the latter. After a certain amount of confluence has taken place, the solution shows a quite sharp front at the ground. A strong jet has formed at the tropopause, and the tropopause itself has been pulled down, forming a very realistic tropopause fold (Fig. 9.10).

9.9 Frontogenesis as a Three-Dimensional Process

The two-dimensional theory of frontogenesis is of course only a crude approximation. In reality, fronts are not straight, and their structure varies considerably from one cross section to another. Only a three-dimensional theory can give a full account of the frontogenetic processes.

The transient cyclonic and anticyclonic disturbances of synoptic scale in middle and high latitudes will necessarily involve areas of horizontal deformation which disturb the isotherms and produce secondary vertical circulations with local frontogenetic effects. These vertical circulations, however, are not, as in the idealized two-dimensional case, transversal to the baroclinic zone, but just as much longitudinal. Thus, in baroclinic waves the ascending motion ahead of wave troughs and the descent in their rear are connected with horizontal divergent velocities along the main isotherm direction.

Many numerical studies have been reported in the literature that indicate that fronts and jet streams intensify in developing cyclones. Perhaps the first clear demonstration of this kind was the work by Edelmann (1963). He made a numerical integration of the development of a baroclinically unstable wave, using a five-level model based on the primitive equations for a dry atmosphere. Starting with a wave disturbance and a very smooth temperature field, the model developed very sharp surface fronts in a rapidly deepening cyclone after a few days.

Mudrick (1974) likewise simulated the development of baroclinically unstable waves by numerical integration of the primitive equations. His model included a distinct tropopause. In addition to quite realistic surface fronts, he also obtained pronounced upper-tropospheric frontogenesis, with jet maximum in the trough, connected with strong descent of warm air on its upstream side. A similar result was obtained by Shapiro (1975).

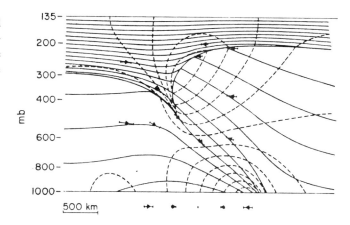

FIG. 9.10. Cross section normal to a baroclinic zone that has been subject to contraction by confluence. The isentropes (solid), alongfront wind isotachs (dashed), and tropopause (heavy solid line) have been calculated from an analytically-defined initial situation on the basis of Hoskins and Bretherton's theory. Arrows indicate short-term particle displacements; basic-state geostrophic deformation field is shown beneath (Hoskins 1972).

A very thorough study of frontogenetic processes in upper jet stream waves has been made by Newton and Trevisan (1984), relating the wave structures and dimensions to changes of baroclinity, vertical shear, lateral shear and static stability. Using a primitive equation, isentropic surface model, they simulated a deepening cyclonic wave which developed a pronounced midtropospheric frontal layer in the trough. They computed the ageostrophic vertical circulations and compared them with theory. In particular, descent in the confluent region behind the upper trough is concentrated near the jet axis, with an indirect circulation in the frontal zone as in the earlier experiments.

As described in the previous sections, the geostrophic momentum approximation has been successfully applied to the development of frontal structure in the idealized two-dimensional case. Hoskins (1975) has generalized this theory to three-dimensional motion. By introducing the semigeostrophic coordinates $X = (x + v_g/f)$, $Y = (y - u_g/f)$, he showed that the dynamics according to the geostrophic momentum approximation can be expressed in these coordinates by equations which are formally nearly identical with the usual quasi-geostrophic equations. The transformation of the geostrophic momentum solution from the coordinates X, Y back to physical space x, y, however, produces a deformation which is of crucial importance to frontogenesis, and which is lacking in quasi-geostrophic theory.

In a series of papers, Hoskins and his coworkers (Hoskins and Draghici 1977; Hoskins and West 1979; Heckley and Hoskins 1982) have used the semigeostrophic equations to demonstrate the development of fronts and jets in growing baroclinic waves. They found that the nature and position of the fronts that form depend much on the structure of the initial baroclinic current. A typical feature in their results is that the surface cold front appears to be disconnected from the warm front (see simulated and observed structures in Section 10.4), in contrast to the conventional picture of a frontal cyclone. This fits in with my own experience as a synoptician (a long time ago), that the inner part of the cold front connecting onto the warm front was usually not discernible in the data.

A likely result of the recent and future research on the detailed structure of developing cyclones may be a revision and refinement of the seventy year-old classical model of frontal cyclones.

REFERENCES

Bennetts, D. A., and B. J. Hoskins, 1979: Conditional symmetric instability—a possible explanation for frontal rainbands. *Quart. J. Roy. Meteor. Soc.,* **105**, 945-962.

Bergeron, T., 1928: Über die dreidimensional verknüpfende Wetteranalyse. *Geofys. Publ.,* **5**, No. 6, 1-111.

Bjerknes, J., 1919: On the structure of moving cyclones. *Geofys. Publ.,* **1**, No. 1, 1-8.

——, and E. Palmén, 1937: Investigations of selected European cyclones by means of serial ascents. *Geofys. Publ.,* **12**, No. 2, 1-62.

Bluestein, H. B., 1986: Fronts and jet streaks: A theoretical perspective. *Mesoscale Meteorology and Forecasting,* P. S. Ray, Ed. American Meteorological Society, 173-215.

Edelmann, W., 1963: On the behavior of disturbances in a baroclinic channel. Summary Rep. No. 2, Research in Objective Weather Forecasting, Part F, Contract AF61 (052)-373. Deut. Wetterd., Offenbach/Main, 35 pp.

Eliassen, A., 1952: Slow thermally or frictionally controlled meridional circulations in a circular vortex. *Astrophys. Norv.,* **5**, 19-60.

——, 1959: On the formation of fronts in the atmosphere. *The Atmosphere and the Sea in Motion* (Rossby Memorial Volume), B. Bolin, Ed. Rockefeller Institute Press, 277-287.

——, 1962: On the vertical circulation in frontal zones. *Geofys. Publ.,* **24**, 147-160.

——, 1966: Motions of intermediate scale: Fronts and cyclones. *Advances in Earth Science,* P. M. Hurley, Ed. MIT Press, 111-138.

Heckley, W. A., and B. J. Hoskins, 1982: Baroclinic waves and frontogenesis in a nonuniform potential vorticity semigeostrophic model. *J. Atmos. Sci.,* **39**, 1999-2016.

Hoskins, B. J., 1971: Atmospheric frontogenesis models: Some solutions. *Quart. J. Roy. Meteor. Soc.,* **97**, 139-153.

——, 1972: Non-Boussinesq effects and further development in a model of upper tropospheric frontogenesis. *Quart. J. Roy. Meteor. Soc.,* **98**, 532-541.

——, 1975: The geostrophic momentum approximation and the semigeostrophic equations. *J. Atmos. Sci.,* **32**, 233-242.

——, 1982: The mathematical theory of frontogenesis. *Ann. Rev. Fluid Mech.,* **14**, 131-151.

——, and F. P. Bretherton, 1972: Atmospheric frontogenesis models: Mathematical formulation and solution. *J. Atmos. Sci.,* **29**, 11-37.

——, and I. Draghici, 1977: The forcing of ageostrophic motion according to the semigeostrophic equations and in an isentropic coordinate model. *J. Atmos. Sci.,* **34**, 1859-1867.

——, and N. V. West, 1979: Baroclinic waves and frontogenesis. Part II: Uniform potential vorticity jet flows—cold and warm fronts. *J. Atmos. Sci.,* **36**, 1663-1680.

Keyser, D., 1986: Atmospheric fronts: An observational perspective. *Mesoscale Meteorology and Forecasting,* P. S. Ray, Ed. American Meteorological Society, 216-258.

——, and M. J. Pecnick, 1985: A two-dimensional primitive equation model of frontogenesis forced by confluence and horizontal shear. *J. Atmos. Sci.,* **42**, 1259-1282.

——, and M. A. Shapiro, 1986: A review of the structure and dynamics of upper-level frontal zones. *Mon. Wea. Rev.,* **114**, 452-499.

——, and M. J. Pecnick, 1987: The effect of along-front temperature variation in a two-dimensional primitive equation model of surface frontogenesis. *J. Atmos. Sci.,* **44**, 577-604.

Mudrick, S. E., 1974: A numerical study of frontogenesis. *J. Atmos. Sci.,* **31**, 869-892.

Namias, J., and P. F. Clapp, 1949: Confluence theory of the high tropospheric jet stream. *J. Meteor.,* **6**, 330-336.

Newton, C. W., and A. Trevisan, 1984: Clinogenesis and frontogenesis in jet-stream waves. Part I: Analytical relations to wave structure; Part II: Channel model numerical experiments. *J. Atmos. Sci.,* **41**, 2717-2734; 2735-2755.

Orlanski, I., B. Ross, L. Polinsky and R. Shaginaw, 1985: Advances in the theory of atmospheric fronts. *Advances in Geophysics,* **28**, 223-252.

Palmén, E., and C. W. Newton, 1969: *Atmospheric Circulation Systems. Their Structure and Physical Interpretation.* Academic Press, 603 pp.

Reeder, M. J., and D. Keyser, 1988: Balanced and unbalanced upper frontogenesis. *J. Atmos. Sci.,* **45**, 3366–3386.

Sawyer, J. S., 1956: The vertical circulation at meteorological fronts and its relation to frontogenesis. *Proc. Roy. Soc. London,* **A234**, 346–362.

Shapiro, M. A., 1975: Simulation of upper-level frontogenesis with a 20-level isentropic coordinate primitive equation model. *Mon. Wea. Rev.,* **103**, 591–604.

——, 1981: Frontogenesis and geostrophically forced secondary circulations in the vicinity of jet stream–frontal zone systems. *J. Atmos. Sci.,* **38**, 954–973.

Solberg, H., 1936: Le mouvement d'inertie de l'atmosphere stable et son rôle dans la théorie des cyclones. *Procès-verbaux, Assoc. de Météor., Mém. et disc., Un. Géod. Géophys. Int.,* Edimbourg, 66–82.

Thorpe, A. J., and K. A. Emanuel, 1985: Frontogenesis in the presence of small stability to slantwise convection. *J. Atmos. Sci.,* **42**, 1809–1824.

Todsen, M., 1964: A study of vertical circulations in a cold front. Part IV, Final Report, Contr. No. AF 61(052)–525.

Williams, R. T., 1967: Atmospheric frontogenesis: A numerical experiment. *J. Atmos. Sci.,* **24**, 627–641.

——, 1972: Quasi-geostrophic versus non-geostrophic frontogenesis. *J. Atmos. Sci.,* **29**, 3–10.

Chapter 10

Fronts, Jet Streams and the Tropopause

M. A. Shapiro
NOAA/ERL/Wave Propagation Laboratory, Boulder, CO 80303

and

Daniel Keyser
Department of Atmospheric Science, State University of New York at Albany, Albany, NY 12222

10.1 Introduction

The advent of kite and balloon-borne meteorograph soundings during the early 1900s and the subsequent deployment of regional rawinsonde networks provided the observational basis for the study of the spatial and temporal evolution of fronts, jet streams and the tropopause. During the mid-century years (1935–1965), researchers focused on the structural characteristics of fronts and their associated jet streams near the tropopause, and on the diagnosis of the frontogenetic processes and secondary circulations governing their life cycles. The pioneering observational study by J. Bjerknes and E. Palmén (1937) showed fronts to be transitional zones of finite width (~100 km) and depth (~1 km), rather than near zero-order discontinuities extending from the surface to the tropopause. Newton (1954) presented the most comprehensive diagnosis of all components of upper-level frontogenesis during this period, and Sawyer (1956) and Eliassen (1962) derived the diagnostic theory for geostrophically forced secondary circulations about fronts based on the semigeostrophic equations, which was later expanded to the temporal dimension by Hoskins (1971) and Hoskins and Bretherton (1972).

In contrast to their upper-level counterparts, surface fronts received less attention from researchers during the period, with the exception of the classic study by Sanders (1955). The conceptual model of surface fronts and their evolution during the life cycle of extratropical cyclones proposed by J. Bjerknes (1919) and J. Bjerknes and H. Solberg (1921, 1922), referred to as the Norwegian frontal cyclone model, received such wide acceptance that it remained virtually unaltered from the time of its inception.

In this chapter, the authors have chosen to review past and present interpretations that have arisen regarding the structure and governing dynamics of fronts, jet streams and the tropopause. It will be shown that new insights and the resolution of previous controversies have been linked, in part, to technological advances in atmospheric observing systems and, more recently, to the utilization of computers for diagnosis and numerical simulation.

For a historical review of fronts, jet streams and the tropopause, readers are referred to the works of Reiter (1975), Palmén and Newton (1969), Kutzbach (1979) and Keyser and Shapiro (1986). Recent advances in the study of surface and upper-level fronts are summarized by Reed in Sections 3.3.1 and 3.3.2 of this volume.

10.2 The Structure and Dynamics of Upper-Level Fronts, Jet Streams and the Tropopause

10.2.1 Structure

The study of the structure of upper-level fronts, associated jet streams and their relationship to the tropopause has resulted in significant differences in interpretation among researchers. Since the earliest frontal-tropopause model by J. Bjerknes (1932), several models have been proposed to describe the structure of fronts and jet streams

in the vicinity of the tropopause (Fig. 10.1). These differences in interpretation stem from the limited availability of upper-air observations in regions of large horizontal gradients in tropopause height across jet streams at the level of maximum wind speed (LMW) (minimum horizontal thermal gradient). In reviews by Reed and Danielsen (1959), Shapiro (1976) and Keyser and Shapiro (1986), Berggren (1952) was cited for proposing a frontal-tropopause model in which the upper front was extended vertically through the "break" between the polar and subtropical tropopause and into the stratosphere above (Figs. 10.1d and 10.2). It has since been recognized that this structural concept was presented earlier by Nyberg and Palmén (1942). Nevertheless, Berggren (1952) is to be credited with utilizing closely spaced wind soundings to describe one example (Fig. 10.2) of ~100 km scale cyclonic wind shear within the vertical portion of an upper-level front at the LMW. Following its inception, the Nyberg–Palmén–Berggren model received limited acceptance, as there was considerable skepticism regarding the notion of vertically oriented fronts near the tropopause, defined by wind-only discontinuities, and the existence of air-mass and frontal discontinuities within the stratosphere. The deployment of meteorologically instrumented high-altitude (> 11 km) aircraft contributed to the resolution of the representativeness of the differing interpretations of frontal discontinuities near the tropopause. Studies based upon this new observing technology provided near-continuous horizontal and vertical profiles of wind velocity, temperature, turbulence and trace constituents (e.g., Shapiro 1974, 1976, 1978, 1980) which clearly

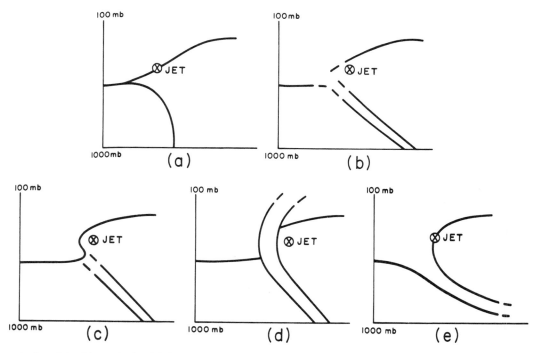

FIG. 10.1. Conceptual models of fronts in the vicinity of the tropopause: (a) J. Bjerknes (1932); (b) Palmén (1933, 1948); (c) Bjerknes and Palmén (1937); (d) Nyberg and Palmén (1942) and Berggren (1952); (e) Newton (1954) and Reed and Danielsen (1959).

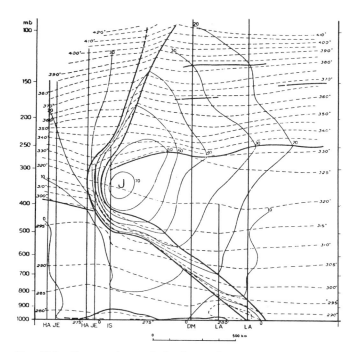

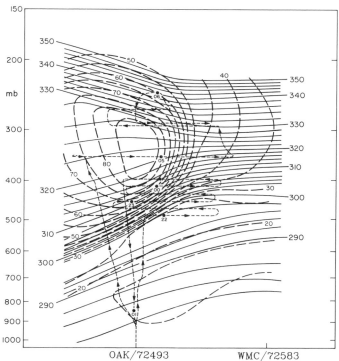

FIG. 10.2. Cross-section analysis of potential temperature (K, dashed lines), wind speed (m s⁻¹, thin solid lines), and frontal boundaries and the tropopause (heavy solid lines) (Berggren 1952).

FIG. 10.3. Composite cross-section analysis for ~00 UTC 16 April 1976 of potential temperature (K, solid lines), wind speed (m s⁻¹, heavy dashed lines), and NCAR Sabreliner aircraft flight track (thin dashed lines, time marks at solid dots, UTC) (Shapiro 1978).

described the ~100-km scale in frontal cyclonic wind speed shear at the LMW (Fig. 10.3). Subsequent measurements with a NASA RB-57F stratospheric aircraft (Shapiro et al. 1980) documented the stratospheric extension of frontal-scale transitions in potential vorticity and ozone to above 100 mb (16 km), verifying the stratospheric air-mass structure proposed by Nyberg, Palmén and Berggren.

Frontal layers have been identified by their discontinuities in horizontal thermal gradient, static stability, lateral and/or vertical wind velocity gradients and potential vorticity (Palmén 1948). The equations defining the physical processes governing the generation and decay of frontal gradients derived by Miller (1948) formed the basis for numerous frontal diagnostic studies (e.g., Reed and Sanders 1953; Newton 1954; Bosart 1970). The individual Miller frontal parameters (e.g., horizontal and vertical gradients of temperature and wind velocity), however, did not show discontinuities throughout the entire frontal domain, leading to questions on the definition of fronts near the tropopause. Consider Fig. 10.4, which illustrates one such jet-front system. Figure 10.4a shows a frontal layer in the troposphere beneath a polar jet-stream core bounded by discontinuities in the horizontal and vertical gradients of potential temperature and wind velocity. Similar discontinuities bound the sloping baroclinic layer within the stratosphere above the jet-stream core. A ~100-km wide frontal region, continuous with the sloping frontal layers above and below and containing large cyclonic wind shear, is situated within the polar stratosphere at the LMW where discontinuities in the horizontal

and vertical gradients of potential temperature vanish. Nyberg and Palmén (1942), Berggren (1952) and Shapiro (1976) termed "frontal" the total jet-stream region which contains hypergradients in either or both wind velocity and potential temperature.

Kleinschmidt (1951) was the first to use isentropic potential vorticity and its discontinuities to define the stratosphere and its interface with the troposphere (the tropopause). In later studies, Reed (1955) and Reed and Danielsen (1959) utilized potential vorticity and its spatial discontinuities (see Fig. 3.9) to establish the dynamical relationship between the folding of the tropopause and upper-level frontogenesis. Although discontinuities in potential vorticity (Fig. 10.4b) bound the mesoscale wind velocity gradients in the layer of maximum wind (see Shapiro 1976, 1978) and define the approximate separation of air of stratospheric versus tropospheric origin, they do not delineate frontal discontinuities in the middle troposphere. In that region, potential vorticity and its discontinuities tend to vanish, as the relative vorticity on isentropic surfaces becomes weakly anticyclonic (see Figs. 10.4a and d). Thus, taken individually, discontinuities in potential temperature, vertical and horizontal wind shear, and potential vorticity do not uniquely define the total frontal domain of upper-level jet-front systems. It remained for future research to define a unifying parameter describing the total frontal domain.

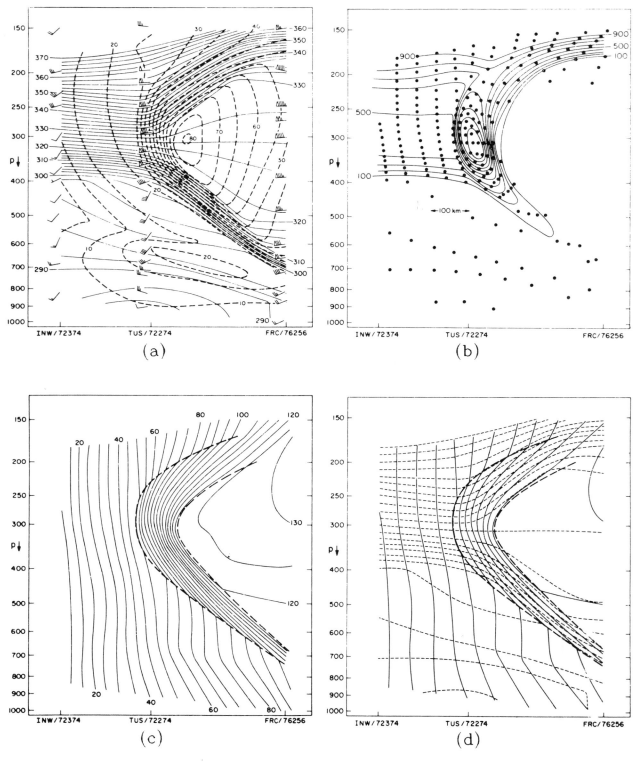

Fɪɢ. 10.4.   Cross sections for 00 UTC 17 April 1976 based on rawinsonde observations at Winslow, Arizona (INW), Tucson, Arizona (TUS), and Guaymas, Mexico (FRC), supplemented with NCAR Sabreliner aircraft data in the layer between 250 and 300 mb: (a) Potential temperature (K, solid lines) and wind speed (m s⁻¹, dashed lines). In this and all ensuing figures, winds are plotted with respect to north at the top of the figure; flags, full barbs and half barbs, respectively, indicate speeds of 25, 5 and 2.5 m s⁻¹. (b) Potential vorticity (10^{-7} K mb⁻¹ s⁻¹, solid lines) and array of dots formed by the intersection of (M, θ) coordinates displayed in panel (d). (c) Absolute momentum, $M = U - fy$ (m s⁻¹, solid lines), with $y=0$ at left side of figure, decreasing toward the right. (d) (M, θ) coordinate grid from patterns in panels (a) and (c), with contour intervals of 10 m s⁻¹ and 4 K. Heavy dashed lines in (c) and (d) indicate first-order discontinuities in M (Shapiro 1981).

Eliassen (1952) introduced the concept of absolute angular momentum (see Section 9.2) in describing forced secondary circulations about an axially-symmetric circumpolar vortex. In later studies, Eliassen (1959, 1962) defined the Cartesian reference frame analogy as absolute momentum, i.e.,

$$M = U - fy, \tag{10.1}$$

where U is the along-front component of geostrophic velocity, f the Coriolis parameter and y the horizontal distance in the cross-front direction (positive toward colder air).

The cross-front vector vorticity $\mathbf{q}$ is

$$\mathbf{q} = -\mathbf{k}\frac{\partial M}{\partial y} - \mathbf{j}\frac{\partial M}{\partial p}, \tag{10.2}$$

with the orientation of $\mathbf{q}$ directed along the vortex lines, i.e., along isopleths of constant M, where $-\partial M/\partial y$ and $-\partial M/\partial p$ are the respective vertical and horizontal components of $\mathbf{q}$. Shapiro (1981) evaluated the distribution of absolute momentum for cases of well-developed upper-level jet-front systems. The results (Fig. 10.4c) revealed that the total hypergradient region of jet-front systems is bounded by discontinuities in the horizontal and/or vertical gradient of absolute momentum. Thus, it was suggested that absolute momentum and its spatial discontinuities be used to define the total hypergradient region of jet stream-frontal zone systems. Figure 10.4d shows the superposition of isopleths of absolute momentum and potential temperature. For adiabatic, inviscid motions, air parcels conserve potential temperature, and changes in their absolute momentum arise from cross-front geostrophic

flow ($dM/dt = -fV_g$). The reference frame composed of the (M, θ) lines forms a stretched Lagrangian coordinate grid, where the horizontal distortion of M lines away from the equally spaced Cartesian y lines is proportional to the vertical component of the vector vorticity. An (M, p) type of coordinate system was used by Hoskins (1971) and Hoskins and Bretherton (1972) for their analytical solutions of semigeostrophic frontogenesis (see Section 9.8).

Conceptual models describing the meridional (pole-to-equator) structure of the tropopause and the positioning of the principal jet streams and frontal zones have also evolved in response to new observational technologies. The research-aircraft-based studies by Shapiro (1985) and Shapiro et al. (1987) presented analyses describing anew the arctic tropopause, jet stream and frontal structure in association with high-latitude polar vortices. The arctic jet stream was found north of the polar jet with well-defined potential vorticity tropopause folds between the lower (~5 km) arctic tropopause to the north and the higher (~7 km) polar tropopause to the south. Earlier models of the key jet streams and tropopause surfaces (e.g., Palmén 1951; Defant and Taba 1957; Palmén and Newton 1969, Fig. 4.7) did not include the arctic jet stream or a low (~5 km) arctic tropopause at high latitudes, nor did they explicitly include the potential vorticity discontinuity between the stratosphere and troposphere and its folding characteristics.

Figure 10.5 presents a revised meridional model of the tropopause, primary jet streams and fronts from Shapiro et al. (1987). The tropopause is defined by the stratospheric-tropospheric potential vorticity discontinuity, and

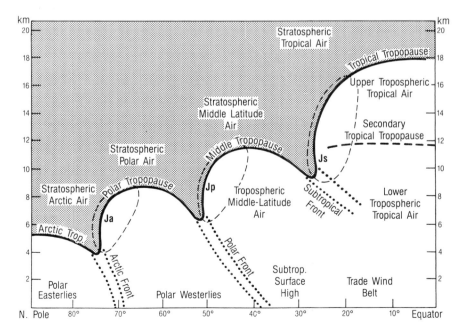

FIG. 10.5. The meridional structure of the tropopause. Potential-vorticity-discontinuity tropopause: heavy solid lines, with stratosphere stippled. The primary frontal zones are bounded by the heavy dotted lines and are labeled accordingly. The 40 m s^{-1} isotach (thin dashed line) encircles the cores of the three primary jet streams: arctic, Ja; polar, Jp; and subtropical, Js. The secondary (thermal) tropical tropopause is indicated by the heavy dashed line. Major tropospheric and stratospheric air masses, tropopause surfaces, and selected wind systems are labeled in the cross section. Individual cross sections may differ spatially and temporally from that presented in this idealized meridional model (Shapiro et al. 1987).

(with this convention) is continuous from pole to equator. It is not a material interface between the stratosphere and troposphere, as stratospheric-tropospheric exchange of air and trace constituents is accomplished through potential-vorticity-altering processes. These range from seasonal radiative processes (e.g., Reiter 1975) to episodic events such as turbulent mixing within tropopause folds (e.g., Shapiro 1978, 1980) and penetrative mesoconvective cloud systems. Three jet streams and their associated tropopause folds are shown in the schematic: the arctic jet (Ja) at 70°N, the polar jet (Jp) at 45°N and the subtropical (Js) jet at 25°N. As in Palmén and Newton's figure, the secondary tropical tropopause at 12 km is shown below the primary tropical tropopause at 18 km. The subtropical jet stream tropopause fold, however, is drawn continuous with the tropical tropopause at 18 km because of the low potential vorticity of the upper-tropospheric tropical air south (anticyclonic shear side) of the subtropical jet in the layer bounded vertically by the primary and secondary tropical tropopause surfaces. With the exception of the addition of the arctic jet stream and the tropopause defined in terms of the potential vorticity, all other primary wind systems and air masses are as in the Palmén and Newton (1969, Fig. 4.7) cross section.

The meridional structure of the tropopause and the position and intensity of the primary wind systems and fronts depicted in Fig. 10.5 can vary considerably, both spatially and temporally. In the extreme, one or more of the primary jet streams and their associated fronts and tropopause folds may not be present in a given cross section on any given day. On occasion, two jet-front systems (i.e., the arctic and polar, or the polar and subtropical) will merge into a single jet-front system, such that roughly half of the midtropospheric pole-to-equator baroclinicity is concentrated within a frontal zone of ~200 km width. Finally, zonally- or seasonally-averaged meridional cross sections would only contain the subtropical jet (Fig. 2.2), and a broad general slope of the mean potential vorticity isopleths (Fig. 5.5) rather than distinct tropopause folds, owing to the localized (spatial) and transient (temporal) character of the polar and arctic jet streams.

10.2.2 Dynamics

The dynamics governing the evolution of fronts in the vicinity of the tropopause have been the focus of numerous investigations during the past half-century. During this period there arose differences in interpretation with regard to the key processes governing the evolution of these systems. The most controversial of the differing interpretations centered on the sense of the transverse (cross-front) secondary circulation associated with the contraction of upper-tropospheric frontal gradients. On the one hand, Namias and Clapp (1949), acknowledging a conception by R. C. Sutcliffe, were the first to discuss the thermally direct circulation relative to the jet stream forced by a confluent geostrophic deformation (Fig. 10.6a). Ascending and descending air currents were found to the

warm and cold sides of the upper-level baroclinic zone, respectively. These diagnostically derived circulations were treated theoretically and/or numerically by Sawyer (1956), Eliassen (1962), Hoskins and Bretherton (1972), Gidel and Shapiro (1979), and Keyser and Pecnick (1985a,b).

Another interpretation of the transverse circulations during upper-level frontogenesis was discussed by Reed and Sanders (1953), Newton (1954), Bosart (1970) and Shapiro (1970). These synoptic studies provided evidence for strong sinking motions within and to the warm side of developing upper fronts, concluding that upper-level frontogenesis was predominantly forced by cross-front differential vertical motions in the thermally indirect sense, acting to increase frontal thermal gradients and vorticity. Newton (1954) stressed that upper-level frontogenesis was a three-dimensional process which did not lend itself to the two-dimensionalization of the Namias and Clapp (1949) confluence theory, as large-scale horizontal deformations associated with evolving upper-tropospheric synoptic waves are more complex than a simple two-dimensional cross-front geostrophic confluence, independent of height, in a straight geostrophic current. Support for the apparent necessity of the three-dimensional treatment of upper fronts came from studies such as those of Mudrick (1974), Shapiro (1975) and Newton and Trevisan (1984a,b), wherein three-dimensional primitive equation numerical

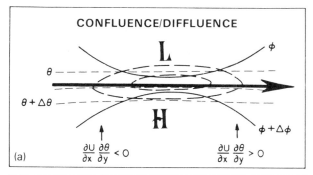

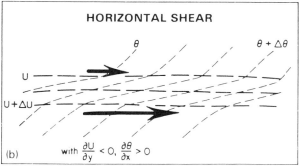

FIG. 10.6. Schematic depictions on a constant pressure surface, of straight frontal zones characterized by (a) confluence and diffluence associated with a jet maximum, and (b) horizontal shear in the presence of a positive along-front thermal gradient. Geopotential height contours, thick solid lines; isotachs of the along-front geostrophic wind component U, thick dashed lines; isentropes, thin dashed lines. Heavy arrows indicate the jet axis in (a) and the sense of cross-front shear of the along-front wind component in (b) (adapted from Shapiro 1982).

simulations produced upper-level frontogenesis, tropopause folding and strong sinking motion at the warm side of the frontal layer, in agreement with the interpretation of the three-dimensional synoptic studies.

The differences in interpretation regarding the sense of the secondary circulations about upper fronts were considered by Shapiro (1981), Keyser and Pecnick (1985a,b) and Reeder and Keyser (1988). Shapiro's (1981) observational study utilized the Sawyer–Eliassen secondary circulation equation, (9.20) in Section 9.3, to show the importance of the previously neglected cross-front horizontal wind shear acting upon along-front thermal gradients (Fig. 10.6b), in addition to cross-front confluence (Fig. 10.6a), in forcing strong sinking motion within and to the warm side of intensifying upper fronts (see Fig. 9.7). Keyser and Pecnick (1985a,b) and Reeder and Keyser (1988) applied a two-dimensional (cross-front) numerical simulation model to study the interplay between geostrophic confluence and cross-frontal geostrophic wind shear acting upon cross-front and along-front thermal gradients, respectively. The results from these studies showed that the effect of horizontal shear upon a positive along-front thermal gradient (cold-air advection) was to displace the thermally direct circulation toward the warm side of developing upper-level fronts (Fig. 10.7). The shift in the position of the axis of the secondary circulation yielded sinking motion which was strongest at the warm side of the front. Thus, the cross-frontal gradient in vertical motion was frontogenetical and had the local appearance of being thermally indirect, while the overall secondary circulation was in the kinetic-energy-generating thermally direct sense as required for the development and maintenance of upper-level jet streams.

The relationship of the forcing of upper-level jet-front secondary circulations to the character of the synoptic-scale flow is illustrated in Fig. 10.8. The schematic shows geostrophic confluence (diffluence) in the entrance (exit) of the jet-front as it propagates through the synoptic wave. In contrast, the thermal advections along the frontal zone range from zero in the pure confluence (diffluence) case (Fig. 10.8a) to cold and warm air advection as the jet-front passes from the northwesterly to the southwesterly wave inflections (Fig. 10.8b and d, respectively). The effect of the cross-jet cyclonic and anticyclonic wind shears upon the varying along-front thermal gradients is to force a variety of cross-front secondary circulations differing from the simplified pure confluent (diffluent) straight-jet secondary circulation (see Keyser and Pecnick 1985a). It is now apparent, in retrospect, that differences in interpretation of upper-level jet-front secondary circulations resulted in part from consideration of these systems during various stages of their life cycles.

10.3 The Scale Contraction of Surface Fronts and its Role in the Initiation of Mesoconvective Precipitation Systems

10.3.1 Frontal Contraction

In reviewing the earlier concepts of surface fronts, one finds that fronts near the ground were first considered to be zero-order discontinuities in density (temperature) and wind velocity between air masses of different origin. The early studies (reviewed by Bergeron 1959) documented the abrupt change in wind direction and the temperature decrease during cold frontal passage. The accompanying

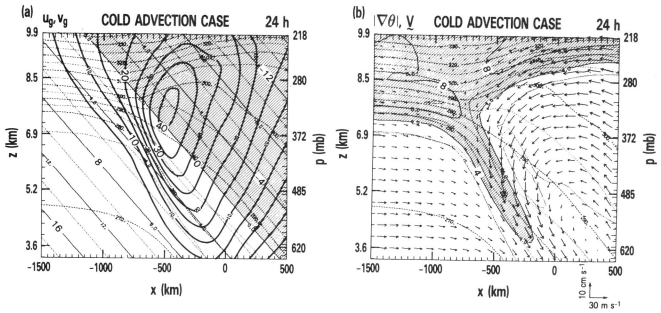

FIG. 10.7. Cross sections at 24 h from a two-dimensional primitive equation model of frontogenesis incorporating horizontal shear: (a) Cross-front geostrophic component u_g (contour interval 2 m s^{-1}, thin solid, negative values shaded) and along-front geostrophic component v_g (interval 5 m s^{-1}, thick solid); (b) $|\Delta\theta|$ [contour interval 2 K (100 km)$^{-1}$, thin solid, values > 4 shaded] and vector arrows of the total flow in the cross-front plane (u,w). Background field is potential temperature (interval 5 K, dashed) (Keyser et al. 1986).

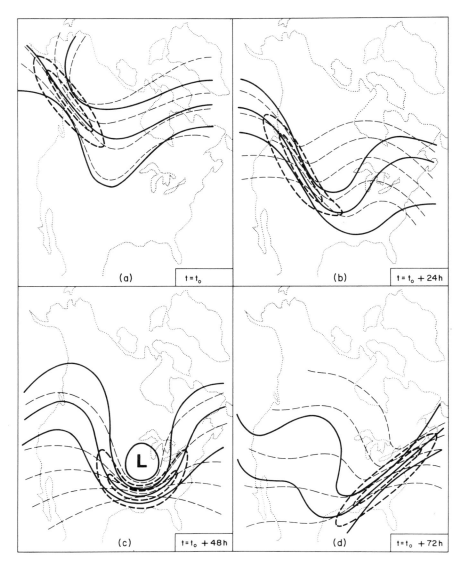

FIG. 10.8. Idealized schematic depiction on a constant pressure surface of the propagation of an upper-tropospheric jet-front system through a midlatitude baroclinic wave over a 72-h period: (a) formation of jet-front in the confluence between mid- and high-latitude currents; (b) jet-front situated in the northwesterly flow inflection of amplifying wave; (c) jet-front at the base of the trough of fully developed wave; (d) jet-front situated in the southwesterly flow inflection of damping wave. Geopotential height contours, thick solid lines; isotachs, thick dashed lines; isentropes or isotherms, thin dashed lines (Shapiro 1982).

theoretical treatments (e.g., Margules 1906) used laws of hydrodynamics applied to "two-density" fluid models containing a sloping frontal interface to describe the motion, slope and vertical circulations of fronts. With the advent of kite and balloon-borne upper-air observations, it was discovered that fronts aloft were actually transition zones of finite width having characteristic vertical and horizontal scales of ~1 km and ~100 km (Bjerknes and Palmén 1937). At this point, the concept of fronts as zero-order discontinuities within synoptic-scale (~1000 km) cyclones was de-emphasized. Fronts thereafter were treated as transition layers which, as demonstrated by Palmén (1948), are bounded by first-order discontinuities in temperature and velocity that are related to the slope of a front. It continued to be appreciated, however, that sharp horizontal discontinuities could exist on very small scales

(0.2–2 km), such as at the outflow boundaries of convective precipitation systems, land-sea breeze convergence lines and orographically-forced flows (e.g., Charba 1974; Goff 1976; Simpson et al. 1977; Matthews 1981; Carbone 1982; Wakimoto 1982; Hobbs and Persson 1982).

We suggest that the shift from the discontinuous "wedge" (two-density) model to the continuous "zone" model resulted from combining synoptically spaced (~400 km) upper-air observations with the ~100 km spacing of the hourly reporting surface stations, along with the decline in the use of single-station (continuous record) analysis of frontal zones. Furthermore, with the expansion of synoptic observing networks and the introduction of the quasi-geostrophic theory, fronts were treated as synoptic-scale (~1000 km) in length, but mesoscale (~100–200 km) in width, with the narrow width resulting from the contractions of synoptic-scale thermal gradients forced by geostrophic deformation and its ageostrophic circulation response.

Bergeron (1928) and Petterssen (1936) first described the deformation fields contributing to the contraction of temperature and velocity gradients into narrow surface frontal zones. Since then, the importance of geostrophic deformation and its coupled vertical secondary circulations has been examined in frontal studies by Sawyer (1956), Eliassen (1959, 1962), Williams (1967) and Hoskins and Bretherton (1972), among others. Eliassen (1959) recognized that secondary circulations give rise to a "self-sharpening" process to accelerate the scale contraction of surface fronts. Williams (1967, 1972) and Hoskins and Bretherton (1972) simulated this process (ageostrophic contraction) through numerical and analytic solutions, respectively (see Section 9.8). In the absence of fine-scale turbulent motions, there are no limits to the scale to which frontal gradients may contract under the combined actions of geostrophic and ageostrophic motions. Inviscid, adiabatic, semigeostrophic frontogenesis theory produces infinitesimally narrow fronts within a finite time (Hoskins and Bretherton 1972). The finite vertical and horizontal scales of frontal zones are presumed to result from a balance between frontogenetical synoptic-scale forcing and frontolytical turbulent-scale mixing (e.g., Williams 1974). Accelerated frontal contractions transpire when latent heat release occurs within the ascending motion at the leading edge of fronts (e.g., Browning and Harrold 1970; Carbone 1982), after the frontal dynamics

are modified by the effects of water vapor phase changes and nonhydrostatic pressure changes. Surface boundary-layer heat and momentum fluxes also contribute to vertical circulations about fronts (e.g., Keyser and Anthes 1982; Shapiro 1982; Koch 1984; Reeder 1986).

Recent observational studies with research aircraft, an instrumented 300-m tower and ground-based remote sensors have documented the cross-frontal scale collapse of the leading edge of nonprecipitating surface cold fronts down to horizontal distances of ≲ 1 km (Shapiro 1984; Shapiro et al. 1985). The example from Shapiro et al. (Fig. 10.9a) shows the passage of a surface cold front by the NOAA/Boulder Atmospheric Observatory (BAO) instrumented 300-m tower. This front had the structural characteristics of a density current: an elevated hydraulic head followed by a turbulent wake. The cross-frontal scale was ~ 1 km and vertical motions at the frontal head exceeded 4 m s^{-1} (Fig. 10.9b). An acoustic sounder documented the structure of the frontal interface as it passed the BAO tower (Fig. 10.9c). Results from these observational studies initiated debate among researchers on the nature of the observed frontal scale collapse in the absence of precipitation processes, revived an earlier controversy regarding the role of "pressure jumps" at or in advance of surface fronts in triggering mesoconvective precipitation systems, and inspired numerical modelers to attempt simulating these structures using nonhydrostatic models (Gall et al. 1987, 1988).

The frontal scale collapse studies of Shapiro (1984) and Shapiro et al. (1985) were received with a degree of skep-

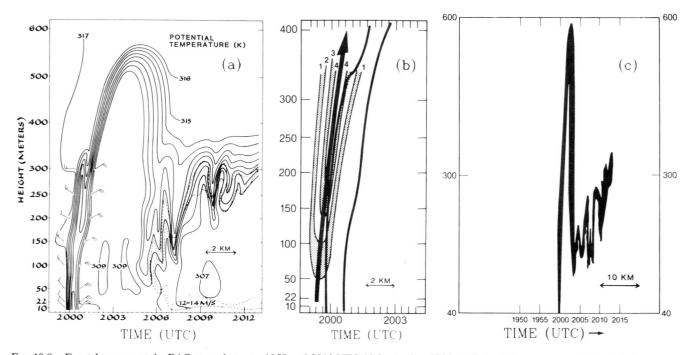

Fig. 10.9.   Frontal passage at the BAO tower between 1959 and 2013 UTC 19 September 1983: (a) Potential temperature (K) derived from tower data up to 300 m and the acoustic record in panel (c) between 300 and 600 m. Region of the 12–14 m s^{-1} wind speed surge, stippled area; wind flags (full barb, 5 m s^{-1}) show tower winds preceding and following the passage of the front. (b) Vertical motion (m s^{-1}) at the leading edge of the front, whose boundaries are indicated by heavy solid lines. (c) Acoustic sounder record between 1950 and 2015 UTC, measured at the BAO tower (Shapiro et al. 1985).

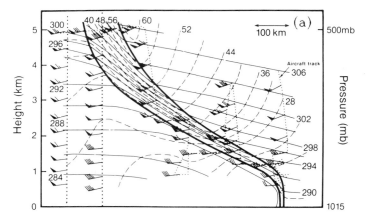

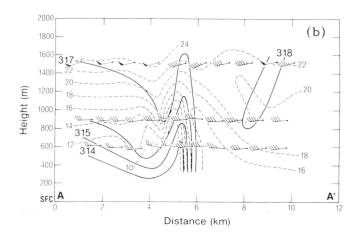

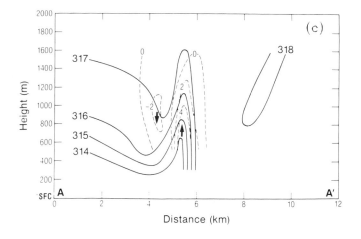

FIG. 10.10. (a) Cross section analysis of potential temperature (K, thin solid lines), along-front wind component (m s⁻¹, dashed lines) and frontal boundaries (heavy solid lines) for an eastern Pacific cold front at ~00 UTC 10 December 1987. NOAA P-3 aircraft flight track, dotted line; dropwindsonde profiles, heavy dotted lines and wind symbols. Left and right endpoints are 44.4°N, 135.3°W and 39.8°N, 130.6°W (cf. Fig. 10.11). (b) The leading edge of the cold front shown in (a) at ~03 UTC: potential temperature, front-parallel wind speed (dashed lines), and selected flight-level wind vectors. (c) Potential temperature and measured vertical velocity (m s⁻¹, dashed). See also Fig. 8.23.

ticism, as it was suggested that these extremely narrow fronts were a manifestation of the steep topography of the eastern slopes of the Rocky Mountains. Orlanski et al. (1985) regarded these observed narrow fronts as atypical, classifying them as orographically-trapped Kelvin waves forced by synoptic-scale fronts impinging on the eastern slopes of the mountains. What was required to resolve this concern was the documentation of such nonprecipitating frontal structure over flat terrain. This opportunity arose during the Ocean Storms 1987 field program, during which a NOAA P-3 research aircraft was used to document the horizontal (cross-frontal) scale of a frontal zone over the eastern Pacific Ocean. In this study, the aircraft was used to deploy dropwindsondes and was flown in a descending "stairstep" profile, tracing the front from the middle troposphere (~500 mb) down to the sea surface (Fig. 10.10a). The microscale structure of the leading edge of the front was observed in vertical profile (Fig. 10.10b), defining the narrow ~1 km frontal discontinuity. Note the ~5 m s⁻¹ ascent at the leading edge of the front (Fig. 10.10c). The companion satellite image (Fig. 10.11) shows the "rope cloud" signature of the enhanced nonprecipitating cumulus band formed by the ascending motion at the leading edge of the front.

It is interesting to observe that interpretations of the transverse scale of surface cold fronts have come full circle. The earlier near zero-order discontinuity model was put aside only to be rediscovered using "modern" instrumentation.

10.3.2 Frontal-Mesoconvective Interaction

Fronts and their associated vertical circulations have long been recognized as a mechanism for lifting moist air to its level of free convection and initiating the release of potential instability through deep mesoconvective cloud systems. An alternative hypothesis for triggering prefrontal thunderstorms was proposed in the theoretical treatments of Freeman (1948) and Abdullah (1949), with extensive observational documentation by Tepper (1950). These studies proposed that frontal and prefrontal squall lines were initiated by hydraulic (nonhydrostatic) pressure waves or "jumps" on an inversion layer, generated by the horizontally accelerated motion of cold fronts. On occasion, these pressure jumps were thought to propagate out in advance of the triggering front. The documentation of these fine-scale phenomena by Tepper (1950) was based upon an automatic 55-station pressure, wind and temperature observing network with ~3-km spacing.

Newton (1950) questioned the applicability of the gravity wave as a triggering mechanism for warm-sector squall lines, noting that a great amount of lifting would be required for condensation in the ordinarily dry air above the inversion, whereas convection from the moist layer beneath would destroy the stable layer necessary for further propagation of the jump wave. Fujita (1955) argued and presented evidence that the pressure jump lines of Tepper (1950) were the result of, rather than the

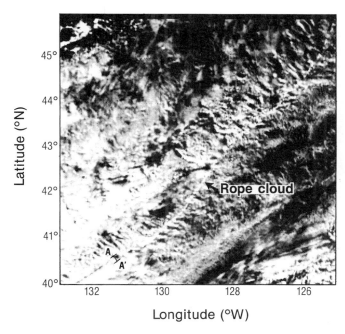

FIG. 10.11. 1-km resolution visible satellite image at 23 UTC 9 December 1987. Line AA′ (SW corner) indicates the front-relative projection line of Fig. 10.10b–c.

cause of, squall lines. We suggest that the limited acceptance of nonhydrostatic frontal phenomena as an initiation mechanism for mesoconvective systems was due in part to the lack of documentation of the vertical structure of the pressure jump lines. It is only recently that instrumented towers and research aircraft have provided some corroborating evidence for density-current (hydraulic-head) characteristics of surface cold fronts. The recent studies have shown examples where nonprecipitating fronts have assumed the characteristics of density-current flows. The large ascending vertical motions (~5 m s^{-1}) at the frontal head are of sufficient magnitude to lift potentially unstable air through the trapping "lid" inversions described by Carlson and Ludlam (1968) and Carlson et al. (1983), which often cap moist surface layers. The frontal head is capable of releasing the potential instability of trapped moist layers on time scales of minutes rather than hours, as would be required for the 20 cm s^{-1} lifting of ~100-km frontal-scale vertical circulations. It is not unreasonable to consider the possibility that the frontal head may separate itself from its parent front and propagate out in advance of the front as a solitary wave, as proposed by Abdullah (1949). The separation process could produce prefrontal pressure waves, as in Tepper (1950), and initiate precipitation systems in the prefrontal environment.

10.4 The Life Cycle of the Marine Extratropical Cyclone and its Fronts

Since its inception, the Norwegian cyclone model (J. Bjerknes 1919; Bjerknes and Solberg 1921, 1922) has formed the conceptual basis for describing the evolution of fronts during the life cycle of extratropical cyclones. Although this model was derived primarily from the analysis of eastern Atlantic Ocean and western European observations, it has been applied in a variety of flow regimes over land, sea and in the vicinity of steep topography. The vertical structure of fronts within this model was conceived from sparse meteorograph and kite soundings, surface observations taken along mountain slopes, and visual observations of differential motions between cloud layers situated at different altitudes above and below fronts. Quite cleverly, these early researchers deduced the three-dimensional thermal structure of cyclones, including the slopes of frontal layers and the vertical wind shear through them, from visually derived cloud-motion winds coupled with the geostrophic thermal wind relationship, in addition to detailed analyses of sea-level pressure and surface temperature observations.

Figure 10.12 presents the conceptual model of the Norwegian cyclone from J. Bjerknes and Solberg (1922). The schematic shows the amplification of the frontal wave from its incipient phase, through cyclogenesis, to its frontal occlusion. Note that the model includes a "seclusion" at the northern tip of the occluded front, denoting the entrapment of initially warm-sector air at the center of the cyclone (shown in Phase IV). This conceptualization included a description of the vertical structure of warm, cold and occluded fronts and their associated cloud and precipitation systems.

As researchers began explorations with the operational upper-air networks during the post-World War II years, the resulting studies revealed cyclone and frontal structure that did not always extend continuously from the surface to the tropopause as previously shown by Bjerknes and Palmén (1937). (See Figs. 3.3 and 9.1.) These new case studies emphasized the vertical separation and differing governing dynamics of upper-level versus lower-level (surface) fronts (e.g., Reed and Sanders 1953; Newton 1954; Sanders 1955; Bosart 1970; Shapiro 1970). It should be noted that these studies of the structural and dynamical separation of fronts near the tropopause from those near the ground were based exclusively on weather events over the central United States during situations of weak lower-tropospheric cyclogenesis, but strong upper-tropospheric synoptic wave amplification. Despite these differences in interpretation of the vertical structures of fronts from the earlier conceptual models, researchers and forecasters were hesitant to suggest significant alternatives to the Norwegian frontal-cyclone model.

The advent of electronic computers during the 1950s provided the technology with which to simulate and predict numerically the life cycles of synoptic-scale weather systems and their embedded mesoscale structures. The most recent advances in computational technology have led to the simulation of idealized and actual cyclogenetic events with such realism that researchers are now turning to numerical model-derived data sets to diagnose the interplay between baroclinic, diabatic and turbulent proc-

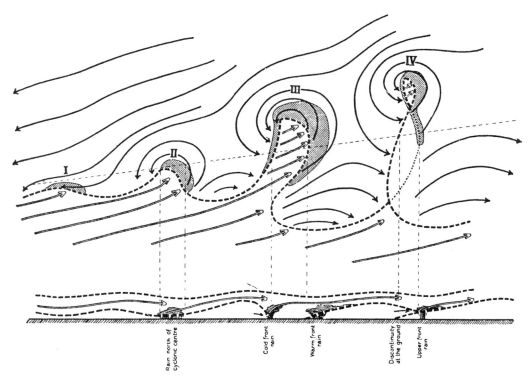

FIG. 10.12.   The Norwegian frontal cyclone model (Bjerknes and Solberg 1922).

esses. This includes the evolution of fronts and jet streams and their associated circulations, precipitation systems and planetary boundary layer processes (e.g., Keyser et al. 1978; Keyser and Uccellini 1987; Whitaker et al. 1988; Kuo and Reed 1988; Kuo et al. 1990). In the following section, we present results from both numerical simulations and field studies which suggest some revisions to the Norwegian frontal-cyclone model.

10.4.1   Numerical Simulations

From the time of the early numerical studies of amplifying baroclinic waves (e.g., Edelmann 1963; Eliassen and Raustein 1968; Mudrick 1974), simulation experiments produced surface frontal configurations that differed markedly from those of the Norwegian frontal-cyclone model. The three-dimensional Eady (1949) wave simulations (e.g., Hoskins 1976; Hoskins and West 1979; Hoskins and Heckley 1981; Schär 1989) also produced unusual frontal configurations which the authors were hesitant to equate with those of the "real" atmosphere, since similar frontal structures had not yet been documented by synoptic meteorologists. Specifically, these studies showed heretofore undescribed frontal aspects such as (1) loss of cold frontal baroclinicity (frontolysis) near the cyclone center during the early phases of cyclogenesis, (2) the subsequent westward migration of warm frontal structure back into the northerly flow west of the intensifying cyclone and (3) the formation of a warm-core frontal seclusion in the post-cold-front cool air in the fully developed cyclone. Quite curiously, these simulations

showed that the largest frontal baroclinicity during the cyclone life cycle occurred within the bent-back warm front to the rear (west) of the cyclone center. It should be noted that these controversial frontal evolutions were simulated with adiabatic models, excluding precipitation and surface boundary-layer processes.

As an example, the three-dimensional Eady-wave simulation by Schär (1989) showed the incipient cyclone developing along broad, zonal baroclinicity (Fig. 10.13a); the bridging of the contracting warm front across the cyclone center, together with cold-front contraction south of, but not in the vicinity of, the cyclone center (Fig. 10.13b); and, finally, the fully developed cyclone with its bent-back warm front and warm-core seclusion (Fig. 10.13c). Note that the warm-core seclusion contains lower temperatures than those initially within the warm sector of the cyclone.

We turn next to a numerical simulation of explosive extratropical marine cyclogenesis that was initialized with real data. The synoptic situation selected for this simulation was named for the Queen Elizabeth II (QE II) ocean liner, which was severely damaged by the fury of this North Atlantic storm. Synoptic discussions of the QE II cyclogenesis are presented in Gyakum (1983a,b) and Uccellini (1986). The present simulation was performed with a high-resolution version of the Penn State/NCAR regional numerical prediction model, documented by Anthes and Warner (1978), initialized at 12 UTC 9 September 1978. The grid resolution was 22.5 km in the horizontal and 15 layers in the vertical between the surface and 100 mb.

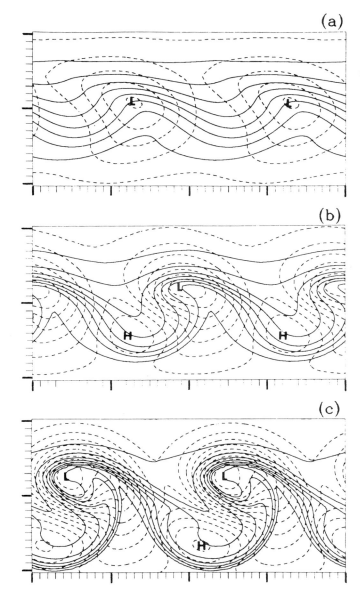

(a)

(b)

(c)

Fig. 10.13. Nonlinear semigeostrophic simulation of a baroclinic development from a small-amplitude disturbance to a cyclone. The diagrams show the surface fields of potential temperature (solid lines) and pressure (dashed lines) in a domain of 8000 × 4000 km. The contour interval is 2 K for potential temperature and 3 mb for pressure. The time interval between (a) and (c) is 96 h (Schär 1989).

Anthes et al. (1983) and Kuo et al. (1990) simulated the QE II cyclogenesis with coarser-resolution versions of the same model. In contrast to the Eady-wave simulations described above, the QE II simulations included boundary layer (air-sea interaction) and precipitation processes.

The high-resolution numerical simulation of the QE II cyclogenesis contained four phases of surface frontal evolution. The incipient cyclone (Fig. 10.14a) formed along a broad (~400 km wide) zonally continuous frontal zone. Twelve hours into the simulation (Fig. 10.14b) the previously continuous front had "fractured" near the center of the intensifying cyclone and the temperature gradients at the warm and cold front had contracted in width to

~100 km. As the cyclone continued intensifying at 18 hours (Fig. 10.14c), the cold front advanced eastward into the narrowing warm sector and the warm front developed westward (in storm-relative coordinates) such that frontogenesis was occurring in the northerly flow to the rear (west) of the cyclone within the cold polar air stream behind the advancing cold front. This phase of the cyclone-frontal evolution is termed the frontal "T-bone" because the advancing cold front had become oriented perpendicular to the "bent-back" extension of the warm front. At 24 hours, the time of maximum cyclone intensity (Fig. 10.14d), the cold front had advanced ~500 km east of the cyclone center and the bent-back warm front and cold polar air had cyclonically encircled the low center, entrapping a pocket of relatively warm air at its center. This warm-core "seclusion" formed within the baroclinicity of the polar air and did not involve air originating from the cyclone warm sector as in Phase IV of the Norwegian model (Fig. 10.12).

It is important to note that most, if not all, prior numerical simulations of both idealized and actual cases of extratropical cyclogenesis failed to reproduce the classical Norwegian cyclone-frontal occlusion. Instead we find, as in the above-described Eady-wave (Fig. 10.13) and QE II simulation (Fig. 10.14), that the warm-core seclusion within the polar air stream represents the final phase in the development of the cyclone. The question whether comparable structures are to be found in the real atmosphere is examined next.

10.4.2 Observational Studies

In their efforts toward advancing the understanding of the mesoscale structure of marine cyclones, researchers mounted extensive field observing programs which relied heavily upon meteorologically instrumented aircraft. Examples of the most recent of these field studies are the Genesis of Atlantic Lows Experiment (GALE) in 1986: U.S. East Coast cyclogenesis (see Dirks et al. 1988); the Alaskan Storm Program (ASP) in 1987: cyclogenesis in the eastern Pacific; and the Experiment on Rapidly Intensifying Cyclones over the Atlantic (ERICA) in 1988–89: western North Atlantic cyclogenesis (see Hadlock and Kreitzberg 1988). For the present illustration, we borrow results from forthcoming articles describing mesoscale evolutions during marine cyclogenesis observed during ASP and ERICA.

The first example of frontal evolution during extratropical marine cyclogenesis was documented with the NOAA P-3 aircraft over the central Pacific on 8–10 March 1987 during the ASP field study. This storm was observed with dropwindsonde and Doppler radar measurements in its T-bone phase (9 March) and fully secluded warm-core phase (10 March) of frontal evolution. The 1-km resolution visible satellite imagery (Fig. 10.15) shows three phases of cloud evolution during the life cycle of this cyclone: the cloud cluster associated with the initial incipient cyclone (Fig. 10.15a), the T-bone head and trailing

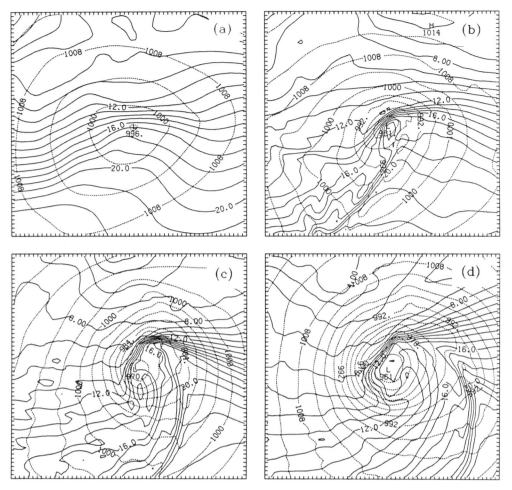

FIG. 10.14. Sea-level temperature (°C, solid lines) and sea-level pressure (mb, dashed lines) from a 24-h numerical simulation of the QE II marine cyclogenesis by the Penn State/NCAR regional model: (a) incipient frontal cyclone; (b) frontal fracture; (c) frontal T-Bone and bent-back warm front; (d) warm-core seclusion.

narrow cold-frontal rope cloud extending southwestward from the storm (Fig. 10.15b) and the fully developed cyclonic comma-shaped cloud signature of the warm-core seclusion (Fig. 10.15c).

The first NOAA P-3 flight into the developing cyclone originated from Adak, Alaska, an island on the Aleutian chain. Sixteen dropwindsondes were deployed from a pressure altitude of ~400 mb during a 5-hour period and space-time adjusted to ~00 UTC 9 March, given the phase velocity of the cyclone estimated from the satellite imagery. This analysis time is within 2 hours of the satellite cloud depiction in Fig. 10.15b.

The 850-mb temperature and geopotential height analysis and dropwindsonde wind vectors at ~00 UTC 9 March (Fig. 10.16) illustrate the frontal T-bone and bent-back warm front phase of this frontal cyclone. At this time, the sea-level pressure at the storm center, 963 mb, was ~20 mb lower than that 12 hours earlier as shown by the ECMWF analysis. The 850-mb temperature analysis was enhanced by incorporating cross-section analyses (discussed below). This analysis (Fig. 10.16) shows the east-west oriented warm front bridging across the cyclone

center into the northerly flow west of the low. The north-south oriented cold-front baroclinicity extends southward from the warm front, forming the T-bone structure simulated in the previously discussed numerical studies (e.g., Fig. 10.14c). The 850-mb wind vectors illustrate the intensity of the storm circulation, as wind speeds exceeding 35 m s^{-1} were observed encircling the cyclone center during this phase of development.

Cross-section analyses of potential temperature and section-normal wind component were prepared along the projection lines AA′ and BB′ of Fig. 10.16. These analyses (Fig. 10.17a,b) intercept the warm front, and the cold front and bent-back warm front, respectively. The warm-front cross section (Fig. 10.17a) shows the front extending upward and northward, with the largest baroclinicity and vertical wind shear situated in the lower portion of the front near the sea surface. The second cross section (Fig. 10.17b) shows the cold front extending from ~400 mb down to the sea surface. The cold front was vertical below 700 mb in the vicinity of the "straight-up" convective cloud system situated at its leading edge. The cold-frontal convective cloud band was clearly evident in

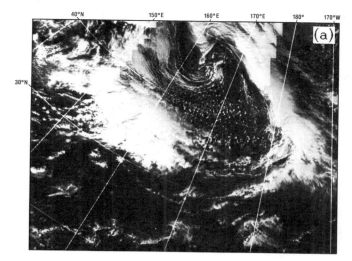

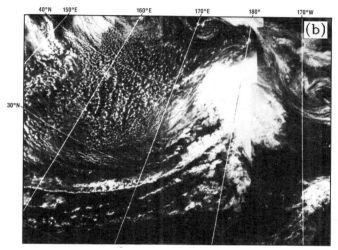

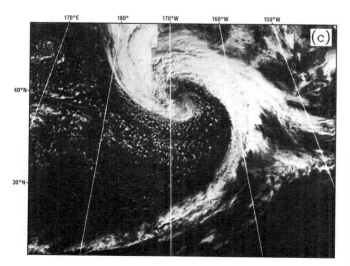

FIG. 10.15. 1-km resolution visible satellite images of three phases of cloud structure during the mid-Pacific cyclogenesis of 7–10 March 1987: (a) the cloud cluster (at left) of the incipient cyclone, 2045 UTC 7 March; (b) the bent-back warm frontal cloud head with the T-bone cold frontal convective cloud line and rope cloud trailing southwestward from the head, 2206 UTC 8 March; (c) the cyclonic spiral cloud signature of the mature cyclone and warm-core seclusion with deep mesoconvective cloud development within the warm sector in advance of the cold front, 2146 UTC 9 March.

the satellite cloud imagery (Fig. 10.15b). The vertical portion of the cold front and its narrow (~10 km) horizontal scale was also characteristic of the conceptualization of a convectively precipitating cold front (see Fig. 8.27) by Browning and Harrold (1970). The leading portion of the bent-back warm front is seen on the northern edge of the cross section.

The second flight into the cyclone originated from Anchorage, Alaska, ~24 hours after the first flight and deployed dropwindsondes to describe the warm-core seclusion phase of the cyclone life cycle. The 700-mb temperature and geopotential height analysis and wind vectors space-time adjusted to ~00 UTC 10 March 1987 (Fig. 10.18) clearly illustrate the −5°C warm-air seclusion (at its level of maximum baroclinicity), with the colder (−13°C) temperatures that cyclonically encircled the storm center along with the bent-back warm front. At this time, the storm central pressure was 973 mb, 10 mb higher than that documented from the aircraft 24 hours earlier, suggesting that cloud signatures such as that shown in Fig. 10.15c are indicative of the mature, and sometimes decaying, phase in the cyclone life cycle. A cross-section analysis of potential temperature and section-normal wind component (Fig. 10.19) was prepared along the projection line AA′ of Fig. 10.18. This analysis shows the vertical profile of the warm-core seclusion and the outward sloping baroclinicity of its encircling bent-back warm front. The

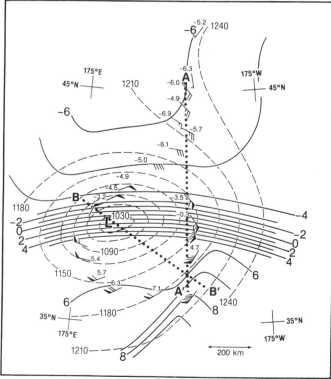

FIG. 10.16. 850-mb temperature (°C, solid lines) and geopotential height analysis (m, dashed lines) at ~00 UTC 9 March 1987, with dropwindsonde wind vectors and plotted temperatures. Lines AA′ and BB′ are cross section projections for Fig. 10.17a and b, respectively.

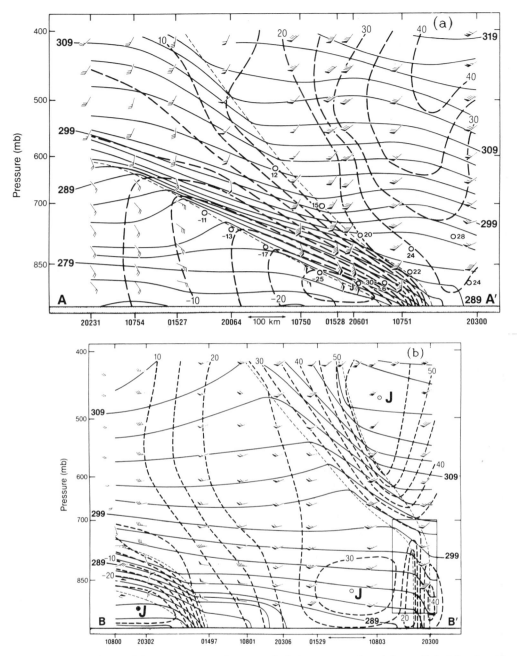

FIG. 10.17. (a) Cross-section analysis of potential temperature, section-normal wind component (m s⁻¹, heavy dashed lines) and frontal boundaries (thin dashed lines) along AA′ in Fig. 10.16. Flags and barbs show winds observed by dropwindsondes (numbered at bottom); Doppler radar wind observations, open circles with wind speeds beneath. (b) Section along line BB′ of Fig. 10.16. Positions of jet stream cores, J; inner boxed area indicates domain of Doppler radar wind observations.

highest wind speeds were found near the sea surface within the low-level jet on the cold side of the secluding front.

An excellent example of the frontal fracture and T-bone phase was observed during the pre-ERICA test flights made on 27 January 1988, one year prior to the full-scale field study. These observations were taken within a rapidly deepening cyclone that formed off the New Jersey coast, reaching its lowest central pressure (962 mb) over the Gulf of Saint Lawrence. This storm was observed with the NOAA P-3 research aircraft, the National Center for Atmospheric Research (NCAR) Loran dropwindsonde

system and operational surface observations and eastern North American rawinsonde soundings. Results from this study are discussed in Neiman et al. (1990).

The 920-mb temperature and geopotential height analysis and wind vectors (Fig. 10.20) were derived from space-time adjustment of the aircraft observations to 12 UTC 27 January 1988, the time of the supporting operational upper-air soundings. The 920-mb temperature analysis shows the warm front extending across Nova Scotia, through the cyclone center, then turning southward as the bent-back warm front in the northerly flow west of

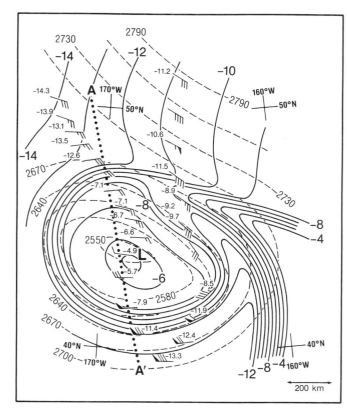

FIG. 10.18. 700-mb temperature (°C, solid lines) and geopotential height (m, dashed lines) analysis at ~00 UTC 10 March 1987, and wind vectors. Line AA′, cross-section projection line for Fig. 10.19.

The cross-section analysis of potential temperature and section-normal wind component (Fig. 10.21) along the projection line AA′ of Fig. 10.20 intercepts the cold front and the bent-back warm front. The frontal structures within this analysis show the cold front sloping upward from the sea surface to the tropopause and its associated vertical and horizontal wind shear beneath the ~90 m s^{-1} polar jet stream at ~250 mb. The shallow bent-back warm front is seen within the cooler air west of the cold front, its warm boundary situated near the center of the cyclone.

Our final example of cyclone-frontal evolution is taken from the analysis of the ERICA field measurements of the extreme cyclogenesis event that occurred over the western North Atlantic on 4–5 January 1989. This storm was observed through its entire life cycle with five NOAA P-3 research flights, sea-surface drifting buoys and an enhanced eastern U.S. upper-air network. The central pressure of this storm decreased by 65 mb (to 935 mb) in 24 hours during its rapid development phase. The NOAA/GOES visible satellite image at 1631 UTC 4 January 1989 (Fig. 10.22) shows the dramatic cloud structure associated with the end of the period of maximum cyclogenesis. Note the large areal coverage of the storm cloud signature, extending meridionally from eastern Cuba to the south coast of Newfoundland (~5000 km) and zonally from the U.S. East Coast to halfway across the North Atlantic (~4500 km).

The second of three low-level flights into the cyclone documented the structure of the bent-back warm front and the cold front. By the mid-time of the flight (~17 UTC 4 January), nearly coincident with the time of Fig. 10.22, the storm central pressure had decreased to ~950 mb. The analysis of 300-m temperature and sea-level pressure and plotted 300-m wind vectors (Fig. 10.23) were prepared from aircraft flight-level and dropwindsonde observations space-time adjusted to 17 UTC. This analysis shows that the frontal evolution had progressed into its bent-back

the storm center. The cold front was situated in the southerly flow east of the cyclone center and extended southward paralleling the East Coast of the U.S. At this time in the cyclone frontal evolution, the warm and cold fronts were distinctly disconnected (fractured), and the warm and cold frontal orientations had formed the above-described frontal T-bone configuration (e.g., Figs. 10.14c and 10.16).

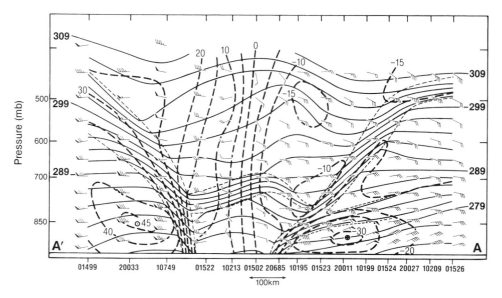

FIG. 10.19. As in FIG. 10.17, but for line AA′ of FIG. 10.18.

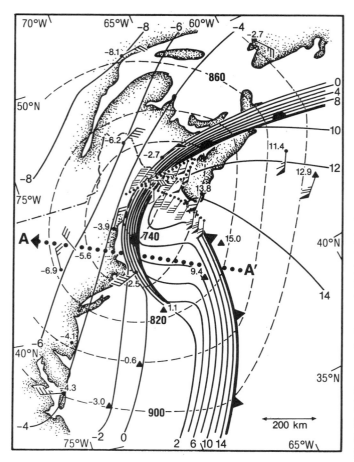

FIG. 10.20. 920-mb temperature (°C, solid lines) and geopotential height (m, dashed lines) analysis at ~12 UTC 27 January 1988. NOAA P-3 920-mb flight track, small-dotted lines with plotted wind vectors. Dropwindsonde deployment positions denoted by triangles. 920-mb temperatures plotted at rawinsonde and dropwindsonde positions. Warm and cold front boundaries indicated with conventional symbols. Line AA', segment of cross-section projection line for Fig. 10.21.

face. The front broadened with height to ~50 km by 600 mb. A prefrontal mesoconvective cloud system was situated at the leading edge of the cold front and extended ~1500 km along the front as shown in the satellite image (Fig. 10.22).

The final low-level flight into the cyclone was made during the period of maximum storm intensity. At this time (~03 UTC 5 January), the storm central pressure had decreased to ~935 mb and its frontal evolution had progressed to the seclusion phase. The analysis of the 300-m temperature and sea-level pressure and plotted 300-m wind vectors space-time adjusted to ~03 UTC 5 January are presented in Fig. 10.25. The 300-m temperature analysis shows that the bent-back warm front and the cold polar air had almost completely encircled the cyclone center, secluding a mesoscale (~100 km) warm pocket of previously post-cold-frontal air near the low center. The seclusion temperatures were ~7 K warmer than those on the cold side of the encircling front. Wind speeds ~40 m s⁻¹ were observed at the cold side of the frontal seclusion and the west-east distance across the seclusion, encircling wind speed maximum and cold air was ~140 km—truly mesoscale.

Cross-section analyses of potential temperature and section-normal wind components were prepared along the lines BB' and AA' of Fig. 10.25 to describe the vertical structure of the bent-back warm front and frontal seclusion, respectively. The warm-front cross section (Fig. 10.26a), constructed north of the cyclone center, shows the narrow (~50 km), shallow (~100 mb) bent-back warm front sloping upward and westward, overlying the ~40 m s⁻¹ low-level (~900 mb) wind speed maximum within the marine boundary layer. This frontal structure is similar to that shown in the previous frontal analyses (Fig. 10.24). Note the shallowness of the strong northerly flow between 57° and 60°W (Fig. 10.26a) associated with

warm front and cold frontal T-bone phase, as the warm front had developed west of the frontal triple point, through the cyclone center, and into the westerly flow to the south. The cold front had advanced ~300 km east of the cyclone center.

Cross-section analyses were prepared to describe the vertical structure of the bent-back warm front (Fig. 10.24a and b, along lines AA' and BB' of Fig. 10.23) and the cold front (Fig. 10.24c, along line CC'). The bent-back warm-frontal cross sections (Fig. 10.24a,b) show the strongest northeast to northerly wind speeds (~40 m s⁻¹) within the marine boundary layer beneath the front. The ~50 km width frontal zone exhibited mesoscale magnitudes of horizontal temperature gradient (~10 K/100 km), cross-frontal wind shear (~10⁻³ s⁻¹) and vertical wind shear (~40 m s⁻¹/100 mb). The cross-section analysis through the cold front (Fig. 10.24c) shows the extreme narrowness (~2 km) and sharpness of its gradients near the sea sur-

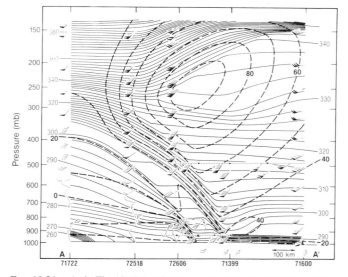

FIG. 10.21. As in Fig. 10.17, but for line AA' of Fig. 10.20. NOAA P-3 flight track and wind vectors as in Fig. 10.20.

FIG. 10.22.   1-km resolution visible image at 1631 UTC 4 January 1989.

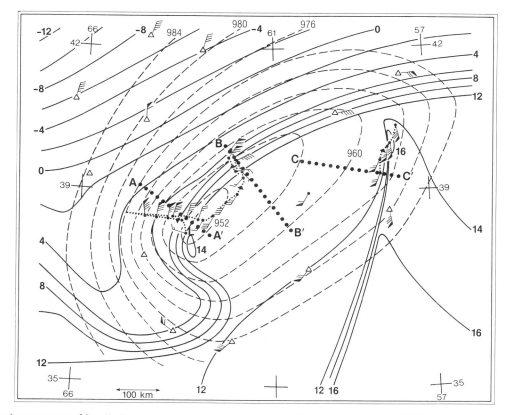

FIG. 10.23.   920-mb temperature (°C, solid lines) and sea-level pressure (mb, dashed lines) analysis at ~17 UTC 4 January 1989. Lines AA′ and BB′, and CC′ are cross-section projection lines for Fig. 10.24a, b and c, respectively. NOAA P-3 flight tracks, dropwindsondes and wind vectors as in Fig. 10.20.

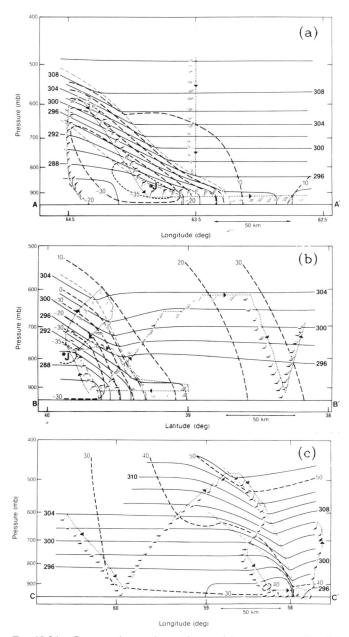

FIG. 10.24. Cross-section analyses of potential temperature (K, solid lines), section-normal wind component (m s⁻¹, dashed lines) and frontal boundaries along the lines AA' (a), BB' (b) and CC' (c) of Fig. 10.23. NOAA P-3 flight track and wind vectors as in Fig. 10.20.

10.4.3 A Conceptual Visualization of Cyclone-Frontal Evolution

We conclude this section by integrating the findings of numerical and observational studies into a conceptual model of the structural evolution of surface fronts during the life cycles of extratropical cyclones. Before proceeding, it should be noted in retrospect that the essence of the frontal evolution described herein was realistically simulated with highly idealized representations of baroclinic flows (e.g., the three-dimensional Eady wave), suggesting that the simulated and observed frontal evolutions are primarily a manifestation of the horizontal deformations and associated vertical circulations within amplifying adiabatic baroclinic waves. Though precipitation and boundary-layer processes act to modulate the time scale and intensity of baroclinic waves and their internal fronts, research results to date suggest that the basic structural evolution of fronts within cyclones is driven by the adiabatic component of the motions.

The proposed conceptual model describing four phases of frontal structure during the life cycle of extratropical cyclones is presented in Fig. 10.27. The model incorporates the results of the previously described simulation and observational studies. The four phases of frontal evolution are: (1) the continuous and broad (~400 km across) front which represents the birthplace of the incipient frontal cyclone (Fig. 10.27I); (2) the frontal fracture in the vicinity of the cyclone center and scale contraction of the discontinuous warm and cold frontal gradients (Fig. 10.27II); (3) the frontal T-bone and bent-back warm front, characteristic of the midpoint of cyclogenesis (Fig. 10.27III); and (4) the warm-core seclusion within the post-cold frontal polar air stream representing the culmination of frontal evolution within the mature, fully developed cyclone (Fig. 10.27IV).

10.5 Future Directions

Having considered selected past and present interpretations of the structure and dynamics of fronts, jet streams and the tropopause, we conclude this chapter with our vision of future directions for advancing the understanding of these weather systems.

From the numerical modeling standpoint, relentless advances in supercomputer technology will shortly lead to regional-scale (~1000 × 1000 km) frontal and jet stream simulations with spatial grid resolutions capable of resolving individual cloud systems, boundary-layer circulations, internal frontal circulations such as gravity waves and shear instabilities, and moist and dry symmetric instabilities. These numerical models will have horizontal and vertical grid resolution ~1 km and ~100 m, respectively, with explicit rather than parameterized representations of "present day" small-scale motions (e.g., cumulus clouds, boundary-layer processes). There will be an entirely new spectrum of microscale processes to be considered, such as cloud microphysics.

the reversal in wind direction to southerly above the frontal zone. The cross section across the warm-core seclusion and cyclone center (Fig. 10.26b) illustrates the intensity of the inner core of the mesoscale circulation near the cyclone center and the shallowness of the warm core structure. Maximum wind speeds in the northerly and southerly flows exceeded 35 and 50 m s⁻¹, respectively. The radius of maximum wind speed at 900 mb measured with respect to the center of the storm circulation was 75 km and increased with height to ≥ 200 km at 700 mb (~3 km). The baroclinicity of the encircling frontal zone sloped outward with height away from the cyclone center.

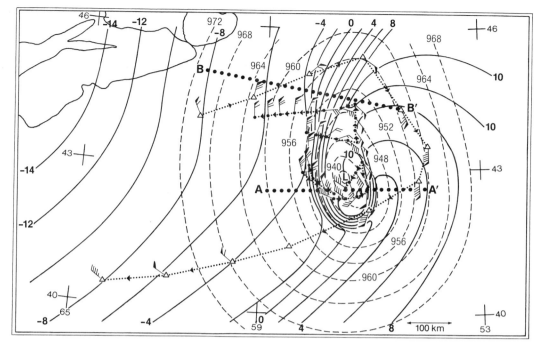

FIG. 10.25. 895-mb analysis of temperature (°C, solid lines) and sea-level pressure (mb, dashed lines) at ~03 UTC 5 January 1989. Lines BB′ and AA′ are cross-section projection lines for Fig. 10.26. Flight tracks, frontal boundaries, dropwindsondes and wind vectors as in Fig. 10.20.

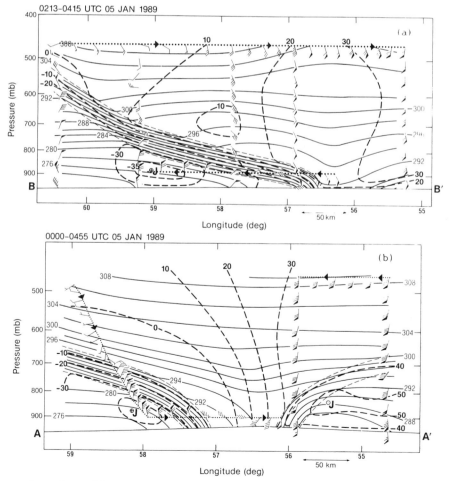

FIG. 10.26. Cross-section analyses of potential temperature (K, solid lines), section-normal wind component (m s^{-1}, heavy dashed lines) and NOAA P-3 flight track with wind vectors along lines BB′ (a) and AA′ (b) of Fig. 10.25. Dropwindsonde winds, vectors without connecting dotted lines.

These models will be used to simulate processes such as frontal-scale contraction from synoptic-scale (>500 km) gradients down to the nonhydrostatic microscale (<1 km), and the interaction of these sharp frontal gradients with precipitation systems and steep topography. The three-dimensionality of numerical models will facilitate the study of phenomena and processes such as mesoscale along-front variability, pre- and post-frontal boundary-layer circulations and their interaction with internal frontal circulations, interactions between fronts and mesoconvective (linear and cellular) precipitation systems, and the impact of physiographic boundaries formed by oceans (coastal and current), ice edges, snow, soil moisture and land use (e.g., forests, urban, agricultural).

By the early years of the 21st century, computing technology will have advanced to the point that microscale frontal-jet stream processes will be explicitly incorporated into global short-range (< 24 hour) through seasonal simulation and forecast models, including frontal interactions with coupled ocean circulation and interactive sea-state (fetch-dependent ocean roughness) models. The coupling of next-generation atmospheric chemistry models with the advanced regional- and global-scale meteorological models will advance the study and prediction of natural and anthropogenic trace constituent transport and chemical transformations. Of special interest will

be a focus upon the fine-scale details of stratospheric-tropospheric exchange and associated chemical processes, including the role of mesoscale and microscale frontal circulations and their associated precipitation systems in the atmospheric chemistry cycle.

From the theoretical standpoint, future considerations will be directed toward extending the theory of fronts and jet streams beyond the limits of the adiabatic, three-dimensional semigeostrophic theory. This will lead to the development of less restrictive diagnostic equations that include accelerations in the ageostrophic rotational and irrotational motions and the effects of nonconservative physical processes (e.g., latent and sensible heating, turbulent mixing). It will also be necessary to determine the importance of internal wave motions (e.g., inertia-gravity waves) in governing the dynamic balance and in forcing vertical circulations in the vicinity of jet-stream frontal-zone systems, as well as to advance the theory of moist mesoscale baroclinic instability and its interaction with synoptic-scale baroclinic/barotropic instability.

Perhaps the greatest challenge to the science resides within the area of technological innovations in atmospheric and oceanographic observing systems. The forthcoming numerical and theoretical advances will require validation through actual observations of the phenomena under investigation. What is necessary are nearly spatially

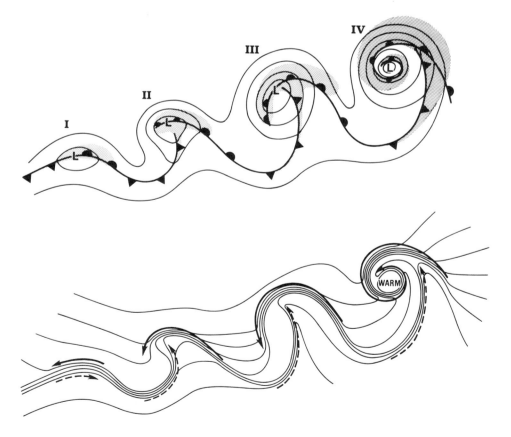

FIG. 10.27. The life cycle of the marine extratropical frontal cyclone: (I) incipient frontal cyclone; (II) frontal fracture; (III) bent-back warm front and frontal T-bone; (IV) warm-core frontal seclusion. Upper: sea-level pressure, solid lines; fronts, bold lines; and cloud signature, shaded. Lower: temperature, solid lines; cold and warm air currents, solid and dashed arrows, respectively.

and temporally continuous observations of all state parameters and velocity components, comparable in resolution to those from the next-generation numerical simulations. It is evident that the observing technology of the future must be of the remote sensing type, since limitations in the spatial and temporal resolutions of in-situ observing systems cannot satisfy the validation and initialization requirements of the simulation models.

Finally, it will be necessary to clarify the interplay between the mesoscale circulations and the synoptic-scale and planetary-scale motions. At the present time, there is considerable debate among researchers regarding the necessity of observing mesoscale weather systems in order to simulate and predict their impact upon larger-scale motions. Fronts, jet streams, mesoconvective systems, mountain waves and sea-breeze circulations have been simulated realistically with models initialized with synoptic-scale resolution data sets. This down-scale viewpoint suggests that mesoscale circulations are primarily a manifestation of the larger-scale motions and/or mesoscale physiography. An alternative viewpoint suggests that, under certain circumstances, upscale forcing by mesoscale phenomena and their associated processes can modulate the synoptic-scale through planetary-scale motions. The resolution of these differing interpretations regarding the interactions between the various scales of motion and their associated internal processes is a current focus of the science and should remain so well into the future.

Acknowledgments

The authors express their gratitude to Dr. N. Bond for providing the frontal analyses in Fig. 10.10a–c, to Ms. E. Donall for the numerical simulation exhibited in Fig. 10.14 and to Mr. P. Neiman for his assistance in preparing the analyses of marine cyclones shown in Section 10.4. We acknowledge Dr. Y.-H. Kuo and the NCAR Mesoscale and Microscale Meteorology Division for providing access to the NCAR/Penn State mesoscale prediction model and the NCAR computing facility. Special thanks are due to Mr. E. Hartnett, ERICA Data Center, Drexel University, for providing the data sets for the ERICA case studies presented herein, and to Prof. C. Kreitzberg, Drexel University, for encouraging our participation in the ERICA field program. We express our appreciation to the NOAA Office of Aircraft Operations and especially to the P-3 flight and engineering crews for their dedication in taking the observations presented in this chapter. Finally, the first author thanks the Office of Naval Research for support of the NOAA Alaskan Storm Program and Ocean Storms Program. The second author thanks the Office of Naval Research and National Science Foundation for supporting his effort in preparing this chapter through Contract N00014-88-K-0074 and Grant ATM-8721478, respectively.

We dedicate this chapter to the memory of Mrs. Mildred Birchfield of NOAA/WPL. Her superb technical assistance in preparing this and prior manuscripts has been invaluable, and she will be dearly missed.

REFERENCES

Abdullah, A. J., 1949: Cyclogenesis by a purely mechanical process. *J. Meteor.,* **6**, 86–97.

Anthes, R. A., and T. T. Warner, 1978: Development of hydrodynamic models suitable for air pollution and other mesometeorological studies. *Mon. Wea. Rev.,* **106**, 1045–1078.

——, Y.-H. Kuo and J. R. Gyakum, 1983: Numerical simulations of a case of explosive marine cyclogenesis. *Mon. Wea. Rev.,* **111**, 1174–1188.

Bergeron, T., 1928: Über die dreidimensional verknüpfende Wetteranalyse (I). *Geofys. Publ.,* **5**, No. 6, 1–111.

——, 1959: Methods in scientific weather analysis and forecasting. An outline in the history of ideas and hints at a program. *The Atmosphere and the Sea in Motion,* B. Bolin, Ed. Rockefeller Institute Press, 440–474.

Berggren, R., 1952: The distribution of temperature and wind connected with active tropical air in the higher troposphere and some remarks concerning clear air turbulence at high altitude. *Tellus,* **4**, 43–53.

Bjerknes, J., 1919: On the structure of moving cyclones. *Geofys. Publ.,* **1**, No. 1, 1–8.

——, 1932: Exploration des perturbations atmosphèriques à l'aide de sondages rapprochés dans le temps. *Geofys. Publ.,* **9**, No. 9, 1–52.

——, and E. Palmén, 1937: Investigations of selected European cyclones by means of serial ascents. *Geofys. Publ.,* **12**, No. 2, 1–62.

——, and H. Solberg, 1921: Meteorological conditions for the formation of rain. *Geofys. Publ.,* **2**, No. 3, 1–60.

——, and ——, 1922: Life cycle of cyclones and the polar front theory of atmospheric circulation. *Geofys. Publ.,* **3**, No. 1, 1–18.

Bosart, L. F., 1970: Mid-tropospheric frontogenesis. *Quart. J. Roy. Meteor. Soc.,* **96**, 442–471.

Browning, K. A., and T. W. Harrold, 1970: Air motion and precipitation growth at a cold front. *Quart. J. Roy. Meteor. Soc.,* **96**, 369–389.

Carbone, R. E., 1982: A severe frontal rainband. Part I: Stormwide hydrodynamic structure. *J. Atmos. Sci.,* **39**, 258–279.

Carlson, T. N., and F. H. Ludlam, 1968: Conditions for the occurrence of severe local storms. *Tellus,* **20**, 203–226.

——, S. G. Benjamin, G. S. Forbes and Y. F. Li, 1983: Elevated mixed layers in the regional severe storm environment: Conceptual model and case studies. *Mon. Wea. Rev.,* **111**, 1453–1473.

Charba, J., 1974: Application of gravity current model to analysis of squall-line gust front. *Mon. Wea. Rev.,* **102**, 140–156.

Defant, F., and H. Taba, 1957: The threefold structure of the atmosphere and the characteristics of the tropopause. *Tellus,* **9**, 259–274.

Dirks, R. A., J. P. Kuettner and J. A. Moore, 1988: Genesis of Atlantic Lows Experiment (GALE): An overview. *Bull. Amer. Meteor. Soc.,* **69**, 148–160.

Eady, E. T., 1949: Long waves and cyclone waves. *Tellus,* **1**, No. 3, 33–52.

Edelmann, W., 1963: On the behavior of disturbances in a baroclinic channel. Summary Rep. No. 2, Research in Objective Weather Forecasting, Part F, Contract No. AF61 (052)-373, Research Division, Deutscher Wetterdienst, Offenbach, 35 pp.

Eliassen, A., 1952: Slow thermally or frictionally controlled meridional circulations in a circular vortex. *Astrophys. Norv.,* **5**, No. 2, 60 pp.

——, 1959: On the formation of fronts in the atmosphere. *The Atmosphere and the Sea in Motion,* B. Bolin, Ed. Rockefeller Institute Press, 277-287.

——, 1962: On the vertical circulation in frontal zones. *Geofys. Publ.,* **24**, No. 4, 147-160.

——, and E. Raustein, 1968: A numerical integration experiment with a model atmosphere based on isentropic surfaces. *Meteor. Ann.,* **5**, 45-63.

Freeman, J. C., Jr., 1948: An analogy between equatorial easterlies and supersonic gas flow. *J. Meteor.,* **5**, 138-146.

Fujita, T., 1955: Results of detailed synoptic studies of squall lines. *Tellus,* **7**, 405-436.

Gall, R. L., R. T. Williams and T. L. Clark, 1987: On the minimum scale of surface fronts. *J. Atmos. Sci.,* **44**, 2562-2574.

——, —— and ——, 1988: Gravity waves generated during frontogenesis. *J. Atmos. Sci.,* **45**, 2204-2219.

Gidel, L. T., and M. A. Shapiro, 1979: The role of clear air turbulence in the production of potential vorticity in the vicinity of upper tropospheric jet stream-frontal systems. *J. Atmos. Sci.,* **36**, 2125-2138.

Goff, R. C., 1976: Vertical structure of thunderstorm outflows. *Mon. Wea. Rev.,* **104**, 1429-1440.

Gyakum, J. R., 1983a: On the evolution of the QE II storm. I: Synoptic aspects. *Mon. Wea. Rev.,* **111**, 1137-1155.

——, 1983b: On the evolution of the QE II storm. II: Dynamic and thermodynamic structure. *Mon. Wea. Rev.,* **111**, 1156-1173.

Hadlock, R., and C. W. Kreitzberg, 1988: The experiment on rapidly intensifying cyclones over the Atlantic (ERICA) field study: Objectives and plans. *Bull. Amer. Meteor. Soc.,* **69**, 1309-1320.

Hobbs, P. V., and P. O. G. Persson, 1982: The mesoscale and microscale structure and organization of clouds and precipitation in midlatitude cyclones. Part V: The substructure of narrow cold-frontal rainbands. *J. Atmos. Sci.,* **39**, 280-295.

Hoskins, B. J., 1971: Atmospheric frontogenesis models: Some solutions. *Quart. J. Roy. Meteor. Soc.,* **97**, 139-153.

——, 1976: Baroclinic waves and frontogenesis. Part I: Introduction and Eady waves. *Quart. J. Roy. Meteor. Soc.,* **102**, 103-122.

——, and F. P. Bretherton, 1972: Atmospheric frontogenesis models: Mathematical formulation and solution. *J. Atmos. Sci.,* **29**, 11-37.

——, and W. A. Heckley, 1981: Cold and warm fronts in baroclinic waves. *Quart. J. Roy. Meteor. Soc.,* **107**, 79-90.

——, and N. V. West, 1979: Baroclinic waves and frontogenesis. Part II. Uniform potential vorticity jet flows—cold and warm fronts. *J. Atmos. Sci.,* **36**, 1663-1680.

Keyser, D., and R. A. Anthes, 1982: The influence of planetary boundary layer physics on frontal structure in the Hoskins-Bretherton horizontal shear model. *J. Atmos. Sci.,* **39**, 1783-1802.

——, and M. J. Pecnick, 1985a: A two-dimensional primitive equation model of frontogenesis forced by confluence and horizontal shear. *J. Atmos. Sci.,* **42**, 1259-1282.

——, and ——, 1985b: Diagnosis of ageostrophic circulations in a two-dimensional primitive equation model of frontogenesis. *J. Atmos. Sci.,* **42**, 1283-1305.

——, and M. A. Shapiro, 1986: A review of the structure and dynamics of upper-level frontal zones. *Mon. Wea. Rev.,* **114**, 452-499.

——, and L. W. Uccellini, 1987: Regional models: Emerging research tools for synoptic meteorologists. *Bull. Amer. Meteor. Soc.,* **68**, 306-320.

——, M. A. Shapiro and D. J. Perkey, 1978: An examination of frontal structure in a fine-mesh primitive equation model for numerical weather prediction. *Mon. Wea. Rev.,* **106**, 1112-1124.

——, M. J. Pecnick and M. A. Shapiro, 1986: Diagnosis of the role of vertical deformation in a two-dimensional primitive equation model of upper-level frontogenesis. *J. Atmos. Sci.,* **43**, 839-850.

Kleinschmidt, E., Jr., 1951: Grundlagen einer Theorie der tropischen Zyklonen. *Arch. Meteor. Geophys. Bioklim.,* **A4**, 53-72.

Koch, S. E., 1984: The role of an apparent mesoscale frontogenetic circulation in squall line initiation. *Mon. Wea. Rev.,* **112**, 2090-2111.

Kuo, Y.-H., and R. J. Reed, 1988: Numerical simulation of an explosively deepening cyclone in the eastern Pacific. *Mon. Wea. Rev.,* **116**, 2081-2105.

——, M. A. Shapiro and E. G. Donall, 1990: Interaction of baroclinic and diabatic processes in numerical simulations of a rapidly developing marine cyclone. *Mon. Wea. Rev.,* submitted.

Kutzbach, G., 1979: *The Thermal Theory of Cyclones: A History of Meteorological Thought in the Nineteenth Century.* American Meteorological Society, 255 pp.

Margules, M., 1906: Über temperaturschichtung in stationär bewegter und ruhender luft. *Hann-Band. Meteor. Zeits.,* **2**, 245-254.

Matthews, D. A., 1981: Observation of a cloud arc triggered by thunderstorm outflow. *Mon. Wea. Rev.,* **109**, 2140-2157.

Miller, J. E., 1948: On the concept of frontogenesis. *J. Meteor.,* **5**, 169-171.

Mudrick, S. E., 1974: A numerical study of frontogenesis. *J. Atmos. Sci.,* **31**, 869-892.

Namias, J., and P. F. Clapp, 1949: Confluence theory of the high tropospheric jet stream. *J. Meteor.,* **6**, 330-336.

Neiman, P. J., M. A. Shapiro, E. G. Donall and C. W. Kreitzberg, 1990: The diabatic modification of an extratropical marine cyclone warm sector by cold underlying water. *Mon. Wea. Rev.,* **118**, in press.

Newton, C. W., 1950: Structure and mechanism of the prefrontal squall line. *J. Meteor.,* **7**, 210-222.

——, 1954: Frontogenesis and frontolysis as a three-dimensional process. *J. Meteor.,* **11**, 449-461.

——, and A. Trevisan, 1984a: Clinogenesis and frontogenesis in jet-stream waves. Part I: Analytical relations to wave structure. *J. Atmos. Sci.,* **41**, 2717-2734.

——, and ——, 1984b: Clinogenesis and frontogenesis in jet-stream waves. Part II: Channel model numerical experiments. *J. Atmos. Sci.,* **41**, 2735-2755.

Nyberg, A., and E. Palmén, 1942: Synoptische-aerologische Bearbeitung der internationalen Registrierballonaufstiege in Europa in der Zeit 17-19 Oktober 1935. *Statens Meteorol.-Hydrol. Anstalt, Medd., Ser. Uppsater* No. 40, 1-43.

Orlanski, I., B. Ross, L. Polinsky and R. Shaginaw, 1985: Advances in the theory of atmospheric fronts. *Advances in Geophysics, 28B*, 223-252.

Palmén, E., 1933: Aerologische Untersuchungen der atmosphärischen Störungen mit besonderer Berüchsichtigung der stratosphärischen Vorgänge. *Soc. Sci. Fenn., Comm. Phys.-Math., 7* , No. 5, 65 pp.

——, 1948: On the distribution of temperature and wind in the upper westerlies. *J. Meteor., 5*, 20-27.

——, 1951: The rôle of atmospheric disturbances in the general circulation. *Quart. J. Roy. Meteor. Soc., 77*, 337-354.

——, and C. W. Newton, 1969: *Atmospheric Circulation Systems. Their Structure and Physical Interpretation.* Academic Press, 603 pp.

Petterssen, S., 1936: Contribution to the theory of frontogenesis. *Geofys. Publ., 11*, No. 6, 1-27.

Reed, R. J., 1955: A study of a characteristic type of upper-level frontogenesis. *J. Meteor., 12*, 226-237.

——, and E. F. Danielsen, 1959: Fronts in the vicinity of the tropopause. *Arch. Meteor. Geophys. Bioklim., A11*, 1-17.

——, and F. Sanders, 1953: An investigation of the development of a mid-tropospheric frontal zone and its associated vorticity field. *J. Meteor., 10*, 338-349.

Reeder, M. J., 1986: The interaction of a surface cold front with a prefrontal thermodynamically well-mixed boundary layer. *Austral. Meteor. Mag., 34*, 137-148.

——, and D. Keyser, 1988: Balanced and unbalanced upper-level frontogenesis. *J. Atmos. Sci., 45*, 3366-3386.

Reiter, E. R., 1975: Stratospheric-tropospheric exchange processes. *Rev. Geophys. Space Phys., 13*, 459-474.

Sanders, F., 1955: An investigation of the structure and dynamics of an intense surface frontal zone. *J. Meteor., 12*, 542-552.

Sawyer, J. S., 1956: The vertical circulation at meteorological fronts and its relation to frontogenesis. *Proc. Roy. Soc. London, A234*, 346-362.

Schär, C. J., 1989: Dynamische Aspekte der aussertropischen Zyklogenese, Theorie und numerische Simulation im Limit der balancierten Strömungssysteme. Dissertation Nr. 8845 der Eidgenossischen Technische Hochschule, Zurich, 241 pp.

Shapiro, M. A., 1970: On the applicability of the geostrophic approximation to upper-level frontal-scale motions. *J. Atmos. Sci., 27*, 408-420.

——, 1974: A multiple structured frontal zone-jet stream system as revealed by meteorologically instrumented aircraft. *Mon. Wea. Rev., 102*, 244-253.

——, 1975: Simulation of upper-level frontogenesis with a 20-level isentropic coordinate primitive equation model. *Mon. Wea. Rev., 103*, 591-604.

——, 1976: The role of turbulent heat flux in the generation of potential vorticity in the vicinity of upper-level jet stream systems. *Mon. Wea. Rev., 104*, 892-906.

——, 1978: Further evidence of the mesoscale and turbulent structure of upper level jet stream-frontal zone systems. *Mon. Wea. Rev., 106*, 1100-1111.

——, 1980: Turbulent mixing within tropopause folds as a mechanism for the exchange of chemical constituents between the stratosphere and troposphere. *J. Atmos. Sci., 37*, 994-1004.

——, 1981: Frontogenesis and geostrophically forced secondary circulations in the vicinity of jet stream-frontal zone systems. *J. Atmos. Sci., 38*, 954-973.

——, 1982: Mesoscale weather systems of the central United States. CIRES/NOAA Tech. Rep., University of Colorado, 78 pp.

——, 1984: Meteorological tower measurements of a surface cold front. *Mon. Wea. Rev., 112*, 1634-1639.

——, 1985: Dropwindsonde observations of an Icelandic low and a Greenland mountain-lee wave. *Mon. Wea. Rev., 113*, 680-683.

——, E. R. Reiter, R. D. Cadle and W. A. Sedlacek, 1980: Vertical mass- and trace-constituent transports in the vicinity of jet streams. *Arch. Meteor. Geophys. Bioklim., B28*, 193-206.

——, T. Hampel, D. Rotzoll and F. Mosher, 1985: The frontal hydraulic head: A micro-α scale (~1 km) triggering mechanism for mesoconvective weather systems. *Mon. Wea. Rev., 113*, 1166-1183.

——, ——, and A. J. Krueger, 1987: The arctic tropopause fold. *Mon. Wea. Rev., 115*, 444-454.

Simpson, J. E., D. A. Mansfield and J. R. Milford, 1977: Inland penetration of sea-breeze fronts. *Quart. J. Roy. Meteor. Soc., 103*, 47-76.

Tepper, M., 1950: A proposed mechanism of squall lines: The pressure jump line. *J. Meteor., 7*, 21-29.

Uccellini, L. W., 1986: The possible influence of upstream upper-level baroclinic processes on the development of the QE II storm. *Mon. Wea. Rev., 114*, 1019-1027.

Wakimoto, R. M., 1982: Investigations of thunderstorm gust fronts with the use of radar and rawinsonde data. *Mon. Wea. Rev., 110*, 1060-1082.

Whitaker, J. S., L. W. Uccellini and K. F. Brill, 1988: A model-based diagnostic study of the rapid development phase of the Presidents' Day cyclone. *Mon. Wea. Rev., 116*, 2337-2365.

Williams, R. T., 1967: Atmospheric frontogenesis: A numerical experiment. *J. Atmos. Sci., 24*, 627-641.

——, 1972: Quasi-geostrophic versus non-geostrophic frontogenesis. *J. Atmos. Sci., 29*, 3-10.

——, 1974: Numerical simulation of steady-state fronts. *J. Atmos. Sci., 31*, 1286-1296.

Chapter 11

Advances in Numerical Prediction of the Atmospheric Circulation in the Extratropics

Lennart Bengtsson

European Centre for Medium-Range Weather Forecasts, Shinfield Park, Reading, Berkshire RG2 9AX, U.K.

11.1 Introduction

The complexity and variability of atmospheric motion and their manifestations in all kinds of weather phenomena constitute a major scientific, technical and practical challenge to the meteorological community. The weather affects practically all meteorological aspects of human affairs and influences society both directly and indirectly. There is no doubt that the prediction of weather and the understanding of atmospheric processes are the primary tasks of the meteorological services. The prediction of the weather requires a fundamental understanding of the laws that govern the atmosphere and of the many feedback processes involving the atmosphere, oceans and the land surfaces. Predicting the weather is primarily an initial value problem and hence the accuracy of weather prediction is directly related to the accuracy of observations and their distribution in time and space.

Numerical prediction using mathematical models of the atmosphere has been in existence for almost forty years. During this period a spectacular development has taken place encompassing the complete field of numerical weather prediction. A global observing system has been established and operational models provide daily routine predictions for the whole global atmosphere, from the surface of the earth to high into the stratosphere. The effect on weather prediction has been dramatic; today 5-day forecasts for the 500 hPa geopotential are as accurate as the 1-day forecasts produced in the early 1950s; see Table 11.1. By far the greatest advances in forecast skill have taken place in the extratropics.

In this chapter we will discuss the physical and mathematical basis for numerical weather prediction, the numerical methods and the modeling techniques, as well as the use and importance of observations. Operational results will be presented and analysed. Particular importance will be devoted to the prediction of intense cyclogenesis in the westerlies; this was an area in which Professor Erik Palmén had particular interests.

11.2 The Physical and Mathematical Basis for Numerical Weather Prediction

Numerical weather prediction and general circulation modeling grew from similar origins in the early 1950s, but modeling for the two applications differed widely. Weather forecasting was concentrated on the time range of at most up to a few days ahead, over which period close attention to the slowly acting physical processes was not of paramount interest. It was also subject to operational time constraints which necessitated the use of simplified equations and limited area domain. The model used by Charney et al. (1950) was based on the principle of conservation of the vertical component of the absolute vorticity for a particle; the model was adiabatic and barotropic, it used the 500 hPa level as an equivalent barotropic model. Although it has severe physical restrictions, the barotropic model was gradually put into operational use by several meteorological services. Despite the obvious limitation the operational results were nevertheless encouraging and generally better than previous forecasts based on subjective and empirical methods. The reader is referred to Bergthorsson et al. (1955) reporting on the experience of the very first real time numerical weather prediction carried out by the Swedish Air Force in 1954. A new era in meteorology had begun.

The extraordinary development in computer technology, with an averaged doubling time in speed and memory storage of less than two years (Fig. 11.1), has removed many of the computational restrictions in atmospheric modeling and numerical weather prediction. The advent of supercomputers with processing speeds of around 50 MIPS in the 1970s was of importance for Europe in establishing a special center with the objective to undertake forecasts in the medium-range covering a time range from 3 to 10 days, the European Centre for Medium-Range Weather Forecasts (ECMWF). This initiative led to operational models for weather forecasting following an approach which previously had been applied only in models for climate simulation and prediction (Bengtsson and Simmons 1983; Bengtsson 1985).

As was recognized already at the outset of numerical modeling and more specifically by Miyakoda et al. (1972), the climatological balance of the forecast model may become of importance after several days of prediction. Moreover, the extension of prediction time necessitated a gradual extension of the integration domain to the whole globe. This development means that the modeling problem in weather forecasting, at least in the medium range, has become very similar to the problem of studying climate processes on short time scales (less than a few months). In fact a clear distinction can no longer be drawn between numerical models for climate studies and for medium-range weather prediction.

The fundamental process driving the earth's atmosphere is the heating by incoming short-wave solar radiation and the cooling by long-wave radiation to space. The heating is

TABLE 11.1

Geopotential height errors (standard deviation) of: (a) 24 operational and quasi-operational 24-h predictions by the barotropic model (data from University of Stockholm 1954). (b) Barotropic forecasts for the Northern Hemisphere during January 1981. Initial state taken from the operational ECMWF analysis. (c) ECMWF operational forecasts for January 1981. (d) ECMWF operational forecasts for January 1984. (e) ECMWF operational forecasts for January 1988.

Forecast time	(a) Nov 1951– Apr 1954 (24 cases) barotr. model	(b) Jan 1981 barotr. model	(c) Jan 1981 ECMWF	(d) Jan 1984 ECMWF	(e) Jan 1988 ECMWF
24 h	76 m	47 m	22 m	21 m	16 m
48 h		97 m	41 m	38 m	31 m
72 h		151 m	62 m	57 m	46 m
96 h			85 m	75 m	60 m
120 h				89 m	73 m

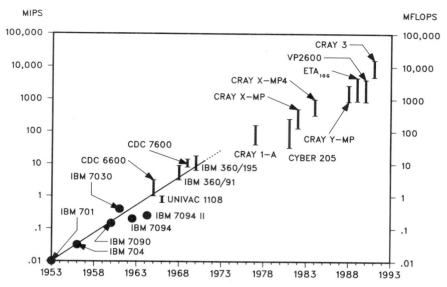

FIG. 11.1. History of supercomputer performance. Performances are given in MIPS (millions of instructions per second) to 1975, thereafter in MFLOPS (millions of floating point instructions per second). See also Fig. 12.1.

strongest in the tropics while cooling predominates at the polar latitudes of at least the winter hemisphere. The bulk of the net incoming solar radiation is absorbed not by the atmosphere, but by the underlying surface. The evaporation of moisture and the heating of the surface lead, however, to much of this energy being transferred to the atmosphere as latent heat and, to a lesser extent, as sensible heat. Thus the dominant direct heating of the atmosphere is found to be the release of latent heat. Although the major source of latent heat is associated with deep tropical convection, release of latent heat plays an important role in the intense and rapid deepening of extratropical depressions. This will be demonstrated in Section 11.6.

The meridional transfer of energy across middle latitudes, which is necessary to offset the heat imbalance set up by the differential radiative heating, is accomplished largely by transient weather systems. These systems, which dominate the circulation at middle latitudes and have time scales of the order of a few days, develop due to baroclinic instability (Charney 1947) in the zonal flow. The flow is further perturbed especially in the Northern Hemisphere by orographic effects and land-sea contrasts (Charney and Eliassen 1949; Bolin 1950; Smagorinsky 1953). These have a strong local influence and on a larger scale lead to a concentration of strong baroclinic zones along the storm tracks of the North Pacific and North Atlantic (Blackmon et al. 1977; see Section 4.2.2). Of particular importance for numerical prediction is the low-frequency variability such as cutoff lows and quasi-stationary blocking anticyclones. Major anomalies in the weather which take place in association with blocking highs over northern Europe are often of great concern to the public. The mechanism leading to blocking is not yet fully understood. Blocking may arise from slowly varying boundary conditions such as sea-surface temperature (e.g., Bjerknes 1966; Namias 1969) or from variability in the dynamical response to a

fixed external forcing (Charney and DeVore 1979; Wiin-Nielsen 1979; Simmons et al. 1983). Numerical experiments (Bengtsson 1981), as well as diagnostic evaluations of operational forecasts, indicate the importance of interaction with small-scale synoptic systems (Tracton 1988).

Many other processes are important in determining the detailed behaviour of the atmosphere on time scales of more than a few days. The turbulent fluxes of heat, moisture and momentum influence successively all larger scales of motion. These fluxes are determined by the large scale flow and by the nature of the underlying surface. The type of surface (e.g., type of vegetation), as characterized by its albedo, determines the proportion of incoming solar radiation that is reflected back toward space, and its evapotranspiration capacities determine the Bowen ratio (the ratio of sensible heat to latent heat flux). The role of clouds in both horizontal and vertical distribution is important in reflecting incoming short-wave radiation and in absorbing and emitting long-wave radiation.

As the models have evolved, it has become feasible to predict the local weather per se instead of statistically relating it to large scale predictors given by models. For this reason a comprehensive modeling of physical processes is also receiving attention from modelers concerned specifically with short-range prediction. Some examples of the prediction of "weather parameters" are given in Section 11.6.

11.3 Numerical Methods and Modeling Techniques

Present models used for numerical weather prediction are almost without exception based on a set of equations known as the primitive equations. These equations were first explored by Richardson (1922) who used height as a vertical coordinate. Hinkelmann (1959) developed a model using pressure as the vertical coordinate, which was to become the first primitive-equation model to be used in operational weather prediction.

As discussed by Phillips (1973) the governing dynamic, thermodynamic and conservation equations for mass and moisture are transformed to a spherical geometry. The reduced set of primitive equations is obtained by assuming the height scale of the motion to be small compared with its horizontal length scale. The basic predicted variables in such a set are the horizontal wind components u and v, temperature T, water vapor normally represented by the specific humidity q, and surface pressure p_S.

We may illustrate the form of the primitive equations using the vertical coordinate system in most common use, namely the "sigma" coordinate system proposed by Phillips (1957). In the sigma system the vertical co-ordinate is given by

$$\sigma = p/p_S \qquad (11.1)$$

where p is pressure and p_S is surface pressure. In this case the governing equations become:

Momentum

$$\frac{D\mathbf{V}}{Dt} + f\mathbf{k} \times \mathbf{V} + \nabla\Phi + RT\nabla(\ell n p_S) = \mathbf{F}_m \qquad (11.2)$$

Thermodynamic

$$\frac{DT}{Dt} - \frac{RT\omega}{c_p p_S \sigma} = F_T \qquad (11.3)$$

Mass conservation

$$\frac{Dp_S}{Dt} + p_S\left(\nabla \cdot \mathbf{V} + \frac{\partial\dot{\sigma}}{\partial\sigma}\right) = 0 \qquad (11.4)$$

Moisture conservation

$$\frac{Dq}{Dt} = F_q \qquad (11.5)$$

Hydrostatic

$$\frac{\partial\Phi}{\partial\sigma} = -\frac{RT}{\sigma}. \qquad (11.6)$$

Here t is time and D/Dt denotes the rate of change for a particle moving with the fluid. In σ coordinates this derivative takes the form

$$\frac{D}{Dt} = \frac{\partial}{\partial t} + \mathbf{V} \cdot \nabla + \dot{\sigma}\frac{\partial}{\partial\sigma}. \qquad (11.7)$$

Here $\mathbf{V}$ is the horizontal velocity vector, $\mathbf{V} = (u,v,0)$ and ∇ is the two-dimensional gradient operator on a constant σ-surface; f is the Coriolis parameter, $\mathbf{k}$ is the unit vertical vector, Φ is geopotential, R is the gas constant, c_p the specific heat of air at constant pressure. F_X denotes the rate of change of variable X due to the parameterized processes of radiation, convection, turbulent vertical mixing and large-scale precipitation. It also represents the rate of change of X due to the explicit horizontal smoothing that is usually included in models in order to prevent an unrealistic growth of the smallest scales which can be represented by the model.

A predictive equation for surface pressure is obtained by integrating (11.4) from $\sigma = 0$ to $\sigma = 1$, using the boundary conditions $\dot{\sigma} = 0$ at $\sigma = 0$ and $\sigma = 1$:

$$\frac{\partial p_S}{\partial t} = -\int_0^1 \nabla \cdot (p_S\mathbf{V})\,d\sigma. \qquad (11.8)$$

Vertical velocities are not explicitly predicted but they can easily be obtained from (11.4).

The form of the primitive equations given above neglects the local mass of water vapor compared with that of dry air, an approximation that can introduce a small, but not always negligible, error in moist and warm conditions. A more accurate form can be obtained by replacing the temperature T, appearing in (11.3) and (11.6), by the virtual temperature, T_v, which is defined by:

$$T_v = T\{1 + [R_v/R - 1]q\} \qquad (11.9)$$

where R_v is the gas constant for water vapor. Equation (11.3) must be corrected in a corresponding way.

As the parameterization schemes become more complex, additional predictive equations may be added to this basic set. Sundqvist (1981) has developed a formulation for a separate prediction of liquid water. A type of boundary-layer parameterization that uses the turbulent kinetic energy as a predicted variable has been tested by Miyakoda and Sirutis (1977).

11.3.1   Numerical Formulation

It will not be possible here to give a comprehensive and systematic presentation of the different numerical formulations used in models. For an extensive review reference is made to Haltiner and Williams (1980) and Cullen (1983). The overall objective has been to develop schemes with the highest possible accuracy with available computer resources. Of particular importance has been the development of efficient time-integration schemes, semi-implicit schemes (Robert 1969; Robert et al. 1972), split-explicit schemes (Marchuk 1974; Burridge 1975; Gadd 1978) and in recent years semi-Lagrangian schemes (Robert 1982; Bates and McDonald 1982; Robert et al. 1985; Staniforth and Temperton 1986; Ritchie 1988). By increasing the time-step by a factor of five in going from an explicit to a semi-implicit or a split-explicit scheme and by another factor of three to five in going to a semi-Lagrangian scheme, we are naturally increasing the time truncation error. As has been demonstrated by many researchers, e.g., Robert (1974), however, time truncation errors are insignificant compared to space truncation errors for explicit or semi-implicit schemes. For this reason a stable scheme such as a semi-Lagrangian scheme could be set up in such a way that the time truncation error is by and large consistent with the space truncation error. Such a procedure would have the additional advantage that subgrid-scale processes could be parameterized in a physically more straightforward way.

Today practically all operational or research models either use semi-implicit or split-explicit schemes. While earlier prediction models used finite difference schemes, finite differences are now mainly used for limited area models. Global or hemispheric models are essentially based on a spectral transform technique first proposed by Eliasen et al. (1970) and Orszag (1970). Present formulations largely follow the approach of the first multilevel spectral model of Bourke (1972), Hoskins and Simmons (1975) and Baede et al. (1979) and hence use vorticity and divergence as predictive variables.

These equations are easily derived from (11.2). The predicted variables are represented in terms of truncated expansions of spherical harmonics

$$X(\lambda, \phi, \sigma, t) = \sum_{m=-M}^{M} \sum_{n=|m|}^{N} X_n^m(\sigma, t) p_n^m(\sin \phi) e^{im\lambda} \quad (11.10)$$

where X is any variable, ϕ is latitude, λ is longitude and the p_n^m are the associated Legendre polynomials.

For equivalent resolution (e.g., the finite difference grid has the same spacing as the Gaussian grid used by the spectral model), and for the same physical parameterization and the same initial data, there are generally small differences between a finite difference model and a spectral transform model. Girard and Jarraud (1982) undertook an extensive intercomparison between the ECMWF grid point model (horizontal resolution of 1.875° latitude/longitude) and the ECMWF spectral transform model at triangular truncation of T63. The spectral model gave slightly better results for the same computational cost. It should be pointed out, however, that differences in mathematical representation (spectral or grid point for instance) generally have less impact on predictive skill than most other aspects on the forecasting system such as resolution, subgrid-scale parameterization and the initial state.

Table 11.2 outlines in a qualitative sense the importance of different atmospheric processes with respect to the prediction of the synoptic flow in the extratropics. In the short time range (1–2 days) a detailed description of the adiabatic processes is of utmost importance. This includes the role of orographic obstacles which may influence the flow via the lower boundary condition. Jet streams and baro-

clinic zones have sharp structures (see, e.g., Defant 1959), and resolutions of 50–100 km in the horizontal and 25–50 hPa in the vertical are required to keep truncation errors comfortably small. Simmons et al. (1989) have demonstrated convincingly the importance of a high horizontal resolution. Further remarks will be made in Section 11.6. (Limited-area fine-mesh models are treated by Anthes in Chapter 12.)

Perhaps the most important effect of an increased horizontal resolution is the benefit it brings in resolving land-sea contrasts and steep orography. Dell'Osso (1984), and Wu and Chen (1985) have demonstrated the effect of resolution in predicting lee-wave cyclogenesis. For such developments, proper resolution of orographic obstacles is essential; hardly any positive effect of increased atmospheric resolution is obtained if there is no simultaneous improvement in resolving the orography. (See Section 7.5.)

11.3.2   Parameterization

Observational and computational restrictions make it necessary to confine the numerical models to a description of phenomena larger than a certain scale. Although this scale has gradually become smaller following computer developments, the minimum scale is still significantly larger than that of many weather systems. These so-called subgrid-scale processes must be related to the macro-scale currently resolved by the models. This step is known as *parameterization*, since the subgrid-scale processes are described in terms of the parameters resolved and predicted by the model.

We will not here give a comprehensive presentation of the parameterization schemes presently used in numerical models. These schemes are being successively modified. The reader is advised to study the latest model documentation from the large forecasting centers. Instead, we will here focus on a few important areas that have been found to be of major importance in weather prediction in the extratropics in the short and medium range.

a) *Cumulus convection*

A proper parameterization of deep cumulus convection is of primary importance for numerical weather prediction in the tropics and plays an important role at middle and high latitudes in the medium and extended range (e.g., Simmons and Miller 1988). Several schemes have been developed which relate the occurrence of convection to the existence of an unstable stratification and a net conveyance of moisture by the large-scale flow and surface friction. For an extensive review see Arakawa and Chen (1987). One of the most common schemes is the one proposed by Kuo (1974) and now used by several models including the ECMWF operational model.

In the scheme proposed by Kuo a partition parameter, b, was introduced in such a way that moistening of the environmental air was proportional to b while heating due to release of latent heat was proportional to $(1-b)$. Currently, however, there is no universally accepted

TABLE 11.2

Relative importance in a qualitative sense of different physical processes on the synoptic scale flow at middle latitudes as a function of the length of the forecast. H = high, M = medium, S = small.

Physical processes	Length of forecast		
	1–2 days	3–5 days	6–14 days
Adiabatic	H	H	H
Radiation	S	M	H
Sensible heat flux	S	M	H
Latent heat flux	S	M	H
Cumulus convection	S	H	H
Stratiform precipitation	M	H	H
Vertical momentum flux	S	M	H
Surface friction	M	H	H
Land surface condition	S	S	M

method of specifying *b*. Anthes (1977) has proposed an empirical formulation for *b* depending on the relative humidity. Krishnamurti et al. (1980) have given an expression for *b* depending on the large-scale vertical velocity and vorticity, derived from multiple regression analysis on the GATE upper air data set. Geleyn (1985) has proposed a modified version wherein the partition is determined locally through the use of the wet-bulb characteristics.

In recent years new conceptual ideas have been proposed. Betts (1986) and Betts and Miller (1986) have developed a convective adjustment scheme where adjustment is also taking place toward a prescribed moisture profile typical of convective situations. Recent evaluation carried out at ECMWF (Simmons and Miller 1988) indicates better performance with this scheme than with the Kuo scheme presently used. (See Fig. 11.2.) Edelmann (1984) and Bougeault (1985) have proposed simplified mass flux schemes with a parameterization of the detrainment and a closure assumption similar to those of the Kuo scheme. The schemes have been implemented in the German and French operational models respectively (Müller et al. 1987; Coiffier et al. 1987). A further development of the mass flux scheme has recently been proposed by Tiedtke (1989) and has been implemented in the ECMWF operational model.

b) *Stratiform precipitation*

The treatment of nonconvective precipitation appears to be one of the simpler elements of the overall parameterization scheme. Stratiform precipitation is normally calculated after the computation of other dynamical and physical processes that change temperature and water vapor content. It generally allows for condensation with associated latent heat release of sufficient vapor to keep the relative humidity below a fixed threshold value. The threshold value is normally set to a value in the range of 80–100 percent relative humidity. Partial evaporation of

raindrops falling through unsaturated layers is normally incorporated following the proposal by Kessler (1969).

c) *Dissipation of momentum*

The term $\mathbf{F}_m$, representing the dissipation of momentum in the momentum equation (11.2), is a comparatively small term outside the boundary layer. Very little observational evidence exists of its distribution in time and space. So far, the main evidence for the existence of a frictional force comes from the residual term in the longitudinally-averaged budget of zonal momentum (Swinbank 1985). Studies of the local momentum budget (e.g., Holopainen et al. 1980) are inconclusive due to lack of data on vertical velocity.

In numerical models we must distinguish between dissipation which is introduced for numerical reasons, and dissipation which is due to real physical subgrid-scale processes. In practice there is no clear way to separate these. The dissipation terms are determined by systematic numerical experiments of selected synoptic cases (e.g., Machenhauer 1988). Figure 11.3 from Simmons and Miller (1988) shows the relation between predictive skill and horizontal diffusion in one particular experiment. In this case the sensitivity to the choice of diffusion factor is probably larger than what normally occurs.

Recent evaluation at ECMWF of the role of vertical diffusion, for example, has indicated that previously used vertical dissipation has been too large and led to an excess reduction of eddy kinetic energy. From January 1988 vertical dissipation was removed in the free atmosphere except in areas of dry static instability. Although there are no indications that the vertical dissipation is zero in the real atmosphere, there are observational indications that dissipation takes place in narrow bands and, during the course of integration it is smoothed by the vertical finite difference scheme. The effect of reduced vertical diffusion (as is further discussed in Section 11.7.2) is an improved

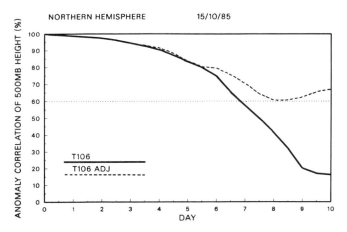

FIG. 11.2. Anomaly correlation of 500 hPa height for the extratropical Northern Hemisphere forecasts from 12 UTC 15 October 1985. Full line: the operational forecast using a Kuo-type convection. Dashed line: forecast with the adjustment-type convection scheme of Betts and Miller (1986) (Simmons and Miller 1988).

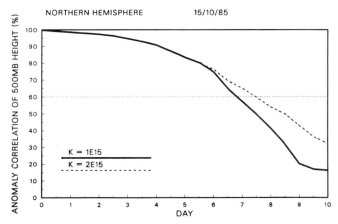

FIG. 11.3. Anomaly correlation of 500 hPa height for the extratropical Northern Hemisphere forecasts from 12 UTC 15 October 1985. Full line: forecast with a horizontal diffusion coefficient of $10^{15} \text{m}^4 \text{ s}^{-1}$. Dashed line: Forecast with a diffusion coefficient of $2 \times 10^{15} \text{m}^4 \text{ s}^{-1}$ (Simmons and Miller 1988).

maintenance of eddy kinetic energy and a better prediction of intense synoptic features (Section 11.6).

A common systematic error in numerical integration is a marked tendency to intensify the westerlies over the continents in middle and high latitudes. The error is most pronounced during the winter. It can be identified clearly in short-range forecasts but becomes serious beyond 4–5 days. The erroneous flow regime is accompanied by unrealistically low values of surface pressure, geopotential height and temperature in high latitudes. Two traditionally neglected processes have recently been investigated as being of importance in alleviating this problem in large-scale numerical models. Both are associated with the occurrences of stable stratified flow over unresolved orography—a common situation in the extratropics in winter.

The first of these is the damming and trapping of cold air by ridges and valleys in mountainous regions. Wallace et al. (1983) suggested a procedure whereby the unresolved orography was accounted for by adding an amount proportional to the standard deviation of the unresolved subgrid-scale orography—a procedure which is the equivalent of partially filling unresolved valleys. This so-called envelope orography was found to improve the skill of the ECMWF model by reducing the magnitude of the westerly error. Later studies by other modelers, e.g., Chouinard et al. (1986), have verified the results obtained at ECMWF.

The second process, which may be of importance in alleviating the westerly flow error, is associated with the occurrence of mesoscale orographically excited gravity-wave systems in stable stratified flow. The idea that such drag forces due to mountain waves may have an important impact on the synoptic and large-scale flow was proposed by Sawyer (1959) and Bretherton (1969). Observational studies by Lilly (1972) and Lilly et al. (1982) reinforced the earlier studies.

The first use of a wave-drag parameterization was in the Canadian Atmospheric Environment Service's general circulation model (Boer et al. 1984). It has recently been incorporated in the U.K. Meteorological Office operational model (Palmer et al. 1986) and in the ECMWF model (Miller et al. 1989). In the model implementation, the drag is proportional to the surface wind speed, the variance of the subgrid-scale orography and the Brunt-Väisälä frequency. In the ECMWF implementation, the variance of the subgrid-scale orography is also dependent on the wind direction relative to the orographic obstacle. Numerical experiments have shown that a combination of envelope orography and gravity wave drag is the best solution (McFarlane et al. 1987). Figure 11.4 shows a similar result from ECMWF.

11.4   Use and Importance of Observations

Numerical weather prediction is an initial value problem, and the accuracy of any forecast is directly related to the accuracy of the initial state. The radiosonde network established after the Second World War is still the cornerstone of the atmospheric observing system, but it has been greatly enhanced with satellite and aircraft measurements. Since the end of the 1970s there has in essence been a global observing system (Fig. 11.5). Despite the impressive development of the observing system over the past fifteen years, however, the present observing system cannot satisfy the observational requirements that ideally would be needed at every grid point of the model consisting of the basic parameters: horizontal wind, temperature, moisture and surface pressure. Additionally, sea surface temperature, soil moisture and snow observations are required.

Fortunately, these very demanding requirements can be relaxed due to the strong dynamical and physical coupling between meteorological observations in space and time. This was pointed out by Smagorinsky (1969) who demonstrated that a dynamical model, for example, was able to reconstitute the humidity field in most of its details within a day or two in an experiment in which humidity initially was prescribed as a zonal mean. It should be stressed, however, that this essentially is valid only in the extratropics when the dynamical forcing is dominating. In the tropics, humidity observations often play a crucial role and, as has been demonstrated by Krishnamurti et al. (1983), are required for an accurate prediction of tropical disturbances. Numerical experiments (e.g., Arpe et al. 1985; Hollingsworth et al. 1985) have shown that an accurate specification of the coupled wind and mass fields in the baroclinic zones is crucial for forecast quality, while a detailed analysis of the boundary layer appears to be less important. The

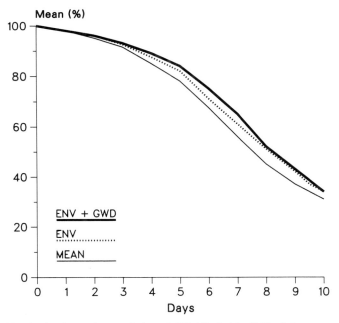

FIG. 11.4. Anomaly correlation of 500 hPa height field of the extratropical Northern Hemisphere forecasts averaged over 11 forecasts with the ECMWF T106-L19 model. Thin full line shows the score using a mean orography, dashed curve with an envelope orography and heavy full line with both envelope orography and gravity wave drag. For further information, see text.

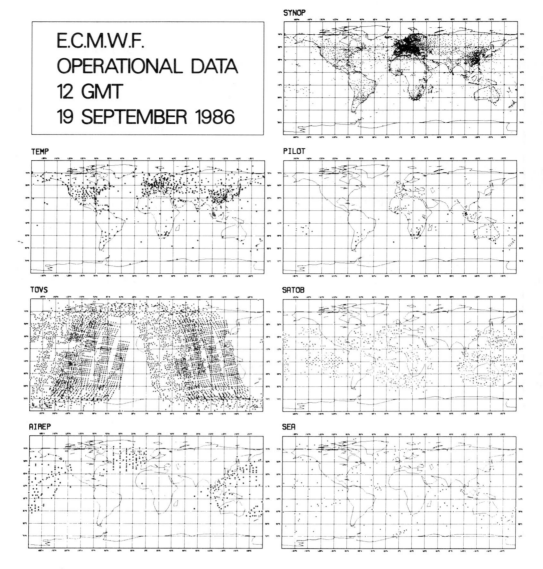

FIG. 11.5.   Coverage of observational data received at ECMWF between 09 UTC and 15 UTC 19 September 1986. The data distribution is typical for the period 1986—1988.

SYNOP: Observations from surface stations including observations from ships of opportunity
TEMP: wind, temperature and moisture observations from radiosondes
PILOT: wind observations by pibal balloons
TOVS: temperature and moisture soundings by polar orbiting satellites (NOAA)
SATOB: wind measurements from geostationary satellites
AIREP: wind measurements from commercial airlines
SEA: pressure observations from drifting buoys.

explanation is again that a numerical model is able to generate missing information, indicating a considerable degree of redundancy among the large-scale atmospheric variables. Consequently the assimilation of observations in four dimensions using a comprehensive numerical model as a tool is a necessary requirement for an accurate determination of the initial state. The development of such systems during the past ten years has played a very important part in the improvement of numerical weather prediction. Moreover, asynoptic data, such as observations from satellites and aircraft, cannot be adequately used without four-dimensional data assimilation.

Most of the operational data-assimilation systems developed so far are not fully four-dimensional but instead arrange data in time slots ranging from a few hours up to 12 hours. There are several advantages in such a procedure, since it creates a possibility for a rational monitoring and checking of the data. As an example, we will describe the data-assimilation system used at ECMWF. This system, outlined in Fig. 11.6, organizes the data in 6-hour time windows. The global atmosphere is analyzed at 17 levels, 1000-10 hPa, four times a day.

A data-assimilation step consists of a first guess, a 6-hour forecast from a previous initial state, an analysis

OPERATIONAL DATA ASSIMILATION - FORECAST CYCLE

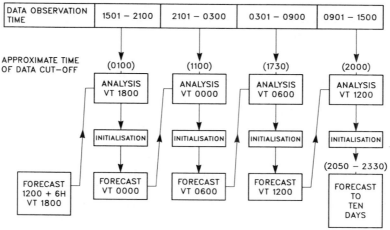

FIG. 11.6.   The ECMWF operational data-assimilation forecast cycle, valid at the end of 1988. The scheme is typical of an intermittent data-assimilation system.

procedure using all available observations within ±3 h and finally an initialization step. After the initialization, integration continues for another 6 hours, whereafter the process is repeated and so on. A numerical forecast for any length of time can be started from any of these initial states.

Objective analysis methods for numerical weather prediction have recently been thoroughly reviewed by Hollingsworth (1987). Most methods are based on an extension of optimum interpolation (Eliassen 1954; Gandin 1963) to a multivariate three-dimensional interpolation of deviation from forecast fields (e.g., Lorenc 1981). The multivariate technique allows for a consistent use of observations with different error characteristics and takes into full account the irregular distribution of these observations. Multivariate methods are consequently convenient for analyzing the mixture of different observing systems that we have today.

As has been demonstrated by Leith (1983) and Bengtsson (1989), the accuracy of the initial state as obtained through a data-assimilation process is determined by (i) the observational error variance at a given time, (ii) the data-assimilation frequency and (iii) the accuracy of the model. It can be demonstrated (Bengtsson 1989) that an extension of predictive skill of at least one day by the ECMWF model is due to the use of an accurate high-resolution model in the data-assimilation process. The smaller the forecast errors are, the more linear will be the multivariate relation between the mass field and the wind components, the smaller will be the changes made by the analysis and the smaller will be the changes made by the initialization. It is essential to use the same model for data-assimilation as for the forecast production, in order to minimize the shocks to the model. The reasons are evident: The background field for the analysis is as accurate as possible; the effects of the forward interpolation are minimized; and the adjustment between physics and

dynamics at the start of the forecast, the "spin-up," is reduced or eliminated entirely.

If analyzed data are used directly as the initial condition for a forecast, imbalance between the mass and wind fields will cause the forecast to be contaminated by spurious, high-frequency gravity-wave oscillations of much larger amplitudes than are observed in the real atmosphere. Although these oscillations tend to die away slowly due to various dissipation mechanisms in the model, they may be quite detrimental to the data-assimilation cycle in that the 6-hour forecast is used as a first-guess field for the next analysis. The synoptic changes over the 6-hour period may thus be swamped by spurious changes due to these oscillations, with the consequence that the next analysis time with good data may be rejected as being too different from the first-guess field. *Initialization may have little direct effect on the forecast skill but the indirect role of initialization is of the greatest importance.*

Of particular importance in the development of efficient initialization procedures has been the idea to utilize the normal modes for separating Rossby and gravity waves. Through such a process, gravity waves can be eliminated (Dickinson and Williamson 1972). As has been shown by Leith (1980), however, this does not work particularly well, and the concept of normal mode initialization was first brought to a practical solution by Machenhauer (1977) and Baer and Tribbia (1977) who independently incorporated the effect of nonlinear terms. The physical meaning of this *nonlinear normal mode initialization was to put the initial tendency of the gravity-wave modes equal to zero.* Andersen (1977), Daley (1979) and Temperton and Williamson (1979) demonstrated that the method also worked well in multilevel models. Briere (1982) modified the technique to be used for limited area models and Wergen (1987) generalized it in order to incorporate the effect of diabatic processes, tidal effects, etc. Nonlinear normal mode initialization, now widely used, has played a major part in the improvement of numerical weather prediction.

An interesting by-product of data-assimilation is the possibility for data control and monitoring. Hollingsworth et al. (1986) have developed very powerful systems for routine monitoring of the global observing system. Figure 11.7 shows the perceived wind and height forecast error for 6-hour forecasts verified against 12 UTC North American radiosonde data for winter 1984-85. The perceived forecast error has been partitioned into spatially correlated errors (prediction errors) and spatially uncorrelated errors (observational errors).

The size of the estimated observational error agrees by and large with independent evaluations carried out by WMO/CIMO. It is interesting to note that *the magnitudes of the 6-hour forecast error and the analysis error are approximately of the same order.* A corresponding study for Europe shows in fact that the observational error is somewhat larger than the forecast error, presumably due to the many different types of radiosonde equipment in Europe compared to North America.

As a consequence of the high performance of the data-assimilation system, ECMWF has started on a systematic basis to inform operators of the global observing system on the likely deficiencies in the observations. This exercise has revealed several radiosonde stations with systematic errors in the data caused by technical errors in the equipment or in operational procedures. Many of these stations have subsequently been corrected to the benefit of all users of these data.

Systematic deficiencies have been identified in satellite wind measurements (Fig. 11.8); such problems are presently being looked into jointly by modelers and producers of satellite data.

11.5   Operational Achievements

As a consequence of the continuous development of numerical models and data-assimilation systems, the quality of numerical forecasts has undergone a significant improvement. This advancement can be seen as (i) an increased quality and accuracy of short-range prediction, (ii) an extension in time of useful predictive skill and (iii) a vast increase in the number of forecast products.

A systematic evaluation of the quality of short-range forecasts has been carried out by the WMO/CAS Working Group of Weather Prediction Research for the past ten years (Bengtsson and Lange 1982; Lange and Hellsten 1983). Under this intercomparison project operational forecasts from several centers have been verified daily. Figure 11.9 presents the standard deviation of the monthly averaged forecast error for 72-hour forecasts of the height field at 500 hPa and 1000 hPa. It can be noted that *the best available model in 1987 has a standard deviation error of only 55 percent of the best model available in 1979.*

In the following presentation we will show results obtained by the ECMWF model. Concentration on the performance of just one forecasting center may seem inappropriate in a volume such as this, but the forecasts to be discussed are unique in providing a regular record over

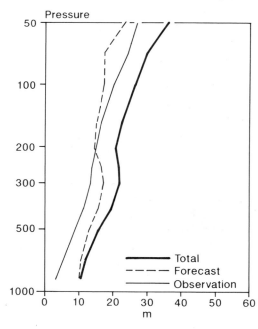

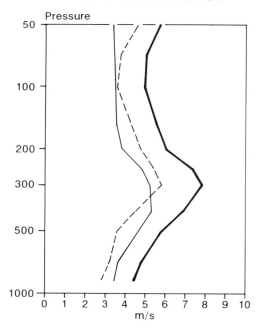

Fig. 11.7.   The perceived height and wind forecast errors over North America. The total perceived error has been divided into a correlated part (forecast error) and an uncorrelated part (observation error) as indicated in the legend. The calculations are based on 6-h forecasts for the first quarter of 1984 with the ECMWF system; units are m (height) and m s^{-1} (wind). Note that the sizes of the prediction error and the observational error are comparable.

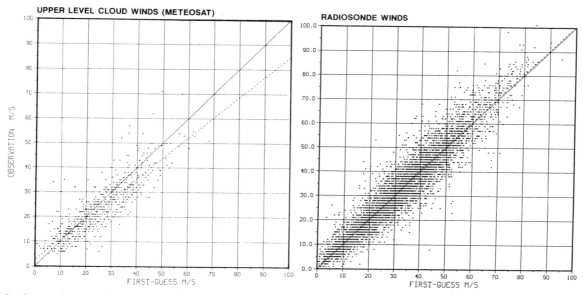

FIG. 11.8.   Scatter diagrams showing the correlation between upper-level cloud winds from Meteosat and 6-h forecasts with the ECMWF operational model for February 1988 in the belt 50°N to 30°N (left) and correlation between radiosonde wind at the levels 275–325 hPa and 6-h forecasts for the same time and in the same area. Only observations which have been used in the analysis are included. The systematic bias of the upper-level satellite winds to be too weak can clearly be seen.

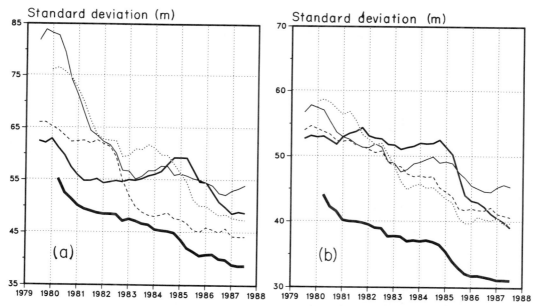

FIG. 11.9.   Standard deviation scores for 72-h operational forecasts for the 500 hPa (a) and 1000 hPa (b) height fields for a period of nine years. The scores have been collected and calculated under the WMO/CAS Forecast Intercomparison Project. Thin full curve, Federal Republic of Germany; dotted curve, France; dashed curve, United Kingdom; heavy curve, NMC, Washington; and thick curve, ECMWF. Verification area is the Northern Hemisphere extratropics. A 12-month time filter has been applied.

a period of almost ten years of atmospheric predictive skill on a time scale as long as 10 days. In addition, as is demonstrated in Fig. 11.9, objective verification has shown the forecasts for the time range of three days produced by the ECMWF system are distinctly more accurate than those produced by other current operational systems. The results described here thus serve to indicate present practical limits of predictability.

ECMWF has undertaken daily operational forecasts up to 10 days since 1 August 1980 (five days a week in the

period 1 August 1979 to 31 July 1980). This set of forecasts constitutes the largest available record of daily global medium-range integrations. As a consequence of successive improvements of the model and the data-assimilation system a gradual extension of predictive skill has taken place. Figure 11.10 shows the monthly means for 1980–1988 as well as the 12-month running averages. The result is given for the Northern and Southern Hemisphere extratropics, respectively. The skill score consists of a weighted average of anomaly correlation and normalized

ECMWF FORECAST SKILL (N. HEMISPHERE)
January 1980 - December 1988

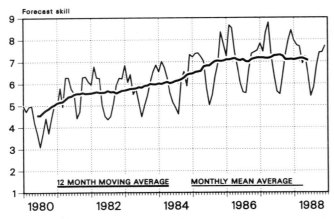

ECMWF FORECAST SKILL (S. HEMISPHERE)
January 1980 - December 1988

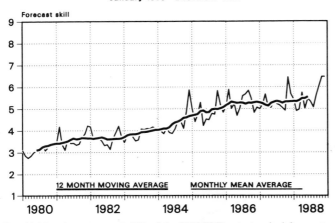

FIG. 11.10. A measure of skill of the ECMWF extratropical forecasts from January 1980 to December 1988. Above: Northern Hemisphere. Below: Southern Hemisphere. The number of days of predictive skill is derived from monthly means of daily averages of the anomaly correlation and standard deviation of the errors of geopotential height and temperature forecasts for the levels 850 to 200 hPa. Thick line, monthly mean values; thin line, 12-month running mean. See also Fig. 12.2.

RMS for tropospheric temperature and height fields.

Two periods of major improvements can be noted, 1980–81 and 1984–85. The largest contribution stemmed from an implementation of refined data-checking (elimination of erroneous and nonrepresentative observations) and changes in the physical parameterization. The major reason for the improvement in 1985 was the implementation of a high resolution spectral model, T106, and further improvements in the physical parameterization, deep and shallow convection and cloud description (Jarraud and Simmons 1985; Tiedtke et al. 1988). The positive interaction between the increased horizontal resolution and the physical parameterization had the interesting result that the combined effect of the two changes was larger than the sum of the two changes taken independently.

The skill of prediction models varies considerably in space and time. An example of the variation in predictive skill as a function of the spatial scale may be gained from

Figure 11.11a which shows the anomaly correlation for three separate groups of zonal wave numbers for the geopotential field in the troposphere. See also Fig. 11.22. The spectral decomposition demonstrates vividly that the larger scales are more accurately predicted in contrast to earlier experience reviewed by Leith (1978) when medium scales were reported to be better predicted than the planetary scales. A poorer forecast of shorter synoptic scales is represented here by zonal wavenumbers 10 to 20. The latter result may be associated with the wrong timing of individual weather events, within an overall weather situation which is better predicted. Examples can also be found in which the erroneous forecast of a small-scale feature is followed by a deterioration of the forecast over a larger scale.

The spatial variability of predictive skill has also been examined by comparing objective measures over more limited areas. In the extratropics predictive skill is generally lower in areas of high dynamic activities where the error growth is strong. It is also lower downstream of data-sparse regions. During the winter the scores over eastern Asia and North America are often higher than those for the European area and western United States. The predictive skill also varies considerably with height. The lower troposphere is strongly influenced by small-scale features, while the upper troposphere and lower stratosphere are dominated by large planetary waves. Figure 11.11b shows the anomaly correlation of the 50 hPa, 500 hPa and 1000 hPa height fields calculated for most of the Northern Hemisphere and averaged over all operational forecasts for winter 1987–88. This shows that 50 hPa has the most accurate forecast and also that the forecast at 500 hPa is generally more accurate than at 1000 hPa, a result in general agreement with synoptic assessment. Using 60 percent as a measure of useful predictive skill, it is found that the predictive skill at the three levels is more than 10 days, 7 days and 6.5 days, respectively. The high predictive skill at 50 hPa during the winter is interesting to note. Bengtsson et al. (1982) have shown an example of an excellent 10-day forecast correctly predicting a split of the polar night vortex into two separate vortices.

As can be seen from Fig. 11.10 there are considerable variations in the temporal variability of the forecasts with a minimum in the summer and a maximum in the winter. In addition, there is a significant interannual variation in predictive skill, as well as considerable variation within the month or season.

Figure 11.12 shows the anomaly correlation scores for every individual day during winter 1987—88 expressed in the form of a cumulative frequency diagram. As can be seen, useful predictive skill for 90 percent of the cases varies between 5 and 10 days. An inspection of the daily scores indicates that there are periods of high and low scores lasting from a week to a few weeks. Superimposed on this pattern, there are occasional low scores occurring in a random fashion. Careful investigation reveals that the isolated cases of low scores are mostly related to data

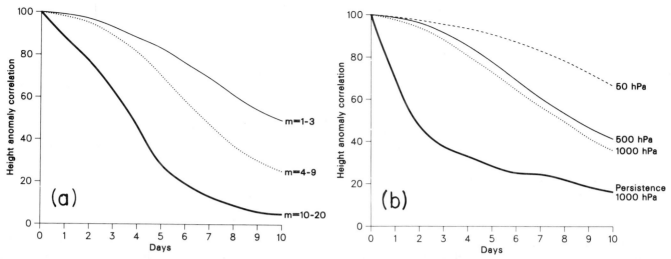

Fig. 11.11. (a) Anomaly correlation of height for zonal wavenumbers 1–3, 4–9 and 10–20, averaged for standard levels 200–1000 hPa. ECMWF Northern Hemisphere forecasts (20–82.5°N), winter 1987-88 (DJF). (b) Height anomaly correlation scores, ECMWF 50, 500 and 1000 hPa Northern Hemisphere forecasts (20–82.5°N) winter 1987-88, and persistence scores from 1000 hPa.

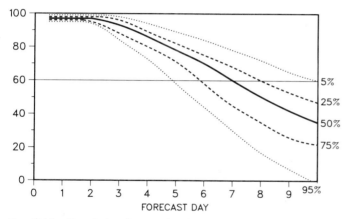

Fig. 11.12. Cumulative diagram showing the 500 hPa height anomaly correlation coefficients for the Northern Hemisphere extra-tropics for every day for January, February and March 1988. Full line, 50 percent; dashed lines show the range within which 50 percent of the cases lie; dotted lines show the range for 90 percent of the cases. It can be seen that useful prediction skill taken as an anomaly correlation of 60 percent varies between 5 and 10 days.

problems; such problems have increased somewhat with the latest version of the ECMWF model due to reduced data filtering in the data assimilation. It is expected that such problems can again be reduced by improved data-checking.

Of more interest from a scientific viewpoint are the more systematic variations of the forecast skill. Removing cases of high or low scores, which simply are artifacts of the verification procedure (there is normally a strong correlation between an anomaly correlation and the size of the anomaly), there still remains a relation between predictive skill and flow pattern. This can, to some extent, be explained as either a data or a model problem.

If for instance the intense baroclinic zones, where error growth is rapid, are found in data-sparse regions, say over the oceans and the Arctic, this is likely to have a more detrimental effect than if the baroclinic zones are in data-

rich regions. Similarly, there are certain weather situations where a particular model is performing worse due to limitations in the physical parameterization; or where one is more exposed to resolution limitations such as cases with a double jet structure, where both horizontal and vertical features are very sharp.

As has been demonstrated recently by Palmer (1988), however, there are also clear indications that *there are circulation patterns which are inherently more predictable.* An example of such a pattern is the so-called PNA pattern (Wallace and Gutzler 1981), which has been found to give rise to more skillful forecasts over the U.S. and eastern Pacific than the reverse PNA pattern (with positive height anomalies over the eastern Pacific and eastern U.S.). By inserting a perturbation off the east coast of China in a barotropic 500 hPa flow pattern, the error growth was significantly larger in the reverse PNA flow pattern than the error growth of the same perturbation in the normal PNA pattern. In other parts of the Northern Hemisphere, such as over Europe, the situation is less clear with more complex relations.

In view of the large variability in predictive skill from episode to episode, there is a considerable practical interest in having an estimate of the possible reliability of a given forecast — a kind of confidence factor. On a trial basis ECMWF has started such quasi-operational experiments. So far the practical value of these experiments has been limited (Palmer and Tibaldi 1988). In the longer term a type of Monte-Carlo forecast is anticipated, in which several forecasts are run from slightly different but equally likely initial states. The difference of such forecasts in space and time will provide users with reliability factors.

11.6 Prediction of Intense Cyclonic Developments

The westerlies are generally baroclinically unstable all through the year, and the development of cyclonic eddies of different scales and intensity is a fundamental feature of the general circulation of the atmosphere. Cyclones are associated with adverse and rapidly changeable weather, such as strong winds and precipitation, and can in their most intense forms constitute a major hazard. Accurate and timely prediction of extratropical cyclones accordingly constitutes a major objective for the meteorological services. As numerical models have developed, so has their ability to predict intense extratropical depressions improved (Gadd et al. 1990).

In this section we will describe the prediction of an intense cyclogenesis which took place over the North Atlantic Ocean on 7–8 February 1988. The period 28 January–8 February was characterized by a very strong westerly flow over the North Atlantic, associated with sharp temperature contrast between north and south. This condition created a very unstable flow in which three intense cyclogeneses took place. Figure 11.13 shows the observed and predicted surface pressure in the center of these depressions as well as the geographical position for the beginning of the development and the position where the cyclone reached its maximum intensity. The latest of these cyclones was the most intense and reached a maximum deepening rate of 3 hPa h^{-1}. The corresponding

forecasts with the operational ECMWF T106-L19 model were quite successful and predicted all the three cyclones with considerable accuracy. The operational forecasts from 12 UTC 4 February 1988 predicted a cyclogenesis which started at the eastern U.S. seaboard around 38°N. The storm moved swiftly along the U.S. and Canadian coastline, rapidly deepening. After 60 hours it had reached the southern part of Davis Strait where it slowly started to fill. On its southern flank very cold arctic air from Canada was advected east and southeast over the Atlantic Ocean with a widespread temperature fall of 15–20°C in 12 hours. The intense cold air advection sharpened the frontal zone over the western Atlantic. This in turn enhanced the conditions for a second cyclogenesis which started to develop around 00 UTC 7 February in the area around 35°N, 65°W. This cyclone developed with extreme intensity with a central pressure fall of almost 30 hPa in 12 hours (Fig. 11.13c). The accuracy of the prediction was quite remarkable as can be seen from Fig. 11.14 showing the surface pressure and 850 hPa temperature as predicted and observed from T+60 h up to T+120 h.

In many ways this storm was a typical textbook development and showed all the characteristic features which we associate with an intense extratropical depression. We

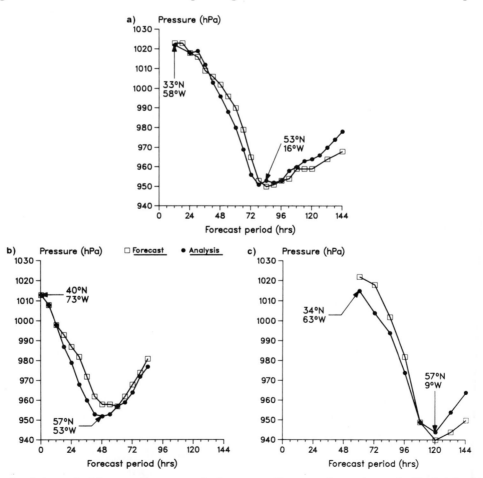

Fig. 11.13.   Predicted and observed minimum surface pressure in three cases of intense cyclogenesis over the North Atlantic, winter 1988: (a) forecast from 12 UTC 28 January 1988; (b) and (c) forecast from 12 UTC 4 February 1988. Position (observed) from an identifiable closed circulation to maximum intensity is given.

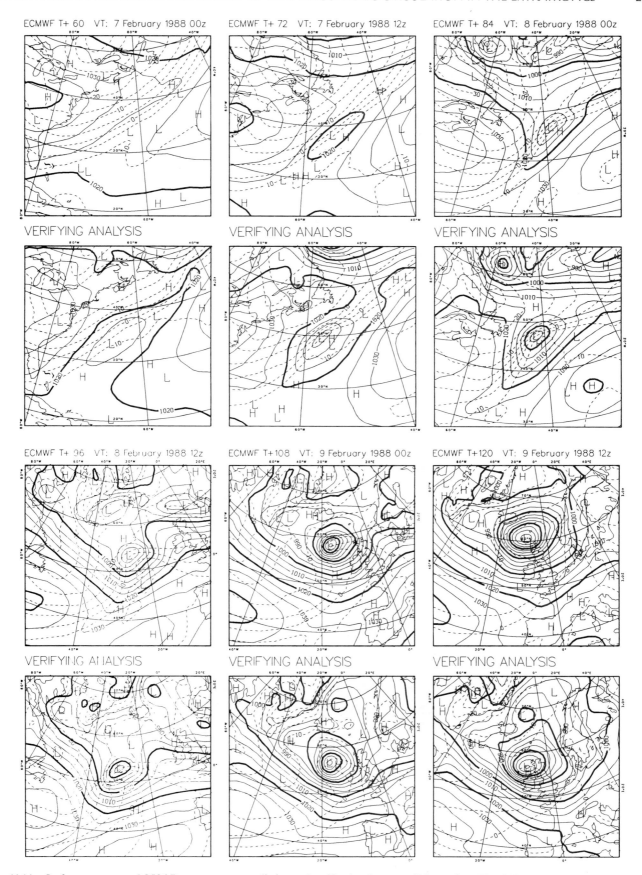

FIG. 11.14.   Surface pressure and 850 hPa temperature prediction and verification for every 12 hours from T + 60 h to T + 120 h for the forecast starting 12 UTC 4 February 1988.

will illustrate this by showing a series of predicted quantities for the most intense phase of the development that took place between T+72 h and T+96 h. Figure 11.15 shows the wind field at the lowest model level, 30 m above the surface. The well-developed discontinuity in the wind field indicates the position of the surface warm and cold fronts; the rapid shrinkage of the warm sector between T+84 h and T+108 h is evident. Twelve hours later the occlusion was completed and a warm sector could no longer be identified at the surface.

Figure 11.16 shows the predicted cloud cover. Low, middle, high and convective clouds are shown separately. The representation of clouds in the ECMWF model is shown in Fig. 11.17. The cloud forecast appears realistic. Infrared cloud images from Meteosat, valid for the same time, are shown in Fig. 11.18. The cloud prediction and their evaluation are in agreement with synoptic experience. It is interesting to see the band of clear air mass gradually increasing in depth; behind the cold front deep convective cloud systems are developing. The transfer of sensible and

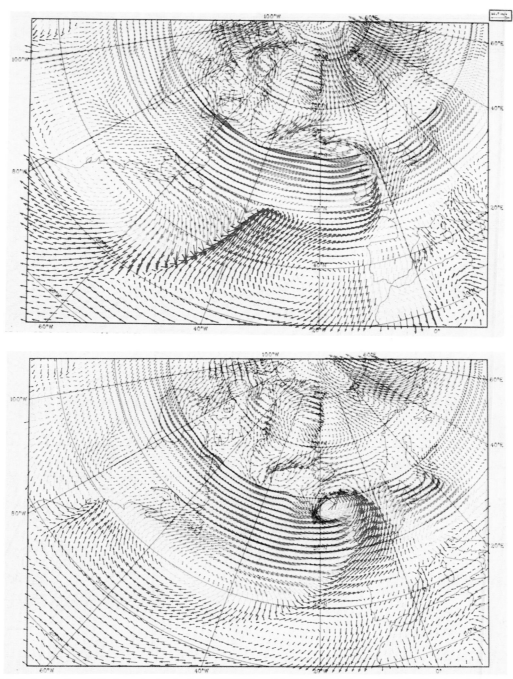

FIG. 11.15.   Predicted wind vectors at the lowest σ-level of the ECMWF model (30 m above the surface) for T + 84 h (top) and T + 108 h. Wind vectors are given a unique color for every 4°C as indicated by the 850 hPa temperature field. Observe the very rapid occlusion process.

latent heat in the cold air mass to the north and west of the cyclone is intense; the total maximum heat flux amounts to more than 1 kW m^{-2}. The magnitude and distribution of sensible and latent heat flux is in excellent agreement with diagnostic calculations (e.g., Petterssen et al. 1962). In Fig. 11.19 we show the instantaneous precipitation expressed in mm (2 h)$^{-1}$ for the stratiform and the convective precipitation, respectively. The stratiform precipitation dominates and amounts to around 4 mm h^{-1} during the most intense phase of the development. Since the stratiform precipitation takes place in the center of the cyclone, it contributes significantly to the rapid deepening process. This is not the case, however, with the surface fluxes which occur in the cold air mass. Their effect is likely to be the reverse with respect to the cyclogenesis process; it will heat the cold air mass and thereby reduce the available potential energy of the storm.

As discussed in Section 11.3, it is expected that the accuracy of the adiabatic calculation (including high resolution) and the release of latent heat are significant for the

FIG. 11.16. Predicted cloud cover at T + 84 h (top) and T + 108 h. Low, middle, high and convective clouds are shown separately. Cloud description in the ECMWF model is shown in Fig. 11.17.

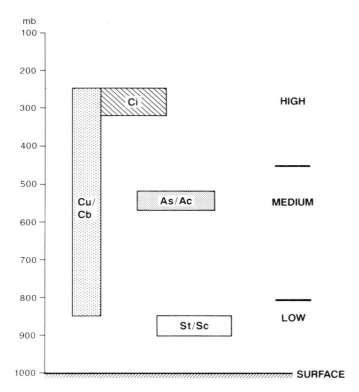

FIG. 11.17. Cloud description in the ECMWF model (Tiedtke et al. 1988).

00 UTC 9 February 1988

FIG. 11.18. Observed clouds from Meteosat (infrared) for 00 UTC 9 February 1988 (corresponding to the T + 108 h forecast in Fig. 11.16b).

prediction of intense cyclogenesis, while other processes such as the detailed description of surface friction are of minor importance. In order to demonstrate this, a series of numerical experiments have been carried out. The results of these studies are described below.

11.6.1 Horizontal Resolution

For the case initiated from 28 January 1988 (Fig. 11.13a), separate forecasts were done with 4 different horizontal resolutions: T21, T42, T63 and T106. The

physical parameterization and the initial state were the same in all cases, but orography and land-sea contrasts were consistent with respectively horizontal resolution. The result is given in Fig. 11.20, which shows the predicted pressure in the center of the cyclone. While the T106 forecast is in good agreement with observation, a steady deterioration can be seen as resolution becomes coarser. The T63 reaches a maximum depth of only 972 hPa, compared to 950 hPa for the T106, and has no clearly defined closed circulation between T+66 h and T+78 h. The T42 calculation has no clearly defined center after T+60 h, but a trough reaching a maximum depth of only 984 hPa. The T21 does not develop any separate cyclone center at all, except a noticeable weak center around T+36 h. The actual forecasts at T+96 h (not shown here) differ considerably; the T106 has positioned the cyclone correctly over northern Scotland, the T63 has its center over southeastern England.

11.6.2 Hydrological Cycle

In another experiment the T106 model was run with the release of latent heat switched off. This forecast failed to develop the storm. Figure 11.21 shows the comparison between the "dry" and "moist" integrations.

11.6.3 Modification of Surface Friction

In this experiment the Charnock formula was replaced by a modified scheme that enhanced the surface friction over ocean areas as a function of the intensity of the surface wind. No noticeable difference in the forecast could be observed.

11.7   Systematic Errors in Numerical Weather Prediction

Due to the general instability of the flow of the atmosphere at middle latitudes, the error growth is large. Several studies indicate an error doubling time of around 2 days for the synoptic-scale flow as determined by the 500 hPa height field (Lorenz 1982; Dalcher and Kalnay 1987). Actual atmospheric models have a larger error growth due to model error. Bengtsson (1989) has recently estimated the error growth by the ECMWF model for winter 1986-87 (DJF). Using an error growth equation of the form

$$\frac{dV}{dt} = (\alpha V + S)\left(V - \frac{V}{V_\infty}\right) \qquad (11.11)$$

where V is the forecast error variance of the 500 hPa height field, α is the rate of growth of the forecast error variance, S the amount of error variance introduced by model deficiencies in one day and V_∞ is the asymptotic value of the error variance. The value of S has been empirically determined to be 144 m². Comparing the result from previous years it was found that S had gradually been reduced; for winter 1980-81 the corresponding value was 324 m².

A more detailed inspection shows that the error of the

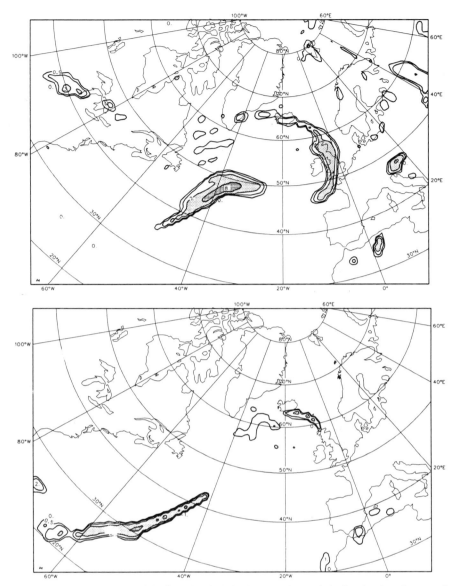

Fig. 11.19. Predicted precipitation intensity in mm $(2 \text{ h})^{-1}$ at T + 84 h for large-scale precipitation (top) and convective precipitation (bottom). Isolines for 0.5, 1, 2, 4 and 8 mm $(2 \text{ h})^{-1}$.

forecast can be split into a "systematic part" or average error for a particular month or season and a "transient part" that changes from day to day. The sum of the systematic and transient error variance constitutes the total error variance. Figure 11.22 from Mureau (1989) shows the growth of error variance for different scales of motion; T40, T10, T7 and T5 for the 500 hPa height field for winter 1980-81 and winter 1987-88, respectively. The stippled area between the pair of curves indicates the systematic error. The figure shows clearly that the predictability increases when the field is truncated, indicating that the largest scales of motion are the most predictable; this was certainly not the case with forecast models from the 1970s or earlier. The improvement in prediction skill during the seven years is evident with a considerable reduction in the systematic error, in particular for the largest scales of motion.

Systematic errors exist in all models. A summary of typical errors is given in Table 11.3 (ECMWF 1988). These errors are common for most models. The reason for the systematic errors is not known but they are sensitive to the parameterization of certain processes. These processes are indicated in the table.

Of particular interest is the behavior of the atmospheric energetics during the course of the integration. These are defined following the original suggestion by Lorenz (1955). The specific procedures applied are described in Arpe et al. (1986). Figure 11.23 shows, in the form of a box diagram, available potential energy and kinetic energy for the zonal and eddy components globally averaged. Integration has been carried out between 1000 and 30 hPa and averaged for winter 1987-88. The conversion terms are calculated from the basic parameters, and the generation and dissipation terms are obtained as residuals. The

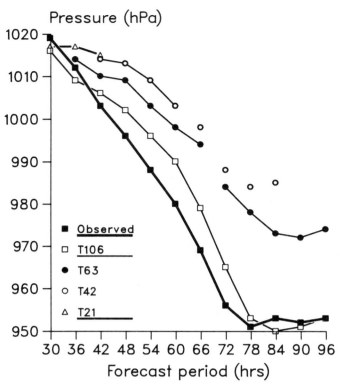

Fig. 11.20. Surface pressure as a function of time in the center of the low, forecast from 12 UTC 28 January 1988 (Fig. 11.13a). Forecasts for T21, T42, T63 and T106 resolutions are shown separately (see legend). The points in the plot are disconnected when the low loses its identity.

values are given for day 1 (averaged over all day-1 forecasts) and for day 10, which is the last day of the ECMWF forecasts. The energetics at day-1 forecasts and the analysis are very similar, but it has been found that the day-1 forecasts are more representative in view of spin-up problems during the early phase of the forecast.

Strictly speaking the generation, conversion and dissipation as developed by Lorenz (1955) are defined as integral quantities preferably over the whole mass of the atmosphere. As will be illustrated below, however, it is nevertheless constructive to discuss the contribution from various regions and to study the way these contributions vary during the course of the forecast.

11.7.1 Eddy Available Potential Energy (AE)

Figure 11.24 shows the zonal mean of AE as a function of pressure, averaged for winter 1987-89 for day-1 forecasts and day-10 forecasts, respectively. During the course of the integration the global average is reduced a little more than 1 percent, from 556 to 549 kJ m^{-2}. The reduction, however, is due to systematic deficiencies in the tropics; in fact a minor increase can be seen in the maximum zones around 50°N and 50°S. The characteristic three maxima in the vertical, two in troposphere and another around 65°N in the stratosphere (in association with the stratospheric polar night jet), are correctly maintained by the model.

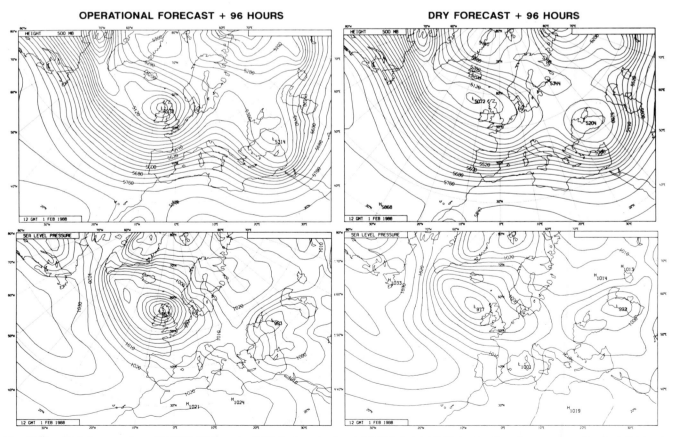

Fig. 11.21. 96-h forecast from 12 UTC 28 January 1988. Left: operational 500 hPa height field (top) and surface pressure (bottom). Right: the forecast obtained by switching off the release of latent heat (dry model). The deep low over Scotland is that described in Fig. 11.13a.

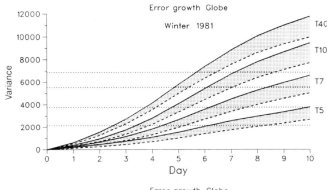

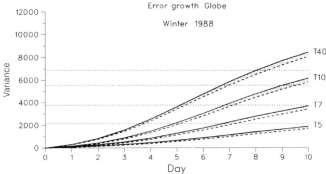

FIG. 11.22. Error growth in the winters of 1980-81 and 1987-88 for four different triangular truncations of spherical harmo̶ s̶ (T40, T10, T7, T5). The solid line represents the total squared e̶ ̶ , a function of forecast day, the dashed line the nonsystemati̶c̶ ̶ ̶ e shaded area represents the squared systematic error. ̶ ̶ s represent the seven-year mean climatological variance. ̶ ̶ ̶ ne is for T5, the uppermost line for T40. Units: m² (Mureau 198̶ ̶ .

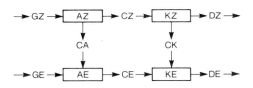

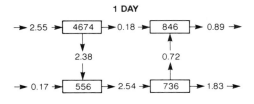

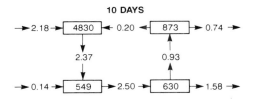

FIG. 11.23. Global energy diagram (1000 hPa—30 hPa) for winter 1987-88. Available potential energy and kinetic energy are given in kJ m⁻² and conversions in W m⁻². The changes between day 1 (average of values at day 1 of each forecast) and day 10 indicate the systematic errors.

TABLE 11.3
Systematic model errors.

Phenomenon	Known to be sensitive to:
A. Extratropics	
• Zonalization of mean midlatitude circulation, i.e., too weak diffluent flow over Europe and northern Pacific. Dipole pattern of 500 hPa height error	Momentum fluxes* Upper boundary condition Radiation in stratosphere
• Reduced variability of standing waves from month to month (too small low frequency variability?)	?
• Poleward and upward shift of subtropical jets	Convection, momentum fluxes
• Reduced ability to predict blocking more than five days ahead	?
• Increase of eddy momentum flux together with increased tilting of troughs and ridges	?
B. Tropics	
• Excessive easterlies in upper tropical troposphere	Convection, momentum fluxes
• Weakening of the trade winds	Radiation, convection
• Upper branch of Hadley circulation too weak and spread over too many layers	Radiation, convection
• Weakening of divergent mean flow over main tropical convection areas in connection with reduced precipitation	Radiation, convection
• Overestimation of ITCZ in eastern Pacific	?
• Weakening of transients in Tropics	Convection, momentum fluxes

*Momentum fluxes including gravity waves, vertical and horizontal diffusion and mountain blocking

11.7.2 Eddy Kinetic Energy (KE)

Figure 11.25 shows similarly the zonal cross section of KE. The units are the same as for AE. Comparing day 1 with day 10, it is found that KE is reduced significantly more than AE with a drop of more than 100 kJ m⁻² or by more than 14 percent. The major reduction takes place around the jet-stream level. In this vicinity the zonal kinetic energy (not shown here) increases slightly. This reduction was even larger, about 20 percent, before the change in the ECMWF model in January 1988.

11.7.3 Conversion between Zonal Available Potential Energy and Eddy Available Energy (CA)

Figure 11.26 shows the zonal cross section of CA. The averaged value is conserved and is practically the same at day 10 as at day 1. A closer inspection, however, reveals interesting changes: a slight intensification of the tropospheric maximum around 40°N and a disappearance of the equatorial maximum around 200 hPa. The weakening of the equatorial maximum is probably related to problems listed in Table 11.3 referring to the weakening of the upper

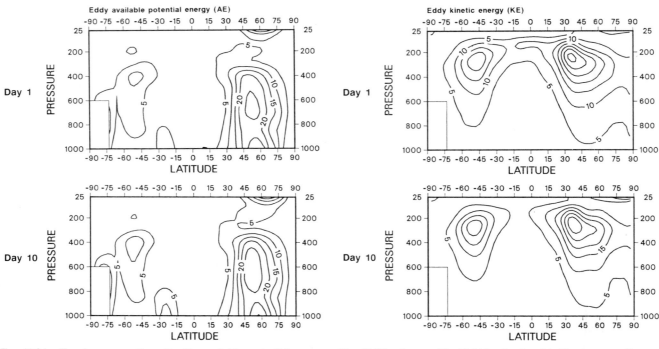

FIG. 11.24. Zonal cross section of eddy available potential energy, winter 1987-88. Unit kJ m^{-2}(bar)$^{-1}$. See text.

FIG. 11.25. Same as Fig. 11.24 but for the eddy kinetic energy. See text.

branch of the Hadley circulation. The slight increase of CA in middle latitudes is related to an overall intensification of the westerlies and the associated generation of eddies.

11.7.4   Conversion between Eddy Available Potential Energy and Eddy Kinetic Energy (CE)

Figure 11.27 shows the zonal cross section of CE. This process is closely connected to cyclone development. (See Section 12.3.4 for energy conversions in individual cyclones.) Generally the model maintains the overall average energy transfer of around 2.5 W m^{-2} but, as can be seen, the level of energy conversion increases during the forecast at middle latitudes of the winter Hemisphere. The systematic errors are very similar to those of CA with a slight intensification in the maximum zone around 45°N and the disappearance of the equatorial maximum around 200 hPa.

11.7.5   Conversion between Zonal Kinetic Energy and Eddy Kinetic Energy (CK)

Figure 11.28 shows the zonal cross section of CK. The absolute value of this transfer has a marked maximum around 25°N at about 250 hPa with a transfer from the eddies to the zonal part. Although there are areas (such as poleward of the jet) where the energy transfer is reversed, the negative transfer dominates. During the course of the forecast the transfer is increased by around 30 percent. The increase in the eddy transfer is by and large consistent with a similar enhancement of the eddy momentum flux (not shown here). *The increase in these fluxes is interesting*

in view of the fact that the eddy kinetic energy is underestimated (Fig. 11.24). The reason is probably too much vertical and horizontal tilt of transient eddies, as pointed out by Arpe and Klinker (1986). An enhancement of the tilt of trailing troughs can easily enhance the eddy momentum flux leading to systematic errors as indicated in Fig. 11.28.

11.7.6   Atmospheric Blocking

As indicated in Table 11.3, a serious deficiency of present models is their reduced ability to predict blocking for more than about five days ahead. Atmospheric blocking has for a long time been recognized as a process of profound dynamical interest and is of great practical relevance to operational weather prediction. The crucial role that the onset, development and decay of block-like structures have on atmospheric low-frequency variability (see Section 4.5.3), and hence on forecasting on different time scales, has made blocking one of the most studied atmospheric processes.

Tibaldi and Molteni (1988) have recently undertaken a diagnostic evaluation of the capability of the ECMWF model to predict blocking. In order to arrive at a simple and yet reasonably realistic definition of blocking, they have used a definition essentially derived from a study by Lejenäs and Økland (1983). Following this idea, the geopotential height gradients are computed between 60°N and 40°N for every 10° longitude. When this gradient is positive, e.g., the geopotential height at 60°N is larger than at 40°N, and where there at the same time exists a negative gradient between 80°N and 40°N (more than 10 m/deg lat)

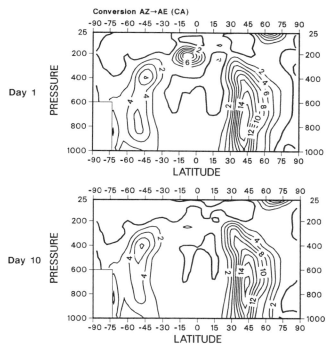

FIG. 11.26. Zonal cross section of the conversion between zonal available potential energy and eddy available potential energy for winter 1987-88. Unit W m^{-2}(bar)$^{-1}$. See text.

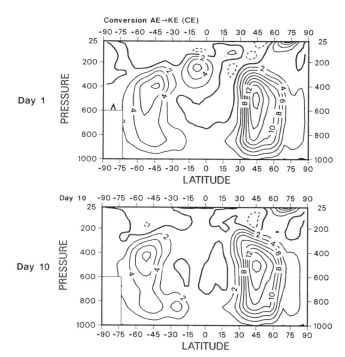

FIG. 11.27. Same as Fig. 11.26 but for the conversion between eddy available potential energy and eddy kinetic energy. See text.

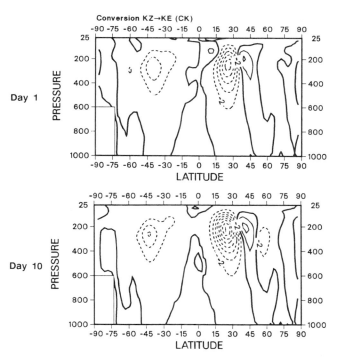

FIG. 11.28. Same as Fig. 11.26 but for the conversion between eddy kinetic energy and zonal kinetic energy. See text.

a state of blocking is defined. This definition agrees conceptually rather well with the original phenomenological definition of blocking as proposed by Rex (1950).

Figure 11.29 shows the percentage frequency of blocking as a function of longitude calculated for the period 1 December to 10 March for the seven years 1980/81-

1986/87 as calculated from the ECMWF operational analyses. Figure 11.30 shows the corresponding prediction of blocking as calculated from the ensemble of forecasts valid at day 1, day 3, day 6 and day 10, respectively. *The reduction in the frequency of blocking as the forecast is extended can clearly be seen.* Although a gradual improvement has taken place in the prediction of blocking during the seven-year period, the characteristic deficiency still remains, particularly in the Pacific sector.

Tibaldi and Molteni (1988) also evaluated the model's ability to predict blocking correctly. It was found that the prediction of blocking was quite successful when the onset signal of blocking did exist initially, as previously demonstrated in case study evaluations by Bengtsson (1981) and Grönås (1982). On the other hand, the performance deteriorated rapidly when the blocking took place 4–5 days into the forecasts. While the prediction of blocking per se may be limited due to the unstable nature of the phenomenon, the development of a model that can generate blocking with the same frequency as observed in nature is certainly a tractable problem. Consequently, before this has been achieved, there is no reason to be overly pessimistic concerning the prediction of blocking.

11.8.   Concluding Remarks

Numerical weather prediction has undergone an exceptional development since its inception almost forty years ago. It has developed from a limited experimental activity into a major function of the meteorological services, without which present-day forecasting services to the public and different special customers would be impossible. The quality of the forecasts has improved in a way

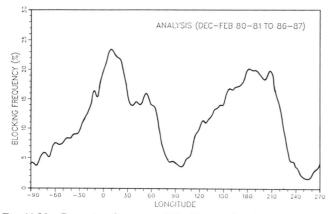

FIG. 11.29. Percentage frequency of blocking as a function of longitude, computed from all ECMWF daily objective analyses for the 500 hPa height field (all winters 1980-81 — 1986-87).

tions, are unique in the sense that they provide data from previously data-empty regions; without them global weather prediction would not be achievable. Other important contributions are aircraft observations (accurate but sparse), observations from drifting buoys, and a slow but steady increase of observations from ships of opportunity; here data collection by satellites has made a great contribution. Furthermore, observations are now better utilized due to improved analysis methods, more accurate initialization and a more accurate and consistent use of the prediction model to provide the first guess.

Computer development has been and continues to be extraordinary. At the leading edge are the supercomputers that by now can perform well over 10^9 floating point operations (1 gigaflop) per second averaged over a complete forecast; this is more than a million times faster than the early electronic calculating machines used in the early 1950s. The increase in storage capacity has been more or less equivalent. The supercomputers have made it possible to develop successively more realistic models of the atmosphere and to undertake the time-consuming data processing required for the assimilation of observations.

Significant scientific progress has taken place in conjunction with the technical achievements. Efficient numerical integration algorithms (such as semi-implicit and semi-Lagrangian time integration) have made it possible to increase the time step, thus speeding up the calculation further. Other contributions have eliminated nonlinear instabilities and made extended integrations possible.

that could hardly be foreseen in the early years; useful forecasts in the extratropics of the Northern Hemisphere have been extended to up to a week ahead and forecast products are now made available for a wide range of products covering the whole globe from the surface of the earth to high into the stratosphere.

The basic conditions that have made this evolution possible are the spectacular developments which have taken place in observational technology and computer technology.

Global observations are regularly made available from polar-orbiting and geostationary satellites. These data, although not of the same quality as radiosonde observa-

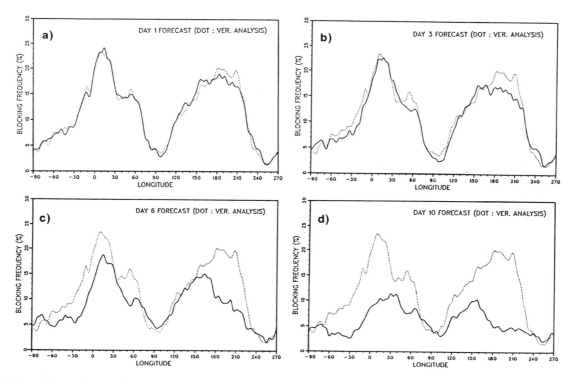

FIG. 11.30.   Dotted lines: observed frequency as in Fig. 11.29. Full lines, blocking frequency computed on the forecast fields for Day 1, 3, 6 and 10 (panels (a) to (d) respectively).

The parameterization of physical (subgrid-scale) processes has developed in an impressive way, although the data required for a deeper understanding of these processes, and the necessary computer resources to undertake the calculations of them in a more accurate way, are still not available.

The ongoing intense development in computer technology means that we may within a few years have computers with an average processing speed of up to 10 gigaflops. This will make it possible to run global models with a horizontal resolution of the order of 50 km and a vertical resolution of 40–50 levels. Such models will be able to resolve and predict the evolution of lee-wave cyclones and tropical cyclones.

Increase of resolution, however, is not only a technical matter but to a high degree a scientific problem. As has been found in recent experiments with high-resolution limited-area models (Imbard et al. 1988) the *parameterization of convective precipitation in particular is sensitive to resolution*; indications are in fact that parameterization may have to be retuned and even perhaps be reformulated when resolution is changed significantly. Other problems are aliasing of frontal systems and mesoscale phenomena, which may take place as horizontal resolution increases beyond certain critical scales. Consequently, major scientific efforts will be required to develop such high-resolution models properly.

There does not seem to be any realistic alternative to the "brute force approach," and future models are likely to be improved through the systematic and meticulous development of all aspects of the forecasting system. An alternative approach can possibly be considered when the forecasts are extended beyond the predictability of the individual weather systems. As has been shown by Miyakoda and Chao (1982) and Shukla (1984), there are indications that useful prediction of time averages can be extended even further, perhaps up to a month or more. The fact that considerable anomalies can exist for this length of time, and that present GCMs can simulate such long-lasting anomalies even in the extratropics (Lau 1981; Volmer et al. 1983), gives us hope that we may be successful.

As has been discussed in Section 11.5, however, there are strong indications that predictability depends on the stability of the large scale flow. Knowledge of the predictability of a particular flow pattern is of great practical importance, and methods for the development of predictive skill on an operational basis are under development at the large forecasting centers. The most likely technique to be applied is a sequence of predictions from slightly different (but equally likely) initial states, a so-called Monte-Carlo technique.

The other necessary condition for better forecasts is a further improvement of the observing system, in particular better observations of the three-dimensional wind field. In the tropics there is also a great demand for more accurate humidity data. For practical and economical reasons we must rely heavily on satellite observations, and substantial research and investments are required for the instrument designers to develop better sensors. It is equally important to direct more research and development to make more efficient use of satellite data and other asynoptic observations in the data-assimilation system. Closer cooperation between experts on satellite instruments and retrieval procedures, and numerical modelers, is essential. For operational reasons, more efficient means for the global exchange of data in real time is required.

Professor Erik Palmén was not directly involved in numerical weather forecasting but he followed the development with great interest into his very last years. The scientific contributions by himself and his coworkers of detailed studies of synoptic systems, however, have provided important insights into the structure and evolution of these systems and their interaction with the large-scale flow. The importance of these studies to understanding significant atmospheric processes cannot be overestimated; they have played a major role in the development of today's advanced forecasting system.

Acknowledgments

The author wishes to acknowledge the assistance of Dr. K. Arpe, Dr. L. Dell'Osso and Dr. A. Woods in preparing part of the background material for this paper. The author is also indebted to the assistance of many scientific colleagues around the world who have provided reference articles and other material. Mrs. A. Dinshawe who did the typing and Mr. R. Hine who prepared the illustrations are gratefully acknowledged.

REFERENCES

Andersen, J. H., 1977: A routine for normal mode initialization with nonlinear correction for multilevel spectral model with triangular truncation. ECMWF Int. Rep. No. 15, 41 pp.

Anthes, R. A., 1977: A cumulus parameterization scheme utilizing a one-dimensional cloud model. *Mon. Wea. Rev.,* **105**, 270–286.

Arakawa, A., and J.-M. Chen, 1987: Closure assumption in the cumulus parameterization problem. *Short- and Medium-Range Numerical Weather Prediction,* T. Matsuno, Ed. Meteorological Society of Japan, 107–131.

Arpe, K., and E. Klinker, 1986: Systematic errors of the ECMWF operational forecasting model in midlatitudes. *Quart. J. Roy. Meteor. Soc.,* **112**, 181–202.

——, A. Hollingsworth, M. S. Tracton, A. C. Lorenc, S. Uppala and P. Kållberg, 1985: The response of numerical weather prediction systems to FGGE level IIB data. Part II: Forecast verification in implication for predictability. *Quart. J. Roy. Meteor. Soc.,* **111**, 67–102.

——, C. Brankovic, E. Oriol and P. Speth, 1986: Variability in time and space of energetics from a long series of atmospheric data produced by ECMWF. *Contr. Atmos. Phys.,* **59**, 321–325.

Baede, A. P. M., M. Jarraud and U. Cubasch, 1979: Adiabatic formulation of ECMWF's spectral model. *ECMWF Tech. Rep.,* **15**, 1–40.

Baer, F., and J. Tribbia, 1977: On complete filtering of gravity modes through nonlinear initialization. *Mon. Wea. Rev.*, **105**, 1536-1539.

Bates, J. R., and A. McDonald, 1982: Multiple-upstream, semi-Lagrangian advective schemes: Analysis and application to multilevel primitive equation model. *Mon. Wea. Rev.*, **110**, 1831-1842.

Bengtsson, L., 1981: Numerical prediction of atmospheric blocking. A case study. *Tellus, 33,* 19-42.

——, 1985: Medium-range forecasting at the ECMWF. *Advances in Geophysics, 28B,* 3-54.

——, 1989: On the growth of error in data-assimilation systems. *ECMWF Seminar Proceedings,* 5-9 September 1988, in press.

——, and A. Lange, 1982: *Results of the WMO/CAS Numerical Weather Prediction Data Study and Intercomparison Project for Forecasts for the Northern Hemisphere in 1979-80.* World Meteorological Organization, Geneva, 26 pp, 71 figs. and Annex.

——, and A. Simmons, 1983: Medium range weather prediction — operational experience at ECMWF. *Large-Scale Dynamical Processes in the Atmosphere,* B. J. Hoskins and R. P. Pearce, Eds. Academic Press, 337-363.

——, M. Kanamitsu, P. Kållberg and S. Uppala, 1982: FGGE 4-dimensional data assimilation at ECMWF. *Bull. Amer. Meteor. Soc., 63,* 29-43.

Bergthorsson, P., B. R. Döös, S. Fryklund, O. Haug and R. Lindqvist, 1955: Routine forecasting with the barotropic model. *Tellus, 7,* 272-276.

Betts, A. K., 1986: A new convection adjustment scheme. Part I: Observational and theoretical basis. *Quart. J. Roy. Meteor. Soc., 112,* 677-691.

——, and M. J. Miller, 1986: A new convective adjustment scheme. Part II: Single column testing using GATE wave, BOMEX, ATEX and arctic air-mass data sets. *Quart. J. Roy. Meteor. Soc., 112,* 693-709.

Bjerknes, J., 1966: A possible response of the atmospheric Hadley circulation to equatorial anomalies of ocean temperature. *Tellus, 18,* 820-829.

Blackmon, M. L., J. M. Wallace, N.-C. Lau and S. L. Mullen, 1977: An observational study of the Northern Hemisphere wintertime circulation. *J. Atmos. Sci., 34,* 1040-1053.

Boer, G. J., N. A. McFarlane, R. Laprise, J. D. Henderson and J.-P. Blanchet, 1984: The Canadian Climate Centre spectral atmospheric general circulation model. *Atmos.-Ocean, 22,* 397-429.

Bolin, B., 1950: On the influence of the earth's orography on the general character of the westerlies. *Tellus, 2,* 184-195.

Bougeault, P., 1985: Parameterization of cumulus convection for GATE. A diagnostic and semipragmatic study. *Mon. Wea. Rev., 113,* 2108-2121.

Bourke, W., 1972: An efficient one-level primitive equation spectral model. *Mon. Wea. Rev., 100,* 683-689.

Bretherton, F. P., 1969: Momentum transport by gravity waves. *Quart. J. Roy. Meteor. Soc., 95,* 213-243.

Briere, S., 1982: Nonlinear normal mode initialization of a limited area model. *Mon. Wea. Rev., 110,* 1166-1186.

Burridge, D. M., 1975: A split semi-implicit reformulation of the Bushby-Timpson 10-level model. *Quart. J. Roy. Meteor. Soc., 101,* 777-792.

Charney, J. G., 1947: The dynamics of long waves in a baroclinic westerly current. *J. Meteor., 4,* 135-162.

——, and Eliassen, A., 1949: A numerical method for predicting the perturbations of middle latitude westerlies. *Tellus, 1,* No. 2, 38-54.

——, and J. G. DeVore, 1979: Multiple flow equilibria in the atmosphere and blocking. *J. Atmos. Sci., 36,* 1205-1216.

——, R. Fjørtoft and J. von Neumann, 1950: Numerical integration of the barotropic vorticity equation. *Tellus, 2,* 237-254.

Chouinard, C., M. Beland and N. McFarlane, 1986: A simple gravity wave drag parameterization for use in medium-range weather forecast models. *Atmos.-Ocean, 24,* 91-110.

Coiffier, J., Y. Ernie, J.-F. Geleyn, J. Clochard, J. Hoffman and F. Dupont, 1987: The operational hemispheric model at the French Meteorological Service. *Short- and Medium-Range Numerical Weather Prediction,* T. Matsuno, Ed. Meteorological Society of Japan, 337-357.

Cullen, M. J. P., 1983: Current progress and prospects in numerical techniques for weather prediction models. *J. Comp. Physics, 50,* 1-37.

Dalcher, A., and E. Kalnay, 1987: Error growth and predictability in operational ECMWF forecasts. *Tellus, 39A,* 474-491.

Daley, R., 1979: The application of nonlinear normal mode initialization to an operational forecast model. *Atmos.-Ocean, 17,* 97-124.

Defant, F., 1959: On hydrodynamical instability caused by an approach of subtropical and polar jet stream in northern latitudes before the onset of strong cyclogenesis. *The Atmosphere and the Sea in Motion,* B. Bolin, Ed. Rockefeller Institute Press, 305-325.

Dell'Osso, L., 1984: High-resolution experiments with the ECMWF model. A case study. *Mon. Wea. Rev., 112,* 1853-1883.

Dickinson, R. E., and D. L. Williamson, 1972: Free oscillations of a discrete stratified fluid with application to numerical weather prediction. *J. Atmos. Sci., 29,* 623-640.

ECMWF, 1988: *Proceedings from the ECMWF Workshop on Diabatic Forcing, 30 November-2 December 1987.* ECMWF, Reading, U.K.

Edelmann, W., 1984: A convection scheme used by the German forecast model. *LAM Newsletter, Number 8* (May 1984). European Working Group on Limited Area Modeling.

Eliasen, E., B. Machenhauer and E. Rasmussen, 1970: On a numerical method for integration of the hydrodynamical equations with a spectral representation of the horizontal fields. *Rep. No. 2, Institut for Teoretisk Meteorologi.* University of Copenhagen.

Eliassen, A., 1954: Provisional report on calculation of spatial covariance and autocorrelation of the pressure field. *Rap. No. 5, Videnskapsakademisk Institutt for Vaer og Klimaforskning,* Oslo, Norway.

Gadd, A. J., 1978: A split explicit integration scheme for numerical weather prediction. *Quart. J. Roy. Meteor. Soc., 104,* 569-582.

——, C. D. Hall and R. E. Kruze, 1990: Operational numerical prediction of rapid cyclogenesis over the North Atlantic. *Tellus, 42A,* 116-121.

Gandin, L. S., 1963: *Objective Analysis of Meteorological Fields.* Gidromet. Izdat., translated from Russian by the Israel Program for Scientific Translations (1965), 242 pp.

Geleyn, J.-F., 1985: On a simple, parameter-free partition between moistening and precipitation in the Kuo scheme. *Mon. Wea. Rev., 113,* 405-407.

Girard, C., and M. Jarraud, 1982: Short- and medium-range

forecast differences between a spectral and a grid-point model. An extensive quasi-operational comparison. ECMWF Tech. Rep. 32, 1–78.

Grönås, S., 1982: Systematic errors and forecast quality of ECMWF forecasts in different large-scale flow patterns. *ECMWF Seminar/Workshop on Interpretation of Numerical Weather Prediction Products, 13–24 September 1982,* 161–206.

Haltiner, G. J., and R. T. Williams, 1980: *Numerical Prediction and Dynamic Meteorology,* 2nd ed. Wiley, 477 pp.

Hinkelmann, K., 1959: Ein numerisches Experiment mit den primitiven Gleichungen. *The Atmosphere and the Sea in Motion,* B. Bolin, Ed. Rockefeller Institute Press, 486–500.

Hollingsworth, A., 1987: Objective analysis for numerical weather prediction. *Short- and Medium-Range Numerical Weather Prediction,* T. Matsuno, Ed. Meteorological Society of Japan, 11–59.

——, K. Arpe, A. C. Lorenc, M. S. Tracton, G. Cats, S. Uppala and P. Kållberg, 1985: The response of numerical weather prediction systems to FGGE level II-b data. Part I. Analysis. *Quart. J. Roy. Meteor. Soc.,* **111**, 1–66.

——, D. B. Shaw, P. Lönnberg, L. Illari, K. Arpe and A. J. Simmons, 1986: Monitoring of observation quality by a data-assimilation system. *Mon. Wea. Rev.,* **114**, 861–879.

Holopainen, E. O., N.-C. Lau and A. H. Oort, 1980: A diagnostic study of the time-averaged budget of atmospheric zonal momentum over North America. *J. Atmos. Sci.,* **37**, 2234–2242.

Hoskins, B. J., and A. J. Simmons, 1975: A multi-layer spectral model and the semi-implicit method. *Quart. J. Roy. Meteor. Soc.,* **101**, 637–655.

Imbard, M., A. Craplet, Pl. Degardin, Y. Durand, A. Joly, N. Marie and J.-F. Geleyn, 1988: Fine-mesh limited area forecasting with the French operational Peridot system. *ECMWF Seminar on the Nature and Prediction of Extratropical Weather Systems, 7—11 September 1987,* Vol. II, 231–270.

Jarraud, M., and A. J. Simmons, 1985: Development of the high-resolution model. ECMWF Tech. Memo. No. 107, 61 pp.

Kessler, E., 1969: *On the Distribution and Continuity of Water Substance in Atmospheric Circulation. Meteor. Monogr.,* **10**, No. 32, 84 pp.

Krishnamurti, T. N., Y. Ramanathan, H. L. Pan, R. J. Pasch and J. Molinari, 1980: Cumulus parameterization and rainfall rate I. *Mon. Wea. Rev.,* **108**, 665–672.

——, K. Ingles, S. Cocke, T. Kitade and R. Pasch, 1983: Details of low latitude medium-range weather prediction using a global spectral model. II. Effects of orography and physical initialization. Florida State Univ. Rep. 83-11, 206 pp.

Kuo, H. L., 1974: Further studies of the parameterization of the influence of cumulus convection on large-scale flow. *J. Atmos. Sci.,* **22**, 40–63.

Lange, A., and E. Hellsten, 1983: Results of the WMO/CAS NWP Data Study and Intercomparison Project for Forecasts for the Northern Hemisphere in 1981-82. *WMO Short- and Medium-Range Weather Predict. Res., Publ. Ser. No. 2,* World Meteorological Organization, Geneva, 30 pp., 68 figs. and Annex.

Lau, N.-C., 1981: Mid-latitude wintertime circulation anomalies appearing in a 15-year GCM experiment. *Large-Scale Dynamical Processes in the Atmosphere,* B. J. Hoskins and R. P. Pearce, Eds. Academic Press, 111–125.

Leith, C. E., 1978: Objective methods for weather prediction. *Ann. Rev. Fluid Mech.,* **10**, 107–128.

——, 1980: Nonlinear normal mode initialization and quasi-geostrophic theory. *J. Atmos. Sci.,* **37**, 958–968.

——, 1983: Predictability in theory and practise. *Large-Scale Dynamical Processes in the Atmosphere,* B. J. Hoskins and R. P. Pearce, Eds. Academic Press, 365–383.

Lejenäs, H., and H. Økland, 1983: Characteristics of Northern Hemisphere blocking as determined from a long time series of observational data. *Tellus,* **35A**, 350–362.

Lilly, D. K., 1972: Wave momentum flux. A GARP problem. *Bull. Amer. Meteor. Soc.,* **53**, 17–23.

——, J. M. Nicholls, R. M. Chervin, P. J. Kennedy and J. Klemp, 1982: Measurements of wave momentum flux over the Colorado Rocky Mountains. *Quart. J. Roy. Meteor. Soc.,* **108**, 625–642.

Lorenc, A. C., 1981: A global three-dimensional, multivariate statistical interpolation scheme. *Mon. Wea. Rev.,* **109**, 701–721.

Lorenz, E. N., 1955: Available potential energy and the maintenance of the general circulation. *Tellus,* **7**, 157–167.

——, 1982: Atmospheric predictability with a large numerical model. *Tellus,* **34**, 505–513.

Machenhauer, B., 1977: On the dynamics of gravity oscillations in a shallow-water model with application to normal mode initialization. *Contr. Atmos. Phys.,* **50**, 253–271.

——, 1988: Objective analysis and numerical forecasting of an explosive deepening cyclone using preoperational HIRLAM systems. *ECMWF Seminar on the Nature and Prediction of Extratropical Weather Systems, 7–11 September 1987,* Vol. 2, 193–230.

Marchuk, G. I., 1974: *Numerical Methods in Weather Prediction.* Academic Press, 277 pp. (Russian edition, 1967).

McFarlane, N., C. Girard and D. W. Shantz, 1987: Reduction of systematic errors in NWP and general circulation models by parameterized gravity wave drag. *Short and Medium-Range Numerical Weather Prediction,* T. Matsuno, Ed. Meteorological Society of Japan, 713–728.

Miller, M. J., T. N. Palmer and R. Swinbank, 1989: Parametrization and influence of subgridscale orography in general circulation and numerical weather prediction models. *Meteor. Atmos. Phys.,* **40**, 84–109.

Miyakoda, K., and J. Sirutis, 1977: Comparative integrations of global models with various parameterized processes of subgrid-scale vertical transports: Description of the parameterizations. *Contr. Atmos. Phys.,* **50**, 445–487.

——, and J. P. Chao, 1982: Essay on dynamical long-range forecasts of atmospheric circulation. *J. Meteor. Soc. Japan,* **60**, 292–308.

——, G. D. Hembree, R. F. Strickler and I. Shulman, 1972: Cumulative results of extended forecast experiments. 1. Model performance for winter cases. *Mon. Wea. Rev.,* **100**, 836–855.

Müller, E., D. Frühwald, I. Jacobsen, A. Link, D. Majewski, J.-U. Schwirner and U. Wacher, 1987: Results and prospects of mesoscale modeling at the Deutscher Wetterdienst. *Short- and Medium-Range Numerical Weather Prediction,* T. Matsuno, Ed. Meteorological Society of Japan, 533–546.

Mureau, R., 1989: The decrease of the systematic error and increased predictability of the long waves in the ECMWF model. ECMWF Tech. Rep., to be published.

Namias, J., 1969: Seasonal interactions between the North Pacific Ocean and the atmosphere during the 1960's. *Mon. Wea. Rev.,* **97**, 173–192.

Orszag, S. A., 1970: Transform method for calculation of vector coupled sums: Application to the spectral form of the vorticity equation. *J. Atmos. Sci.,* **27**, 890–895.

Palmer, T. N., 1988: Medium and extended range predictability and stability of the Pacific/North American mode. *Quart. J. Roy. Meteor. Soc.,* **114**, 691–713.

——, and S. Tibaldi, 1988: On the prediction of forecast skill. *Mon. Wea. Rev.,* **116**, 2453–2480.

——, G. J. Shutts and R. Swinbank, 1986: Alleviation of a systematic westerly bias in general circulation and numerical weather prediction models through an orographic gravity wave drag parameterization. *Quart. J. Roy. Meteor. Soc.,* **112**, 1001–1039.

Petterssen, S., D. L. Bradbury and K. Pedersen, 1962: The Norwegian cyclone models in relation to heat and cold sources. *Geofys. Publ.,* **24**, 243–280.

Phillips, N. A., 1957: A coordinate system having some special advantages for numerical forecasting. *J. Meteor.,* **14**, 184–185.

——, 1973: Principles of large scale numerical weather prediction. *Dynamical Meteorology,* P. Morel, Ed. Reidel, 1–95.

Rex, D. F., 1950: Blocking action in the middle troposphere and its effect upon regional climate. II: The climatology of blocking actions. *Tellus,* **2**, 275–302.

Richardson, L. F., 1922: *Weather Prediction by Numerical Process.* Cambridge University Press, 236 pp.

Ritchie, H., 1988: Application of the semi-Lagrangian method to a spectral model of the shallow water equations. *Mon. Wea. Rev.,* **116**, 1587–1598.

Robert, A. J., 1969: The integration of a spectral model of the atmosphere by the implicit method. *Proc. WMO/IUGG Symposium on Numerical Weather Prediction in Tokyo, 1968.* Meteorological Society of Japan, vii-19—24.

——, 1974: Computational resolution requirements for accurate medium-range numerical prediction. *Difference and Spectral Methods for Atmosphere and Ocean Dynamics Problems. Proc. Symp. Novosibirsk, 1973, Part I,* 82–102.

——, 1982: A semi-Lagrangian and semi-implicit numerical integration scheme for the primitive meteorological equations. *J. Meteor. Soc. Japan,* **60**, 319–324.

——, J. Henderson and C. Turnbull, 1972: An implicit time integration scheme for baroclinic models of the atmosphere. *Mon. Wea. Rev.,* **100**, 329–335.

——, T.-L. Yee and H. Ritchie, 1985: A semi-Lagrangian and semi-implicit numerical integration scheme for multilevel atmospheric models. *Mon. Wea. Rev.,* **113**, 388–394.

Sawyer, J. S., 1959: Introduction of the effects of topography into methods of numerical weather forecasting. *Quart. J. Roy. Meteor. Soc.,* **85**, 31–43.

Shukla, J., 1984: Predictability of time averages. *Problems and Prospects in Long and Medium-Range Weather Forecasting,* D. M. Burridge and E. Källén, Eds. Springer-Verlag, 109–206.

Simmons, A. J., and M. J. Miller, 1988: The prediction of extratropical weather systems—some sensitivity studies. *ECMWF Seminar on the Nature and Prediction of Extratropical Weather Systems, 7–11 September 1987,* Vol. II, 271–315.

——, J. M. Wallace and G. W. Branstator, 1983: Barotropic wave propagation and instability, and atmospheric teleconnection patterns. *J. Atmos. Sci.,* **40**, 1363–1392.

——, D. M. Burridge, M. Jarraud, C. Girard and W. Wergen, 1989: The ECMWF medium-range prediction models. Development of the numerical formulations and the impact of increased resolution. *Meteor. Atmos. Phys.,* **40**, 28–60.

Smagorinsky, J., 1953: The dynamical influences of large-scale heat sources and sinks on the quasi-stationary mean motions of the atmosphere. *Quart. J. Roy. Meteor. Soc.,* **79**, 342–366.

——, 1969: Problems and promises of deterministic extended-range forecasting. *Bull. Amer. Meteor. Soc.,* **50**, 286–311.

Staniforth, A., and C. Temperton, 1986: Semi-implicit semi-Lagrangian integration schemes for barotropic finite-element regional models. *Mon. Wea. Rev.,* **114**, 2078–2090.

Sundqvist, H., 1981: Prediction of stratiform clouds: results from a 5-day forecast with a global model. *Tellus,* **33**, 242–253.

Swinbank, R., 1985: The global atmospheric angular momentum balance inferred from analyses made during FGGE. *Quart. J. Roy. Meteor. Soc.,* **111**, 977–996.

Temperton, C., and D. L. Williamson, 1979: Normal mode initialization for a multi-level gridpoint model. ECMWF Tech. Rep. No. 11, 91 pp.

Tibaldi, S., and F. Molteni, 1988: On the operational predictability of blocking. *ECMWF Seminar on the Nature and Prediction of Extratropical Weather Systems, 7–11 September 1987.* ECMWF, 329–371.

Tiedtke, M., 1989: A comprehensive mass flux scheme for cumulus parameterization in large-scale models. *Mon. Wea. Rev.,* **117**, 1779–1800.

——, W. A. Heckley and J. Slingo, 1988: Tropical forecasting at ECMWF: The influence of physical parameterization on the mean structure of forecasts and analyses. *Quart. J. Roy. Meteor. Soc.,* **114**, 639–664.

Tracton, M. S., 1988: Predictability and its relationship to cyclone/planetary scale interactions. *Palmén Memorial Symposium on Extratropical Cyclones,* Helsinki, oral presentation.

University of Stockholm, Staff members, Institute of Meteorology, 1954: Results of forecasting with the barotropic model on an electronic computer (BESK). *Tellus,* **6**, 139–149.

Volmer, J.-P., M. Deque and M. Jarraud, 1983: Large-scale fluctuations in a long-range integration of the ECMWF spectral model. *Tellus,* **35**, 173–178.

Wallace, J. M., and D. S. Gutzler, 1981: Teleconnections in the geopotential height field during the Northern Hemisphere winter. *Mon. Wea. Rev.,* **109**, 784–812.

——, S. Tibaldi and A. J. Simmons, 1983: Reduction of systematic errors in the ECMWF model through the introduction of an envelope orography. *Quart. J. Roy. Meteor. Soc.,* **109**, 683–717.

Wergen, W., 1987: Diabatic nonlinear normal mode initialization for a spectral model with a hybrid vertical coordinate. ECMWF Tech. Rep. No. 59.

Wiin-Nielsen, A., 1979: Steady states and stability properties of a low-order barotropic system with forcing and dissipation. *Tellus,* **31**, 375–386.

Wu, Q. X., and S. J. Chen, 1985: The effect of mechanical forcing on the formation of a mesoscale vortex. *Quart. J. Roy. Meteor. Soc.,* **111**, 1049–1070.

Chapter 12

Advances in the Understanding and Prediction of Cyclone Development with Limited-Area Fine-Mesh Models

Richard A. Anthes

National Center for Atmospheric Research, Boulder, Colorado 80307-3000

12.1 Introduction

Since the early scientific theories of the development of extratropical cyclones in the 19th century (Kutzbach 1979), meteorologists have sought a complete and quantitative description of the physics of these atmospheric systems that dominate weather in middle latitudes. The earliest studies were descriptive and based almost entirely on surface observations. With the advent of instrumented aircraft in the early 1930s, operational rawinsondes in the 1940s and satellites in the 1960s, a more complete three-dimensional picture of the structure of extratropical cyclones emerged, as described by others in this volume.

Professor Palmén contributed much to the early documentation of the three-dimensional structure of extratropical cyclones through his careful analyses of ra-

* The National Center for Atmospheric Research is sponsored by the National Science Foundation.

winsonde observations. For example, his vertical cross section analysis through a frontal system of 17 January 1947 is one of the earliest conclusive documentations of the narrow jet stream and its relationship to upper-level fronts (Palmén 1948a). With Chester Newton, Palmén constructed a 12-case composite vertical cross section through upper-level fronts to show the typical kinematic and thermodynamic structure of these systems (Palmén and Newton 1948).

Shortly after these synoptic studies, Palmén and his colleagues carried out a series of diagnostic studies on cyclones. For example, Palmén and Newton (1951) evaluated the meridional and vertical mass fluxes in a polar-air outbreak from time changes of the frontal contours, and also computed three-dimensional trajectories on isentropic surfaces, to show the importance of cyclones in the north-south exchange of mass, heat and angular momentum (see Section 1.4.2). Later, Palmén and Holopainen (1962) computed moisture budgets and kinetic energy budgets for a deepening cyclone using carefully analyzed rawinsonde data. These early diagnostic and budget studies added much to our early understanding of the energetics of cyclones and demonstrated their importance in the general circulation.

Although the focus of this work is extratropical cyclones, Palmén was also a pioneer in describing the three-dimensional structure of tropical cyclones. His composite analysis of data observed over the period 17–20 September 1947 showed a remarkably representative temperature cross section through a hurricane (Palmén 1948b). A few years later, he used mean tropical storm data to estimate the conversion of potential to kinetic energy and the rate of dissipation of kinetic energy in tropical cyclones (Palmén and Jordan 1955). From these energy conversion rates he concluded that tropical cyclones had a "half-life" of somewhat less than a day. These estimates have since been confirmed by many observational and modeling studies (Anthes 1982).

Since Palmén's pioneering studies of the 1940s and '50s, new and improved observational systems have added to our knowledge of the development and structure of cyclones. Satellites have shown a rich variety of clouds and their organization associated with cyclones, and have contributed observations of temperature, moisture and winds as well. Improved aircraft instrumentation, Doppler radars, and ground-based wind, temperature and moisture profilers have added additional details to the picture. The basic three-dimensional structure of cyclones revealed by the studies of Palmén and his colleagues, however, has not been changed by studies using these new systems.

Prior to the 1960s, the basic theoretical method for explaining the observed development and structure of cyclones was the linear perturbation method (Haurwitz 1951). In this method, a set of nonlinear equations that describe atmospheric motions is linearized about a basic state. After assuming wave-like forms for the behavior of small perturbations superimposed on this basic state and

choosing appropriate boundary conditions, exact mathematical solutions describing the growth or decay and the movement of the perturbations can be obtained. These methods were successful in providing significant insight into the dynamics of waves in the westerlies and cyclones through barotropic and baroclinic processes (Rossby 1940; Bjerknes and Holmboe 1944; Charney 1947; Eady 1949). The assumption of linearity, however, restricts this method to small perturbations with the neglect, or great simplification, of diabatic and frictional processes such as latent heat release, radiation and turbulence.

The advent of automatic electronic calculators, or "stored program" computers, in the 1940s permitted meteorologists and mathematicians to begin realizing the early dreams of Vilhelm Bjerknes in 1904 and Lewis Fry Richardson in 1922. Their vision was the prediction of weather by numerical integration of the full set of nonlinear equations including physics (latent heating, friction, radiation, turbulent mixing, sensible heating, evaporation). Thompson (1983) and Tribbia and Anthes (1987) provide reviews of the history of numerical weather prediction and summarize the scientific basis for numerical models of the atmosphere.

Because of the slow speed of the early computers, the first numerical models had to be highly simplified and provided only coarse vertical and horizontal resolution of the atmosphere. The first numerical models that were suc-

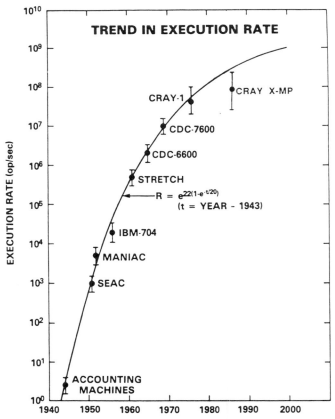

FIG. 12.1. Trend in single processor computational performance (Hack 1989). See also Fig. 11.1.

cessfully initialized with real data were two-dimensional barotropic models based on the conservation of absolute vorticity (Charney et al. 1950). The first operational weather prediction model, which began running daily at the Joint Numerical Weather Prediction Unit (JNWP) in Washington, D.C. on 15 May 1955, was a three-layer, quasi-geostrophic model (Thompson 1983).

The rapid increase in computing power from the machines in the late 1940s, which computed at rates of about 1000 operations per second (Thompson 1983), to the supercomputers 40 years later in which speeds approach 10^8 operations per second (Fig. 12.1), have permitted the development of higher-resolution models with more realistic and complete physics. The result of these improved models, together with the parallel development of improved analysis and initialization techniques and new observations such as satellites, has been a steady increase in forecast skill (Fig. 12.2). This is demonstrated by Bengtsson in Section 11.5.

With present-day computers, global models are capable of running with horizontal resolutions as fine as 100 km. Until very recently, however, such resolutions were obtainable only over regions of limited extent. Hence it was recognized early that there was a need for *Limited-Area fine-mesh Models* (LAMs), and in 1972 the U. S. National Meteorological Center began running the best-known of many models of this type, the NMC Limited-area Fine-mesh Model, or LFM (J. G. Howcroft and A. Desmaris, personal communication).

The main (perhaps the only) early motivation for developing numerical models of the atmosphere was to improve weather prediction, and it was quickly confirmed that even the simplest numerical models could provide forecasts that were superior to subjective methods beyond about 24 hours (Fig. 12.2). As the skill of the early numerical models became apparent, it was recognized that models are powerful tools for research as well as operational purposes. Global models were developed for the study of climate and the general circulation (e.g., Smagorinsky et al. 1965) while higher-resolution LAMs were developed for the study of particular phenomena such as tropical cyclones (Kasahara 1959, 1961; Syōno 1962).

Since these early studies, great progress has been made in developing LAMs and applying them to the study of many atmospheric systems, including planetary boundary layer (PBL) turbulence, convective clouds and cloud systems, topographically forced flows, land and sea breezes, fronts and tropical and extratropical cyclones. As discussed by Keyser and Uccellini (1987), these models have become valuable research tools that complement and extend observational and other theoretical methods. They alleviate the problem of inadequate spatial and temporal coverage of observations by providing high-resolution, idealized data sets. Although the model data sets contain errors, they, unlike observational data sets, are dynamically and thermodynamically consistent in that they satisfy exactly the approximate dynamical and thermodynamical equations used in the model. Numerical models extend linear theories by permitting the evolution of large-amplitude nonlinear disturbances and the feedback of these disturbances to larger and smaller scales. Finally, numerical models are a *theoretical laboratory* for the atmospheric scientist, who can isolate particular physical processes through sensitivity studies in a way analogous to laboratory research in which chemists or physicists vary parameters and compare the effect to a control experiment. For example, the role of mountains in cyclone development can be studied by comparing a numerical

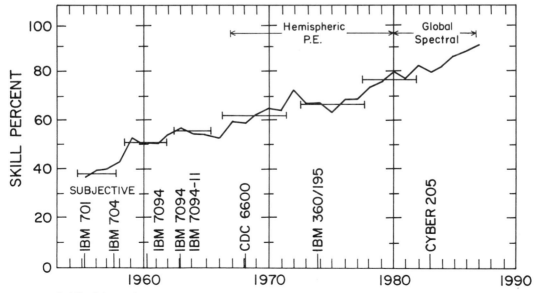

FIG. 12.2. Average annual skill of the National Meteorological Center's 36-h forecast of the 500-mb height field over an area defined by 65° to 145°W and 25° to 55°N. The skill is defined as: SKILL = $100 + 2(20 - S_1)$ where S_1 is the skill score defined by Teweles and Wobus (1954). The original figure appeared in the NMC Annual NWP Progress Report for 1985; the figure has been updated with data kindly provided by Dr. Joseph P. Gerrity, Jr., of NMC. See also Fig. 11.10.

model forecast with the mountains present (the control experiment) and a second model forecast with the mountains removed.

This paper first reviews some of the recent contributions of LAMs to the study of the evolution and structure of extratropical cyclones. Recent results are emphasized to limit the length of the paper, and because recent models are significantly better in spatial resolution, numerical methods and in their treatment of physical processes than earlier models. The paper then concludes with an example of the application of a LAM to the study of the transformation of Hurricane Hazel (1954) into an extratropical cyclone. Palmén (1958) studied this case using rawinsonde data; I believe he would have enjoyed the opportunity afforded by today's research models to revisit this extraordinary cyclone.

12.2   Limited-Area Models

Tribbia and Anthes (1987) review the scientific basis for numerical weather prediction models in general, and Anthes (1983b) reviews regional models in particular; hence only a short summary will be presented here. The components of global and LAMs include: (1) numerical aspects, including grid structure, finite-difference or spectral representation and temporal integration; (2) data analysis and initialization; and (3) treatment of physics, including diabatic and frictional processes. An important additional component peculiar to the LAMs is (4) the treatment of the lateral boundary conditions (LBC). Anthes (1983b) summarizes these components, and there are many other references that treat them in detail (e.g., Haltiner and Williams 1980; Pielke 1984).

Each of the above four components contributes to errors in a numerical forecast or simulation of a LAM. The distinction between a forecast and a simulation is that a forecast uses real data at an initial time and integrates forward without any additional use of observations after the initial time. In contrast, a simulation may not use real data at all, through the specification of idealized initial conditions. Or, simulations may be initialized with real data and use additional observations after the initial time to influence the integration, for example, through the use of analyzed LBC or four-dimensional data assimilation. With the high horizontal and vertical resolutions of present LAMs and their accurate numerical methods, the numerical aspects probably contribute least to the total error. The other three components, however, may contribute significant errors in any one forecast or simulation, and their relative contributions may vary greatly from case to case.

In a recent study, Anthes et al. (1989) analyzed the results from 72-hour simulations and forecasts from the Penn State/NCAR model (Anthes et al. 1987) to investigate the contribution to model error introduced by the initial data, horizontal resolution and domain size, LBC and physical parameterizations. The simulations and forecasts were verified for 12 individual cases and for the

ensemble average of the 12 cases using several objective measures of skill.

A major result of this study was that the use of analyzed LBC exerts a strong control on the growth of errors over a domain size 3600 × 4800 km (the inner box in Fig. 12.3). Initial errors showed little growth beyond about 36 hours, so that 72-hour errors were nearly as low as the 36-hour errors (Fig. 12.4). These results agree with other studies of

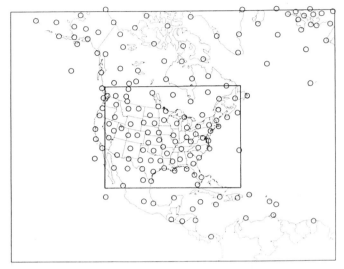

FIG. 12.3. Large and small domains used in sensitivity studies of Anthes et al. (1989). The circles represent the locations of rawinsonde stations.

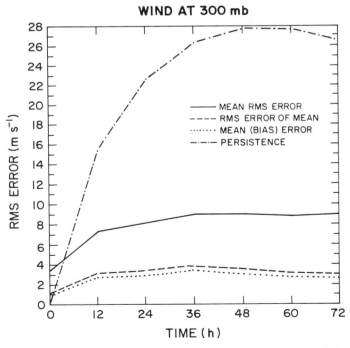

FIG. 12.4. Time series of 12-case average errors of the 300-mb wind associated with control simulation of Anthes et al. (1989). Plotted are the mean (12-case average) root-mean-square error (solid line), the RMS error of the 12-case-average forecast (dashed line), the 12-case average of the mean (bias) error (dotted line) and the 12-case average RMS of a persistence forecast.

single cases (Anthes et al. 1985; Anthes 1986; Orlanski and Katzfey 1987; Paegle and Vukicevic 1987). *On these time and space scales, the quality of the LBC was more important than any other factor tested by Anthes et al. (1989) in determining the error of the simulation. Small variations in the initial conditions had little effect on the model skill beyond 12–24 hours.* The control of error growth through the use of analyzed LBCs adds to the accuracy and credibility of regional model simulations in their use as research tools.

In contrast to the minor impact of random differences in the initial conditions, latent heating effects associated with condensation and precipitation, and with sensible heat transfer and evaporation at the earth's surface, had a statistically significant beneficial effect on the simulations.

The above conclusions were based on the 12-case average skill scores; individual cases showed large variations in model skill. Thus while these results are probably valid when large numbers of cases are considered, they may be misleading for individual cases of importance. For example, the average results of the Anthes et al. (1989) study showed that variations in initial conditions were the least important of all factors tested in determining the average

skill score of the model. Individual cases, however, may show greater sensitivity to variations in initial conditions. Chang et al. (1986) showed that the omission of a single wind sounding over northwestern Mexico had a significant effect on a 24-hour simulation of the Severe Environmental Storms and Mesoscale Experiment (SESAME)-I (10 April 1979) cyclone case.

Figure 12.5 shows the two initial analyses for the 500-mb height and wind speed and the 300-mb relative vorticity and wind speed fields. In the analysis without the wind sounding in Mexico (Experiment E1), the wind field is close to the geostrophic first guess, and is too strong by about 20 percent in the base of the deep trough over Mexico where the cyclonic curvature is large. When the Mexican wind sounding, is inserted into the analysis scheme (Exp. E2), the maximum wind speed in the jet is decreased from about 55 m s^{-1} to about 45 m s^{-1} at 500 mb and 75 to 65 m s^{-1} at 300 mb. These differences produced noticeable differences in the 24-hour forecasts. A closed upper-level low formed in both forecasts; the E1 forecast without the Mexican wind sounding, however, developed a 500-mb low that was 100 m deeper than the observed and the E2 forecast (Fig. 12.6). The overly

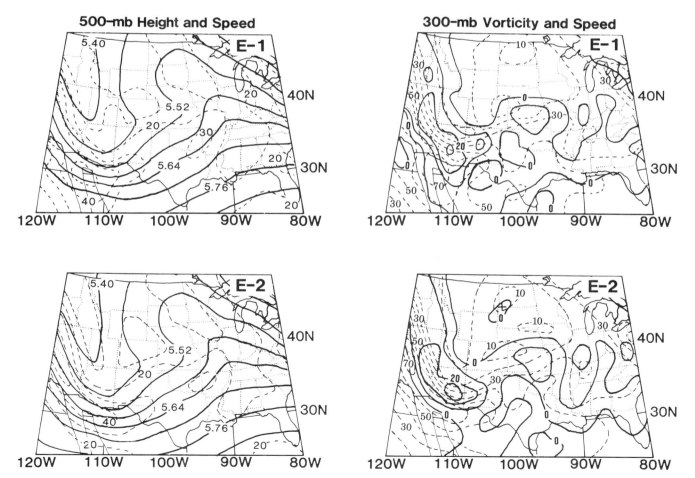

Fɪɢ. 12.5.   Initial (12 UTC 10 April 1979) 500-mb conditions (left) for simulation without wind observation over Mexico (E-1) and with wind observation (E-2). Solid lines are height contours (km) and dashed lines are isotachs (m s^{-1}). Also shown on right are initial 300-mb conditions. Solid lines are absolute vorticity (10^{-5} s^{-1}) and dashed lines are isotachs (m s^{-1}) (Chang et al. 1986).

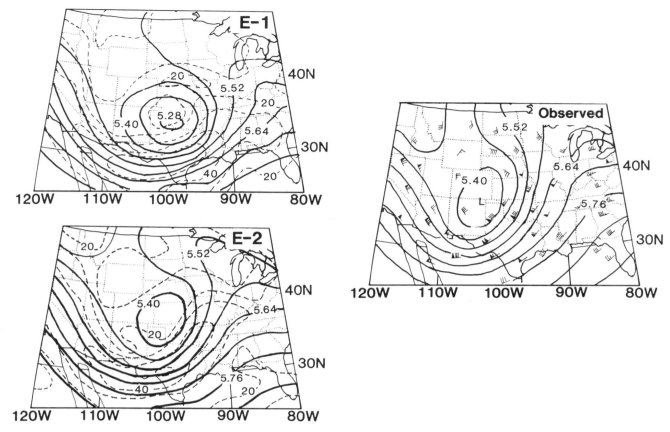

FIG. 12.6.   Simulated 24-h 500-mb height (solid lines, km) and wind speed (dashed lines, m s^{-1}) for E-1 and E-2. Also shown are observed conditions (Chang et al. 1986).

intense upper-level circulation in Exp. E1 also produced significant differences in the 24-hour precipitation patterns (not shown).

The results for the single case by Chang et al. (1986) are consistent with the results of Källén and Huang (1988a, 1988b). In their 1988b study, they examined the behavior of perturbation growth in 152 cases using the European Centre for Medium-Range Weather Forecasts (ECMWF) model. They found that there was a very large variability in growth. In general, the most rapid growth occurred in regions of strong baroclinity.

In another LAM study that considered the effect of differences in initial conditions on cyclone development, Duffy and Atlas (1986) showed that proper incorporation of wind estimates from the Seasat scatterometer had a major positive impact on a 36-hour forecast of the Queen Elizabeth II (QE II) storm. This storm began as a weak, shallow disturbance west of Atlantic City, New Jersey on 8 September 1978 and developed explosively over the Atlantic, deepening 60 mb to a minimum pressure of 945 mb at 12 UTC 10 September (Gyakum 1983). The storm caused extensive damage to the *Queen Elizabeth II* luxury liner and sank the fishing trawler *Capt. Cosmo.*

Figures 12.7a and b show the forecasts with and without the use of Seasat winds in the initial conditions; the Seasat forecast shows a more intense cyclone that is much closer

to the observed storm intensity. There are two major reasons for the large positive impact found by Duffy and Atlas. First, the analyses without the Seasat data were significantly in error over much of the domain because of the absence of conventional data over the ocean and seriously underestimated the intensity of the circulation at the initial time. Second, the addition of the Seasat data produced *large* (typically 5 m s^{-1}) and *systematic* differences in the initial winds through deep layers of the troposphere. The influence of the surface winds on the winds above the surface was computed by adding corrections to the winds at all levels based on the difference between the Seasat wind estimates at the surface and the winds in the control analysis. When the Seasat winds were used to modify only the surface winds of the control analysis, they had little impact on the forecast.

The results of the Chang et al. (1986) and the Duffy and Atlas (1986) experiments indicate that *differences in initial conditions, when they are of sufficient amplitude, add substantially to the information in the analysis and affect significant portions of the model atmosphere in a physically consistent way, can have a major impact on model forecasts.* In contrast, small-amplitude, random perturbations or errors in the initial conditions that are dynamically unbalanced generally have little impact on LAM forecasts or simulations. From a series of simulations studying the

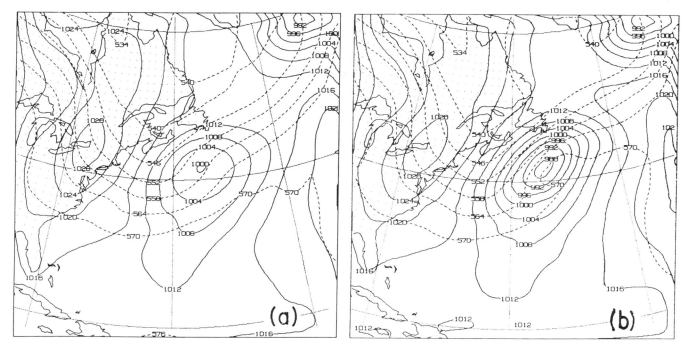

FIG. 12.7. Simulated 36-h sea level pressure (solid lines, mb) and 1000–500 mb thickness (dashed lines, dam) for experiments (a) without Seasat data and (b) using Seasat data (Duffy and Atlas 1986).

impact of VAS (visible and infrared spin-scan radiometer atmospheric sounder) data on numerical simulations of a Pacific cyclone, Douglas and Warner (1987) conclude that the impact of initial data also depends on the stage of evolution of the cyclone and the physical parameterizations in the model.

Keyser and Uccellini (1987) discuss three uses of LAMs for basic research:

(1) use of the model data for synoptic analyses;
(2) sensitivity studies in which one or more parameter is varied to isolate a particular effect; and
(3) diagnostic studies in which the model data are used to compute energy, heat, or moisture budgets and other diagnostic properties such as ageostrophic circulations.

To these three methodologies I add a fourth: (4) Observational Systems Simulation Experiments (OSSEs) in which the impact of different observing systems is evaluated (a particular type of sensitivity study). Examples of each of these methodologies are given in the following section.

12.3 Application of Models to the Study of Cyclones

12.3.1   Idealized Simulation of Cyclones

High-resolution data from model simulations or forecasts can be used to study the development and structure of cyclones. Models permit the specification of initial states that are simple compared to the real atmosphere, yet too complex to be studied by other theoretical means. Examples of the use of LAMs in idealized simula-

tions of extratropical cyclones include Shapiro (1975), Trevisan (1976), Buzzi et al. (1977), Simmons and Hoskins (1978), Newton and Trevisan (1984) and Nuss and Anthes (1987).

Simmons and Hoskins (1978) investigated the nonlinear behavior of midlatitude baroclinic waves using a primitive equation model. The simulations were initialized with a small-amplitude disturbance of a prescribed wavelength on a balanced zonal flow. These initial disturbances grew through the mechanism of baroclinic instability and reached a mature stage that showed many characteristics similar to those of observed cyclones. The disturbances then went through a decaying phase similar to the occlusion phase of cyclones. Barotropic processes were important during the decaying phase.

Newton and Trevisan (1984) examined frontogenesis in a model based on the isentropic model developed by Eliassen and Raustein (1968). The model was adiabatic and inviscid, in order to isolate dynamical from physical processes in the cyclogenesis. Newton and Trevisan specified idealized initial distributions of temperature, static stability, tropopause height and winds that gave a zonal jet stream with realistic shears. A weak cyclone-anticyclone couplet in the lower troposphere initiated cyclogenesis by the "self-development" mechanism (Sutcliffe and Forsdyke 1950; Palmén and Newton 1969, pp. 324–326). North-south advection of temperature by the initially perturbed flow distorted the initial temperature field and resulted in an amplifying wave perturbation. Ageostrophic motions induced by the resulting unbalanced wind and mass fields led to upper-level divergence over the cyclone and further intensification of the perturbation circulation

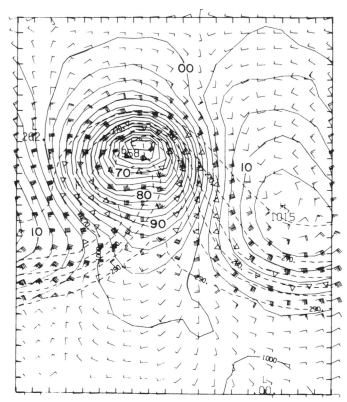

FIG. 12.8. Simulated 1000-mb heights (solid lines, contour interval 50 m), 1000–500 mb thickness (dashed lines at 100 m intervals) and low-level winds (barb, 5 m s^{-1}; pennant, 25 m s^{-1}) at 72 h for model cyclone (Newton and Trevisan 1984).

12 hours using the Sanders (1971) model, indicating the importance of diabatic processes in the model cyclone.

Large surface heat and moisture fluxes and boundary-layer mixing produced a layer of saturation behind the cold front, which resembles stratocumulus clouds in the cold air to the rear of cyclones over the oceans. The latent heating in the stratocumulus clouds and the sensible heating counteract the cold advection behind the front, so the horizontal temperature gradient in the cold air was relatively weak. A deep moist band developed over the surface cold front, which indicates the presence of a deep vertical circulation associated with the front.

12.3.2   Sensitivity Studies

a)   Surface moisture availability

Evaporation from the surface is a major factor in determining the structure of the daytime planetary boundary layer (PBL). The availability of surface moisture for evaporation, either from a wet surface or from transpiring vegetation, determines the partitioning of net radiation between sensible and latent heat fluxes, and these in turn determine the depth, temperature and humidity of the PBL. One-dimensional modeling studies by McCumber and Pielke (1981) and Zhang and Anthes (1982) showed that *the surface moisture availability M,* which varies from 0 for a dry surface to 1 for a wet surface, *was the single most important surface parameter in determining the evolution and structure of the PBL during the daytime.*

Several sensitivity studies with LAMs have shown that three-dimensional simulations and forecasts over time periods as short as 12 hours are sensitive to the magnitude and horizontal distribution of surface moisture availability. Lanicci et al. (1987) used the Penn State/NCAR model to simulate a Great Plains cyclone of 9–10 May 1979 (SESAME IV case) with different distributions of moisture availability. In the control simulation, which used realistic values of M, low soil moisture over the Mexican plateau allowed for strong sensible heating there and development of a deep mixed layer. This deep mixed layer was advected northward over cooler, more moist air in eastern Texas and formed a capping inversion (lid) which prevented deep convection there. This deep mixed layer failed to form when M was increased from the realistic value of 0.02 to 0.05, to a uniform value of 0.4 (Fig. 12.9).

The gradient of M over Texas and Oklahoma affected the motion of the dryline through its effect on differential heating and vertical mixing. Low values of M over west Texas and the associated strong PBL heating caused an increase in the ageostrophic flow over east Texas and the Gulf of Mexico, and this flow contributed to the westward advection of the dryline during the evening. These changes in PBL winds, temperature and moisture affected the intensity and location of precipitation.

b)   Surface fluxes of sensible and latent heat

In two 12-hour model simulations of cyclonic circulations over the western U.S. (10 April 1979—SESAME I,

in a positive feedback process. The model cyclone at 72 hours (Fig. 12.8) resembles intense observed cyclones. North-south vertical cross sections through the cyclone at this time (not shown) show a steeply sloping cold front and a more shallow warm front, with associated upper-tropospheric jet-stream wind maximum exceeding 90 m s^{-1}. Other simulations in which the initial conditions were varied showed that development was faster for lower static stability and greater baroclinicity, as predicted from linear theory. These experiments show that realistic cyclogenesis can be produced by purely adiabatic processes.

In another series of idealized simulations, Nuss and Anthes (1987) investigated the physical and dynamical factors that lead to explosive cyclogenesis over oceans. Using analytic mathematical functions, they specified idealized initial conditions characterized by strong low-level baroclinicity and a weak upper-level trough. Variations in the initial conditions and in the physical processes of latent heating and sensible and latent heat fluxes from the surface produced different evolutions of the model cyclone. In the control simulation, an intense storm deepened by 23 mb from the initial minimum pressure of 1009 mb. Although the development during the first few hours resembled closely the "self-development" process found in Newton and Trevisan's adiabatic simulation, the 24-hour deepening rate was more than three times the quasi-geostrophic rate computed from the model data at

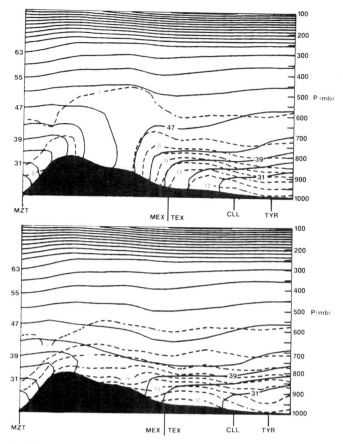

FIG. 12.9. Vertical cross sections from Mazatlan, Mexico to northeastern Texas of potential temperature (solid lines, °C) and mixing ratio (dashed lines, g kg⁻¹) from 12-h simulations with (a) realistic variable surface moisture availability and (b) greater, spatially constant moisture availability. The time is 00 UTC 9 May 1979 (Lanicci et al. 1987).

and 9 May 1979—SESAME IV) Benjamin and Carlson (1986) demonstrated the *significant effect that sensible heating at the earth's surface can have on cyclones over land, even for these short time periods.* Figure 12.10a shows the 12-hour forecast of the 10 April case; this forecast contained surface sensible and latent heat fluxes. Figures 12.10b and c show the differences in sea-level pressure and PBL wind flow at 12 hours between the forecast with surface fluxes and a forecast without. Differences in sea-level pressure range from +3.2 to −4.2 mb; the resulting difference in PBL pressure-gradient force produces perturbation winds exceeding 7.5 m s⁻¹ in magnitude. The greater southeasterly flow in the simulation with surface fluxes increased the low-level transport of moisture toward northern Texas and helped destabilize the air there; these effects contributed to the outbreak of severe convective storms in this region. Benjamin and Carlson noted a similar effect in the 9 May simulation.

As shown by the sensitivity of short-range forecasts to surface heat and moisture fluxes in the SESAME cases, surface energy fluxes can have a significant effect on cyclone development over land. Studies by Anthes (1983a), Anthes et al. (1983), Chen et al. (1983), Nuss

and Anthes (1987) and Kuo and Reed (1988) have shown a complex role of surface energy fluxes in the development of cyclones over the oceans. In model simulations of the QE II storm, Anthes (1983a) and Anthes et al. (1983) showed that the surface energy fluxes had a modest positive effect on cyclone development. Under the strong surface winds around this cyclone, sensible and latent heat fluxes exceeded 350 and 1000 W m⁻² respectively. Difference fields between simulations with and without surface energy fluxes showed that these fluxes produced lower surface pressures at the cyclone center and along the front, with resulting stronger low-level convergence. They also produced a warmer and moister PBL. This energy was distributed upward by strong vertical motions associated with the cyclone and fronts and resulted in a more intense storm.

Chen et al. (1983) have presented model results from a case of cyclogenesis off the east coast of Asia during the period 13–15 February 1975. A 24-hour simulation that included surface energy fluxes and the latent heat of condensation showed cyclogenesis that was close to the observed. As shown by the difference fields of sea-level pressure (not shown) and 300-mb winds (Fig. 12.11), latent heating and surface energy fluxes were important to this development, together contributing more than 50 percent to the total deepening. Another experiment, in which latent heating was excluded but sensible heating was included, indicated that the sensible heating alone contributed about 20 percent to the total deepening. Thus, as in the QE II case, *the major effect of surface fluxes was to enhance the condensation heating, which was a major source of energy for the storm.*

In the two cases summarized above, surface energy fluxes had a positive effect on the cyclogenesis. They may also, however, have little effect, or even a negative effect, depending upon where they occur in relation to the low-level thermodynamic and moisture structure of the cyclone and how they interact with the release of latent heat. For example, Kuo and Reed (1988) found that surface energy fluxes had little immediate effect on the development of an intense cyclone over the eastern Pacific.

The importance of the relative phase of the sensible heating and low-level temperature wave was shown by Nuss and Anthes (1987) in simulations of an idealized cyclone over the ocean. In the control simulation, sensible heating in the cold air behind the surface cold front reduced the low-level baroclinicity; a much stronger cold front was produced when sensible heating was neglected. This increased baroclinicity resulted in a stronger cyclone; at 36 hours the minimum pressure of the cyclone simulated *without* surface energy fluxes was 10 mb lower than the minimum of the simulation with the fluxes included. In contrast, when an alternative sea-surface temperature distribution was specified that resulted in a sensible heat flux enhancing the low-level baroclinicity, a more intense storm developed. The different effect of surface energy fluxes depending on the detailed structure of individual

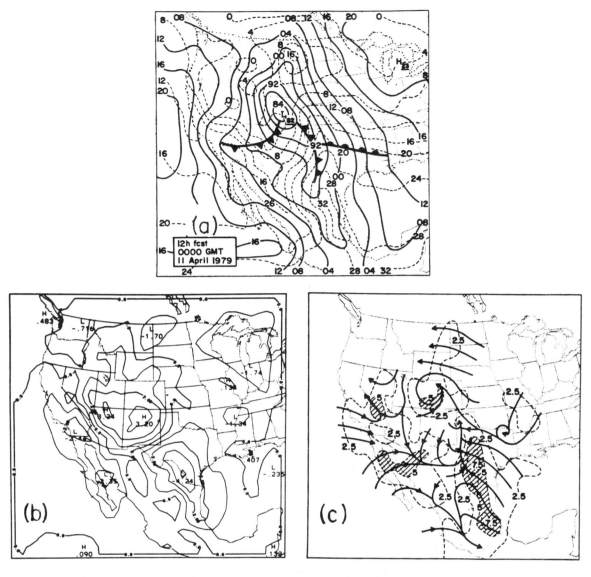

FIG. 12.10.   (a) 12-h simulation valid at 00 UTC 11 April 1979 of sea-level pressure (solid lines, mb) and screen-level temperature (dashed lines, °C). This simulation contained sensible and latent heat fluxes from the surface. (b) Surface pressure differences (contour interval 1 mb) between 12-h simulations with and without surface heat fluxes, for same time. (c) As in (b) but for low-level ($\sigma = 0.96$) wind speed. Isotachs are in m s^{-1} (Benjamin and Carlson 1986).

cyclones shows the value of numerical models in isolating important physical effects in real atmospheric storms.

c)   *Release of latent heat*

It is well recognized that the release of latent heat associated with condensation and precipitation is the major energy source in tropical cyclones; without latent heating, tropical cyclones would not exist. Extratropical cyclones, in contrast, may develop without the latent heat of condensation as shown, for example, by the simulations of Newton and Trevisan (1984). Many studies with LAMs, however, have shown that *latent heating can significantly affect extratropical cyclogenesis* (Anthes and Keyser 1979; Fritsch and Maddox 1981; Maddox et al. 1981; Chang et al. 1982; Anthes et al. 1982).

The effect of latent heating on cyclogenesis can be shown by running the model with and without latent heating included and comparing the simulations or forecasts. For example, Fig. 12.12 shows the difference fields in the upper- and lower-level wind fields at 6 and 18 hours of simulations of the SESAME II case (25 April 1979) with and without latent heating (Anthes et al. 1982). The difference fields show the development of an upper-level anticyclonic perturbation flow that exceeds 15 m s^{-1} in magnitude by 18 hours, and the development of a lower-level cyclonic perturbation flow of the same magnitude. The sea-level pressure field in the region of heaviest precipitation is more than 7 mb lower at 18 hours when latent heating is included. Similar differences are evident in the simulation of the cyclogenesis in Fig. 12.12 and in another case by Chang et al. (1982, 1984).

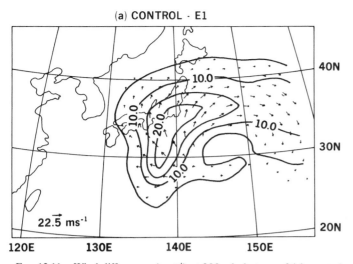

(a) CONTROL - E1

FIG. 12.11. Wind differences (m s⁻¹) at 300 mb, between 24-h control simulation and simulation without the effects of latent heating and surface energy fluxes (Chen et al. 1983).

In their 1984 study, Chang et al. computed kinetic energy budgets for a domain centered over the cyclone for the dry and moist simulations. They found that latent heating increased the generation of kinetic energy at all levels, with a maximum increase occurring in the lower troposphere. Although the maximum release of latent heat was in the middle to upper troposphere, the most significant dynamic response to the latent heating was in the lower troposphere, where the ageostrophic flow was a significant source of kinetic energy.

The release of latent heat can be particularly important in cases of explosive cyclogenesis over the ocean (Anthes et al. 1983; Chen et al. 1983; Kuo and Reed 1988). These studies show that baroclinic instability is responsible for the initiation of the cyclogenesis, but that once a vertical circulation is established and condensation begins, the release of latent heat can double the rate of intensification. Kuo and Reed used a 40-km resolution model to investigate the role of conditional symmetric instability (Emanuel

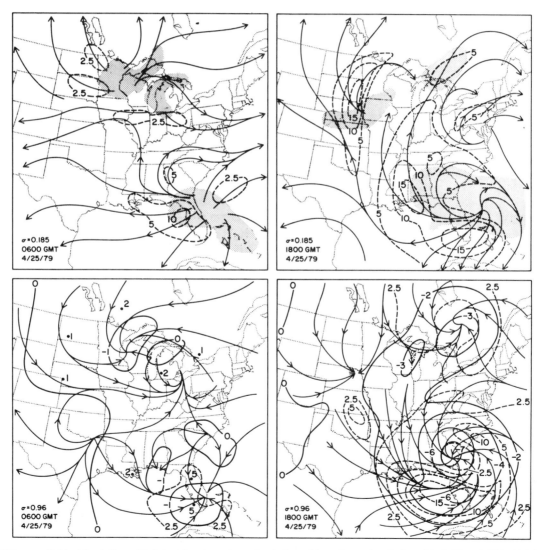

FIG. 12.12. Difference fields (simulation with latent heating minus simulation without latent heating) at 6 h (left) and 18 h (right). Shaded areas depict regions that received more than 0.19 cm of rain in the previous 3 h. Top two panels show wind differences in m s⁻¹ at $\sigma = 0.185$ (about 307 mb level). Lower two panels show boundary layer ($\sigma = 0.96$) wind differences in m s⁻¹ and surface pressure differences in mb (Anthes et al. 1982).

1983) in a case of explosive cyclogenesis over the North Pacific (13–14 November 1981). A vertical cross section of equivalent potential temperature and absolute momentum (M) through the warm front of the cyclone (Fig. 12.13) show that the air is generally weakly statically stable but symmetrically neutral (θ_e lines parallel to M lines). Over limited areas, the air is symmetrically unstable (θ_e lines more vertical than M lines; see Section 5.2.1). In this region the air ascends rapidly in a narrow, sloping sheet; vertical velocities exceed 75 cm s^{-1}. This rising air is associated with vertical stretching of the air column and a strong spin-up of low-level vorticity. In this simulation, the strong upward motion made possible by the symmetric instability was responsible for the rapid intensification of the cyclone.

On 18–19 February 1979, an intense cyclone developed along the East Coast of the U.S. Called the Presidents' Day storm because it occurred over the national holiday by that name, it produced heavy snowfall from Virginia to New York. Because of the intensity of the storm, its large impact on people and the failure of operational models to predict it well, it has been the object of numerous observational and theoretical investigations (Atlas 1987).

Orlanski and Katzfey (1987) studied the effects of latent heating on the Presidents' Day cyclone. Using a mesoscale model developed by the Geophysical Fluid Dynamics Laboratory (GFDL), they showed that latent heating had a major effect in producing the correct intensification of this storm and also strongly influenced the 500-mb heights. Near the center of the storm differences in sea-level pressure and 500-mb heights between simulations with and without latent heating were −13 mb and +36 m, respectively. These results agreed with those of other modeling studies of this storm (Atlas 1987; Uccellini et al. 1987).

d) *Effect of frictional dissipation*

Despite the importance of frictional dissipation in cyclones, there have been relatively few sensitivity studies isolating this effect. Anthes and Keyser (1979) studied the effect of surface friction on the model development of an extreme case of cyclogenesis over land, the "Ohio blizzard" of 26 January 1978 in which a 998-mb low over Mississippi deepened to 958 mb 24 hours later as it moved northward through the Ohio Valley. In the experiment with surface friction, the drag coefficient was between 5.0 and 10.0 × 10^{-3}; in the frictionless simulation it was zero. The effect of surface friction in this case of extreme cyclogenesis was large, the minimum pressure was 978 mb compared to 955 mb; the PBL winds were slower by a factor of about 2, and the cross-isobar flow angle was markedly greater than in the frictionless forecast. *The greater frictional convergence resulted in greater rainfall, despite the weaker storm intensity.*

In addition to including the effects of surface friction, numerical models parameterize the effects of horizontal and vertical mixing in the free atmosphere. These parameterizations are typically based on a down-gradient mixing theory and require coefficients of horizontal and vertical diffusivity. Although horizontal and vertical diffusion occur in the real atmosphere, the physical validity of these mixing parameterizations in models is often questionable; nevertheless some type of diffusion or smoothing mechanism must be included in the models to prevent nonlinear instability.

Orlanski and Katzfey (1987) investigated the sensitivity of the GFDL model simulations of the Presidents' Day cyclone to the value of horizontal diffusivity. They found that the intensity of the model cyclone varied considerably as K_h varied from 1.0×10^5 to 5.0×10^6 m^2 s^{-1}. The character and location of the development, however, did not change significantly with the magnitude of K_h. The sensitivity of the intensity of the development indicates that horizontal diffusion must be formulated carefully in LAMs.

e) *Cloud-radiation interactions*

As shown in Secs. 12.3.2a-b, sensible heating at the earth's land surface, driven by solar radiation, has an important effect on the planetary boundary-layer structure and low-level circulations associated with extratropical cyclones, even on time scales as short as a day. Therefore clouds at any level, because of their effect on the solar radiation reaching the surface, also must affect extratropical cyclones. In addition clouds, through their large effects on short- and long-wave radiation, may also affect extratropical cyclone structure through radiative heating and cooling in the free atmosphere. Hobgood (1986) has shown a significant effect of cloud-radiation interactions in a tropical cyclone model. To my knowledge, however, systematic modeling studies of the effect of cloud-radiation interactions on extratropical cyclones have not been done.

Sundqvist et al. (1989) described an innovative parameterization scheme for stratiform clouds and its behavior in a LAM with 50-km horizontal resolution. The scheme included four categories of clouds (high, middle, low and fog), longwave radiation and shortwave radiation with diurnal variation. This scheme was tested on a rapidly deepening storm that crossed southern Scandinavia on 5–6 September 1985 and caused heavy precipitation and a record-breaking early snowfall in eastern Norway. The results from a 36-hour integration indicated that this scheme gave improved results compared to simpler models and that the prediction of clouds compared favorably with satellite photographs.

f) *Orographic effects on cyclogenesis*

High mountain ranges, including the Alps, Himalayas, Rockies and Andes, have a major effect on cyclones. Because Tibaldi et al. discuss these effects in Chapter 7, I will present only a brief summary of several LAM studies of orographic effects on cyclones. Most of these have considered the effect of the Alps on cyclogenesis in the Gulf of Genoa. Egger (1972) showed that blocking of the low-level flow was crucial to a case of cyclogenesis; without the

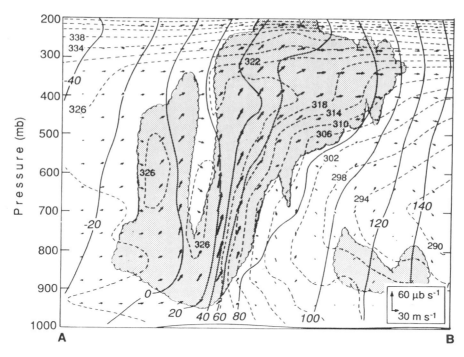

Fɪɢ. 12.13. South-north vertical cross section (A–B ~ 1550 km) through model warm front, of absolute momentum (solid contours, m s⁻¹) and equivalent potential temperature (dashed contours in K) at 12 UTC 13 November 1981. Arrows show motion in plane of cross section; shading denotes clouds (Kuo and Reed 1988).

mountain, no cyclogenesis occurred. Subsequent simulations by Trevisan (1976), Buzzi and Tibaldi (1978) and Tibaldi et al. (1980) emphasized a variety of complex physical factors including deformation of the low-level wind and temperature fields, and the resultant effects on energy transformations and baroclinic development. Bleck's (1977) real-data experiments showed that an elevation of the model Alps of at least 2000 m was necessary to obtain low-level cyclogenesis.

In 48-hour simulations with a LAM developed at GFDL, Mesinger and Strickler (1982) studied four cases of Genoa cyclogenesis. The model had a horizontal resolution of about 80 km and was adiabatic. In two of the four cases, cyclogenesis occurred without the presence of mountains; the mountains, however, significantly modified the storm structure in these cases. In the other two cases, mountains were essential for cyclogenesis. In three of the four cases, the primary or parent cyclone that moved eastward across northern Europe was 5 to 10 mb too intense when the mountains were removed, indicating that the effect of the Alps is to weaken large-scale cyclones passing to their north.

g) *Synergism of physical effects*

In the real atmosphere, individual physical processes rarely act in isolation. In the studies of cyclogenesis over oceans summarized above, sensible and latent heating were shown to interact, with a major effect of surface latent energy fluxes being to enhance the moisture available for condensation heating, which then affected deep layers of the atmosphere. Numerical models are particularly useful

in diagnosing such feedbacks, or the *synergism* of different physical and dynamical processes.

In a modeling study of the February 1979 Presidents' Day cyclone Uccellini et al. (1987) stressed the importance of the interactions among physical processes including sensible heating and evaporation from the surface, latent heating associated with precipitation, and adiabatic dynamical effects, particularly ageostrophic motions associated with upper- and lower-tropospheric jets (see Section 6.4). Figure 12.14a shows the analyzed surface map for 00 UTC 19 February 1979. Figures 12.14b-c show corresponding maps from simulations with a model that contained no diabatic or frictional effects, and a model that contained full physics. Without physical processes, the model failed to simulate the development of the cyclone and coastal front off the southeast coast. Other simulations with the model in which only partial physics were included failed to simulate the observed development. These simulations showed that neither physical processes nor adiabatic dynamical processes alone were sufficient to produce cyclogenesis. Instead, a synergistic interaction among dynamically-induced ageostrophic motions in the free atmosphere, heating and moistening of the PBL over the ocean, and latent heating associated with condensation and precipitation in the upward branch of the ageostrophic circulation, produced the observed cyclogenesis.

In a similar study, Zack and Kaplan (1987) modeled the evolution of the Atmospheric Variability Experiment (AVE)–SESAME I (10 April 1979) cyclone and showed the interactions between differential surface fluxes of heat

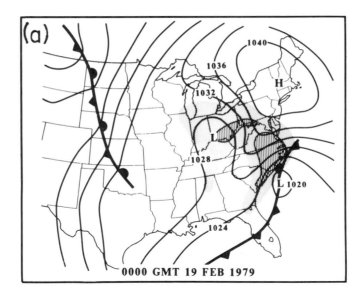

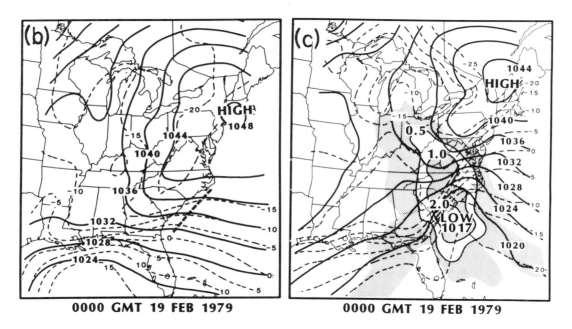

FIG. 12.14. (a) Surface analysis at 00 UTC 19 February 1979. Solid lines are sea-level isobars in mb; shading represents precipitation, with hatched shading representing moderate to heavy precipitation. (b) Sea-level pressure and isotherms (dashed, °C) for lowest model level (near 1000 mb) at 24 h of an adiabatic simulation. (c) As in (b) except for a model simulation containing diabatic and frictional effects (Uccellini et al. 1987). See also Fig. 6.18.

and momentum and the ageostrophic motions associated with upper- and lower-tropospheric jets. Differential vertical fluxes of sensible heat developed as a result of a boundary between clear and cloudy air. The resulting differential heating of the PBL produced a low-level pressure anomaly of 5 mb and an enhancement of the low-level isallobaric wind created by quasi-adiabatic mass adjustments induced by an upper-level jet. A significant downward flux of momentum occurred within the heated clear-air PBL, and this flux enhanced the low-level winds and convergence. The combination of adiabatic dynamical processes and the diabatic and frictional processes

increased the strength of a low-level jet.

In a third example of the synergistic interactions between diabatic and adiabatic processes, Chen and Dell'Osso (1987) used a limited-area version of the ECMWF global model to simulate a case of cyclogenesis along the East Asian coast. In the control experiment, which included all physical processes, the simulated cyclone developed similarly to the observed cyclone. When the effects of latent heating were excluded, however, only a shallow cyclone was simulated. The role of latent heating in this case was to create a strong vertical coupling between the upper- and lower-level circulations

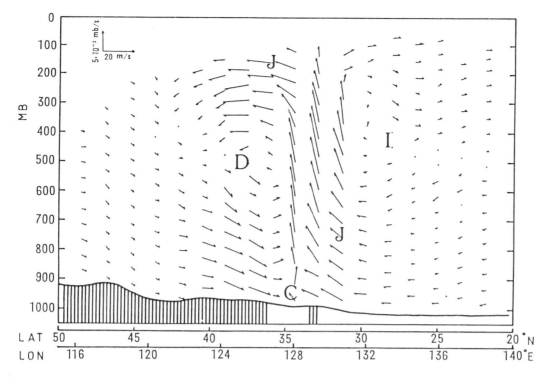

Fig. 12.15. Difference of 36-h simulated vertical transverse circulations between simulations with and without latent heating. Arrows are proportional to the speed. "J" denotes jet streams, "C" indicates place where cyclone developed and "I" and "D" indicate indirect and direct circulations, respectively (Chen and Dell'Osso 1987).

(Fig. 12.15). Chen and Dell'Osso also isolated the impact of sensible heating over the water; sensible heating contributed nearly 18 percent to the development. It created a baroclinic zone along the coast, much as it did in the case of the Presidents' Day cyclone. This coastal front enhanced the moisture convergence and the release of latent heat.

The above examples show the value of limited-area models in understanding complex atmospheric interactions. Because of the highly nonlinear and three-dimensional nature of these interactions, and the small scale of some of the processes, a high-resolution numerical model with complete physics is the most suitable research tool for the understanding of these cases of cyclogenesis.

12.3.3 Diagnostic Studies

Diagnostic studies using model data are useful in understanding the behavior of cyclones. When the diagnostic quantities are compared with the same quantities computed from observations, the results are also useful in verifying the models and in understanding their strengths and weaknesses.

Ageostrophic circulations associated with cyclones are known to be important in generating kinetic energy, transporting heat and moisture, changing the static stability of the atmosphere and inducing precipitation and severe weather. Because they are usually an order of magnitude smaller than the geostrophic circulations, however, they are difficult to resolve using conventional observations. In

a study of a tornado outbreak in Ohio on 10–11 May 1973, Uccellini and Johnson (1979) hypothesized that an indirect vertical circulation (sinking motion on the warm, anticyclonic side of the jet and rising motion on the cold cyclonic side) in the exit region of an upper-level jet caused lower-tropospheric mass changes that led to the development of a low-level jet. The resulting differential advection of heat and moisture destabilized the atmosphere and created an environment favorable for the development of severe convective storms.

In a synoptic case study using the British Meteorological Office's LAM, McCallum et al. (1983) investigated the airflow through a cyclone that produced extensive rainfall over England on 22 June 1982. The airflow through the cyclone was illustrated by examining trajectories of air parcels as computed from the model data. Figure 12.16 represents the low-level airflow over a 24-hour period as deduced from many model trajectories. North of the frontal zone (indicated by the dashed line), the air moves westward and sinks. South of the frontal zone, the air moves northward without significant vertical displacement until it reaches the front, where it ascends rapidly. At upper levels (450 mb), air to the north sinks and splits into two streams, one moving eastward and the other westward (not shown). To the south, the rising airstream also splits into eastward and westward flowing branches.

Orlanski and Ross (1984) analyzed the development and structure of an observed cold front using a LAM developed at the GFDL. Ross and Orlanski (1982) de-

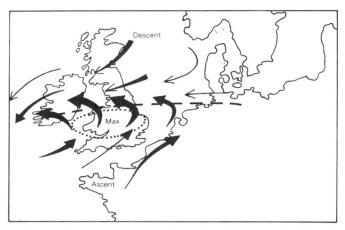

FIG. 12.16. Schematic diagram of airflow near 950 mb at 12 UTC 22 June 1982. Rising air parcels are indicated by arrows that thicken toward their heads and descending parcels by arrows that thicken toward their tails (McCallum et al. 1983).

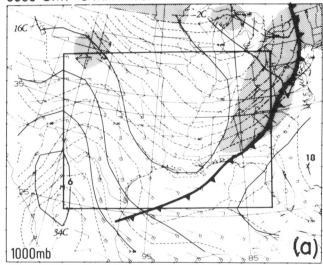

scribe the model and two 48-hour simulations, a dry simulation and one with moisture effects included. Figure 12.17 shows the observed low-level flow at 12 UTC 2 May 1967 and the corresponding 36-hour simulation from the moist model. Orlanski and Ross's (1984) analysis focused on the kinematics and dynamics of the frontal zone and the development of moist convection in the zone. Analysis of the vorticity and divergence equations showed that during the intensification phase of the front (0–12 hours), the vorticity and convergence maxima were superimposed, which produced strong vortex stretching. In the mature phase (24–36 hours), the convergence maximum was located ahead of the vorticity maximum and the front was in a quasi-steady state. From 42 to 48 hour, ageostrophic effects produced frontolysis by displacing the convergence maximum farther from the vorticity maximum.

When moisture was included in the model through the addition of an explicit prediction equation for cloud water, the frontogenesis during the first 24 hours was similar to that in the dry simulation because there was little condensation. After the outbreak of moist convection in the frontal zone at 24 hours, however, the simulations differed significantly. The increased vertical motions associated with the moist convection intensified the vortex stretching and increased the low-level vorticity.

In order to show the dynamic and thermodynamic balances that existed in the front, Orlanski and Ross (1984) computed the individual terms in the prognostic equations for five variables: horizontal components of wind in the plane of a cross section through the front (u) and perpendicular to the cross section (v), potential temperature θ, water vapor mixing ratio q_v and cloud water mixing ratio q_c. In the momentum equations, the coriolis and pressure-gradient terms tend to balance in the u-equation, reflecting the quasi-geostrophic balance of the large-scale jet stream. Horizontal advection modifies this

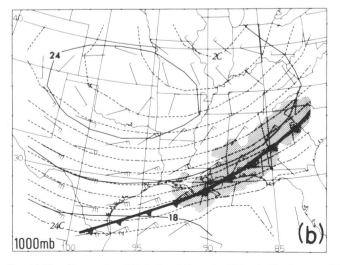

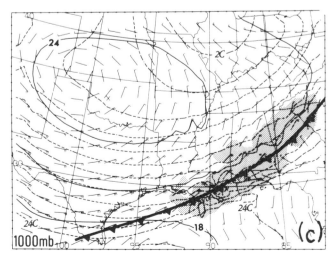

FIG. 12.17. Observed and 36-h simulation of cold front. Charts are on 1000-mb surface for (a) observed fields and, within the inner frame, (b) fine-mesh solution smoothed to coarse grid and (c) unsmoothed fine-mesh solution. Solid lines are geopotential height (dam); dashed lines, temperature (°C). Winds are in knots. Regions in which precipitation was measured during the preceding 6 h are indicated by stippling (Ross and Orlanski 1982).

balance in the upper troposphere. In the *v*-equation, horizontal and vertical advection are large in the frontal zone. In the potential temperature equation, diabatic heating and adiabatic cooling tend to balance in the frontal zone of moist convection. This zone is characterized by a near balance between vertical advection and condensation in the equation for water vapor mixing ratio. Finally, the cloud-water equation is dominated by the condensation and rain production terms.

Brill et al. (1985) used the Penn State/NCAR LAM to verify Uccellini and Johnson's hypothesis. In a 12-hour adiabatic simulation, they found a clearly defined indirect circulation as hypothesized. Figure 12.18 shows vertical cross sections at 9 hours of the simulation perpendicular to the upper-level jet in the exit region. At the level of the upper jet on the anticyclonic side, the horizontal wind in the plane of the section is directed from north to south; while at lower levels the flow is from south to north. This horizontal flow, coupled by the sinking motion between 32° and 35°N and rising motion between 35° and 44°N, is the indirect circulation. *Through differential advection of heat and moisture, this circulation destabilized the model*

environment as hypothesized. In a second simulation in which the initial upper-level jet was weakened by smoothing, the indirect circulation and the resultant destabilization were considerably less, indicating that the mass imbalances associated with the propagating upper-level jet were the major cause of the indirect vertical circulation.

12.3.4 Energy Budget Studies

Numerical simulations using LAMs have been useful in studying the energetics of extratropical cyclones. Chen and Dell'Osso (1987) computed the kinetic energy budget for the control and dry simulations of cyclogenesis off the east coast of Asia. The kinetic energy equation for the model in sigma (σ) coordinates is

$$\frac{\partial}{\partial t}(p_S k) = -\nabla_\sigma \cdot (p_S k \overline{V}) - \frac{\partial}{\partial \sigma}(p_S k \dot{\sigma})$$
$$\text{A} \qquad\qquad \text{B} \qquad\qquad \text{C} \qquad\qquad (12.1)$$
$$- p_S \overline{V} \cdot (\nabla_\sigma \Phi + RT \nabla_\sigma \ell n p_S) + p_S R_k$$
$$\text{D} \qquad\qquad\qquad \text{E}$$

where p_S is surface pressure, T is temperature, Φ is geopotential height, V is horizontal vector velocity, $\dot{\sigma}$ is the

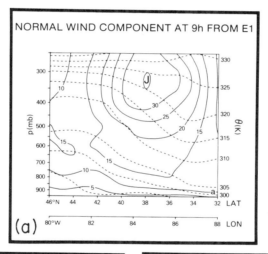

(a)

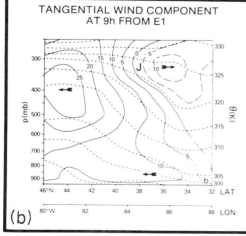

(b)

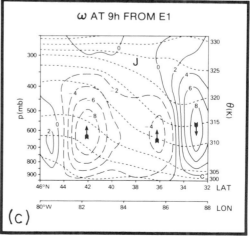

(c)

Fɪɢ. 12.18.   Vertical cross sections at 9 h of simulation valid at 21 UTC 10 May 1973. Dashed lines are potential temperature in K. (a) Component of wind normal to the cross section in m s⁻¹. (b) Component of wind in the plane of the section in m s⁻¹. (c) Vertical velocity ω in μb s⁻¹. "J" marks the location of the maximum normal wind component (Brill et al. 1985).

vertical velocity in sigma coordinates, k is kinetic energy $(u^2 + v^2)/2$ and R_k is the dissipation of kinetic energy through surface and internal friction. The area-averaged, vertically-integrated kinetic energy budget for the two simulations is shown in Table 12.1. Without latent heating, the region lost rather than gained kinetic energy over a 24-hour period. The gain in generation of kinetic energy associated with the latent heat release, with an intensified vertical and transverse circulation (Fig. 12.15), more than offset the increased frictional dissipation.

Robertson and Smith (1983) computed energy budgets for two cases of extratropical cyclone development using the Drexel-NCAR Limited Area Mesoscale Prediction System (LAMPS). The total kinetic energy K, integrated over mass per unit area, is defined as

$$K = \frac{1}{g} \int_{P_U}^{P_S} \left[\overline{\frac{\mathbf{V} \cdot \mathbf{V}}{2}} \right] dp \qquad (12.2)$$

where the overbar is a zonal averaging operator, [ ] is an averaging operator in the meridional direction and subscripts S and U refer to the surface and upper level pressures, respectively.

The total kinetic energy K is expanded into the zonal mean and the eddy kinetic energy

$$K = KZ + KE \qquad (12.3)$$

where KZ and KE are given by

$$KZ = \frac{1}{g} \int_{P_U}^{P_S} \left[\frac{\overline{\mathbf{V}} \cdot \overline{\mathbf{V}}}{2} \right] dp \qquad (12.4)$$

and

$$KE = \frac{1}{g} \int_{P_U}^{P_S} \left[\overline{\frac{\mathbf{V}' \cdot \mathbf{V}'}{2}} \right] dp . \qquad (12.5)$$

The temporal rate of KE change is

$$\underbrace{\frac{\partial KE}{\partial t}}_{\text{DKEDT}} = \underbrace{-\frac{1}{g} \int_{P_U}^{P_S} \overline{[\mathbf{V}' \cdot \nabla_p \Phi']} \, dp}_{\text{GKE}} + \underbrace{\frac{1}{g} \int_{P_U}^{P_S} \overline{[\mathbf{V}' \cdot \mathbf{F}']} \, dp}_{\text{DE}}$$

$$\underbrace{-\frac{1}{g} \int_{P_U}^{P_S} \overline{\left[\nabla_p \cdot \left(\frac{\mathbf{V}' \cdot \mathbf{V}'}{2} \right) \mathbf{V} \right]} dp}_{\text{HFKE}}$$

Table 12.1.

For an East Asiatic coastal cyclogenesis, the area-averaged, vertically-integrated kinetic energy budget in the dry and moist simulations for 24–28 h initiated 00 UTC 28 November 1982. Integrands are identified beneath Eq. (12.1); term C vanishes in the vertical integration. Units in W m^{-2} (Chen and Dell'Osso 1987).

	$\frac{1}{g}\int_0^1 [A] \, d\sigma$ local change	$-\frac{1}{g}\int_0^1 [B] \, d\sigma$ convergence of KE flux	$-\frac{1}{g}\int_0^1 [D] \, d\sigma$ generation of KE	$[E]$ dissipation (residual)
Moist	3.1	−9.5	19.7	−7.1
Dry	−2.4	−8.1	7.8	−2.1

$$\underbrace{-\frac{1}{g} \int_{P_U}^{P_S} \overline{\left[\frac{\partial}{\partial p} \left(\omega \frac{\mathbf{V}' \cdot \mathbf{V}'}{2} \right) \right]} dp}_{\text{VFKE}}$$

$$\underbrace{-\frac{1}{g} \int_{P_U}^{P_S} \overline{[\mathbf{V}' \cdot (\mathbf{V}' \cdot \nabla_p)\overline{\mathbf{V}}]} \, dp - \frac{1}{g} \int_{P_U}^{P_S} \overline{\left[\mathbf{V}' \cdot \omega' \frac{\partial \overline{\mathbf{V}}}{\partial p} \right]} dp}_{\text{CK}}$$

$$\underbrace{+\frac{1}{g} \left[\frac{\overline{\mathbf{V}'_S \cdot \mathbf{V}'_S}}{2} \, \frac{\partial p_S}{\partial t} \right]}_{\text{KPSE}} \qquad (12.6)$$

where ω is the vertical motion in pressure coordinates and $\mathbf{F}$ the frictional force. The terms in (12.6) represent the local change (DKEDT), mechanical generation (GKE), dissipation (DE); horizontal flux convergence (HFKE), vertical flux convergence (VFKE) of eddy kinetic energy; conversion of zonal to eddy kinetic energy (CK); and the change in KE due to the change in mass of the domain (KPSE). In (12.5) and (12.6) the prime indicates the eddy departure from the zonal average.

The first case studied by Robertson and Smith consisted of a slowly developing cyclone characterized by relatively weak baroclinic forcing and heavy precipitation. The energetics of two model simulations, one with moist physics included and one without moist physics, were computed; the individual terms are shown in Table 12.2. The KPSE term is small and is not shown; the VFKE term vanishes as a result of the vertical integration and the upper- and lower-boundary conditions by assumption of $\omega = 0$ at the top isobaric surface and the ground. The results summarized in Table 12.2 showed that both models lost eddy kinetic energy over a 24-hour period through the conversion of eddy to zonal kinetic energy (CK) and dissipation (DE). The effect of latent heat of condensation resulted in a significantly greater positive generation of

Table 12.2.

Vertically integrated, area-averaged KE budgets for moist and dry model forecasts initialized at 12 UTC 20 May 1977. Units are W m^{-2} except KE which is 10^5 J m^{-2}. Values are rounded to nearest tenth (Robertson and Smith 1983).

Date/time	KE	$\partial KE/\partial t$	HFKE	GKE	CK	DE
Moist forecast						
20/12	6.8		0.1	2.6	−2.1	
20/18	5.7	−4.7	0.0	3.4	−2.1	−5.6
21/00	5.2	−2.6	−0.5	1.7	−2.0	−2.9
21/06	4.7	−2.2	−0.4	2.5	−1.6	−2.1
21/12	4.4	−1.6	−0.2	1.8	−1.3	−2.0
Mean	5.3	−2.8	−0.2	2.4	−1.9	−3.1
Dry forecast						
20/12	6.8		0.1	2.6	−2.1	
20/18	5.7	−4.9	−0.1	1.6	−2.1	−4.9
21/00	5.0	−3.1	−0.5	0.3	−1.9	−1.8
21/06	4.3	−3.3	−0.3	0.6	−1.5	−1.7
21/12	3.8	−2.6	−0.5	−0.0	−1.2	−1.1
Mean	5.1	−3.5	−0.3	0.9	−1.8	−2.4

eddy kinetic energy through the eddy cross-contour flow (GKE). Thus the moist model produced a stronger eddy flow field.

The second cyclone case contained much stronger baroclinic forcing, and both dry and moist models showed an increase in eddy kinetic energy over a 48-hour period. In contrast to the first case, the flux of KE across the lateral boundaries (HFKE) was the dominant process. The generation of KE was significantly different in the dry and moist models. While GKE was negative throughout the period in the dry forecast, it became positive during the last 18 hours of the moist forecast. Thus in both cases the effects of latent heating were to increase the eddy kinetic energy.

Dare and Smith (1984) computed eddy kinetic energy budgets for moist and dry 48-hour forecasts of a developing winter extratropical cyclone. They computed area-average, vertically integrated values of KE and the terms in (12.6) for five time periods for a model forecast that contained moist physics, a dry version of the model, and from analyses of the developing storm. Table 12.3 shows the individual terms in the area-averaged KE budgets for the moist and dry model forecasts.

Both models show less of an increase of KE than observed, with the moist model doing somewhat better than the dry model. The primary source of KE in this case was advection through the lateral boundaries, represented by the HFKE term in Table 12.3; the models, however, showed significantly smaller values of HFKE than observed, suggesting that the numerical treatment of the LBC did not permit the proper advection of KE into the domain.

The major sinks of KE were GKE, indicating that the eddy cross-isobar flow was generally from lower to higher

heights, and frictional dissipation, DE. The negative GKE indicates that the eddy flow was mainly supergradient. The observed and modeled CK was positive during the first part of the period and negative in the latter stages. Positive (negative) values of CK indicate that KE is increasing (decreasing) at the expense of zonal kinetic energy.

The salient results of the Dare and Smith (1984) study were: (1) the primary source of KE was horizontal advection into the limited-area domain associated with the upper-level jet; (2) the models underestimated this horizontal advection because of inadequate treatment of the LBC, hence underpredicting the development of the storm; and (3) latent heating enhanced the generation of KE.

12.3.5 Observing Systems Simulation Experiments

LAMs have been increasingly useful in recent years in testing the impact of different types of observing systems in initialization of forecasts and in the subsequent forecast skill of the model. In an observing system simulation experiment (OSSE), a model is used to generate a four-dimensional data set; these high-resolution data are considered to represent the evolution of the atmosphere. They are used as verification data for subsequent forecasts that are initialized with data extracted from some time in the control run, usually after the control run has adjusted to initial imbalances and reached a slowly varying quasi-balanced state. The data are selected to represent certain observing systems, such as satellite winds or temperature retrievals, balloon systems, or ground-based wind, thermodynamic or moisture profilers. Arnold and Dey (1986) provide a review of OSSEs. It should be noted that OSSEs tend to overestimate the impact of increased accuracy and/or density of observations, especially when the model used to generate the pseudo-observations is the same as the model used to assimilate the pseudo-observations. When real observations are assimilated into models, the models often tend to reject the observations.

Recent OSSEs using limited-area models include those by Kuo and Anthes (1984, 1985), Kuo et al. (1985), Lee and Houghton (1984), Cram and Kaplan (1985) and Gal-Chen et al. (1986). As an example of the use of LAMs in OSSEs, I review the study of the impact of a network of profilers on short-term weather prediction by Kuo et al. (1987). They studied the impact of various observing systems on simulations of the cyclone of 22–25 April 1981, which crossed the central and eastern U.S. This cyclone was typical of those baroclinic developments that occur over this region in winter and spring. In these OSSEs a relatively coarse-resolution (80 km), large-domain forecast was initialized at 00 UTC 22 April and integrated for 72 hours; these data were used to provide LBC to subsequent higher-resolution (40 km) small-domain simulations. The data at 12 hours of this simulation were also used to initialize the 60-hour control experiment. The 12-hour forecast of the control experiment provided initial

TABLE 12.3.

Area-averaged, vertically-integrated eddy kinetic energy budget (KE in 10^5 J m^{-2}; other quantities in W m^{-2}), for a cyclone over North America in January 1975 (Dare and Smith 1984).

	Day/time	KE	DKEDT	HFKE	GKE	CK	DE
Observed	9/12	10.2		29.0	−4.4	3.1	
	10/00	16.1	13.7	25.1	−4.8	2.4	−11.4
	10/12	22.0	13.7	30.3	2.4	−4.3	−11.6
	11/00	26.0	9.3	39.5	−19.9	−6.5	−11.1
	11/12	30.7	10.9	43.1	−14.9	2.4	−10.8
	Average	21.1	11.9	32.7	−8.0	−1.4	−11.2
Moist model	9/12	12.7		29.2	−9.7	2.1	
	10/00	16.5	8.8	17.6	−12.7	2.0	−5.6
	10/12	19.5	6.9	10.1	0.0	−0.5	−1.3
	11/00	20.0	1.2	16.3	5.2	−4.9	−11.7
	11/12	22.1	4.9	11.9	6.2	−11.1	−6.7
	Average	18.4	5.5	16.1	−2.3	−2.0	−6.2
Dry model	9/12	12.7		29.2	−9.7	2.1	
	10/00	16.3	8.3	17.4	−13.7	1.8	−5.5
	10/12	18.3	4.6	13.5	−9.2	0.6	−0.6
	11/00	18.2	−0.2	17.9	−8.9	−1.8	−6.0
	11/12	19.1	2.1	9.1	−1.8	−6.1	−1.8
	Average	17.2	3.7	17.0	−9.4	−0.4	−3.4

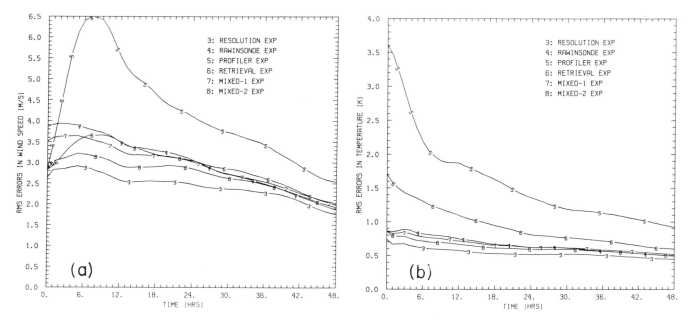

FIG. 12.19. Time series of vertically-integrated RMS errors in (a) wind speed and (b) temperature for six OSSEs. The text describes the different simulations (Kuo et al. 1987).

data of varying spatial density and error characteristics to a series of 48-hour forecasts in the OSSEs.

The impact of different observing systems on the 48-hour forecasts was indicated by the temporal evolution of vertically and horizontally averaged root-mean-square (RMS) errors of temperature and winds. Figure 12.19 illustrates these errors for six experiments. Experiment 3, which shows the smallest wind and temperature errors, was initialized with perfect data extracted from the control, but at a resolution of 360 km rather than 40 km. In Exp. 4, these soundings were degraded by adding errors typical of operational rawinsondes. The RMS temperature errors were 1°C, RMS relative humidity errors were 10 percent, and the RMS wind errors increased linearly with decreasing pressure from 1 m s^{-1} at 1000 mb to 6 m s^{-1} at 100 mb.

In Exp. 5, called the profiler experiment, the initial data were modified by adding random errors to represent observations from a network of wind, temperature and moisture profilers supplemented by satellite observations. A 1 m s^{-1} RMS error was added to the wind data and 2°C and 10 percent RMS errors were added to the temperature and relative humidity data. These soundings were then heavily smoothed in the vertical to reduce the vertical resolution to vary from about 130 mb near the surface to 270 mb near the top of the model. In Exp. 6 (retrieval experiment), the initial temperatures were derived from the profiler-simulated wind data of Exp. 5 from a form of the divergence equation following Kuo and Anthes (1985).

Experiments 7 and 8 include a mixture of rawinsonde and profiler data. Experiment 7 is the same as the rawinsonde experiment (Exp. 4) except that a wind profiler was placed in the middle of every grid square defined by the rawinsonde network. In Exp. 8, the radiosonde tempera-

tures and humidities of Exp. 4 are retained, but the rawinsonde winds at these points are replaced by the more accurate profiler winds. If the winds in current operational networks were provided by profilers as simulated in Exp. 8, a less expensive balloon system could be used.

The results in Fig. 12.19 indicate that *profiler wind observations have a small but positive impact on the forecasts* (Exps. 7 and 8 versus Exp. 4). The forecasts initialized with only profiler data (Exps. 5 and 6) were significantly inferior to those initialized with rawinsonde data; the forecast initialized with temperatures derived from the profiler winds, however, was significantly better than the one initialized with radiometric temperatures (Exp. 6 versus Exp. 5). The accuracies of the forecasts rank as follows: (1) profiler wind with radiosonde temperature and moisture, (2) mixed profiler and rawinsonde winds with radiosonde temperature and moisture, (3) rawinsonde wind, temperature and moisture, (4) profiler wind and moisture with retrieved temperatures and (5) profiler wind, temperature and moisture.

12.4 The Metamorphosis of Hurricane Hazel Revisited

During the 36-hour period beginning at 03 UTC 15 October 1954, an intense tropical cyclone—Hurricane Hazel—crossed the coast of North Carolina and moved northward along a path east of the Appalachians, passing over the western suburbs of Washington, D.C. Rather than weakening rapidly over land, as is typical of tropical cyclones, Hazel interacted with an unusually intense upper-level trough over the Ohio Valley (see Fig. 1.10a) and underwent a metamorphosis into a major extratropical cyclone. This intense storm crossed Pennsylvania, western

New York, passed directly over Toronto and eventually began to decay in northern Canada (Fig. 12.20a). As shown in Fig. 12.20b, rainfall along the path of the storm was typically 10–20 cm (4–8 inches), with some local points receiving more than 25 cm (10 inches). Although causing about 60 deaths and property losses in excess of $460 million, Hazel provided beneficial rains over a large area; for many places in the drought-stricken southeastern United States, Hazel provided the first soaking rain in months. This unusual event, described by Krueger (1954), Mook (1955), Davis (1954), Knox (1955) and Hughes et al. (1955), attracted the attention of Palmén, who carried out detailed analyses of the storm structure and calculated water and energy budgets from the rawinsonde data over the eastern United States (Palmén 1958, 1959, 1961). From these analyses, Palmén reached a number of important conclusions about the three-dimensional airflow through the system, the importance of the release of latent heat to the development and maintenance of the transformed cyclone and the overall contribution of the storm to the energetics of the Northern Hemisphere (see Sections 1.6.1, 1.7.1). His diagnostics, however, were necessarily limited by the quality and temporal and spatial resolution of the rawinsonde network.

This section revisits the metamorphosis of Hurricane Hazel using a three-dimensional numerical model. Three simulations are conducted to examine the evolution and structure of the tropical and extratropical cyclone with a high-resolution model data set and to help answer two questions raised by Palmén and others in the 1950s—the relative contribution of the hurricane circulation to the

development of the extratropical cyclone and the importance of the release of latent heat to this development. In the control simulation, a model with complete physics is initialized with a combination of real data and hypothetical, but plausible, data designed to represent a realistic atmospheric structure containing Hurricane Hazel. In a second simulation, the release of latent heat is neglected; a comparison of this "dry" simulation with the control indicates the importance of latent heat in the evolution of the system. In the third simulation, the hurricane circulation is removed from the initial conditions; this simulation helps show the significance of the hurricane to the extratropical cyclone development.

12.4.1 The Numerical Model and the Initial Conditions

The numerical model is an improved version of the Penn State/NCAR model, and is described by Anthes et al. (1987). It is a hydrostatic model in sigma coordinates. In all three simulations, the model contains 15 layers with a top at 100 mb and a horizontal resolution of 80 km. The planetary boundary layer physics is based on the model of Blackadar (Zhang and Anthes 1982). The moisture cycle in the model includes both resolvable-scale precipitation and subgrid-scale cumulus convective precipitation, based on Anthes' (1977) scheme.

The initial conditions (03 UTC 15 October 1954) and the lateral boundary conditions were determined from rawinsonde data archived at the National Center for Atmospheric Research and subjectively-derived sound-

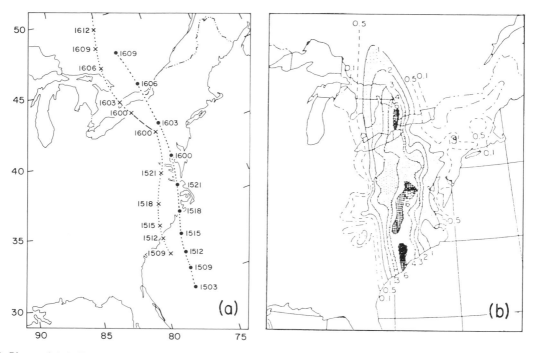

Fig. 12.20. (a) Observed (×) (Knox 1955) and control model simulation (●) track of Hurricane Hazel during the period 03 UTC 15 October (denoted by 1503 in figure) to 12 UTC 16 October 1954. (b) Precipitation in inches during the 24-h period ending 06 UTC 16 October (Palmén 1958).

ings based on Palmén's (1958) analyses of 1000-mb, 850-mb, 700-mb, 500-mb and 300-mb constant pressure surfaces. The subjective soundings were obtained by computing layer-mean temperatures from the geopotential height values in Palmén's analyses. The winds for these soundings were approximated by estimates of the gradient wind, also made from Palmén's maps. Relative humidities were estimated to range from 80 percent in the environment of the storm to 95 percent near the storm center.

The soundings were analyzed on constant pressure surfaces by a series of successive scans. The inner structure of the hurricane was determined by specifying a central pressure of approximately 975 mb and a temperature sounding at the center of the storm; the central pressure and temperatures were estimated from the geopotential heights of the constant pressure surfaces in Palmén's analyses. The winds in the vicinity of the hurricane were obtained from a weighted average of the gradient wind computed from the analyzed geopotential heights and the wind observations in the environment. The gradient tangential winds v_λ were computed from

$$v_\lambda = \frac{r}{2}\left[-f+\left(f^2+\frac{4}{r}\frac{\partial\Phi}{\partial r}\right)^{1/2}\right] \qquad (12.7)$$

where the radius of curvature r was assumed to be the distance from the storm center. The gradient u and v components are related to the tangential wind by

$$u_{gr} = -v_\lambda\frac{y}{r},$$

$$v_{gr} = v_\lambda\frac{x}{r}. \qquad (12.8)$$

The final wind components used to initialize the model were derived from

$$u = F(r)\,u_{gr} + [1.0 - F(r)]\,u_{an}$$
$$\qquad\qquad\qquad\qquad (12.9)$$
$$v = F(r)\,v_{gr} + [1.0 - F(r)]\,v_{an}$$

where u_{an} and v_{an} are the analyzed wind components based on the soundings in the storm's environment and $F(r)$ is given, after Fiorino and Warner (1981), by

$$F(r) = \cos\left(\frac{\pi r}{2R}\right). \qquad (12.10)$$

Here $R = 3\Delta s = 240$ km.

Figure 12.21a shows the initial sea-level pressure field. A 997-mb extratropical cyclone is centered over the Great Lakes region; a strong cold front extends southward from this low to the Gulf Coast. High pressure dominates the western U.S. Hurricane Hazel, located about 400 km east of Jacksonville, Florida, is embedded completely within a warm, moist tropical air mass. The initial 500-mb chart (Fig. 12.21b) shows an unusually intense trough with a cyclone centered over the upper Midwest. A strong front is also present at 500 mb, with the temperature ranging from greater that $-10°$C over the eastern U.S. to less than $-28°$C over the Midwest. Jet-stream winds around this trough

exceed 55 m s^{-1} at 500 mb and 90 m s^{-1} at 300 mb (not shown).

12.4.2 Control Simulation

In the control simulation, Hurricane Hazel moves rapidly northward, following a path about 100 km east of the observed path (Fig. 12.20a). The model storm lags behind the observed storm by about 3 hours; this slow and eastward bias is present very early in the simulation, and is probably related to imbalances in the initial conditions.

The 12-hour forecast sea-level pressure map is shown in Fig. 12.22a. Hurricane Hazel has moved northward to a location about 50 km south of the North Carolina coast and deepened slightly to a minimum pressure of 973 mb. Although the simulated storm lags the observed storm by about 100 km, the simulated sea-level pressure field is similar to Palmén's 1000-mb analysis (Fig. 12.22b).

A west-east vertical cross section through the model-simulated Hurricane Hazel at 15 UTC 15 October (not shown) reveals a warm-core structure ahead of the surface cold front with a deep cyclonic circulation that is clearly

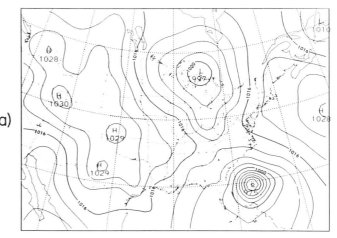

(a)

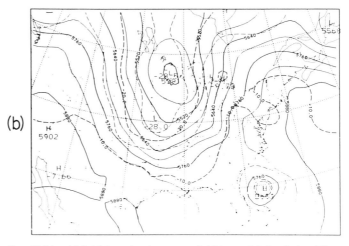

(b)

FIG. 12.21. (a) Initial sea-level pressure field in model simulation. The contour interval is 4 mb. The time is 03 UTC 15 October 1954. (b) As in (a) but for 500-mb height (solid lines, interval 60 m) and temperature (dashed lines, interval 5°C).

separate from the upper-level extratropical cyclonic system to the west.

Figure 12.23a and b compares west-east vertical cross sections along approximately 45°N from Palmén's analysis and the 12-hour model simulation. These cross sections depict the cold air mass in the upper Midwest and the unusually intense tropospheric fronts on both sides of the cold dome, with their associated southerly and northerly jets. The structure of the model atmosphere has many features in common with Palmén's analysis, including the two baroclinic zones that extend throughout most of the troposphere, the northerly and southerly jets and the warm stratosphere above the cold dome. The model cross section shows a narrow tongue of extremely dry air extending from the stratosphere to near the surface on the eastern side of the cold dome; the two soundings in the cold dome confirm the presence of this dry air by the symbol "MB"—motorboating—named after the staccato sound produced by the rawinsonde receiver when the relative humidity is too low to measure.

During the next 12 hours Hazel moved rapidly northward and interacted with the upper-level trough and baroclinic zone, becoming an intense 975-mb low centered over Lake Ontario (Fig. 12.24a). The model hurricane behaved in a similar fashion (Fig. 12.24b), although the early slow bias persisted. The forecast and observed low-level pressure fields and circulation, however, are remarkably similar. Figure 12.25a and b shows observed and model cross sections through the cyclone center. Although the air directly above and to the east of the model cyclone is warm and moist, the distinct warm core that was present 12 hours earlier has disappeared and the transformation into a typical extratropical cyclone is nearly complete (remnants of a separate low-level cyclonic circulation associated with the hurricane are still present at this time). Both model and observed cross sections show a strong baroclinic zone on the eastern side of the cold dome, with a weaker baroclinic zone on the west side. The circulation in the plane of the cross section (denoted by arrows in Fig. 12.25b) shows a stream of rapidly moving air approaching the cyclone at low levels from the southeast and rising in a narrow branch over the cold front; it is this branch of the circulation that produced the heavy rainfall.

Figure 12.26a and b shows the vertical motion fields at 600 mb as computed kinematically by Palmén (1961) and the instantaneous vertical motions from the model simu-

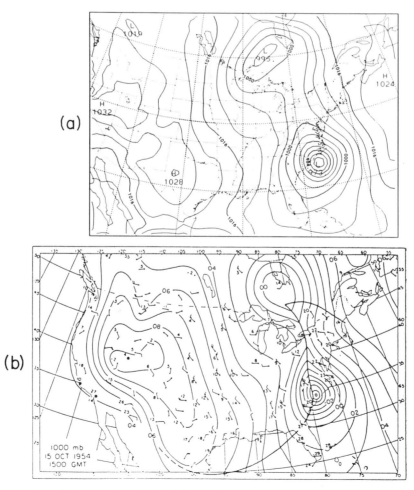

(a)

(b)

FIG. 12.22. (a) Sea-level pressure from 12-h control model simulation, verifying 15 UTC 15 October 1954. The contour interval is 4 mb. (b) Analyzed 1000-mb chart (Palmén 1958) at same time. Solid lines are heights in hundreds of feet, winds are in knots, surface temperatures are plotted in °C.

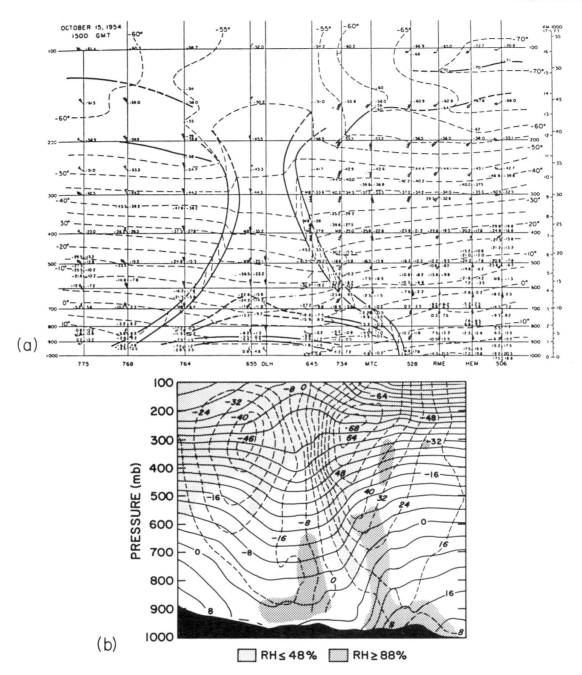

FIG. 12.23.   (a) Vertical cross section at 15 UTC 15 October 1954, approximately along parallel 45°N. Thin dashed lines are isotherms in °C; heavy lines, frontal boundaries or tropopauses. Temperature, dewpoint and wind (knots) are indicated at standard levels and significant points (Palmén 1958). (b) Cross section from control simulation along same line and at same time. Solid lines are isotherms (interval 4°C), dashed lines are speeds (interval 8 m s^{-1}) of wind component normal to cross section, with positive into cross section.

lation at 12 hours. Although the model shows much greater small-scale structure, the two major features of intense upward motion over North Carolina and Virginia and the sinking motion center over Arkansas are present in both fields. The agreement of the maximum values in both these centers within 10 percent is remarkable. Palmén noted the high correlation between rising motion and warm air and sinking motion and cold air, with the resulting strong conversion of potential to kinetic energy. He estimated that only 2 to 3.5 disturbances of the size

and intensity of Hazel would be required to furnish the whole hemisphere north of 30°N with the kinetic energy necessary for the maintenance of the circulation against frictional dissipation.

Figure 12.27a and b shows the observed and forecast 300-mb circulations. Both show a deep closed low centered over Illinois, with winds in excess of 50 m s^{-1} on the east and west sides of the trough. The southeasterly jet at 300 mb extending northwestward from the surface cyclone over the Great Lakes exceeds 77 m s^{-1}. Palmén

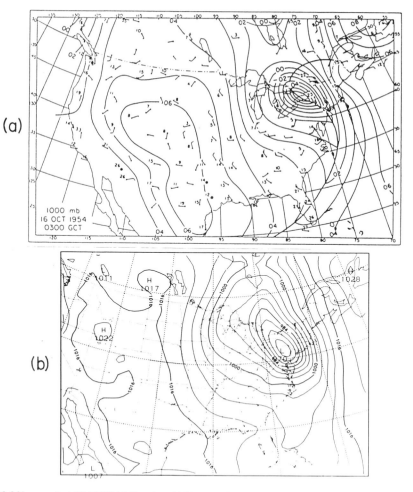

FIG. 12.24. (a) As in Fig. 12.22b except at 03 UTC 16 October 1954 (Palmén 1958). (b) As in Fig. 12.22a except for 24-h simulation verifying at same time.

showed that this jet represented a large net export of kinetic energy from the region of the storm (see Fig. 1.10):

> The kinetic energy produced by the sinking cold air and ascending warm air in the extratropical cyclone "Hazel" was to a very large extent available for export out of the source region. This export occurred . . . between 400 and 200 mb in the form of an upper jet stream leaving the active disturbance [Palmén 1958, p. 20].

Figure 12.27c shows 24-hour trajectories computed from the model simulation. Parcels of air near the surface in the vicinity of Hurricane Hazel are caught in the cyclonic flow and are carried northward with the hurricane system. Many ascend in the upward branch of the hurricane circulation and arrive over Canada in the upper troposphere; for example the trajectory ending just southeast of James Bay started at 937 mb and ended at 218 mb. This stream of tropical air that originated near the ocean surface near the hurricane and ended up in the upper troposphere over southeastern Canada was diagnosed by Palmén from an analysis of the potential wet-bulb temperature:

The potential wet-bulb temperature of this upper air equalled that of the surface layer over the ocean to the southeast of the American continent, whereas the air at the same levels to the west of the upper trough was considerably colder. This analysis shows that this warm and moist air could not have been brought around the upper trough, but was oceanic tropical air which had been lifted from the surface layers in the central parts of the tropical cyclone.

The southeasterly flow of warm, moist tropical air ahead of Hurricane Hazel produced the heavy band of precipitation as it was lifted over the colder air to the west. The relatively narrow band of heavy precipitation, with an especially intense gradient on the western side, was reasonably well-simulated by the model (compare Fig. 12.28a with Fig. 12.20b). The model, however, failed to reproduce the extreme values of 25 cm that were observed; maximum grid-point (80-km average) values of precipitation were about 10 cm.

12.4.3   The Importance of Latent Heat in the Hazel Metamorphosis

Palmén (1958, 1959) noted the large amounts of latent heat release associated with the heavy precipitation in the

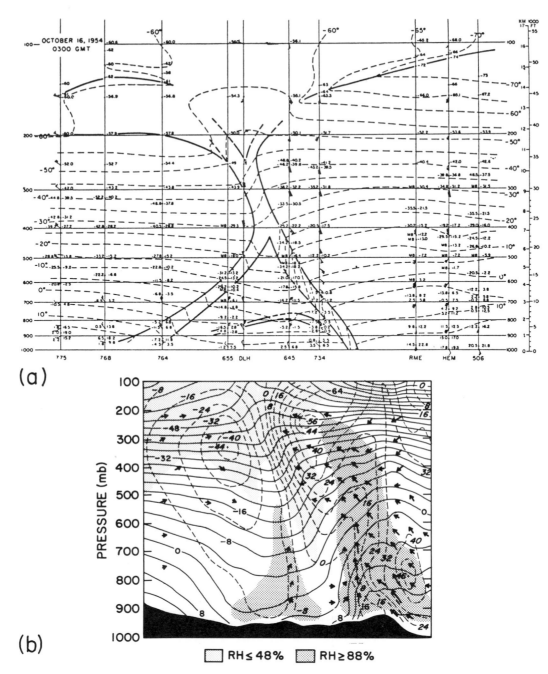

FIG. 12.25.   (a) As in Fig. 12.23a except for 03 UTC 16 October 1954 (Palmén 1958). (b) Model cross section at 24 h of simulation along same path (through center of cyclone). Arrows denote circulation in plane of cross section.

Hazel case and speculated on its importance in the energetics of the system:

> In extratropical storms the kinetic energy is mainly derived from the "available" potential energy due to juxtaposition of air masses of different temperature. However, considering the large amount of latent heat released in the precipitation area of cyclone "Hazel," it seems probable that the role of the condensation of water vapor is far from unimportant for the development [Palmén 1958, p. 14].

Palmén estimated that the total amount of precipitation falling over the southeastern United States during a 24-

hour period was 53×10^{12} kg of water, corresponding to an average latent heating rate of 155×10^{13} W (which greatly exceeds that in an average hurricane).

As noted in results reviewed earlier in this paper, numerical models are well-suited for isolating the effects of physical processes such as the release of latent heat on cyclogenesis. In order to study this effect on Hurricane Hazel, a second simulation was run that was identical to the control with the exception that the latent heat of condensation was neglected in the thermodynamic equation.

It is well known that hurricanes derive their major

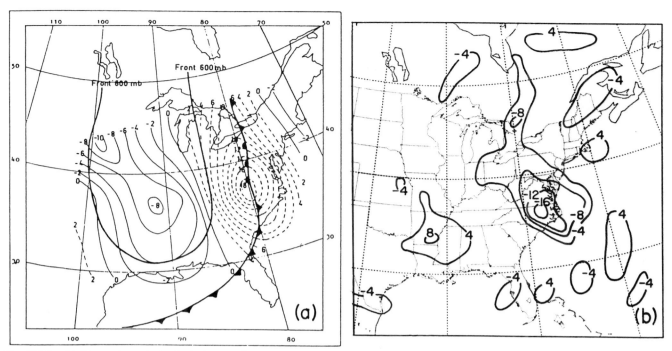

FIG. 12.26. (a) Kinematic vertical velocity in cm s⁻¹ at 600-mb level for 15 UTC 15 October 1954 (Palmén 1961). (b) Model vertical velocities at 600-mb level (interval 4 μb s⁻¹) at 12 h of simulation, for same time.

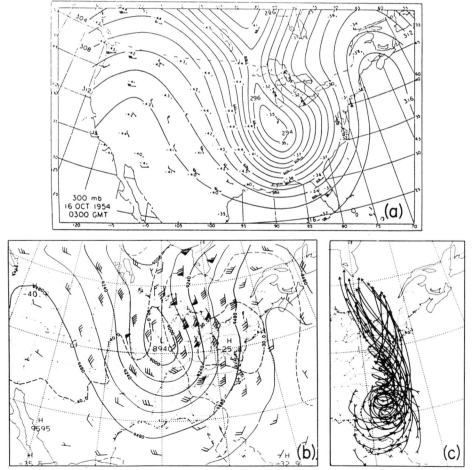

FIG. 12.27. (a) Analyzed 300-mb chart at 03 UTC 16 October 1954, contour interval 200 ft. Temperatures plotted in ° C; winds plotted in knots (Palmén 1958). (b) Simulated 300-mb chart for same time. Solid lines are height contours (interval 120 m), dashed lines are isotherms (interval 5°C). Winds are plotted in m s⁻¹. (c) 24-h trajectories of air parcels originating in the boundary layer ($\sigma = 0.95$) at 03 UTC 15 October.

source of energy from the release of latent heat, so it is not surprising that Hurricane Hazel begins to weaken immediately without latent heating. Table 12.4 lists the minimum pressure at 3-hour intervals in the control simulation and Exp. 2. Without latent heating, the model hurricane weakens rapidly during the first 12 hours of the simulation, unlike the observed and model hurricane in the control simulation.

The impact of latent heating on the evolution of the storm system is broader than its effect on the intensity of the hurricane. The sea-level pressure field at 24 hours of the simulation in Exp. 2 (Fig. 12.29) is dramatically different from the observed (Fig. 12.24a) and the control (Fig. 12.24b). Not only is the storm much weaker without latent heating, it is centered over the extreme eastern border of Virginia and North Carolina instead of central Pennsylvania, a difference in position of more than 600 km. The low-level circulation over the northeastern U.S. and southeastern Canada differs greatly between the simulations with and without latent heating. Without latent heating, the 24-hour rainfall is generally lighter and the maximum rainfall is less concentrated in area (compare Fig. 12.28a and b). The rainfall pattern associated with the control is qualitatively more similar to the observed (compare Figs. 12.28a and 12.20b).

The comparison of the simulations with and without latent heating confirms Palmén's conclusion that *latent heating played a major role in the intense development of Hurricane Hazel and the subsequent transformation into the equally intense extratropical cyclone.* Without latent heating, the model storm is much weaker than observed, follows a different track, and the circulation over a large area differs significantly from that observed.

12.4.4   The Importance of Hurricane Hazel in the Development of the Extratropical Cyclone

The metamorphosis of Hurricane Hazel raises the question of the relative importance of the preexisting

TABLE 12.4.

Minimum pressure (mb) associated with Hurricane Hazel (observed), the control model simulation (Exp. 1) and the simulation without latent heating (Exp. 2).

Forecast time (h)	Observed	Exp. 1	Exp. 2
00	975	975	975
03	975	978	986
06	975	976	988
09	975	974	989
12	974	973	990
15	974	972	993
18	974	970	994
21	975	969	994
24	975	970	995

hurricane circulation versus the intense upper-level trough and baroclinicity in the strong extratropical cyclone development. The previous section showed that latent heating played a major part in the overall development. In the third simulation of this evolution, the initial hurricane vortex is removed from the initial conditions; all other factors, including the physics and lateral boundary conditions, remain the same as in the control simulation.

The removal of Hurricane Hazel from the initial conditions was done in a subjective manner. The first step was a manual reanalysis of the sea-level pressure field over the southeastern portion of the domain outlined in Fig. 12.30. The next step was a similar subjective reanalysis of the temperature structure over the same region; the major change in this step included the removal of the warm-core temperature structure associated with the hurricane. From the modified sea-level pressure and temperature analyses, 16 soundings were constructed at a horizontal spacing of about 400 km. The winds for these soundings were estimated from the control analysis, again with a subjective removal of the hurricane circulation. All real soundings in the vicinity of the hurricane circulation were removed, and the remaining soundings, including the 16 subjectively-derived soundings in the vicinity of the hurricane, were reanalyzed using the successive scan method. In this reanalysis, the original relative humidities remained nearly the same as the control; thus the atmosphere in the southeastern portion of the domain remained extremely moist in Exp. 3.

In contrast to the original analysis (Fig. 12.21a), the modified analysis in Fig. 12.30 shows a broad area of low pressure over the Bahamas, with minimum pressure about 1010 mb. The upper-level temperature and wind analyses (not shown) contain no evidence of the hurricane, and instead represent smooth, large-scale extensions of the major large-scale features, including the trough to the west and the subtropical high to the east. While clearly arbitrary, these conditions represent a plausible atmospheric state in the absence of a hurricane.

Without Hazel in the initial conditions, the evolution of the model atmosphere is quite different from that of the control. Because of the presence of a moist, unstable atmosphere over a warm ocean surface, the weak area of low pressure at the surface, and a weak upper-level wave over the area, a tropical disturbance develops over the Bahamas about 400 km SE of the original position of Hazel. This disturbance, which doubtless is driven by the release of latent heat associated with rainfall in excess of 20 cm (8 inches) (Fig. 12.28c), moves slowly northward to a position about 250 km E of the North Carolina coast by 24 hours. The 24-hour simulation of the sea-level pressure (Fig. 12.31) is quite different from the control simulation (Fig. 12.24b) and the simulation without latent heat (Fig. 12.29). The development of the intense extratropical cyclone that occurred in the control simulation does not occur in the simulation without the hurricane circulation present in the initial conditions, despite the warm, moist

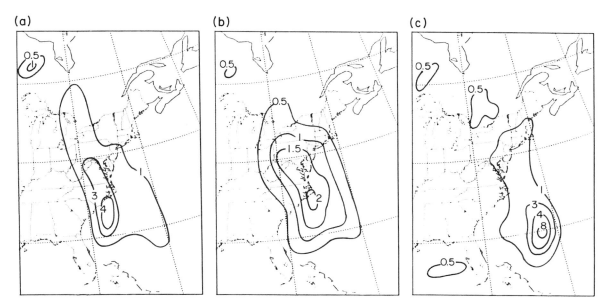

FIG. 12.28.   24-h rainfall amounts (inches) ending at 03 UTC 16 October 1954 in (a) control simulation, (b) simulation without latent heating and (c) simulation with initial hurricane vortex removed. Compare with observed rainfall in Fig. 12.20b.

atmosphere, full physics in the model and the strong upper-level baroclinic system to the west. Instead, a broad, weak cyclone is present over Ontario, clearly separated from the weak tropical disturbance far to the southeast. The atmospheric structure between these two cyclones is completely different in the two simulations. For example, the strong cyclonic flow over western Pennsylvania in the control simulation is replaced by a weak ridge of high pressure in Exp. 3. The rainfall over the eastern U.S. is much lighter in Exp. 3 compared to both the control simulation and Exp. 2 (Fig. 12.28c).

These results show that indeed, as hypothesized by Palmén and others, *the initial hurricane circulation, as well as the high moisture content and the release of latent heat, was essential for the strong development of the extratropical cyclone over the northeastern U.S. and southern Canada.*

The interactions among the initial hurricane vortex, the strong baroclinic zone, and the release of latent heat are complex and deserve more study than presented here; these results, however, illustrate the use of limited-area models to study such complex interacting atmospheric processes.

12.5   Summary

This chapter has reviewed some of the contributions made by limited-area numerical models to the understanding and prediction of cyclone development, with references to the related research studies of Palmén as appropriate. Developed originally for the purpose of improved operational weather forecasts, LAMs have become powerful research tools for the atmospheric scientist, complement-

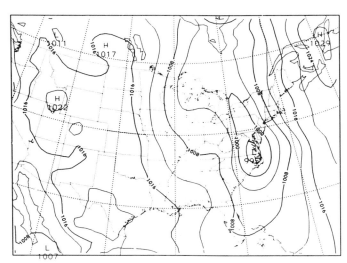

FIG. 12.29.   As in Fig. 12.24b except for simulation without latent heating.

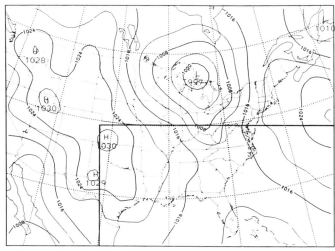

FIG. 12.30.   Initial sea-level pressure field for simulation in which initial hurricane vortex is removed. (Compare with Fig. 12.21a.)

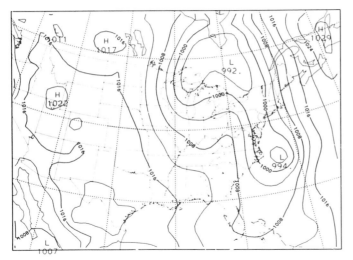

FIG. 12.31. As in Fig. 12.24b except for simulation with initial hurricane vortex removed.

ing analytical mathematical studies and observational studies. High-resolution, nonlinear LAMs, with diabatic and physical processes included, serve as an analog to a physicist's or a chemist's laboratory. Using a LAM, the atmospheric scientist may vary parameters and isolate the effect of physical processes (such as latent heating, radiation and topography) on atmospheric phenomena.

Four classes or types of application of LAMs to research are reviewed in this paper. When initialized with observed or hypothetical data, the model forecast or simulation produces a dense, dynamically consistent four-dimensional data set that may be used in *synoptic studies*. Several examples of the use of models in synoptic studies of extratropical cyclones are presented. These studies have contributed to the understanding of the physical processes leading to the evolution and decay of extratropical cyclones, and of the importance of different aspects of the initial conditions, such as static stability and wind shear, on this evolution. They have also been useful in revealing the detailed dynamical, kinematic and thermodynamic structure of cyclones and related features such as fronts and precipitation systems.

A second use of LAMs is *sensitivity studies*. In a typical sensitivity study, a control simulation is first run with a particular set of initial data, lateral boundary conditions and physics. In subsequent simulations, one or more aspects of the model are varied, and the impact of this change is assessed by comparing the "experimental" simulation with the "control" simulation. The sensitivity of model-simulated extratropical cyclones to initial data, lateral boundary conditions, surface moisture availability, orography, sensible and latent heat fluxes from the surface, release of latent heat of condensation and friction is discussed. It is shown that each of these factors alone can be important in specific cases; in addition, the *synergism* of different physical processes through feedback processes can also produce significant effects on cyclones.

Diagnostic studies are a third type of use of LAMs. The

high-resolution, dynamically consistent data sets may be used to calculate diagnostic quantities such as ageostrophic motions, divergence, water budgets and energy conversions. These quantities are often difficult to compute reliably from observations because of their sensitivity to small errors and to inadequate temporal and spatial density of observations. Examples of the use of models to diagnose the secondary circulations around cold fronts and the kinetic energy conversions in extratropical cyclones are presented.

The fourth type of use of LAMs is *Observing Systems Simulation Experiments* (OSSEs). In an OSSE, a model is used to generate a four-dimensional data set, which is assumed to represent the evolution of the real atmosphere. This data set is used to verify subsequent forecasts that are initialized with a limited portion of the data taken from some time in the control simulation, usually after the control simulation has reached a quasi-balanced state. The data are selected to represent certain observing systems such as satellite winds or temperature retrievals, balloon systems or ground-based temperature and wind profilers. The impact of various observational errors, and of spatial and temporal densities of observations, can be assessed quantitatively by comparing the simulation initialized with a particular data set with the control simulation. Examples of OSSEs to study the impact of a network of ground-based wind and thermodynamic profilers are presented.

In the final part of this chapter, the metamorphosis of Hurricane Hazel (1954) into an extratropical cyclone is revisited using a modern limited-area model. This example was selected both to illustrate how a LAM can be used to understand a complex atmospheric event, and because Palmén produced several important diagnostic studies of this case, including water and energy budgets, based on rawinsonde observations during the late 1950s and early 1960s. In this unusual event Hazel, a hurricane of moderate intensity, crossed the coast of North Carolina and moved northward along a path east of the Appalachians. When the storm reached Pennsylvania, a remarkable transformation from the tropical cyclone to an extratropical cyclone occurred. A LAM is used to study the effects of latent heating, and of the initial hurricane circulation, on this evolution and transformation. The model results are compared with those from Palmén's observational studies 30 years ago. In many ways, the evolution and structure of the model cyclone resemble those diagnosed by Palmén. In addition, it is shown that both the release of latent heat and the initial hurricane circulation played essential roles in the observed metamorphosis.

Acknowledgments

Phil Haagenson provided expert assistance with the Hurricane Hazel simulations. Susan Tufte prepared the manuscript and Chester Newton contributed thorough and thoughtful editorial comments. I thank Hilding Sundqvist and an anonymous reviewer for their helpful reviews.

REFERENCES

Anthes, R. A., 1977: A cumulus parameterization scheme utilizing a one-dimensional cloud model. *Mon. Wea. Rev.,* **105**, 270–286.

——, 1982: *Tropical Cyclones—Their Evolution, Structure and Effects. Meteor. Monogr.* No. 41. American Meteorological Society, 208 pp.

——, 1983a: Modeling sea-air energy fluxes and their effects on explosive marine cyclogenesis. *Papers in Meteor. Res.,* **6**, 1–12.

——, 1983b: Regional models of the atmosphere in middle latitudes. *Mon. Wea. Rev.,* **111**, 1306–1335.

——, 1986: The general question of predictability. *Mesoscale Meteorology and Forecasting,* P. S. Ray, Ed. American Meteorological Society, 636–656.

——, and D. Keyser, 1979: Tests of a fine-mesh model over Europe and the United States. *Mon. Wea. Rev.,* **107**, 963–984.

——, Y.-H. Kuo, S. G. Benjamin and Y.-F. Li, 1982: The evolution of the mesoscale environment of severe local storms: Preliminary modeling results. *Mon. Wea. Rev.,* **110**, 1187–1213.

——, —— and J. R. Gyakum, 1983: Numerical simulations of a case of explosive marine cyclogenesis. *Mon. Wea. Rev.,* **111**, 1174–1188.

——, ——, D. P. Baumhefner, R. M. Errico and T. W. Bettge, 1985: Predictability of mesoscale atmospheric motions. Contribution to "Issues in Atmospheric and Oceanic Modeling," *Advances in Geophysics,* **28B**, 159–202.

——, E.-Y. Hsie and Y.-H. Kuo, 1987: Description of the Penn State/NCAR Mesoscale Model Version 4 (MM4). NCAR Technical Note, NCAR/TN-282 + STR, 66 pp.

——, Y.-H. Kuo, E.-Y. Hsie, S. Low-Nam and T. W. Bettge, 1989: Estimation of skill and uncertainty in regional numerical models. *Quart. J. Roy. Meteor. Soc.,* **115A**, 763–806.

Arnold, C. P., and C. H. Dey, 1986: Observing-systems simulation experiments: Past, present, and future. *Bull. Amer. Meteor. Soc.,* **67**, 687–695.

Atlas, R., 1987: The role of oceanic fluxes and initial data on the numerical prediction of an intense coastal storm. *Dyn. Atmos. Oceans.,* **10**, 359–388.

Benjamin, S. G., and T. N. Carlson, 1986: Some effects of surface heating and topography on the regional severe storm environment. Part I: Three-dimensional simulations. *Mon. Wea. Rev.,* **114**, 307–329.

Bjerknes, J., and J. Holmboe, 1944: On the theory of cyclones. *J. Meteor.,* **1**, 1–22.

Bleck, R., 1977: Numerical simulation of lee cyclogenesis in the Gulf of Genoa. *Mon. Wea. Rev.,* **105**, 428–445.

Brill, K. F., L. W. Uccellini, R. P. Burkhart, T. T. Warner and R. A. Anthes, 1985: Numerical simulations of a transverse indirect circulation and low-level jet in the exit region of an upper-level jet. *J. Atmos. Sci.,* **42**, 1306–1320.

Buzzi, A., and S. Tibaldi, 1978: Cyclogenesis in the lee of the Alps: A case study. *Quart. J. Roy. Meteor. Soc.,* **104**, 271–287.

——, T. Nanni and M. Tagliazucca, 1977: Midtropospheric frontal zones: Numerical experiments with an isentropic coordinate primitive equation model. *Arch. Meteor. Geophys. Bioklim.,* **A26**, 155–178.

Chang, C. B., D. J. Perkey and C. W. Kreitzberg, 1982: A numerical case study of the effects of latent heating on a developing wave cyclone. *J. Atmos. Sci.,* **39**, 1555–1570.

——, —— and ——, 1984: Latent heat induced energy transformations during cyclogenesis. *Mon. Wea. Rev.,* **112**, 357–367.

——, —— and ——, 1986: Impact of missing wind observations on the simulation of a severe storm environment. *Mon. Wea. Rev.,* **114**, 1278–1287.

Charney, J. G., 1947: The dynamics of long waves in a baroclinic westerly current. *J. Meteor.,* **4**, 135–162.

——, R. Fjørtoft and J. von Neumann, 1950: Numerical integration of the barotropic vorticity equation. *Tellus,* **2**, 237–254.

Chen, S.-J., and L. Dell'Osso, 1987: A numerical case study of East Asian cyclogenesis. *Mon. Wea. Rev.,* **115**, 477–487.

Chen, T.-C., C.-B. Chang and D. J. Perkey, 1983: Numerical study of an AMTEX '75 oceanic cyclone. *Mon. Wea. Rev.,* **111**, 1818–1829.

Cram, J. M., and M. L. Kaplan, 1985: Variational assimilation of VAS data into a mesoscale model: Assimilation method and sensitivity experiments. *Mon. Wea. Rev.,* **113**, 467–484.

Dare, P. M., and P. J. Smith, 1984: A comparison of observed and model energy balance for an extratropical cyclone system. *Mon. Wea. Rev.,* **112**, 1289–1308.

Davis, W. R., 1954: Hurricanes of 1954. *Mon. Wea. Rev.,* **82**, 370–373.

Douglas, S. G., and T. T. Warner, 1987: Utilization of VAS satellite data in the initialization of an oceanic cyclogenesis simulation. *Mon. Wea. Rev.,* **115**, 2996–3012.

Duffy, D. G., and R. Atlas, 1986: The impact of Seasat-A scatterometer data on the numerical prediction of the Queen Elizabeth II Storm. *J. Geophys. Res.,* **91**, 2241–2248.

Eady, E. T., 1949: Long waves and cyclone waves. *Tellus,* **1**, No. 3, 33–52.

Egger, J., 1972: Numerical experiments on the cyclogenesis in the Gulf of Genoa. *Beitr. Phys. Atmos.,* **45**, 320–346.

Eliassen, A., and E. Raustein, 1968: A numerical integration experiment with a model atmosphere based on isentropic coordinates. *Meteor. Ann.,* **5**, 45–63.

Emanuel, K., 1983: On assessing local conditional symmetric instability from atmospheric soundings. *Mon. Wea. Rev.,* **111**, 2016–2033.

Fiorino, M., and T. T. Warner, 1981: Incorporating surface winds and rainfall rates into the initialization of a mesoscale hurricane model. *Mon. Wea. Rev.,* **109**, 1915–1928.

Fritsch, J. M., and R. A. Maddox, 1981: Convectively driven mesoscale weather systems aloft. Part II: Numerical simulations. *J. Appl. Meteor.,* **20**, 20–26.

Gal-Chen, T., B. D. Schmidt and L. W. Uccellini, 1986: Simulation experiments for testing the assimilation of geostationary satellite temperature retrieval into a numerical prediction model. *Mon. Wea. Rev.,* **114**, 1213–1230.

Gyakum, J. R., 1983: On the evolution of the Queen Elizabeth II Storm. I. Synoptic aspects. *Mon. Wea. Rev.,* **111**, 1137–1155.

Hack, J. J., 1989: On the promise of general-purpose parallel computing. *Parallel Computing,* **10**, 261–275.

Haltiner, G. J., and R. T. Williams, 1980: *Numerical Prediction and Dynamic Meteorology.* Wiley, 477 pp.

Haurwitz, B., 1951: The perturbation equations in meteorology. *Compendium of Meteorology,* T. F. Malone, Ed. American Meteorological Society, 401–420.

Hobgood, J. S., 1986: A possible mechanism for the diurnal oscillation of tropical cyclones. *J. Atmos. Sci.,* **43**, 2901–2922.

Hughes, L. A., F. Baer, G. E. Birchfield and R. E. Kaylor, 1955: Hurricane Hazel and a long-wave outlook. *Bull. Amer. Meteor. Soc.,* **36**, 528–533.

Källén, E., and X.-Y. Huang, 1988a: The influence of isolated observations on short-range numerical weather forecasts. *Tellus,* **40A**, 324–336.

——, and ——, 1988b: Perturbation sensitivity on the cyclone scale in the ECMWF model. Preprints, *Palmén Memorial Symposium on Extratropical Cyclones,* Helsinki. Amer. Meteor. Soc., 314–317.

Kasahara, A., 1959: A comparison between geostrophic and nongeostrophic numerical forecasts of hurricane movement with the barotropic steering model. *J. Meteor.,* **16**, 371–384.

——, 1961: A numerical experiment on the development of a tropical cyclone. *J. Meteor.,* **18**, 259–282.

Keyser, D., and L. W. Uccellini, 1987: Regional models: Emerging research tools for synoptic meteorologists. *Bull. Amer. Meteor. Soc.,* **68**, 306–320.

Knox, J. L., 1955: The storm "Hazel": Synoptic résumé of its development as it approached southern Ontario. *Bull. Amer. Meteor. Soc.,* **36**, 239–246.

Krueger, A. F., 1954: The weather and circulation of October 1954. *Mon. Wea. Rev.,* **82**, 296–300.

Kuo, Y.-H., and R. A. Anthes, 1984: Accuracy of diagnostic heat and moisture budgets using SESAME-79 field data as revealed by observing system simulation experiments. *Mon. Wea. Rev.,* **112**, 1465–1481.

——, and ——, 1985: Calculation of geopotential and temperature fields from an array of nearly continuous wind observations. *J. Atmos. Oceanic Technol.,* **2**, 22–34.

——, M. Skumanich, P. L. Haagenson and J. S. Chang, 1985: The accuracy of trajectory models as revealed by the observing system simulation experiments. *Mon. Wea. Rev.,* **113**, 1852–1867.

——, E. G. Donall and M. A. Shapiro, 1987: Feasibility of short-range numerical weather prediction using observations from a network of profilers. *Mon. Wea. Rev.,* **115**, 2402–2427.

——, and R. J. Reed, 1988: Numerical simulation of an explosively deepening cyclone in the eastern Pacific. *Mon. Wea. Rev.,* **116**, 2081–2105.

Kutzbach, G., 1979: *The Thermal Theory of Cyclones.* American Meteorological Society, 255 pp.

Lanicci, J. M., T. N. Carlson and T. T. Warner, 1987: Sensitivity of the Great Plains severe-storm environment to soil-moisture distribution. *Mon. Wea. Rev.,* **115**, 2660–2673.

Lee, D. K., and D. D. Houghton, 1984: Impact of mesoscale satellite wind data on numerical model simulation: A case study. *Mon. Wea. Rev.,* **112**, 1005–1016.

Maddox, R. A., D. J. Perkey and J. M. Fritsch, 1981: Evolution of upper tropospheric features during the development of a mesoscale convective complex. *J. Atmos. Sci.,* **38**, 1664–1674.

McCallum, E., J. R. Grant and B. W. Golding, 1983: A synoptic case study using a numerical model. *Meteor. Mag.,* **112**, 275–288.

McCumber, M. C., and R. A. Pielke, 1981: Simulation of the effects of surface fluxes of heat and moisture in a mesoscale numerical model. 1. Soil layer. *J. Geophys. Res.,* **86**, 9929–9938.

Mesinger, F., and R. F. Strickler, 1982: Effect of mountains on Genoa cyclogenesis. *J. Meteor. Soc. Japan,* **60**, 326–338.

Mook, C. P., 1955: The distribution of peak wind gusts in Hurricane Hazel 1954. *Weatherwise,* **8**, 92–96.

Newton, C. W., and A. Trevisan, 1984: Clinogenesis and frontogenesis in jet-stream waves. Part II: Channel model numerical experiments. *J. Atmos. Sci.,* **41**, 2735–2755.

Nuss, W. A., and R. A. Anthes, 1987: A numerical investigation of low-level processes in rapid cyclogenesis. *Mon. Wea. Rev.,* **115**, 2728–2743.

Orlanski, I., and B. B. Ross, 1984: The evolution of an observed cold front. Part II. Mesoscale dynamics. *J. Atmos. Sci.,* **41**, 1669–1703.

——, and J. J. Katzfey, 1987: Sensitivity of model simulations for a coastal cyclone. *Mon. Wea. Rev.,* **115**, 2792–2821.

Paegle, J., and T. Vukicevic, 1987: The predictability of low-level flow during ALPEX. *Meteor. Atmos. Phys.,* **36**, 45–60.

Palmén, E., 1948a: On the distribution of temperature and winds in the upper westerlies. *J. Meteor.,* **5**, 20–27.

——, 1948b. On the formation and structure of tropical hurricanes. *Geophysica,* **3**, 26–38.

——, 1958: Vertical circulation and release of kinetic energy during the development of Hurricane Hazel into an extratropical storm. *Tellus,* **10**, 1–23.

——, 1959: On the maintenance of kinetic energy in the atmosphere. *The Atmosphere and the Sea in Motion* (Rossby Memorial Volume), B. Bolin, Ed. Rockefeller Institute Press, 212–224.

——, 1961: On conversion between potential and kinetic energy in the atmosphere. *Geofis. Pura e Appl.,* **49**, 167–177.

——, and C. W. Newton, 1948: A study of the mean wind and temperature distribution in the vicinity of the polar front in winter. *J. Meteor.,* **5**, 220–226.

——, and ——, 1951: On the three-dimensional motions in an outbreak of polar air. *J. Meteor.,* **8**, 25–39.

——, and C. L. Jordan, 1955: Note on the release of kinetic energy in tropical cyclones. *Tellus,* **7**, 186–188.

——, and E. O. Holopainen, 1962: Divergence, vertical velocity and conversion between potential and kinetic energy in an extratropical disturbance. *Geophysica,* **8**, 89–113.

——, and C. W. Newton, 1969: *Atmospheric Circulation Systems.* Academic Press, 603 pp.

Pielke, R. A., 1984: *Mesoscale Numerical Modeling.* Academic Press, 612 pp.

Robertson, F. R., and P. J. Smith, 1983: The impact of model moist processes on the energetics of extratropical cyclones. *Mon. Wea. Rev.,* **111**, 723–744.

Ross, B. B., and I. Orlanski, 1982: The evolution of an observed cold front. Part I: Numerical simulation. *J. Atmos. Sci.,* **39**, 296–327.

Rossby, C.-G., 1940: Planetary flow patterns in the atmosphere. *Quart. J. Roy. Meteor. Soc.,* **66** (Supp.), 68–87.

Sanders, F., 1971: Analytic solutions of the nonlinear omega and vorticity equations for a structurally simple model of disturbances in the baroclinic westerlies. *Mon. Wea. Rev.,* **99**, 393–407.

Shapiro, M. A., 1975: Simulation of upper-level frontogenesis with a 20-level isentropic coordinate primitive equation model. *Mon. Wea. Rev.,* **103**, 591–604.

Simmons, A. J., and B. J. Hoskins, 1978: The life cycles of some nonlinear baroclinic waves. *J. Atmos. Sci.,* **35**, 414–432.

Smagorinsky, J., S. Manabe and J. L. Holloway, Jr., 1965: Numerical results from a nine-level general circulation model of the atmosphere. *Mon. Wea. Rev.,* **93**, 727–768.

Sundqvist, H., E. Berge and J. E. Kristjánsson, 1989: Condensation and cloud parameterization studies with a mesoscale numerical weather prediction model. *Mon. Wea. Rev.,*117, 1641–1657.

Sutcliffe, R. C., and A. G. Forsdyke, 1950: The theory and use of upper air thickness patterns in forecasting. *Quart. J. Roy. Meteor. Soc.,* **76**, 189–217.

Syōno, S., 1962: A numerical experiment on the formation of tropical cyclones. *Proc. Intl. Symp. on Num. Wea. Pred.* Meteorological Society of Japan, 405–418.

Teweles, S., and H. Wobus, 1954: Verification of prognostic charts. *Bull. Amer. Meteor. Soc.,* **35**, 455–463.

Thompson, P. D., 1983: A history of numerical weather prediction in the United States. *Bull. Amer. Meteor. Soc.,* **64**, 755–769.

Tibaldi, S., A. Buzzi and P. Malguzzi, 1980: Orographically induced cyclogenesis: Analysis of numerical experiments. *Mon. Wea. Rev.,* **108**, 1302–1314.

Trevisan, A., 1976: Numerical experiments on the influence of orography on cyclone formation with an isentropic primitive equation model. *J. Atmos. Sci.,* **33**, 768–780.

Tribbia, J. J., and R. A. Anthes, 1987: Scientific basis of modern weather prediction. *Science,* **237**, 493–499.

Uccellini, L. W., and D. R. Johnson, 1979: The coupling of upper and lower tropospheric jet streaks and implications for the development of severe convective storms. *Mon. Wea. Rev.,* **107**, 682–703.

——, R. A. Petersen, K. F. Brill, P. J. Kocin and J. J. Tuccillo, 1987: Synergistic interactions between an upper-level jet streak and diabatic processes that influence the development of a low-level jet and a secondary coastal cyclone. *Mon. Wea. Rev.,* **115**, 2227–2261.

Zack, J. W., and M. L. Kaplan, 1987: Numerical simulations of the subsynoptic features associated with the AVE–SESAME I case. Part I: The preconvective environment. *Mon. Wea. Rev.,* **115**, 2367–2394.

Zhang, D., and R. A. Anthes, 1982: A high-resolution model of the planetary-boundary-layer-sensitivity tests and comparisons with SESAME-79 data. *J. Appl. Meteor.,* **21**, 1594–1609.

List of Symbols

The following symbols are used consistently among chapters, unless other meanings are specified. Any additional special symbols are defined in the text as they are introduced.

a	Earth radius
a, g	(subscripts) ageostrophic, geostrophic
c_p	specific heat of air at constant pressure
$d/dt, D/Dt$	individual change following a fluid element
f	Coriolis parameter, $2\Omega\sin\phi$
g	acceleration of gravity
k	kinetic energy per unit mass
p	pressure
p_S	surface pressure
q	specific humidity; quasi-geostrophic potential vorticity
q_e	moist potential vorticity (on θ_e surface)
t	time
u, v, w	eastward, northward and upward components of motion
x, y, z	distance east, north, height above sea level
K	total kinetic energy within a specified volume
L	latent heat of condensation; wavelength
M	absolute momentum ($U - fy$)
N	Brunt–Väisälä (buoyancy) frequency [$N^2 = (g/\theta)(\partial\theta/\partial z)$]
P	potential vorticity
R	gas constant for air
T	temperature
U	basic current speed
V	horizontal wind speed
β	df/dy
ζ, ζ_a	relative vorticity, absolute vorticity ($\zeta + f$)
ζ_θ	vorticity in isentropic surface
θ	potential temperature
θ_e	equivalent potential temperature
θ_w	wet-bulb potential temperature
ρ	density
σ	vertical coordinate p/p_S; perturbation growth rate
ϕ	latitude
ψ	stream function
ω	vertical velocity (dp/dt); frequency
Φ	geopotential (gz)
Ω	angular velocity of earth rotation
$\overline{X}$	time mean of quantity X
X'	deviation from time mean ($X - \overline{X}$)
$[X]$	zonal mean
X^*	deviation from zonal mean ($X - [X]$)

Index